# 365 CROSSWORD PUZZLES



hinkler

Published by Hinkler Books Pty Ltd
45–55 Fairchild Street
Heatherton Victoria 3202 Australia
www.hinkler.com.au



Cover design: Sam Grimmer
Typesetting: MPS Limited
Prepress: Graphic Print Group



ISBN: 978 1 4889 0321 2

Printed and bound in China

# PUZZLES

# CROSSWORD 1

### ACROSS

1. Blinded by light
4. Strikes with foot
7. Disgraceful
8. Quay
9. Outward appearance
12. Giving (medal)
15. Seafood crustaceans
17. Shocking ordeal
18. Work (dough)
21. Senselessly
22. Speech impediments
23. Loosen

### DOWN

1. Ruination
2. Move in jagged course
3. Adds soundtrack
4. Understood
5. Made of clay
6. Ride waves
10. Relieves
11. Girth
13. Spiral motion
14. Protests
16. Pungent clove
18. Execute
19. Fades
20. Practical jokes

# CROSSWORD 2

## ACROSS

1. Land measurer
5. Army car
7. Nuclear weapon, ... bomb
8. Hiker's pack
9. Voices
12. Petitions to God
15. Feud
19. Transgressed
21. Beaten
22. Lose your footing
23. Extinct
24. Changes hairdo

## DOWN

1. Scant
2. Disgorge
3. Oxen harnesses
4. Library user
5. Rightly
6. Embers stirrers
10. Charismatic air
11. Always
12. Buddy
13. Opposed to
14. Make (wage)
15. Reported speech
16. Return to custody
17. Engraver
18. Modifies
19. Fizzy drinks
20. Spiteful

# CROSSWORD 3

## ACROSS

1. Uncompromising person (3-4)
4. Stretch (for)
7. Solarium
8. Burn with steam
9. Lessened in severity
12. Twelve-month-old horse
15. Tested
17. Kindle (interest)
18. Become ready to pick
21. Sloping letters
22. Book leaves
23. Requiring

## DOWN

1. Mild repugnance
2. Visits as ghost
3. Twosomes
4. Spectacles frames
5. Water-related
6. Contained
10. Subsiding, ... down
11. Endangered bamboo-eater
13. Smiling broadly
14. Sleeping in tents
16. Speared
18. Win easily, ... home
19. Pen points
20. Benefit

# CROSSWORD 4

## ACROSS

1. Small notches
7. Brightened up
8. Join
10. German cabbage dish
12. Circus swings
14. Precious metal
16. Belonging to you
17. Fort
20. Meteorologist
23. Craze
24. Style
25. Surrendered

## DOWN

1. French confectionery item
2. Sets of tools
3. Now, at ...!
4. Levels of command
5. Eight-sided
6. Reworked (text)
9. Lessens, ... off
11. Drenched
13. Have a meal
15. Shoo!
16. Opened mouth wearily
18. Swell
19. Tied bundle
21. Speed contest
22. Back of neck

# CROSSWORD 5

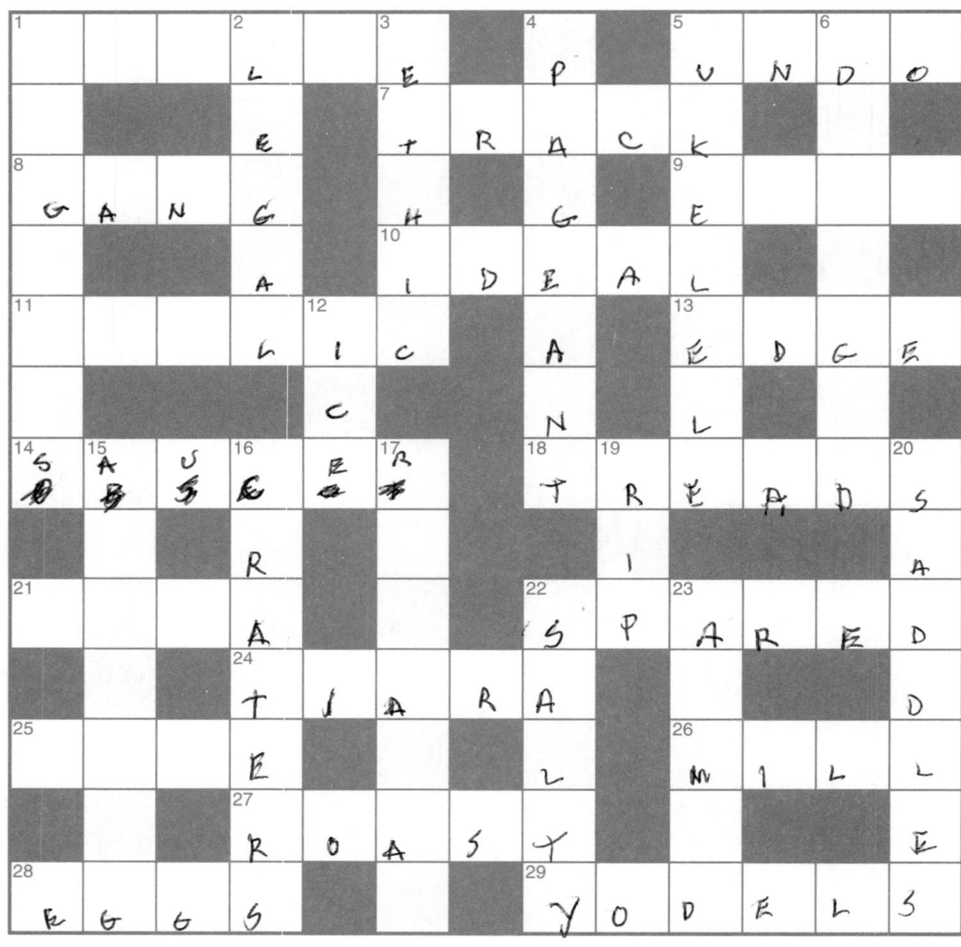

## ACROSS

1. Metal grating
5. Loosen
7. Athletics circuit
8. Power group
9. Brings into play
10. Standard of perfection
11. Strikingly unusual
13. Furthermost limits
14. UFO, flying ...
18. Tramples
21. Temporary visitor document
22. Pardoned
24. Little crown
25. Quote
26. Flour factory
27. Bake in oven
28. Bird's unhatched young
29. Sings like Swiss mountaineer

## DOWN

1. Wine cups
2. Lawful
3. Job attitude, work ...
4. Beauty contest
5. Four-stringed guitar
6. Greatly feared
12. Chill
15. Complying with, ... by
16. Meteor impact holes
17. Absconder
19. Dangerous current
20. Jockeys' seats
22. Briny
23. Meant

# CROSSWORD 6

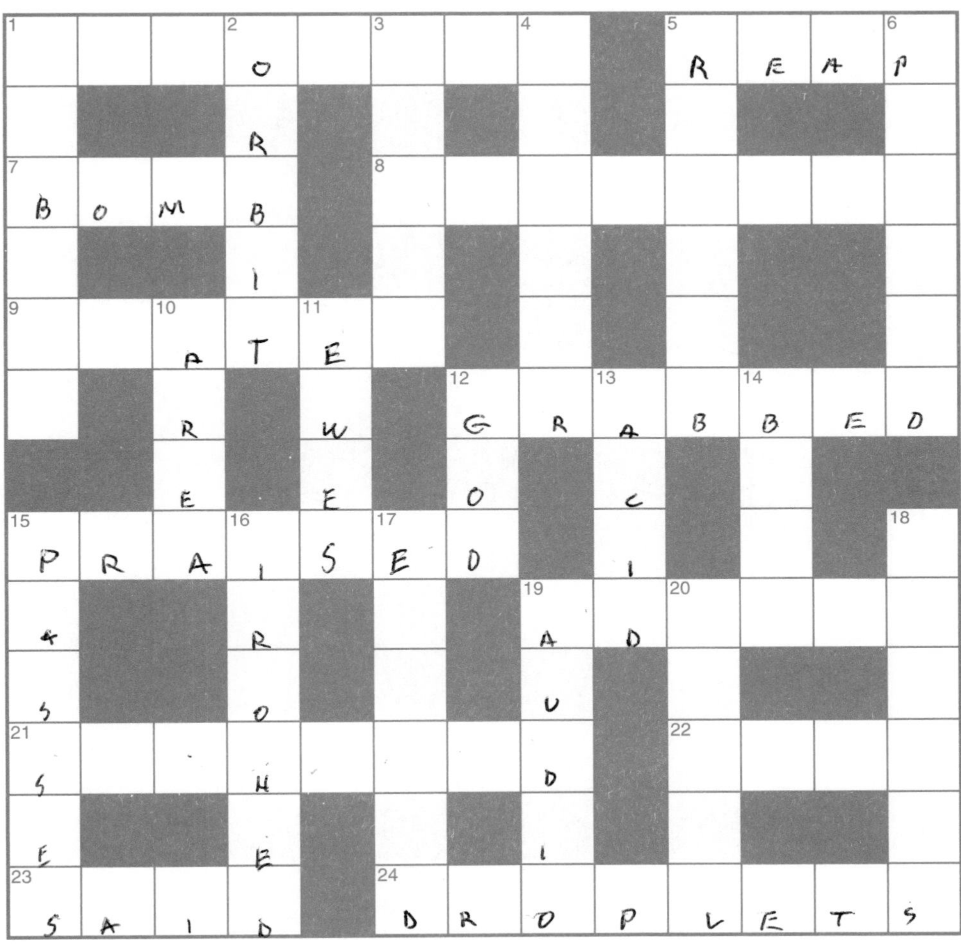

## ACROSS

1. Without ceremony
5. Harvest
7. Grenade
8. Depressed
9. Exhilarated
12. Seized
15. Expressed admiration
19. Wise sayings
21. Average
22. Peel or skin
23. Declared
24. Beads of liquid

## DOWN

1. Innate
2. Planet's path
3. Pondered
4. Paying guest
5. Angelic being
6. Cushioned
10. Zone
11. Rams' mates
12. Deity
13. Corrosive substance
14. Cask stopper
15. Walks on by
16. Pressed (clothes)
17. Fetching task
18. Incidental comments
19. Of sound system
20. Ear test, ... examination

# CROSSWORD 7

## ACROSS

1. Energetic
4. Financial obligations
7. Levering tool
8. Signified
9. Japanese martial art
12. Closeness
15. Rush headlong (of herd)
17. Deep shock
18. Bear-like marsupial
21. Receives (ball)
22. Track down
23. Treated unfairly

## DOWN

1. Pub patrons
2. Taken from plane (of photo)
3. Ears of corn
4. Sleeping hall
5. Cried (of lamb)
6. Place to sit
10. Put in (data)
11. Hotel employee
13. Sprayed
14. Tropical disease
16. Cave chamber
18. Retained
19. Pimple rash
20. Hotpot

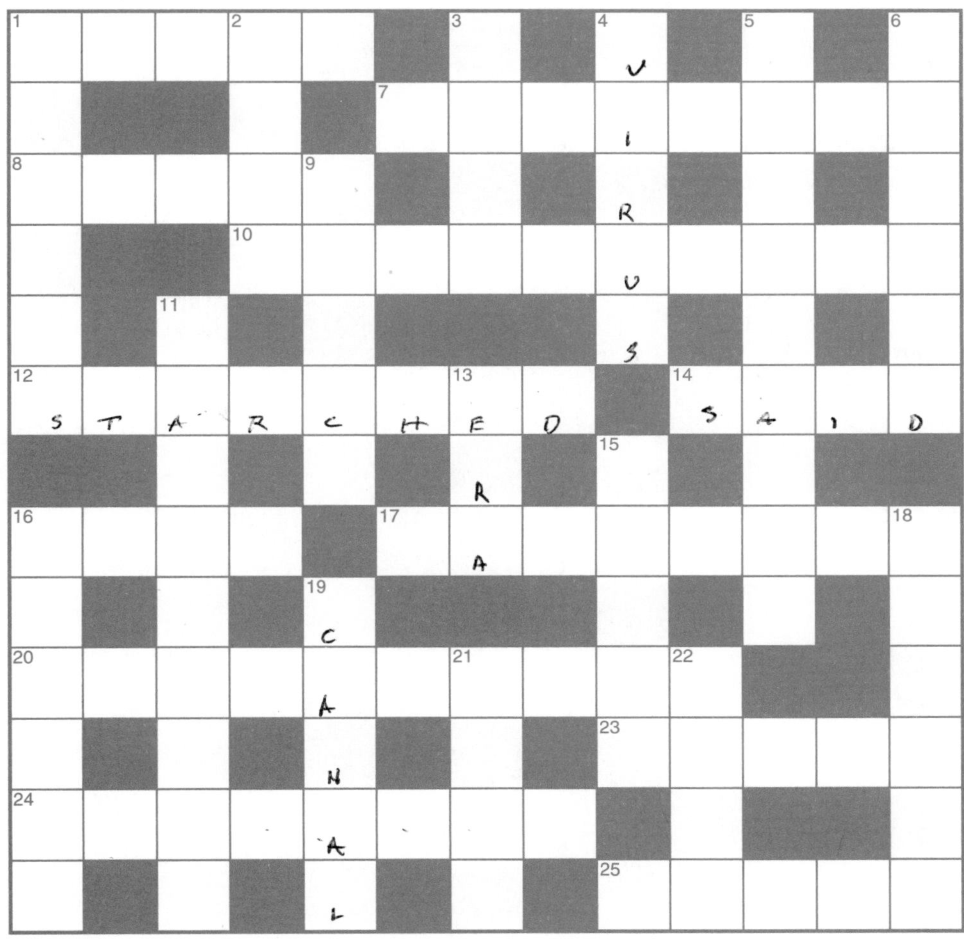


## ACROSS

1. Pretend (injury)
7. Certifying (accounts)
8. Enclosed areas
10. Dark outline
12. Stiffens (fabric)
14. Uttered
16. Melt
17. Legally
20. Science investigator
23. Concerning ships
24. Wound dressings
25. Gives go-ahead to

## DOWN

1. Lobbies
2. Gallivants (about)
3. Exclamation of pain
4. Computer bug
5. Almost
6. Consented
9. Because
11. Bothering
13. Geological age
15. Much of the time
16. Pulsates
18. Crop harvests
19. Venetian waterway
21. Gnaw
22. Display frame

# CROSSWORD 9

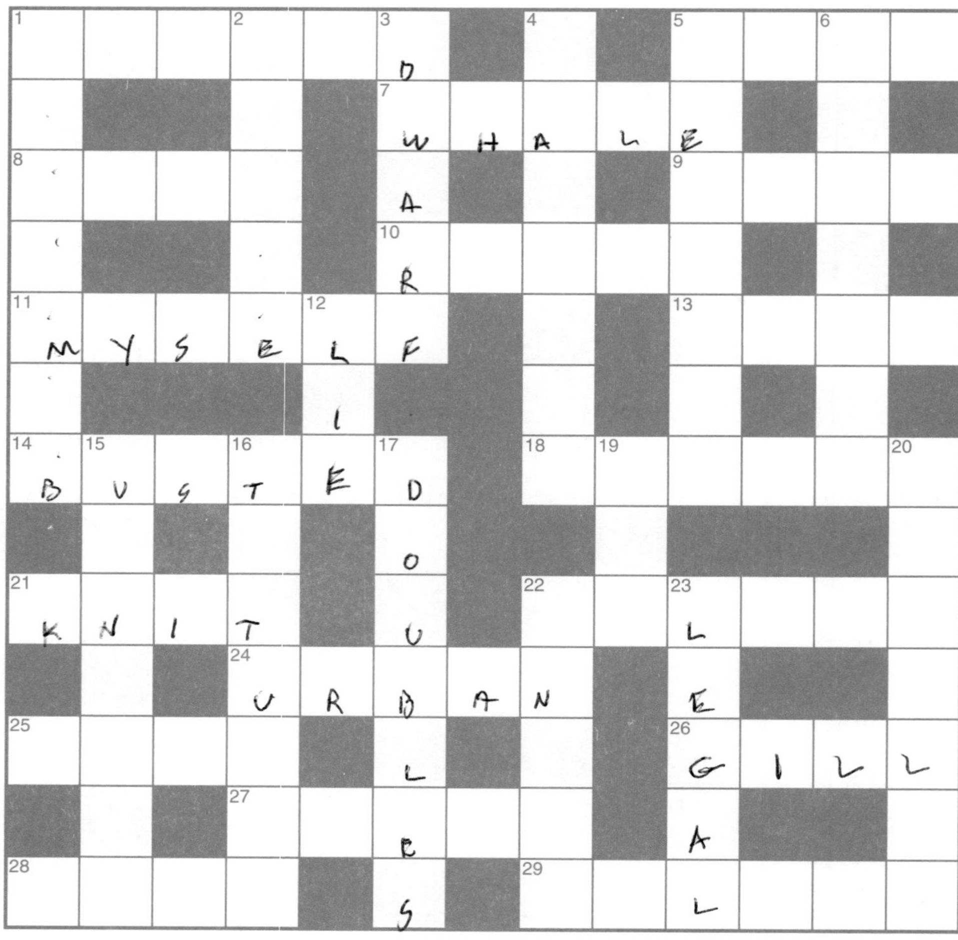

## ACROSS

1. Risk
5. Situate
7. Large sea mammal
8. Without sensation
9. Infuriate
10. Hebrew academic
11. Me
13. Transfixed
14. Caught in the act
18. Cease
21. Make with wool
22. Castrated (horse)
24. Of the city
25. Motion picture
26. Fish breathing organ
27. Pitchers
28. Religious choral work
29. Assistant

## DOWN

1. Letter-guessing game
2. Leisurely walk
3. Fairy tale creature
4. Wagered
5. Episodic TV shows
6. Helms
12. Fib
15. Yearly stipend
16. Asphalt ingredient
17. Tennis pairs
19. Ogle
20. Small child
22. Grind (teeth)
23. Within the law

# CROSSWORD 10

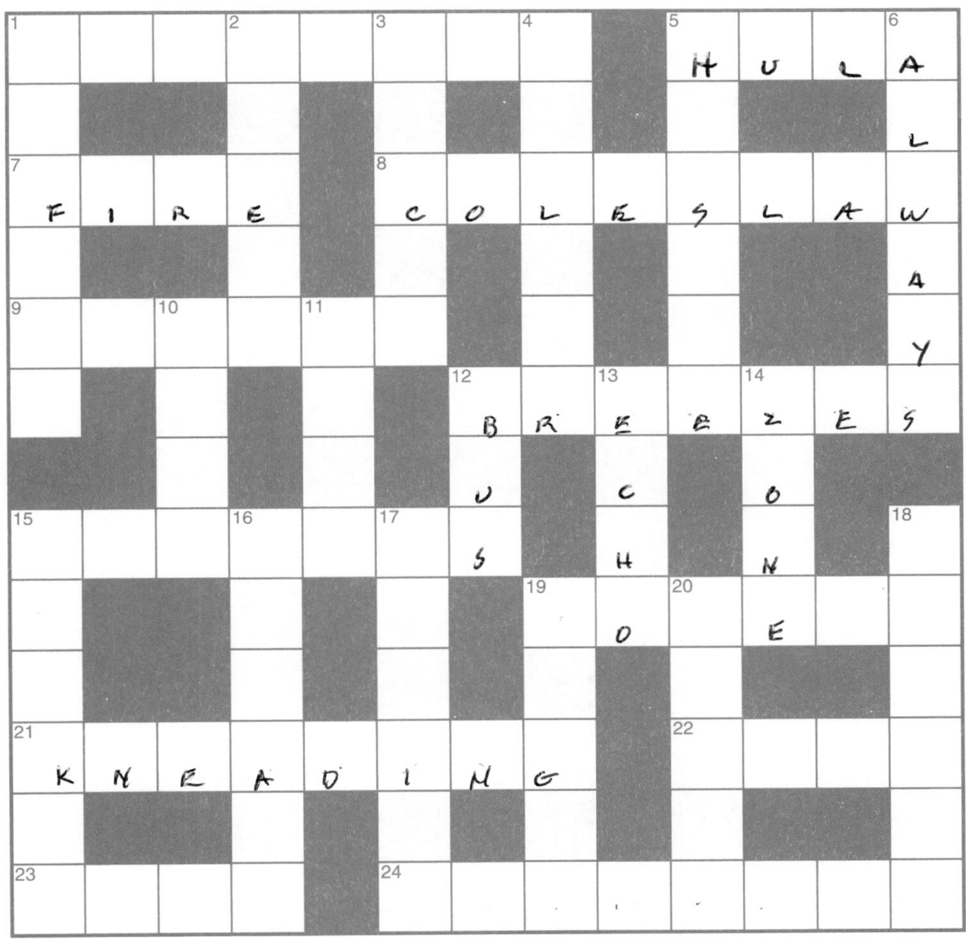

## ACROSS

1. Utmost
5. Honolulu dance
7. Blaze
8. Shredded cabbage salad
9. Let for rent
12. Gentle winds
15. Runners
19. Up-to-date
21. Working (dough)
22. Tofu bean
23. Overdue
24. Joined armed forces

## DOWN

1. Unwrap
2. Objects
3. Formed a curve
4. French pastry
5. Harass
6. Every time
10. Open-mouthed
11. Heavy fencing sword
12. Public transport
13. Reverberate
14. Defined region
15. Wild African canine
16. Spin
17. Filter out impurities
18. Away from coast
19. Ski slope mound
20. Office tables

# CROSSWORD 11

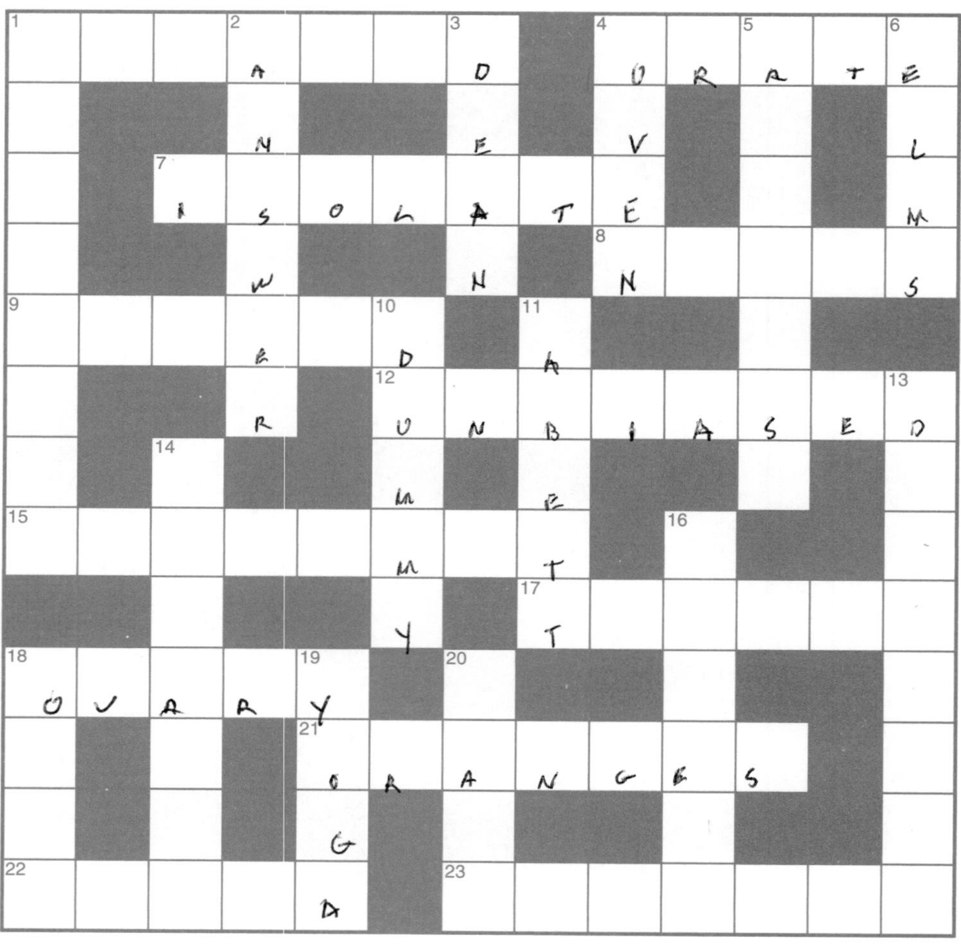

## ACROSS

1. Pierced with lance
4. Speak publicly
7. Set apart
8. Narrow land links
9. Folk tale
12. Not prejudiced
15. Send (message)
17. Wireless crackle
18. Reproductive gland
21. Citrus crop
22. Musical drama
23. Giving autograph

## DOWN

1. Impertinent
2. Reply
3. College head
4. Furnace
5. Gum infection
6. Deciduous trees
10. Ventriloquist's doll
11. Aids (felon)
13. Discarding
14. Competent
16. Pub
18. In contact with
19. Meditation art
20. Raps lightly

# CROSSWORD 12

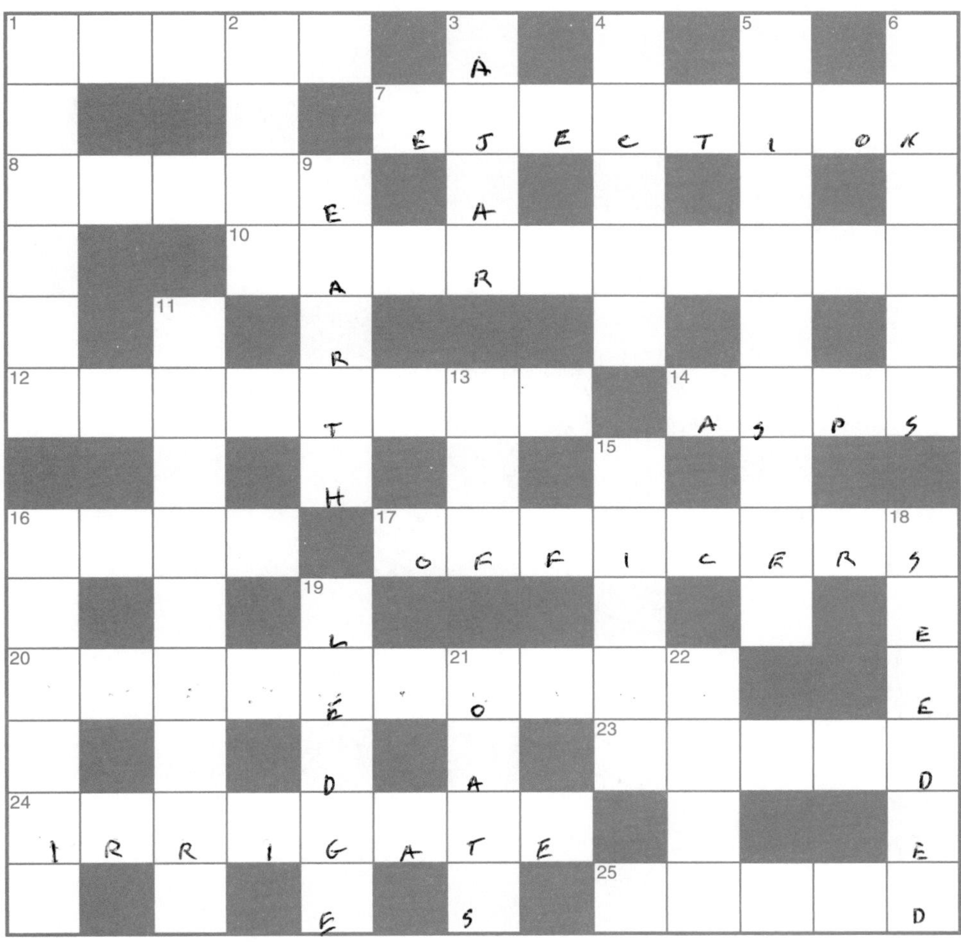

## ACROSS

1. Glances
7. Expulsion
8. House
10. Went without
12. More petite
14. Small vipers
16. Violently attack
17. High-ranking soldiers
20. Aristocratic female
23. Coated (with mud)
24. Supply with water
25. Refashioned

## DOWN

1. Allowed to borrow
2. Young goats
3. Almost closed
4. Mock
5. Talks over
6. Charged electrodes
9. Planet we live on
11. Eldest child (5-4)
13. Sprite
15. Pale violet
16. Outlaw
18. Sown (with grain)
19. Brink
21. Porridge cereal
22. Nominate

# CROSSWORD 13

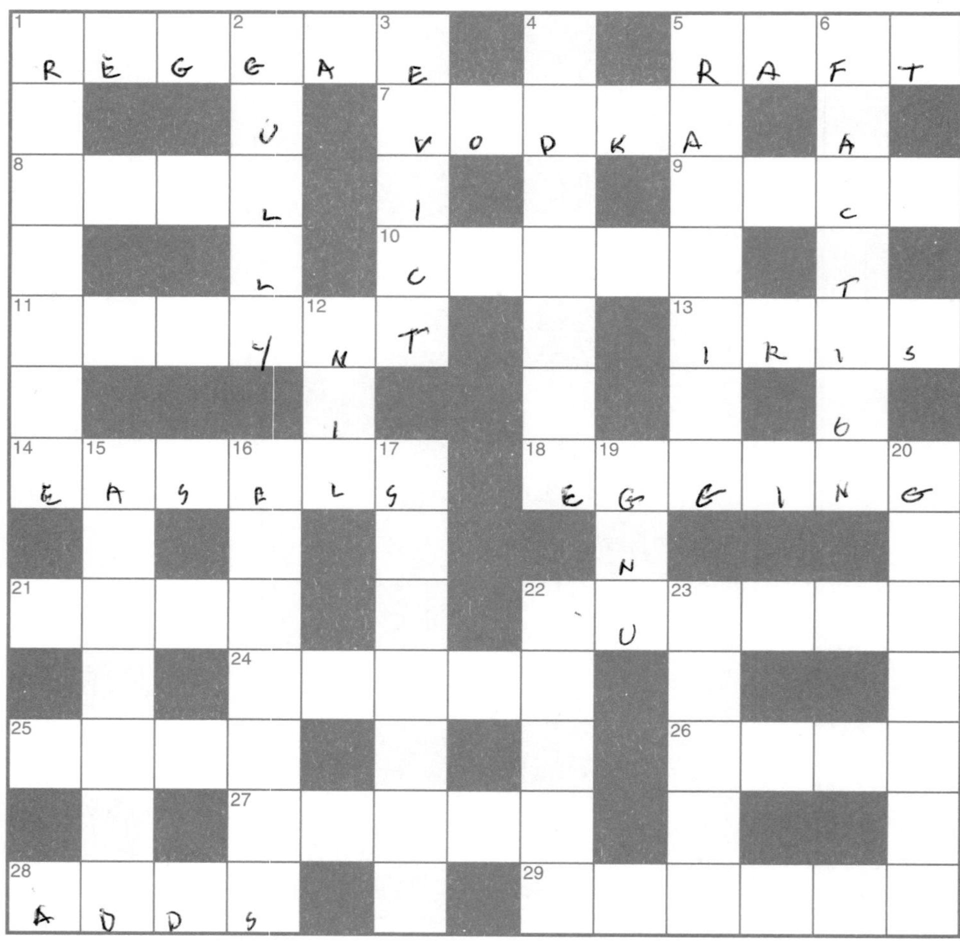

## ACROSS

1. Jamaican music
5. Log vessel
7. Russian liquor
8. Inheritor
9. Linear measure
10. Move on knees
11. High-priority
13. Part of eye
14. Painters' stands
18. Urging, ... on
21. Give (party)
22. Dicing
24. Fire fragment
25. Inactive
26. Ellipse
27. Showily virile
28. Counts up
29. Showed assent

## DOWN

1. Resettle
2. Canyon
3. Turn out (tenant)
4. Loan, cash ...
5. Metal fence
6. Political clique
12. Zero
15. Bypassed
16. Respects
17. Unforeseen complication
19. African antelope
20. Laughed
22. Sing
23. Wide

# CROSSWORD 14

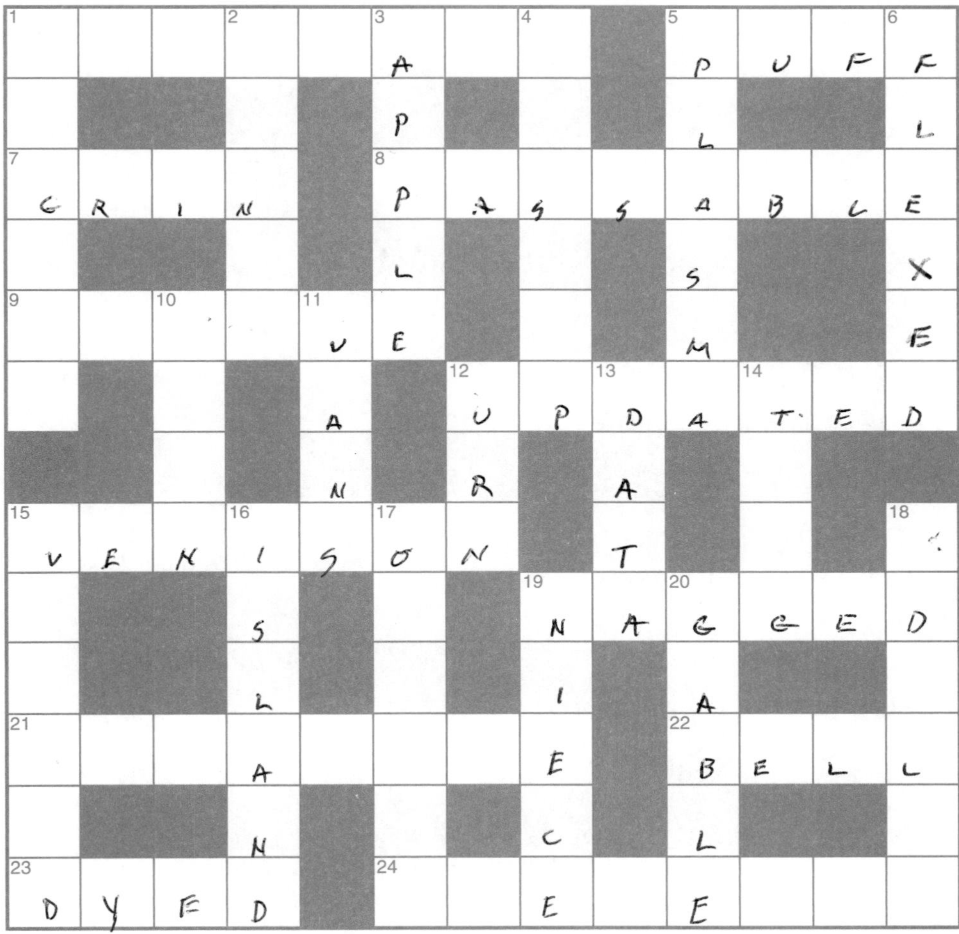

## ACROSS

1. Squid
5. Swell, ... up
7. Broad smile
8. Adequate
9. Develop
12. Made current
15. Deer flesh
19. Scolded repeatedly
21. Living being
22. Chiming instrument
23. Tinted
24. Speared

## DOWN

1. Young swan
2. Cancel
3. Cider fruit
4. Foot arch
5. Blood fluid
6. Tightened (muscle)
10. Bullocks
11. Delivery vehicles
12. Grecian pot
13. Information
14. Bully
15. Expressed
16. Land enclosed by water
17. Comes to pass
18. Muddled
19. Nephew's sister
20. Classic actor, Clark ...

# CROSSWORD 15

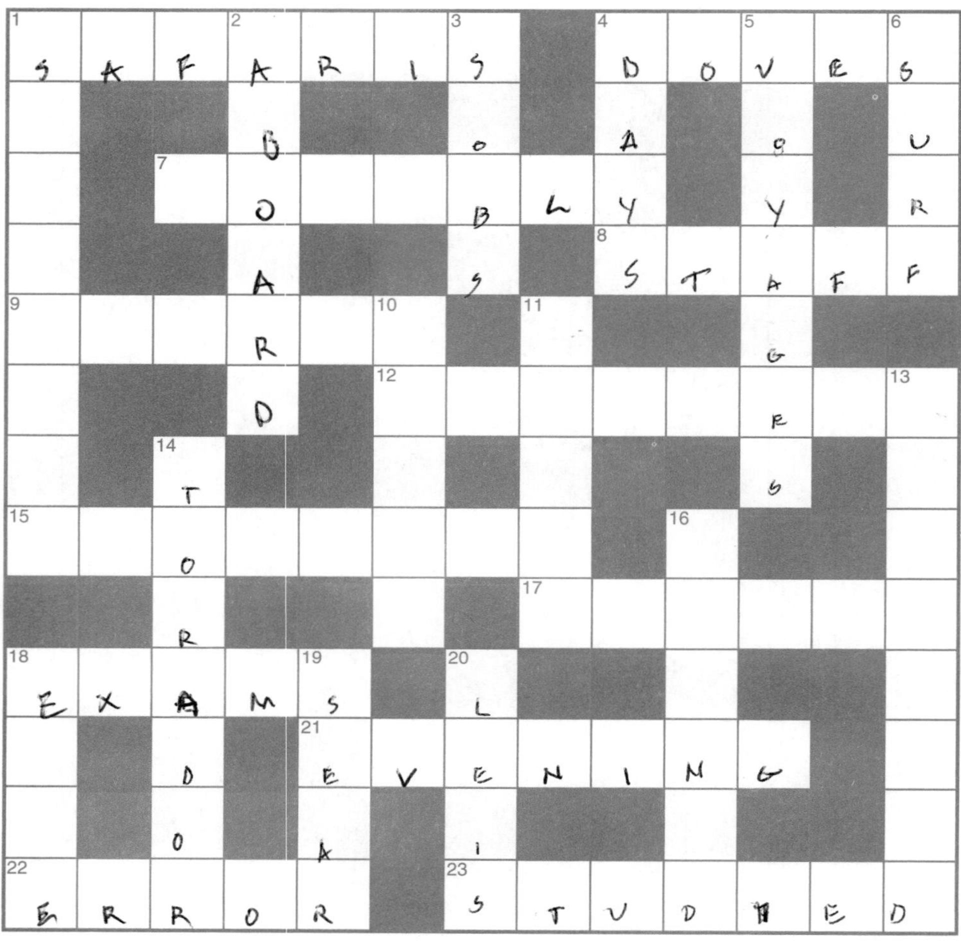

## ACROSS

1. African wildlife tours
4. Birds of peace
7. Remarkably
8. Employees
9. Craves
12. Team coaches
15. Degree-holder
17. Eluded (capture)
18. Written tests
21. After sunset
22. Mistake
23. Did research into

## DOWN

1. Wandering off
2. On train
3. Cries
4. Week divisions
5. Travels by sea
6. Ride the waves
10. Mist of water droplets
11. Person paid
13. Followed closely
14. Spanish bullfighter
16. Tinned
18. Different
19. Brown (meat) quickly
20. Hawaiian garlands

# CROSSWORD 16

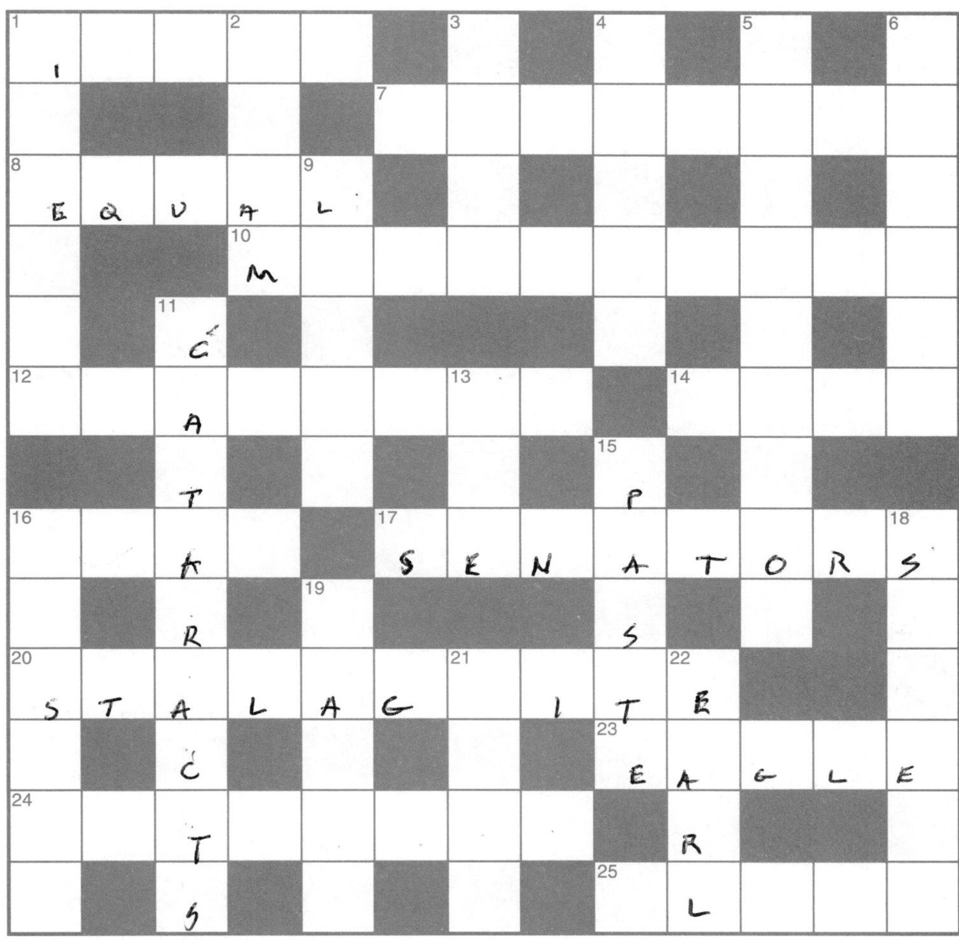

## ACROSS

1. Wharves
7. Stand astride
8. On a par with
10. Downpours
12. Theatrical
14. Collar button
16. Smooth
17. Roman statesmen
20. Limestone cave formation
23. Predatory bird
24. Perceiving
25. Book publicity hype

## DOWN

1. Waited in line
2. Annually, per ...
3. Daze
4. Endures
5. Blind devotion
6. Flexed (muscles)
9. Tibetan monks
11. Cloudy eye condition
13. Rage
15. Adhesive
16. Blending by melting
18. Excellent
19. Gravy
21. Tiny (version)
22. Fragrant tea, ... Grey

# CROSSWORD 17

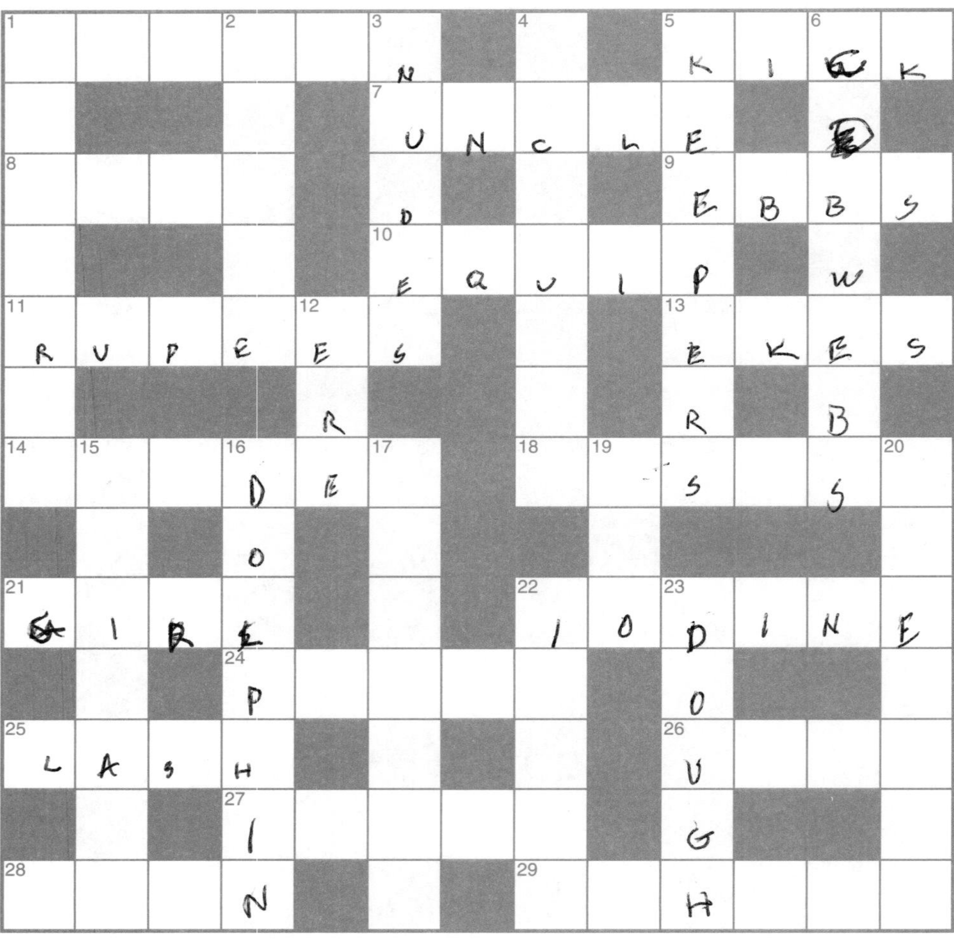

## ACROSS

1. Country
5. Strike with foot
7. Aunt's husband
8. Forearm bone
9. Tide movements, ... & flows
10. Provide with gear
11. Indian money units
13. Scrapes (out a living)
14. Docked
18. Oppose
21. Young woman
22. Abrasion disinfectant
24. Simple
25. Eyelid hair
26. Encourage
27. Intimate (thoughts)
28. Streak in cheese
29. Alternatives

## DOWN

1. Impartial
2. Idiotic (remark)
3. Artist's naked models
4. Abrasive pad
5. Zoo custodians
6. Spider traps
12. Poet's word for before
15. Shake
16. Playful sea mammal
17. Spheres of influence
19. Self-image
20. Hovers (on brink)
22. Prelude
23. Uncooked bread

# CROSSWORD 18

## ACROSS

1. Straw-roofed (cottage)
5. Carnival
7. Attire
8. Contempt
9. Freedom fighters
12. Paper fasteners
15. Frugal
19. Injured (look)
21. Intricate (pattern)
22. Leave hurriedly
23. Incursion
24. Magnifies

## DOWN

1. Striped big cats
2. Dining surface
3. Stays out of sight
4. Straight
5. Idle talk
6. Records
10. Male pig
11. Block of bread
12. Heavens
13. Vocal solo
14. Pork cut
15. Sore to touch
16. ... or outward
17. Dozen
18. Cows' milk sacs
19. Bike footrest
20. Surmise

# CROSSWORD 19

## ACROSS

1. Bows & scrapes
4. Fermenting agent
7. Recognition
8. Pours carelessly
9. Balloon gas
12. Inert
15. Collecting
17. Boats
18. Roamed
21. Envisage
22. Possibly
23. Male rower

## DOWN

1. Pony competition
2. Casualty
3. Wound mark
4. Starchy tubers
5. Of heart/lung exercises
6. Foot digits
10. Imitate
11. Pungently tasty
13. Discharge
14. Innocently
16. Perfumes
18. Space
19. Dreadful
20. Ring of light

# CROSSWORD 20

## ACROSS

1. Resident
7. Security latches
8. Room base
10. Insignificant
12. Overpowered by sound
14. Firm
16. Chinese pans
17. No longer in style
20. Self-appointed lawmen
23. Classified
24. US cattle farmers
25. Magazine copy

## DOWN

1. Hit high in the air
2. Author unknown
3. Timber fastener
4. Toils
5. Sword sheaths
6. Climb up
9. Reaffirm (promise)
11. Wrapping or container
13. Large bird
15. Fossil resin
16. Falters
18. Dally
19. First Greek letter
21. Average
22. Sinks in middle

# CROSSWORD 21

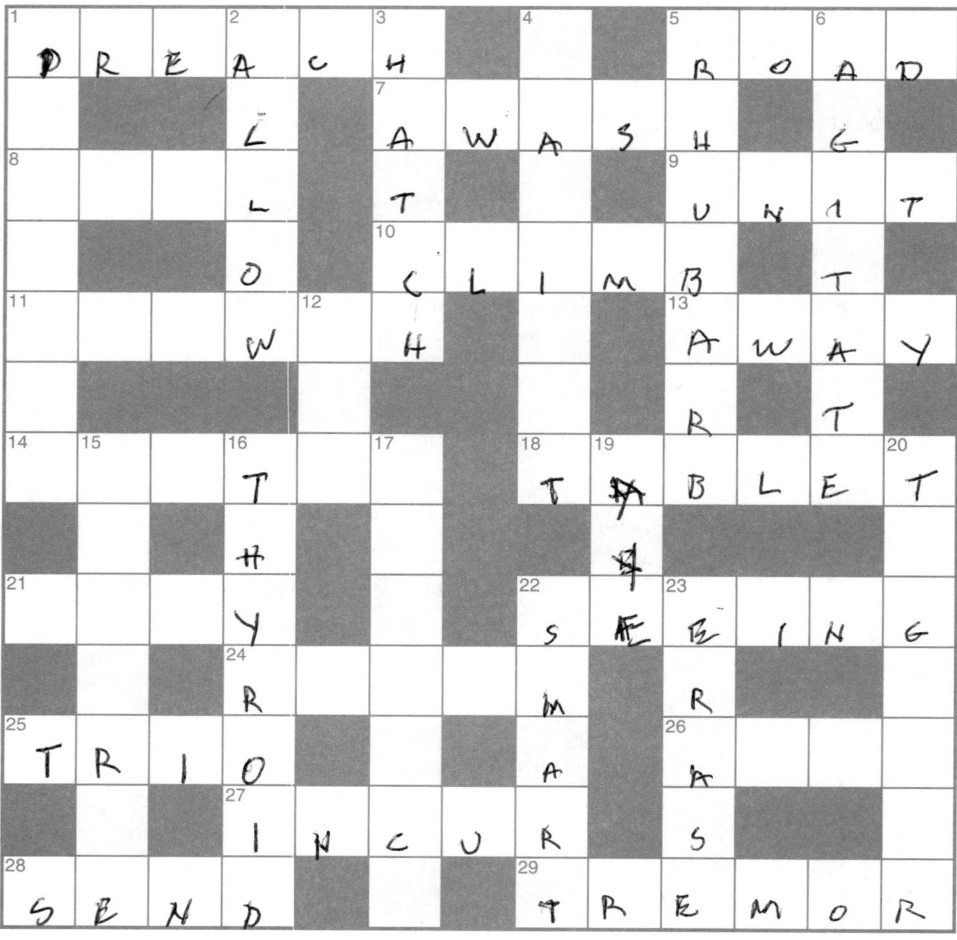

## ACROSS

1. Deliver sermon
5. Thoroughfare
7. Flooded (of decks)
8. Wicked
9. Module
10. Scale (mountain)
11. Spasm
13. Leave, go ...
14. Cleaning cloth
18. Pill
21. Resentful longing
22. Witnessing
24. Domain
25. Three-piece combo
26. Border on
27. Attract (penalty)
28. Transmit
29. Small quake

## DOWN

1. Sewn in folds
2. Allocate
3. Emerge from egg
4. Most work-shy
5. Edible leafstalk
6. Enliven
12. Reminder
15. Disconcert
16. Neck gland
17. Return game
19. Yes vote
20. Closer (of fit)
22. Clever
23. Eradicate

# CROSSWORD 22

## ACROSS

1. Ready to explode
5. Four-wheel vehicle, ... bike
7. Bluefin creature
8. Make larger
9. Freshest
12. Nasty
15. Telling untruth
19. Trouser pouch
21. Public protests
22. Mausoleum
23. Slithered
24. Preserve as sacred

## DOWN

1. Casting ballot
2. Informed
3. Simpleton
4. Enclose in box
5. Searches
6. Profoundly
10. Uterus
11. Half
12. Gigantic
13. Too
14. Long elephant tooth
15. Inundates
16. Reinforced
17. Local inhabitant
18. Horse barn
19. Sits for artist
20. More appealing

# CROSSWORD 23

## ACROSS

1. Natural (of food)
4. Moves listlessly
7. Property, personal ...
8. Rogue
9. Leave empty
12. Strolls aimlessly
15. Orderliness
17. Howled shrilly
18. Leg joints
21. Sad play
22. Bereaved woman
23. Surpassed

## DOWN

1. Obscurity
2. Public disturbance
3. Male bird
4. Perfume ingredient
5. Buccaneers
6. Painful
10. Lodge firmly
11. Common flower
13. Combination of symptoms
14. Playfully skipped
16. Flew without power
18. Was conversant with
19. Store (cargo)
20. Palm starch

# CROSSWORD 24

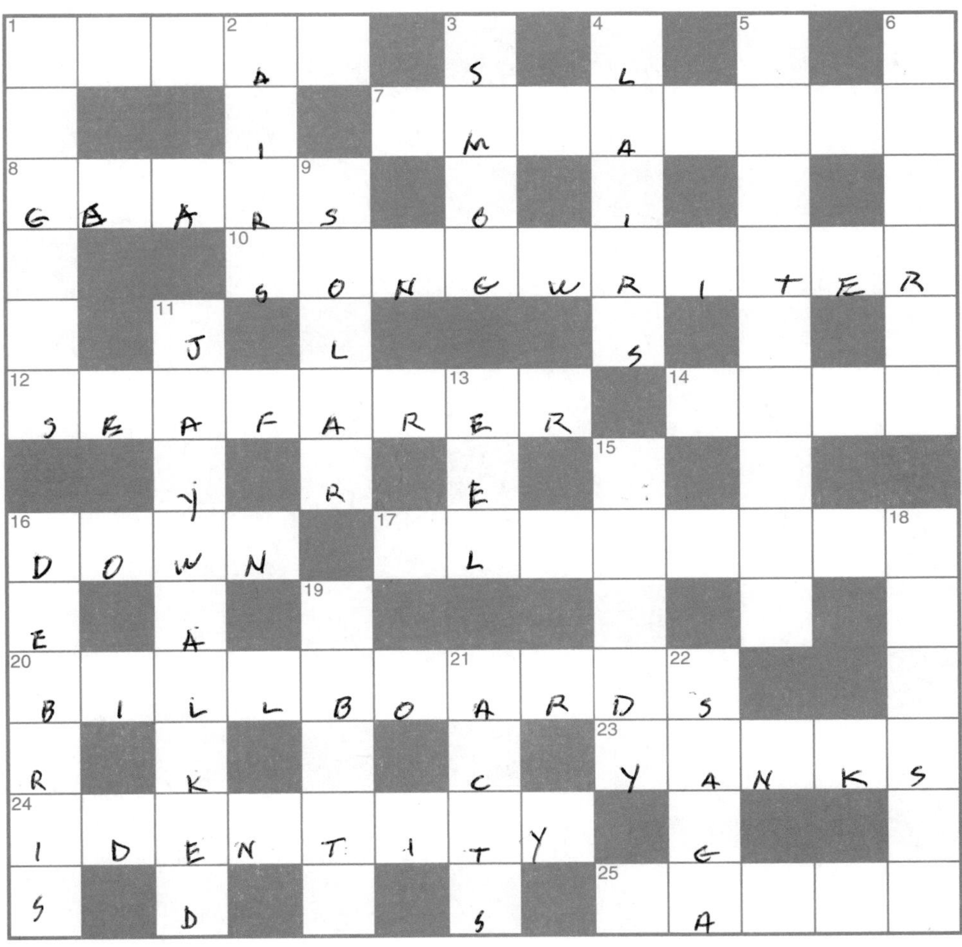

## ACROSS

1. Person, ... being
7. Went aboard ship
8. Cogwheel set
10. Lyricist
12. Sailor
14. In this way
16. Small, soft feathers
17. Pact
20. Advertising signs
23. Tugs sharply
24. ID, ... card
25. Young deer

## DOWN

1. Scottish dish
2. Ventilates
3. Smoke & fog
4. Animal dens
5. Drawing
6. Beautifies
9. Of the sun
11. Crossed street carelessly
13. Conger fish
15. Squally
16. Wreckage
18. Survives
19. Ease off
21. Performs on stage
22. Lengthy story

# CROSSWORD 25

## ACROSS

1. Forceful request
5. Unseat
7. In need of scratching
8. Smear
9. Doe's mate
10. Skin transplant
11. Sedately
13. Inscribe
14. Sound mental health
18. Final option, last ...
21. Taken off air
22. Swirled
24. Proprietor
25. Letterhead insignia
26. Japanese wine
27. Mountain chain
28. Invites
29. Dictator

## DOWN

1. Subtracts
2. Snapshots book
3. Dirty-looking
4. Paint-removing tool
5. Pearl-bearers
6. Less abundant
12. Large amount
15. Worried
16. Within building
17. Opening mouth wide
19. Culminate
20. Most orderly
22. Miscalculated
23. Gives medicine to

# CROSSWORD 26

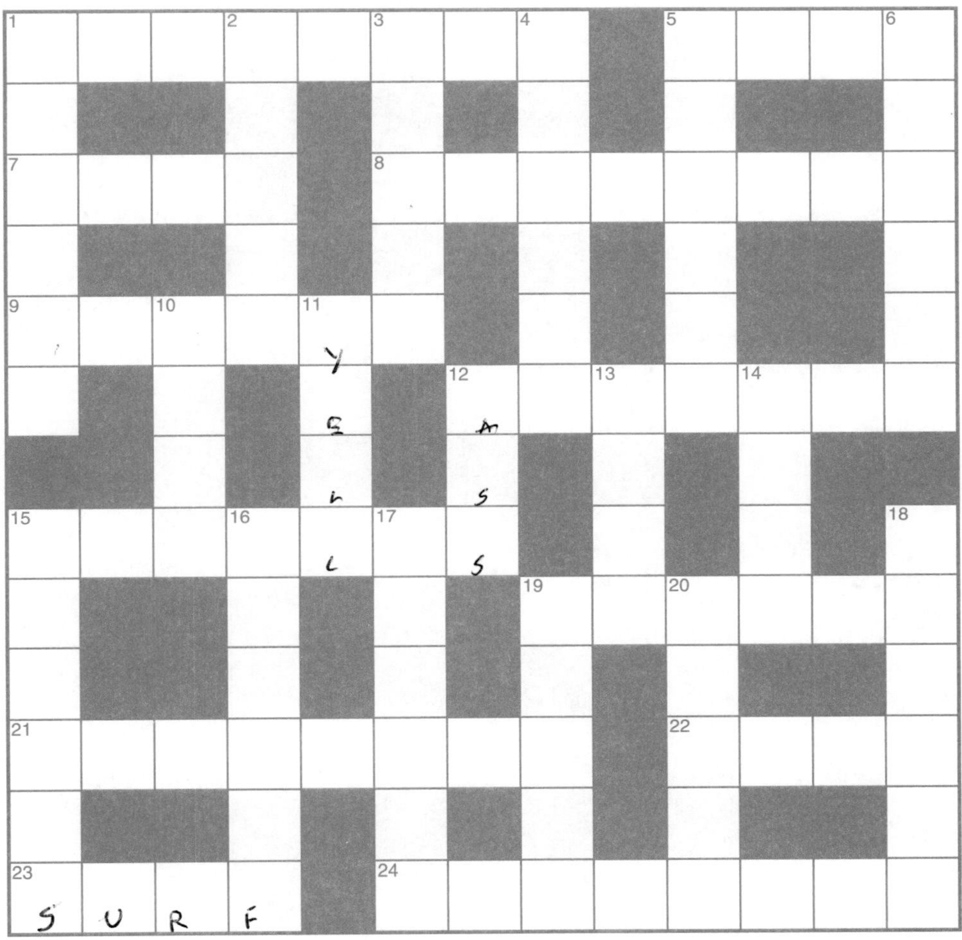

## ACROSS

1. Baby water bird
5. Unchanged, the ...
7. Unconscious state
8. Seepages
9. Charge with crime
12. Postal destination
15. Trembles
19. Take care of
21. Connective tissue
22. Rein in
23. Ride waves
24. Pungent roots

## DOWN

1. Treachery
2. Dull brownish-yellow
3. Cove
4. Fed on pasture
5. Beard trimmer
6. Eventuates
10. Speechless
11. Cry out
12. Horse-like animal
13. Test-drive car, ... model
14. Leave
15. Planets
16. For, on ... of
17. Make beloved
18. Extended family groups
19. Entertained lavishly
20. Gets rid of (employee)

# CROSSWORD 27

## ACROSS

1. Soldiers' sacks
4. Tropical fruit
7. Ice performers
8. Store away greedily
9. Subtle shade of meaning
12. Become stale
15. Study the heavens
17. Hung in folds
18. Metallic (of sound)
21. Made possible for
22. Of the nose
23. Go over again

## DOWN

1. Humanity
2. Cooking
3. Prosecuted
4. Deep cut
5. Yearbook of forecasts
6. Mimicked
10. Student's written assignment
11. Walked back & forth
13. Courtroom testimony
14. Heavy weapons
16. Profession
18. Change direction
19. Scream
20. Set of two

# CROSSWORD 28

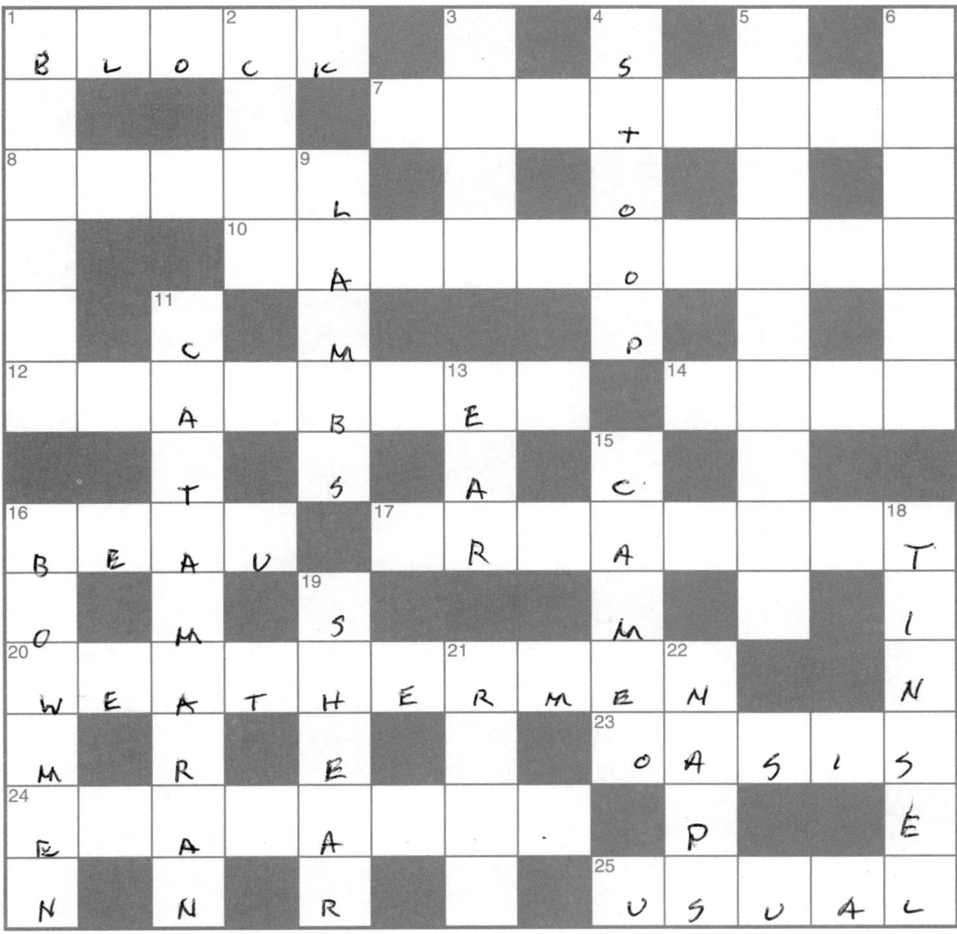

## ACROSS

1. Prevent entry of
7. Keep going
8. Essential
10. Convalescent home
12. More threadbare
14. Cater for
16. Suitor
17. Adornment
20. Meteorologists
23. Fertile desert spots
24. Proceeds (from)
25. Customary

## DOWN

1. Low couches
2. Woe!
3. Fizzy drink
4. Bend down
5. Brightened up
6. Appeared
9. Ewe's offspring
11. Twin-hulled vessel
13. Listening organ
15. Raised carving on brooch
16. Archers
18. Glittery decoration
19. Cut fleece off
21. Regretted
22. Dozes

# CROSSWORD 29

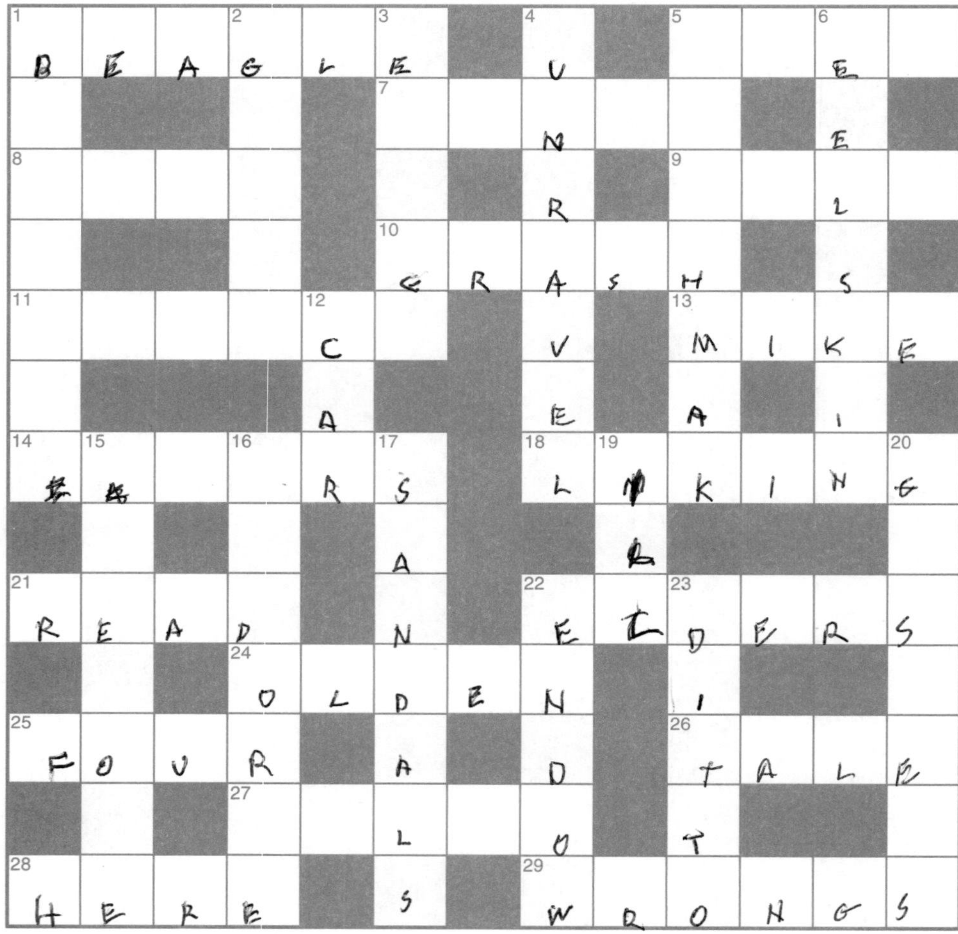

## ACROSS

1. Short-legged hound
5. Harness (oxen)
7. Red dye
8. Chamber
9. Soap bubbles
10. Fail (of computer)
11. Assail
13. Actor, ... Myers
14. Restaurant patrons
18. Fondness
21. Enjoyable book, good ...
22. Tribal seniors
24. Ancient
25. Twice two
26. Story
27. Volley of bullets
28. In this place
29. Injustices

## DOWN

1. Bombardment
2. South American dance
3. Dense
4. Come undone
5. Muslim woman's veil
6. Soft leather
12. Motor vehicle
15. Stupendous
16. Second (motion)
17. Strappy shoes
19. Edgy, ... at ease
20. Sealants
22. Bequeath
23. Repeat symbol

# CROSSWORD 30

## ACROSS

1. Criminal acts
5. Three feet
7. Achievement
8. Task-completion date
9. Voice box
12. Twist together
15. Run amok, go ...
19. Gratify
21. Dislodge (jockey)
22. Cattle meat
23. Wool
24. Males' clothing department

## DOWN

1. Violin
2. Peculiarly
3. Tabulated list
4. Flower part
5. Egg-yolk shade
6. Haul up (from depths)
10. Back section
11. Cat's lives
12. Large antlered animal
13. Above average height
14. Minuscule amount
15. Attractiveness
16. Wrench (ankle)
17. Haphazard
18. Young cow
19. Groom feathers
20. Arm joint

# CROSSWORD 31

## ACROSS

1. Imagine, ... up
4. Wishes
7. Daunt
8. Startle
9. Announce
12. Partaking of liquor
15. Greatness
17. Hypnotic state
18. Articulate
21. Surrendered
22. Taunt
23. Unbridled

## DOWN

1. Cold symptom, ... spasm
2. Jolly
3. Ages
4. Weeding implements
5. Egyptian burial building
6. Fully satisfy
10. Eater
11. Call off
13. Ruled (country)
14. Eyelash darkener
16. Photo device
18. Volcano shaft
19. Ancient stringed instrument
20. Restaurant list

# CROSSWORD 32

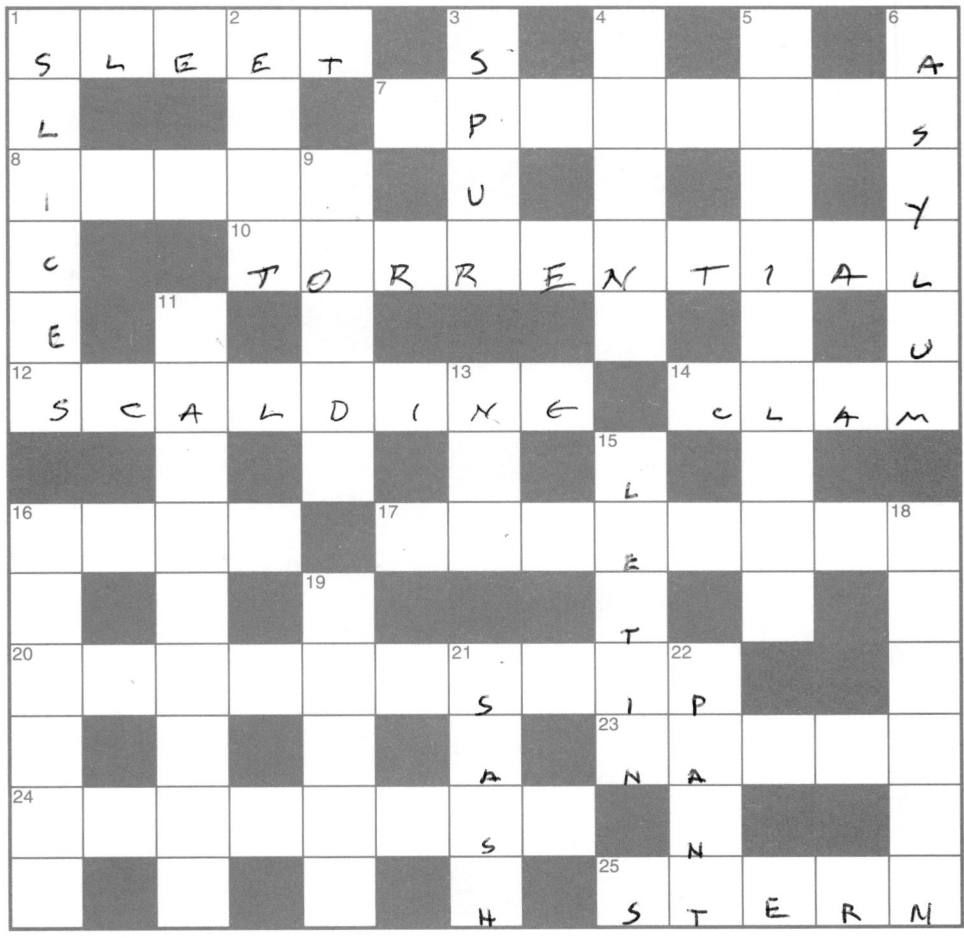

## ACROSS

1. Falls in icy flakes
7. Speechmakers
8. Parish minister
10. Heavy (rain)
12. Burning with hot water
14. Giant shellfish
16. Part of speech
17. Blushed
20. Command
23. Applied levy
24. Most in want
25. Rear of ship

## DOWN

1. Cuts off
2. Which?
3. Cowboy's boot spike
4. Repairs (knitwear)
5. Topping up
6. Psychiatric hospital
9. Noisy
11. Drenches
13. Formerly named
15. Allow inside
16. Sheer hosiery
18. Benumb
19. Earn
21. Silk band
22. Breathe rapidly

# CROSSWORD 33

## ACROSS

1. Sikh headwear
5. Chew like rat
7. Degrade
8. Paw nail
9. Acceptable
10. Dreadful
11. Medieval
13. Was obliged to pay
14. Cavalry spears
18. Most introverted
21. Brass instrument
22. Called (of donkey)
24. Lifting device
25. Mixed-up mess
26. Coffee seed
27. Do well (at)
28. Castrate (horse)
29. Goes into

## DOWN

1. Diplomatic
2. Curtsied
3. Of birth
4. Confounds
5. Study of rocks
6. Emerges from sleep
12. Unreturnable tennis serve
15. Flatter to excess
16. Trained (team)
17. Graze
19. Him or ...
20. News
22. Prettiest girl, ... of the ball
23. Monastery superior

# CROSSWORD 34

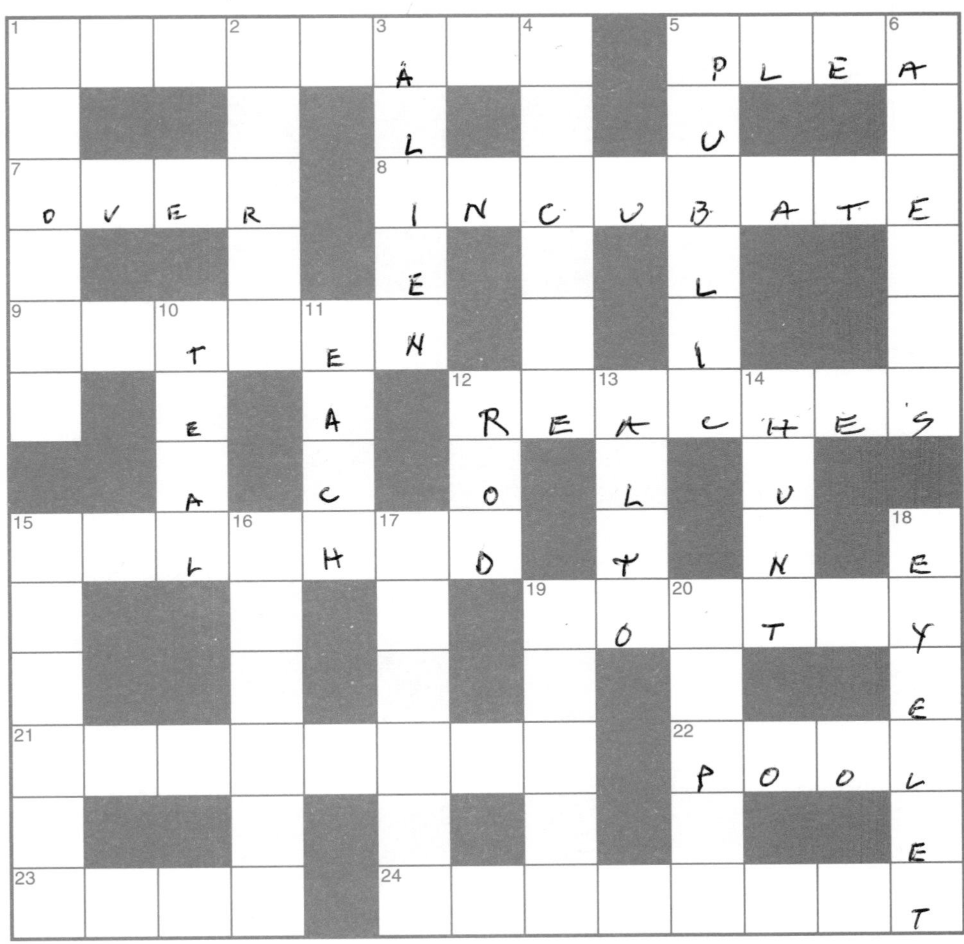

## ACROSS

1. In this day & age
5. Fervent request
7. Expired
8. Warm (eggs) to hatch
9. Heavy (heart)
12. Stretches (for)
15. Cooked (salmon)
19. Verse
21. Exposed film
22. Swimming area
23. Arrived
24. Monarchist

## DOWN

1. Lump of mineral in rock
2. Lent a hand to
3. Foreign
4. Safe
5. General populace
6. Makes correct
10. Greenish-blue
11. To ... their own
12. Baton
13. Highest male singing voice
14. Stalk prey
15. Outdoor meal
16. Assistant clergyman
17. More nervous
18. Opening for laces
19. Religious devotion
20. Dismiss

# CROSSWORD 35

## ACROSS

1. Unkind
4. Sedate (character)
7. Impudent newcomer
8. Colloquial usage
9. Did penance (for)
12. Leftover pieces
15. Vacate (threatened area)
17. Flipped (through book)
18. Mix
21. Stretch tape
22. Sports teams
23. King or queen

## DOWN

1. Migraine
2. Writing by machine
3. Trimmed of fat
4. Complete collections
5. Achieves
6. Medication
10. Great fear
11. Drive forward
13. Bread snack
14. Placed bet
16. Dribble
18. Foundation garments
19. Criminals' hide-outs
20. Cultivate land

# CROSSWORD 36

## ACROSS

1. Common cereal
7. Gun levers
8. Dog parasites
10. Galloper's track
12. Studies closely
14. Tower (over)
16. Dowdy
17. Odd-job person
20. Milk dessert
23. Lessened
24. Raises
25. Recurrent pattern

## DOWN

1. Belgian breakfast treat
2. At a distance
3. Costing nothing
4. Snow house
5. Old family treasures
6. Admiration
9. Sri Lankan robes
11. Information banks
13. Due time (1,1,1)
15. Proverb
16. Lightly touched
18. Asian food item
19. Atlantic or Indian
21. Matured
22. Simple

# CROSSWORD 37

## ACROSS

1. Respect paid
5. Winter garment
7. Offensively showy
8. Hairless
9. Force of troops
10. Alcoves
11. Noisily
13. Terrace level
14. Side dishes
18. Signify
21. Raised (livestock)
22. Moved closer towards
24. Corpulent
25. Those people
26. Expensive
27. Pass (law)
28. Whirled
29. Simmered slowly

## DOWN

1. Limps
2. Totted up
3. Hard black wood
4. Enticed
5. Reprove
6. Seat divider
12. ... & lass
15. Zeppelin
16. Stomach
17. Quite a few
19. Make last, ... out
20. Survived
22. Ants' homes
23. Muddle

# CROSSWORD 38

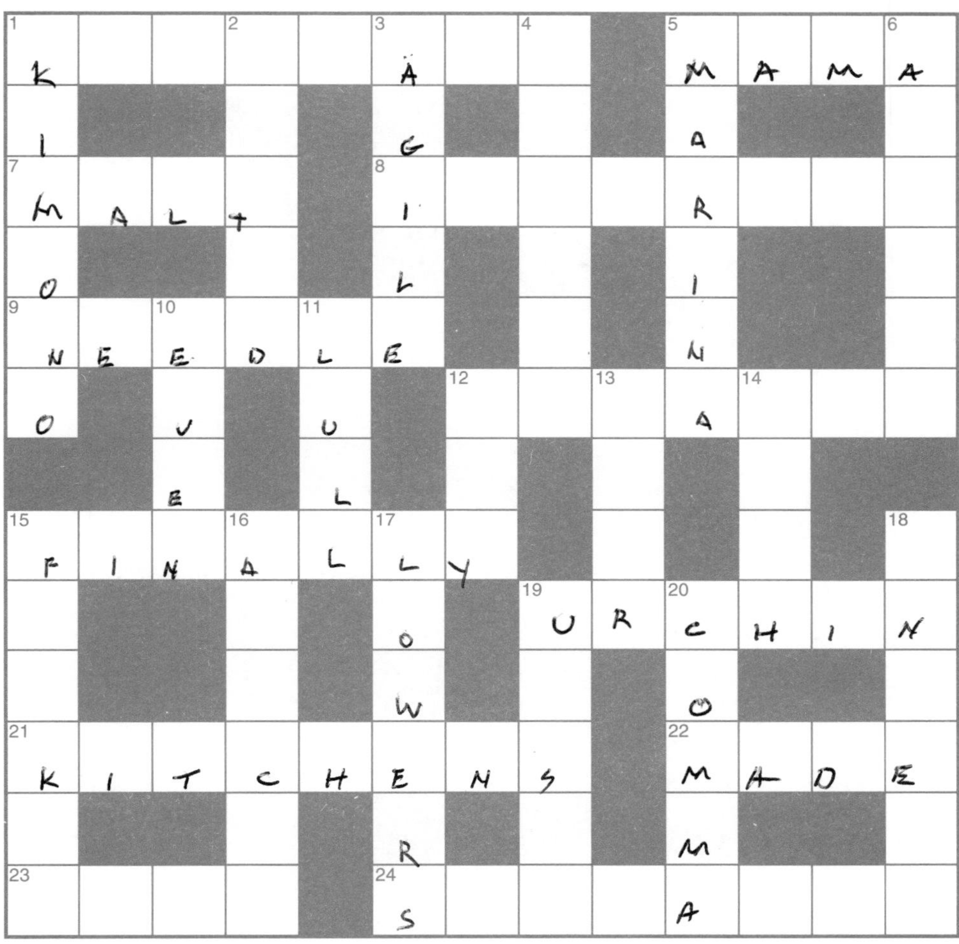

## ACROSS

1. Data entry pad
5. ... & papa
7. Honey liquor
8. Internally
9. Syringe spike
12. Preferably
15. In conclusion
19. Spiny creature, sea ...
21. Rooms for cooking
22. Fabricated
23. Drains
24. Placed

## DOWN

1. Japanese dress
2. Waited
3. Nimble
4. Arrived (of day)
5. Yacht basin
6. Besides
10. Level
11. Pause (in storm)
12. Very cold
13. Large pitcher
14. Luxuriant
15. Snow crystals
16. Bead-frame calculator
17. Reduces
18. Straighten
19. Unnerve
20. Punctuation mark

# CROSSWORD 39

## ACROSS

1. Outrun
4. Mania
7. Ineffective
8. Glorify
9. Large lizard
12. Lodgers
15. Relationships
17. High-gloss paint
18. Corn husks
21. Jumbled letter puzzle
22. Pursuit
23. Seizes (aircraft)

## DOWN

1. Unique
2. Of mail
3. Viewed
4. Detective's assignment
5. Attire
6. Prepare (manuscript)
10. Dislike intensely
11. Make happen
13. Stars' wardrobe specialists
14. Card game
16. Curved fruit
18. Fashionable
19. Celebrity status
20. Tub

# CROSSWORD 40

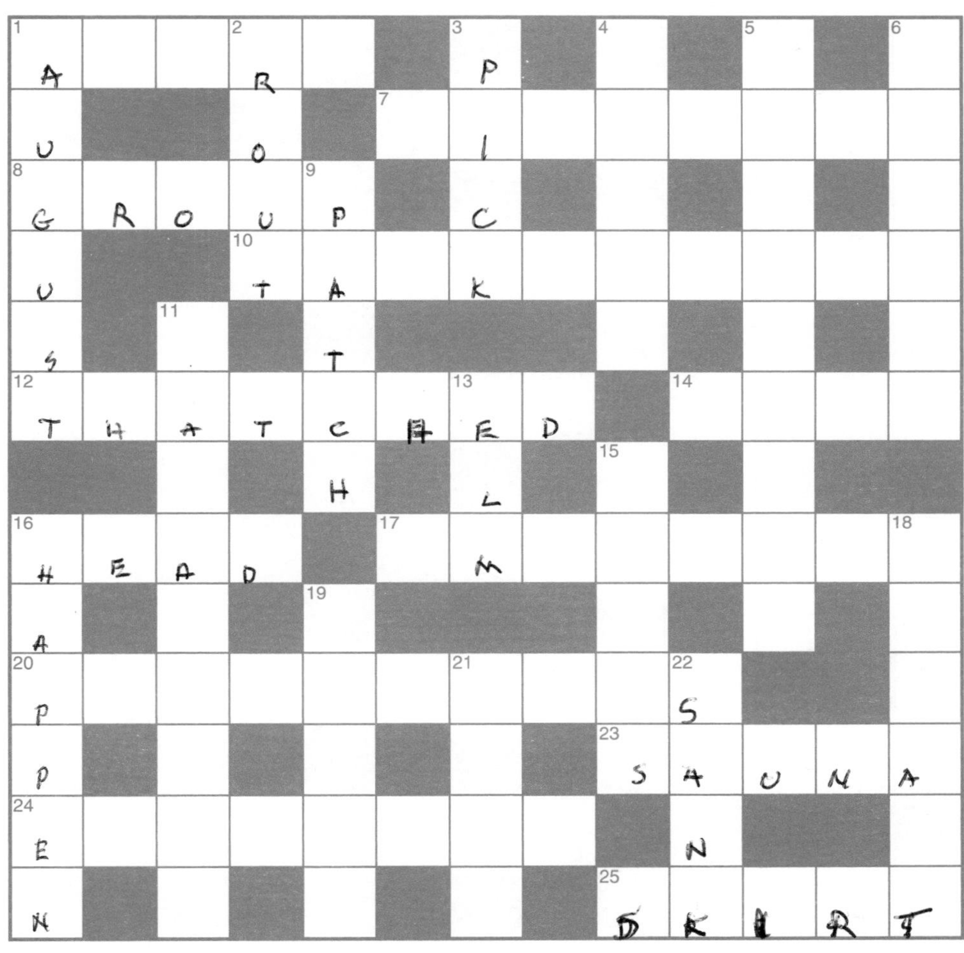

## ACROSS

1. Ward off
7. Provided funds for
8. Collection
10. Harsh boss
12. Roofs with straw
14. Split apart
16. Skull
17. Impending
20. Practical jokers
23. Steam-room
24. Overshadows
25. Woman's garment

## DOWN

1. Eighth month
2. Severe defeat
3. Select
4. Festivals
5. Strewn
6. Loved deeply
9. Eye cover
11. Pleasant tasting
13. Deciduous tree
15. Wharves
16. Occur
18. Rent payer
19. Jumps rope
21. Adolescent
22. Became submerged

# CROSSWORD 41

## ACROSS

1. Vulgarly
5. Nitrogen-rich soil additive
7. Ellipses
8. 100th of dollar
9. Cure
10. Illustrious
11. Aromatic spice
13. Smell strongly
14. Come into view
18. Brutality
21. Wound crust
22. Blunt refusal
24. Picture
25. Coffin stand
26. Replenish
27. Sewn folds
28. Net
29. Prolong

## DOWN

1. Grant permit to
2. Information item
3. Not old
4. Wagers
5. Escorted
6. Pencil rubbers
12. Poultry product
15. Mechanical device
16. New beginning
17. Improve
19. Alcoholic brew
20. Dampened (sound)
22. Recycle
23. Suit

## ACROSS

1. De-ices (freezer)
5. Groan
7. Actor, ... Damon
8. Impel
9. Trophies
12. Associations
15. Convent
19. Wimbledon sport
21. Vows
22. Shrek is one
23. Hand rest
24. Human frame

## DOWN

1. Lower dignity of
2. Helicopter blade
3. Drainage pits
4. Sofa
5. Budging
6. Sibling's daughters
10. Prayer's final word
11. Valley
12. Produce (egg)
13. Land measure
14. Onto
15. Crab claw
16. Ordinary
17. Heightens
18. Rearward (nautical)
19. Mouth sensors, ... buds
20. Lasso loop

# CROSSWORD 43

## ACROSS

1. Trenches
4. Aggravated
7. Duo
8. Warning bell
9. Every 60 minutes
12. Absconders
15. Wavered
17. Gazed fixedly
18. Embezzlement
21. Passes (of time)
22. Funeral song
23. Poisoning by fumes

## DOWN

1. Ring-shaped cake
2. Scared person
3. Cease
4. Clueless, no ...
5. Massaged
6. Grim fate
10. Annual periods
11. Corrosive substances
13. Young plant
14. For that reason
16. Clothing tags
18. Forgery
19. Say it isn't so
20. Sharp twinge

# CROSSWORD 44

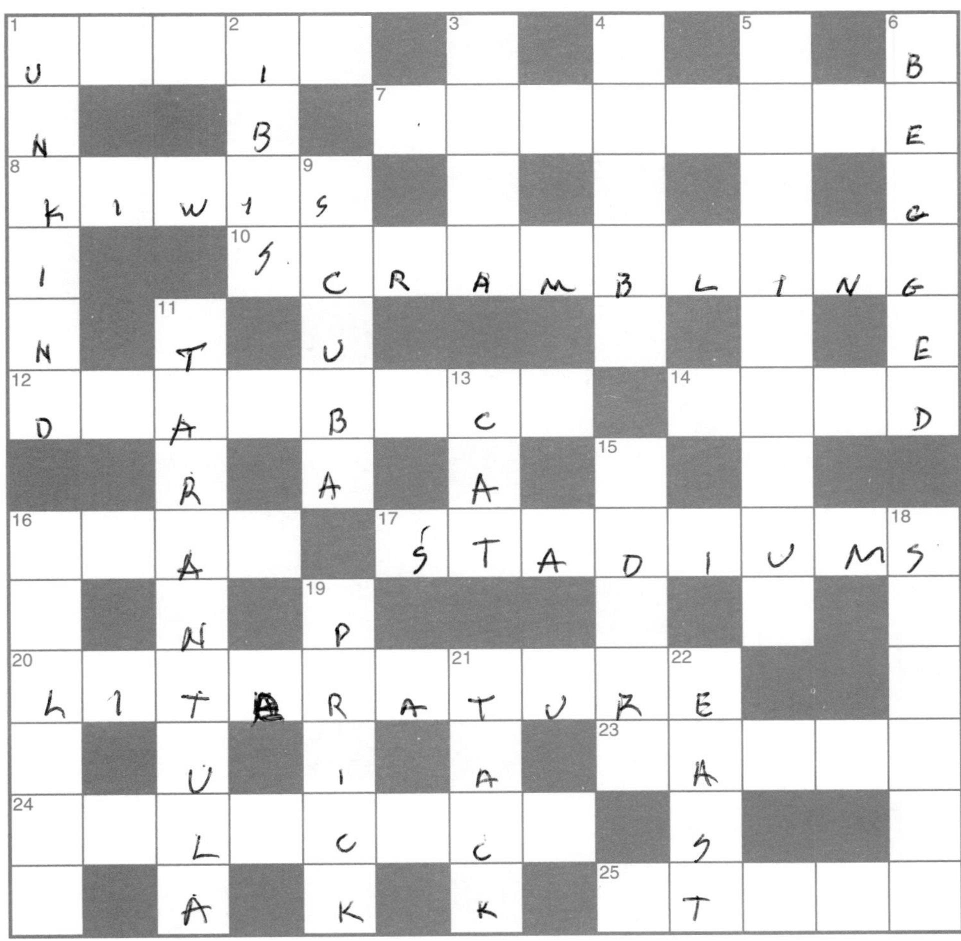

## ACROSS

1. Up to the time
7. Clamber
8. New Zealand birds
10. Scurrying
12. Snag
14. Unearth
16. Edible flesh
17. Sports arenas
20. Reading material
23. Gullible
24. Tasty morsel
25. Remained upright

## DOWN

1. Cruel
2. Spoonbill relative
3. Swindle
4. Candle
5. Unaware
6. Sought alms
9. Skin-diving gear
11. Huge spider
13. Purring animal
15. Decorate
16. Tune
18. Astute
19. Needle stab
21. Change yacht's course
22. Opposite of west

# CROSSWORD 45

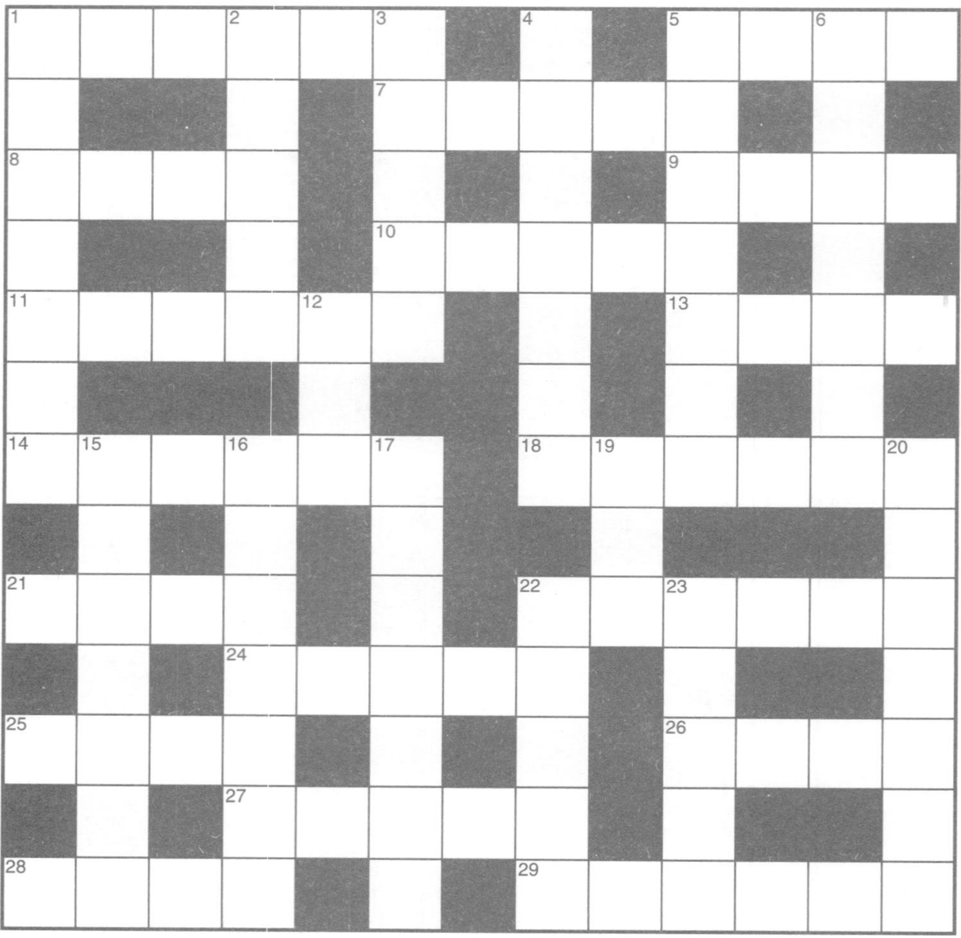

## ACROSS

1. Tile-chip design
5. Samples (wine)
7. Not censored
8. Stun
9. Raise (eyebrows)
10. Swigged
11. Oversights
13. Single thing
14. Hold back (growth)
18. Absorb (nourishment)
21. Cramped (space)
22. Inbred
24. Tasteless (food)
25. Weight unit
26. Social custom
27. Reside
28. Purely
29. Perspires

## DOWN

1. Interfering person
2. Zones
3. ... & whey
4. Scuffed (shoes)
5. Watching covertly, ... out
6. Strike lines
12. Misjudge
15. Feeling
16. Anyone
17. Impairs
19. Tavern
20. Contract bids
22. Objects of worship
23. River vessel

# CROSSWORD 46

## ACROSS

1. Likely
5. Mellow
7. Fix
8. Sauerkraut vegetables
9. Commands
12. Daily record
15. Type of herb
19. Outlook
21. False appearance
22. Taste defeat
23. Sleepy sigh
24. Water outlets

## DOWN

1. Cheerleader's accessory
2. Shift
3. Gives support to
4. Plant seed part
5. Nastier
6. Scatter
10. Room entrance
11. Tumble over & over
12. Gladness
13. Cremation vessels
14. Agreeable
15. Wages hand-out time
16. Campaign motto
17. Improve
18. Horses
19. In the lead
20. Spotted pattern, ... dots

# CROSSWORD 47

## ACROSS

1. Most heated
4. Gorge
7. Impales
8. Do business
9. Curiously coincidental
12. Public addresses
15. Craving
17. Waning
18. Peruvian mammal
21. Tribal leader
22. Social gathering
23. Frenzied

## DOWN

1. Terribly
2. Symbols
3. Neckwear items
4. Throw (fishing line)
5. Pilot
6. Wordless acting
10. Gripe pain
11. Emblem
13. Cuddled (up)
14. Administrator
16. Chafe
18. Rope circle
19. Nautical greeting
20. Abandoned infant

# CROSSWORD 48

## ACROSS

1. Tin or iron
7. Grainy polishing substance
8. Unfasten (garment)
10. Moons
12. Dough ball
14. Uncontrolled slide
16. Hogs
17. Nominates
20. Castle moat crossing
23. Chaos
24. Hurling out
25. Small islands

## DOWN

1. Manhandled
2. Line of rotation
3. Reed instrument
4. Insanely
5. Getting wrong
6. Discontinued
9. Wooden buckets
11. Settles in another country
13. Snooze
15. Unedited film, ... cut
16. Army chaplains
18. Voids
19. Lies adjacent to
21. Charged particles
22. Listening organs

# CROSSWORD 49

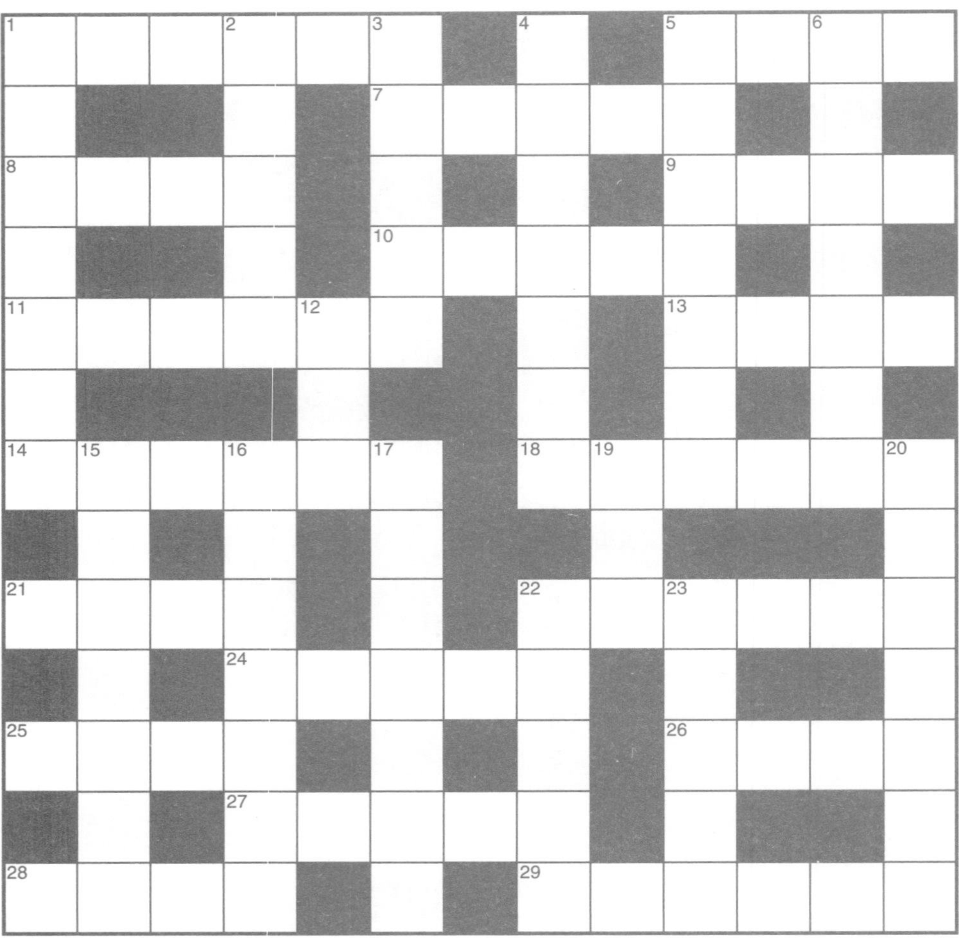

## ACROSS

1. Drumming insect
5. Other way, ... versa
7. Local vegetation
8. Solemn vow
9. Bring in (harvest)
10. Suggest
11. For men or women
13. Involved in
14. Double bike
18. Overwhelm
21. Use computer keyboard
22. Hold tenderly
24. Pour clumsily
25. Excavates
26. Leer
27. Fencing blades
28. Stitched garment edges
29. Film-background performers

## DOWN

1. Hoop/mallet sport
2. Fire remains
3. Fasten (to)
4. Assemble (list)
5. Differing
6. Of the beach
12. Ram's mate
15. Soon, ... now (3,4)
16. Puts clothes on
17. Drove
19. And not
20. Tentacles
22. Selected
23. Concerning

# CROSSWORD 50

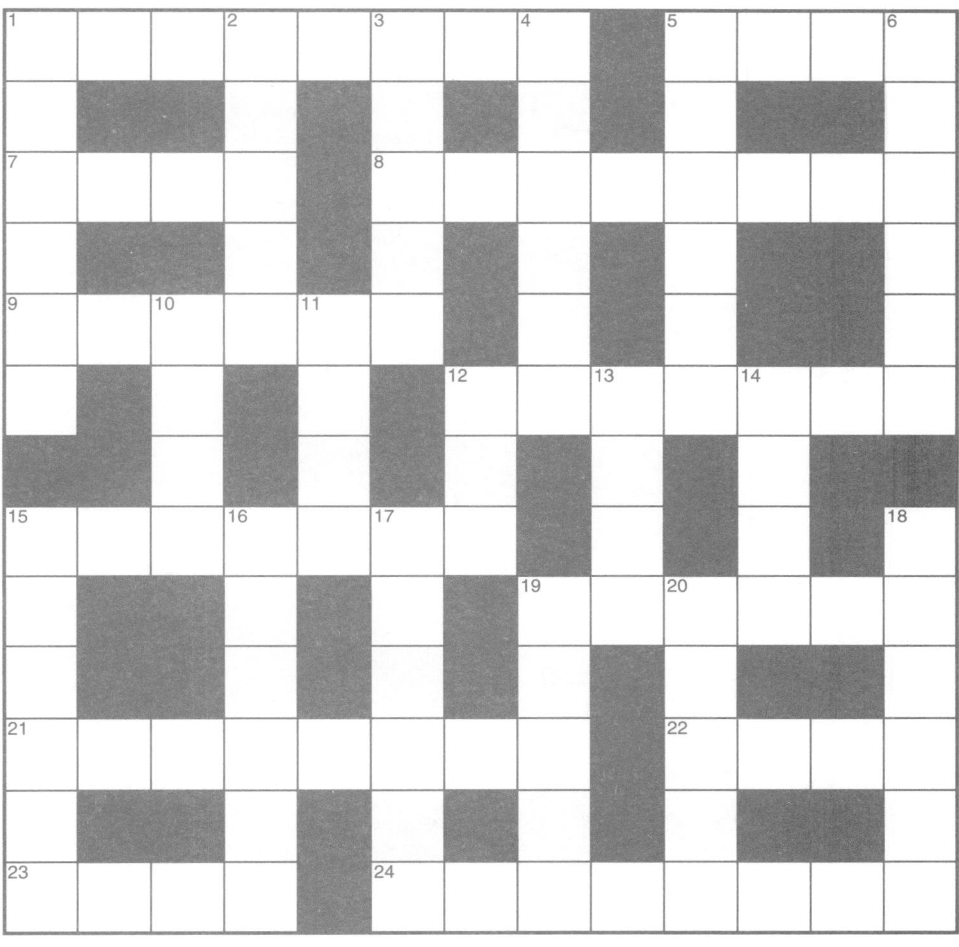

## ACROSS

1. Legal representative
5. Wet weather
7. Money
8. Relating to Vesuvius or Etna
9. Not as wealthy
12. Weirdness
15. Pistol sheath
19. Expresses (opinion)
21. Fashion accessories
22. Tibet's Dalai ...
23. Snow vehicle
24. Paraffin oil

## DOWN

1. Receive
2. Different
3. Under no circumstances
4. Shouted
5. Cause
6. Wall recesses
10. Cloudy gem
11. Give off
12. Belonging to us
13. Extinct bird
14. Grand-scale
15. Silences
16. Screened from sun
17. Venture forth
18. Landed property
19. Helmet face protector
20. Lazes

# CROSSWORD 51

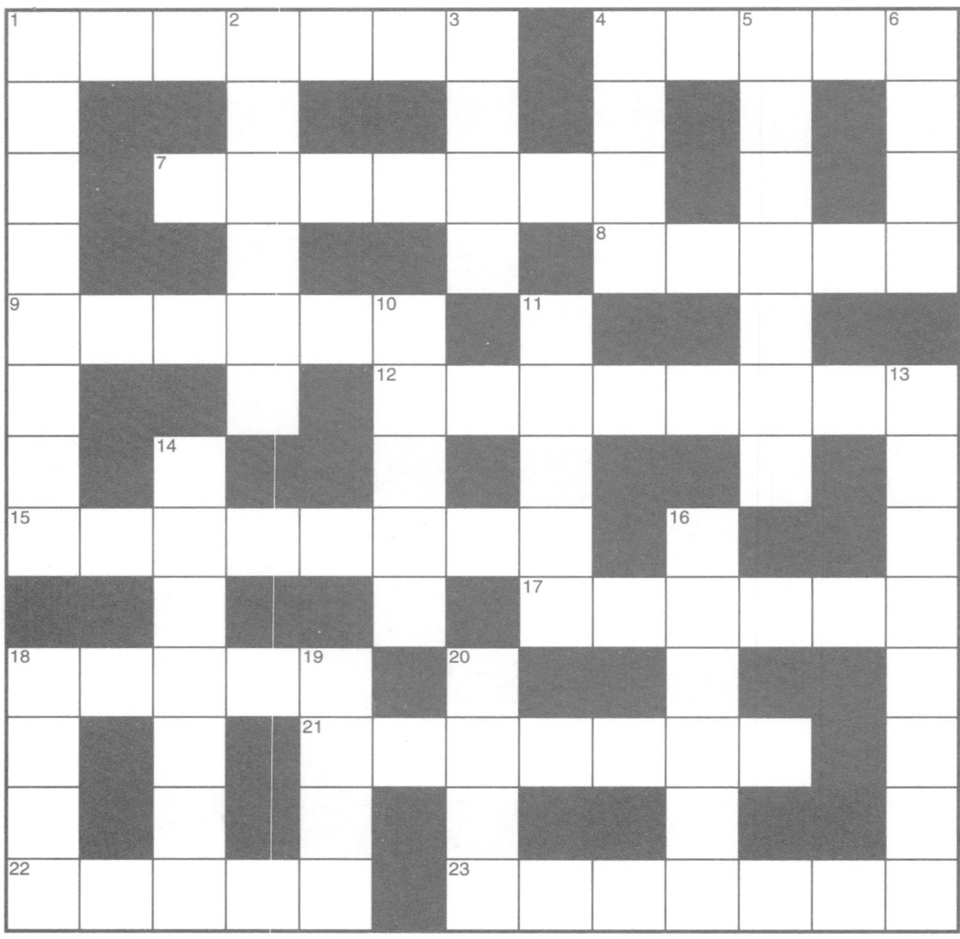

## ACROSS

1. Law officer
4. Day & ...
7. Attack with missiles
8. Remain upright
9. Steering devices
12. Gladdens
15. Sword sheath
17. Humbled
18. Detected sound
21. Angrily
22. Large pieces
23. Hunter-gatherer

## DOWN

1. Laterally
2. Resume business
3. Brave deed
4. Bobs head
5. Lubricates
6. Frog-like animal
10. Submerged sandbank
11. Tarot items
13. Shabbier
14. Model of virtue
16. Mexican flower
18. Tall
19. Short swims
20. Baby whale

# CROSSWORD 52

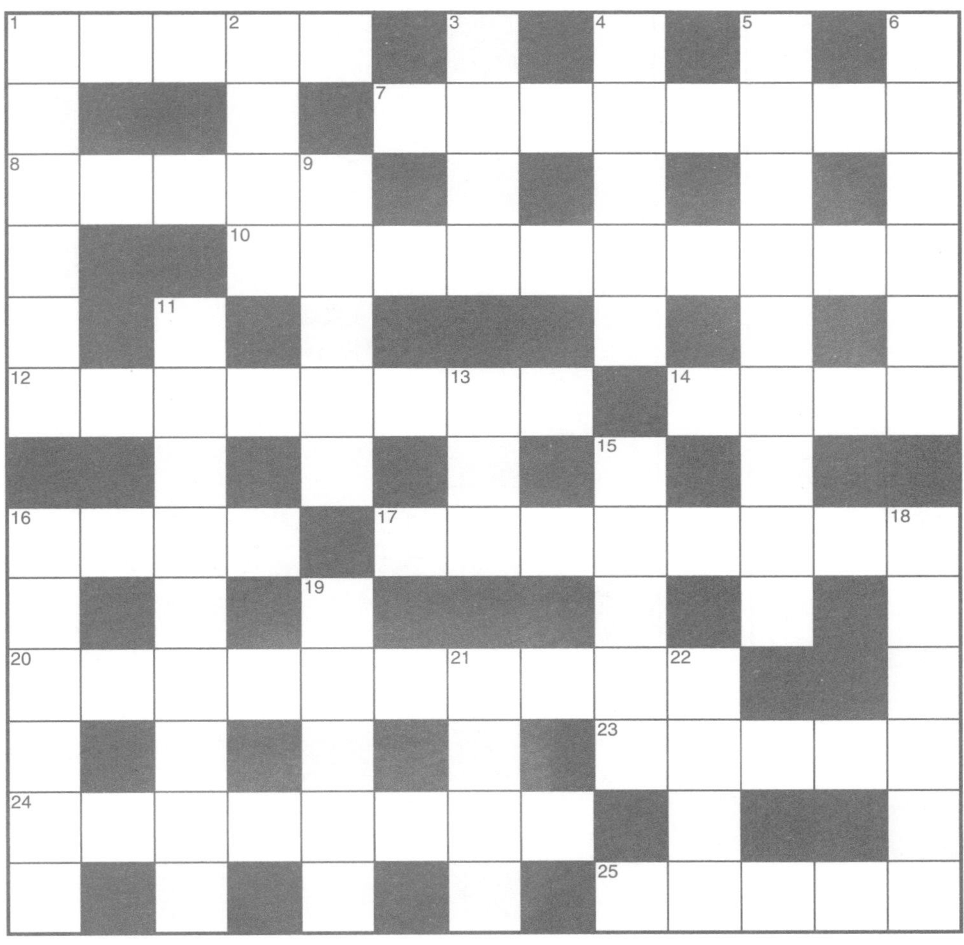

## ACROSS

1. Inserted piece
7. Military occupiers
8. Smooths out (shirt creases)
10. Sixtieth, ..., eightieth
12. Defames
14. Roman garment
16. Annoys constantly
17. Waste discharge
20. Revived (interest)
23. Animal trainer
24. Precious stones
25. Son or daughter

## DOWN

1. Simpletons
2. Geological periods
3. The A of AM
4. Taunts
5. Evolved
6. Respiratory disorder
9. Transmits
11. Dialects
13. Football arbiter
15. Group of warships
16. Ward workers
18. Hot (of climate)
19. Scanning device
21. Small whirlpool
22. Morse symbols, dot & ...

# CROSSWORD 53

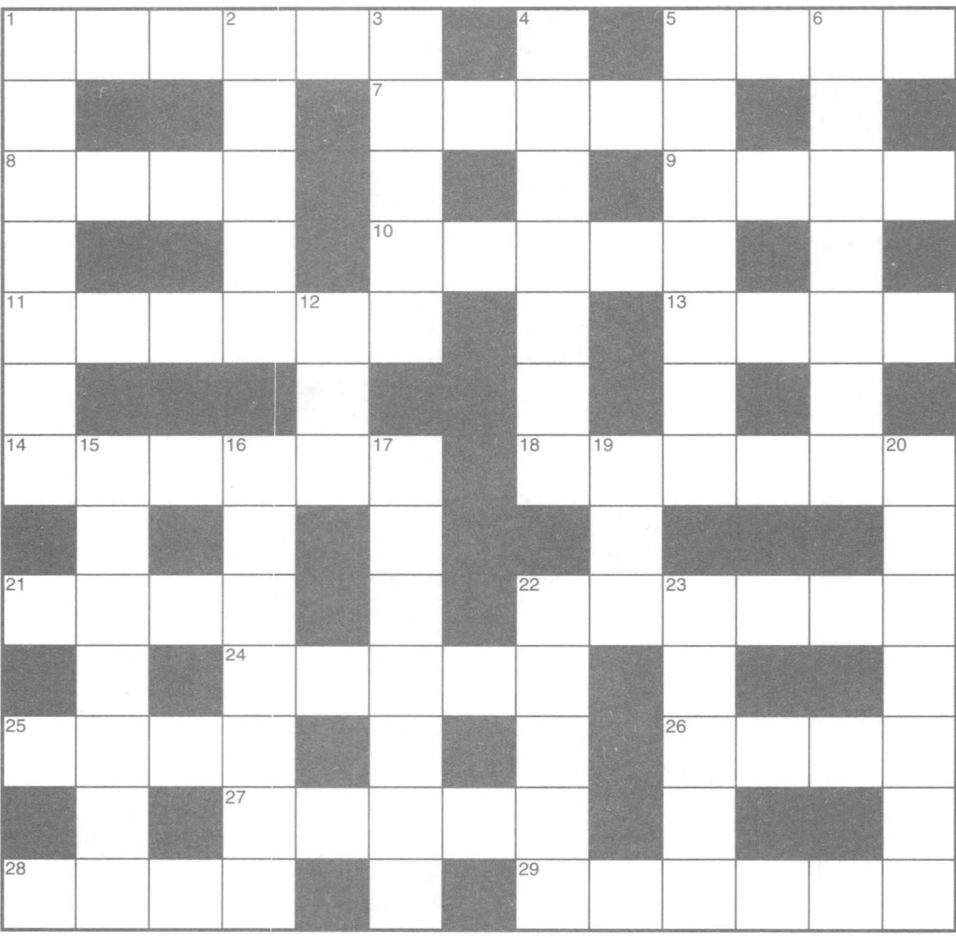

## ACROSS

1. Held for trial, on ...
5. Bird's bill
7. Bury
8. Intellect
9. Rainbow shapes
10. Colloquial saying
11. Gained knowledge
13. Donkey cry
14. Holy people
18. Saturate
21. Suggestion
22. Doubters
24. Train (team)
25. Golly!
26. Medieval guitar
27. More senior
28. Exercise clubs
29. Pit workers

## DOWN

1. Crumples
2. Viper
3. Single number
4. Tarnished
5. Blackberry shrub
6. Old-fashioned
12. Almond or pecan
15. Divorce payment
16. Nicks
17. Maroons
19. Beam of sunlight
20. Speeds up
22. Lucky trinket
23. Synthetic fabric

# CROSSWORD 54

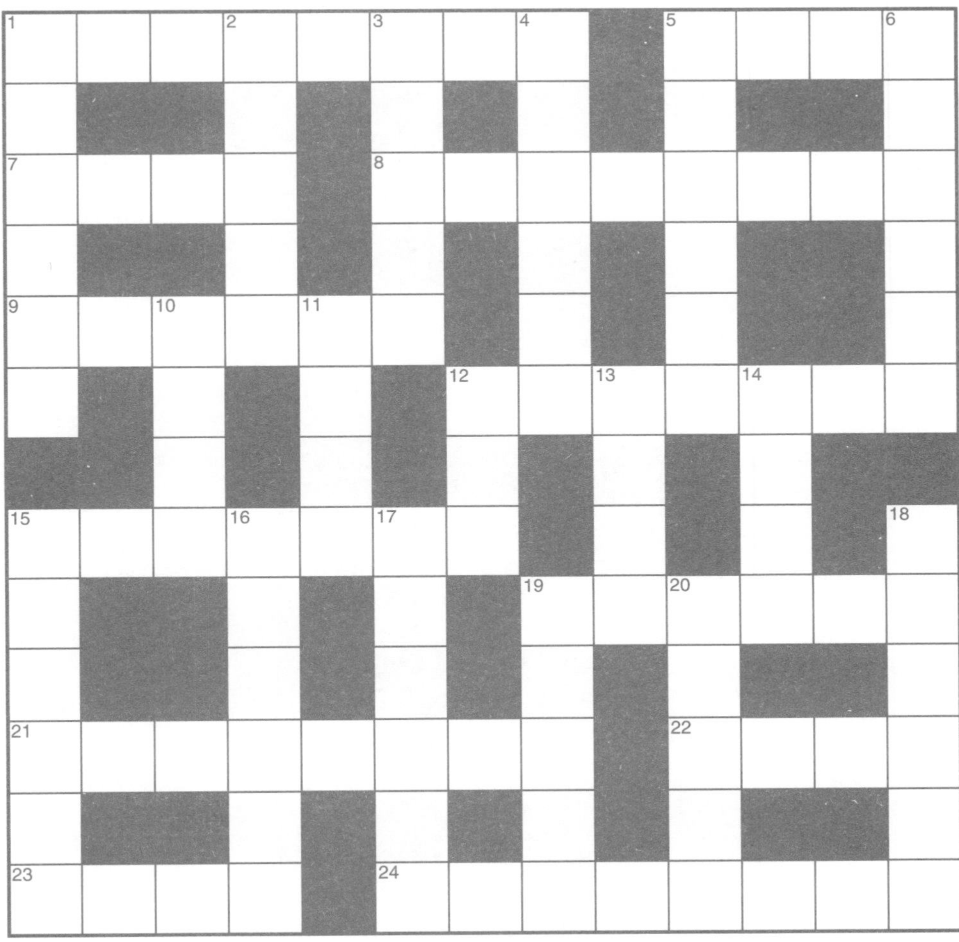

## ACROSS

1. Soldiers on watch
5. Respiratory organ
7. Wisecrack
8. Circling (planet)
9. Votes for
12. Characteristic
15. Retitled
19. Deep gorge
21. Leaving empty
22. Loud laugh
23. No longer living
24. Aimed at

## DOWN

1. Follow-up book
2. Point of discussion
3. Cultural symbols
4. Pacify
5. Dormant
6. Stare with bulging eyes
10. Merit
11. Light-rail car
12. Passing fashion
13. Saintly radiance
14. Unattractive
15. Raced (motor)
16. Fearful
17. Join army
18. Accustomed
19. Cuban smoke
20. Sense receptor

# CROSSWORD 55

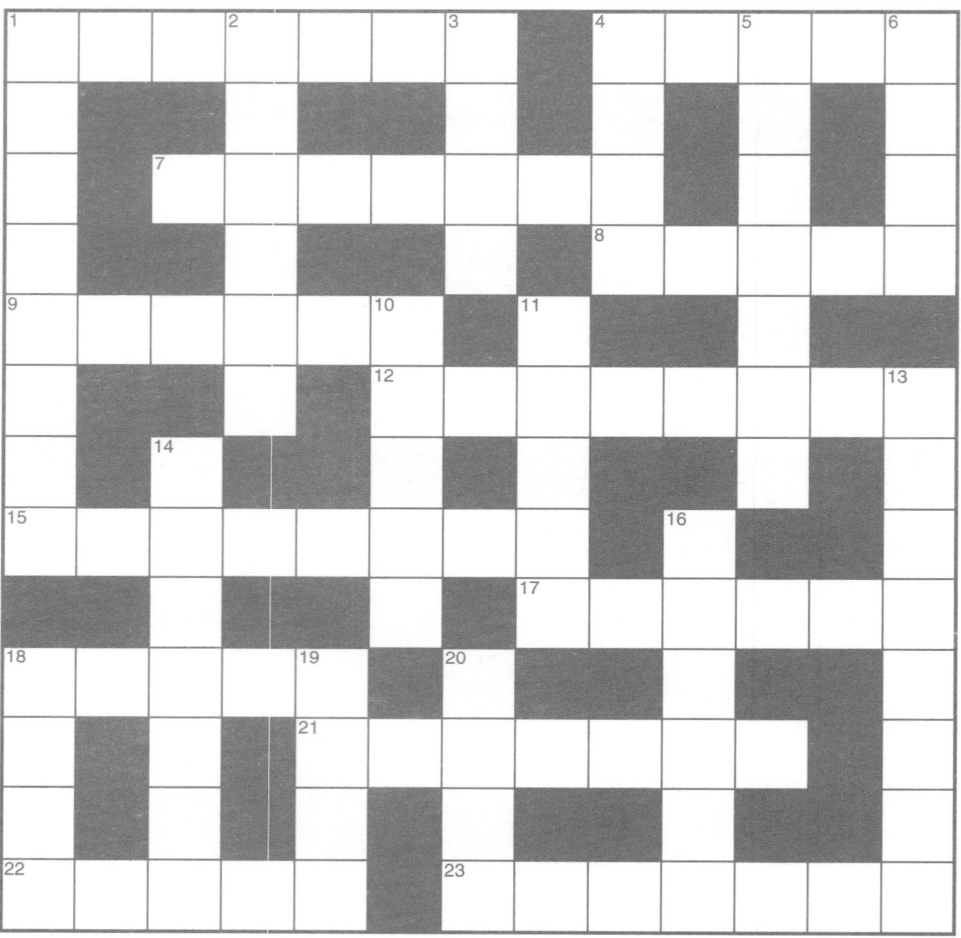

## ACROSS

1. Rapped
4. Australian wild dog
7. Vital
8. Rental agreement
9. Poked abruptly
12. Busy
15. Marine creature's home
17. Warbles alpine-style
18. Ore veins
21. Sloping typeface
22. Tennis delivery
23. Contemplative

## DOWN

1. Fun-spoilers
2. Goes up (stairs)
3. Specks
4. Girl's plaything
5. Wandering (tribesman)
6. A single time
10. Drugged (horse)
11. Rough-skinned
13. Deter
14. More robust
16. Decrees
18. Chops (branches)
19. Father (children)
20. Many-stringed instrument

# CROSSWORD 56

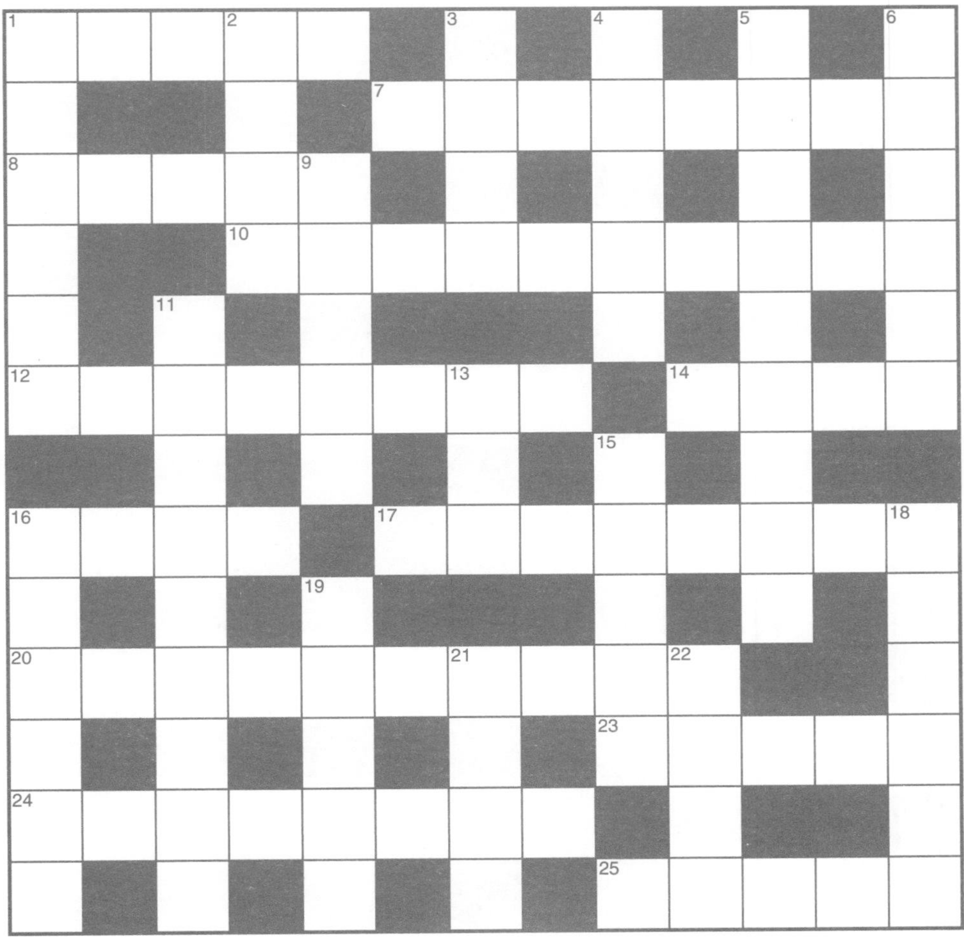

## ACROSS

1. Large jet plane
7. Essential nutrients
8. Occasion
10. Musical instrument
12. Intimidating
14. Curl of smoke
16. Little terrors
17. Acquired
20. Bass or lead players
23. Accumulated money
24. Strangle
25. Consent

## DOWN

1. Mocked
2. Not straight
3. Branch
4. Ruined
5. Non-military personnel
6. Slumbering
9. Flans
11. Providers
13. Arrest
15. Sections
16. Bricks of precious metal
18. Aimless scrawl
19. Prickly desert plants
21. Troubles
22. Performed in opera

# CROSSWORD 57

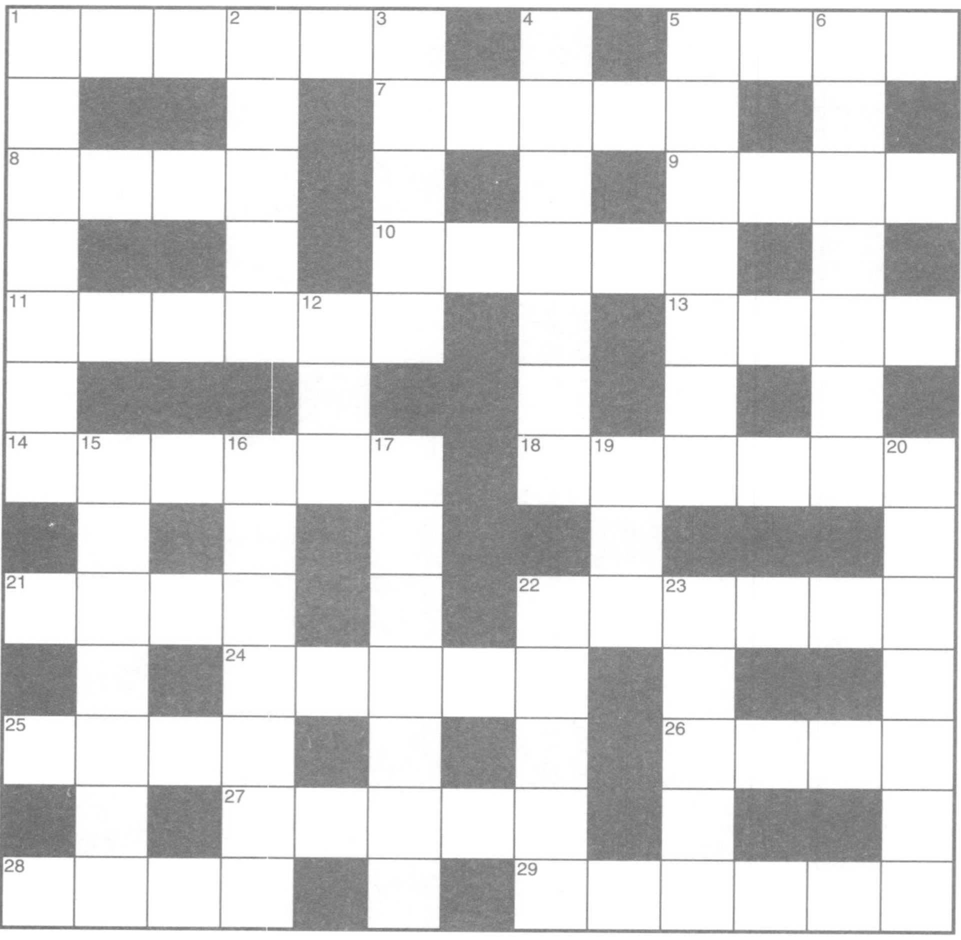

## ACROSS

1. Soldier on watch
5. Outstanding loan
7. Astound
8. Lessen
9. Pen tips
10. Great Depression drifters
11. Trusty
13. Congers
14. Painted roughly
18. Loathe
21. Went quickly
22. Put on (event)
24. Extend arm
25. Mexican food shell
26. Greek liquor
27. Surpass
28. Expression
29. Pokes fun at

## DOWN

1. Fumed
2. Subject matter
3. Sailing boat
4. Talked incessantly
5. Most impenetrable
6. Air balls
12. Seek damages from
15. Pacify
16. Sleeping chamber
17. Pours (wine)
19. Feed on
20. Monotonous
22. Fire (gun)
23. Scent

# CROSSWORD 58

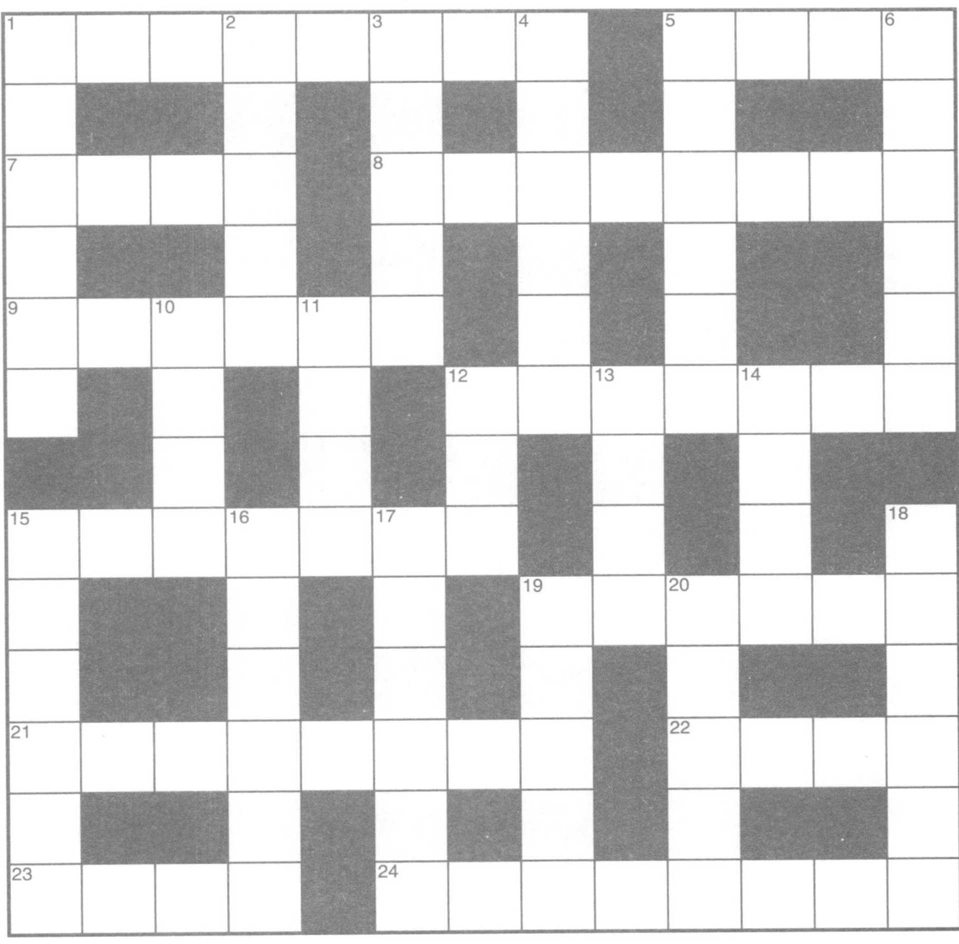

## ACROSS

1. One million watts
5. Click (fingers)
7. Martial art
8. Arched bridges over valley
9. Regretful
12. Broad-bladed knife
15. Layered timber
19. Higher-priced
21. Kings or queens
22. Round door handle
23. Traded for money
24. Made unhappy

## DOWN

1. Army officers
2. Icily detached
3. Metal-working block
4. Harrowing ordeal
5. Crush
6. Mortar & ...
10. Nervous
11. Unbutton
12. Wet soft earth
13. Manage
14. Not often, hardly ...
15. Feathers
16. Sorcerer
17. Liquid units, fluid ...
18. Delved
19. Gave medicine to
20. Leg/foot joint

# CROSSWORD 59

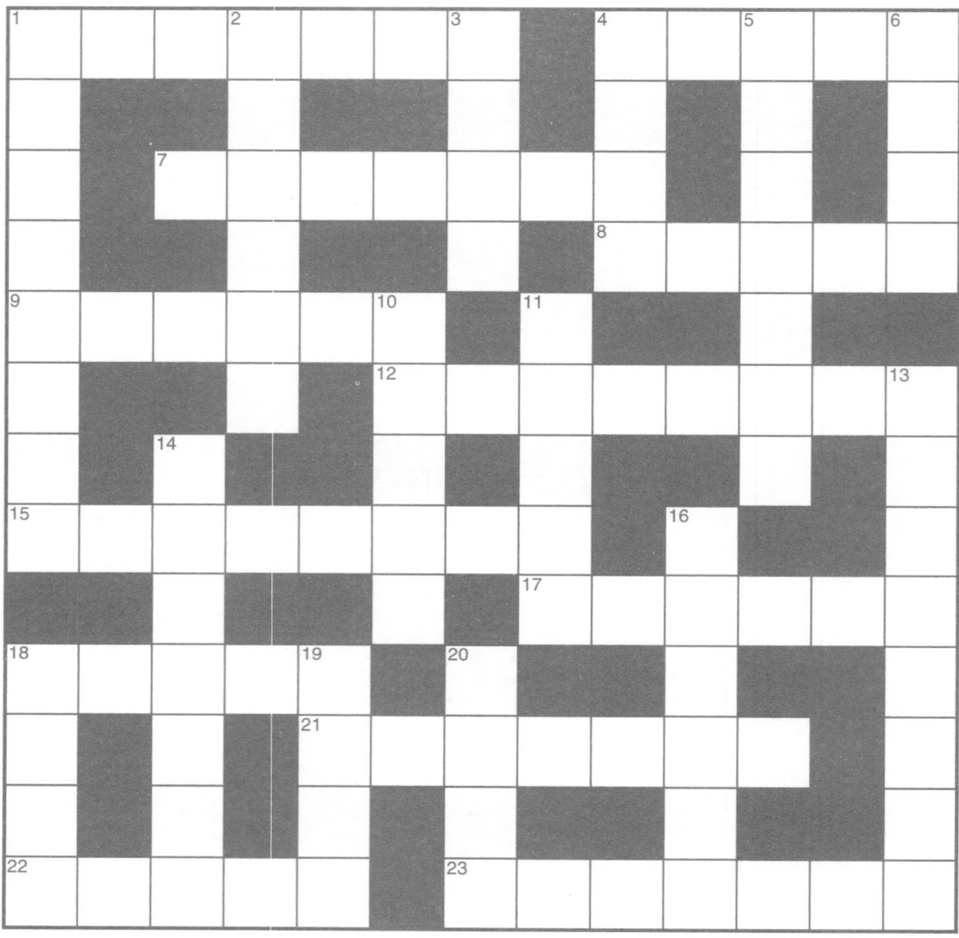

## ACROSS

1. Of water
4. Crop harvest
7. Magazine issue
8. Aptitude
9. Surface wood layer
12. Angrily
15. Lucky charm
17. Attack from hiding
18. Building block
21. Subtleties of meaning
22. Readjust
23. Hoards

## DOWN

1. Campaigner for political change
2. Confuses
3. Voucher
4. Pull with a jerk
5. Enlarges
6. Unlit
10. Nursery verse
11. Flora & ...
13. Muslim veils
14. Pure white animals
16. Nunnery boss
18. Rude person
19. Tangle
20. Dad

# CROSSWORD 60

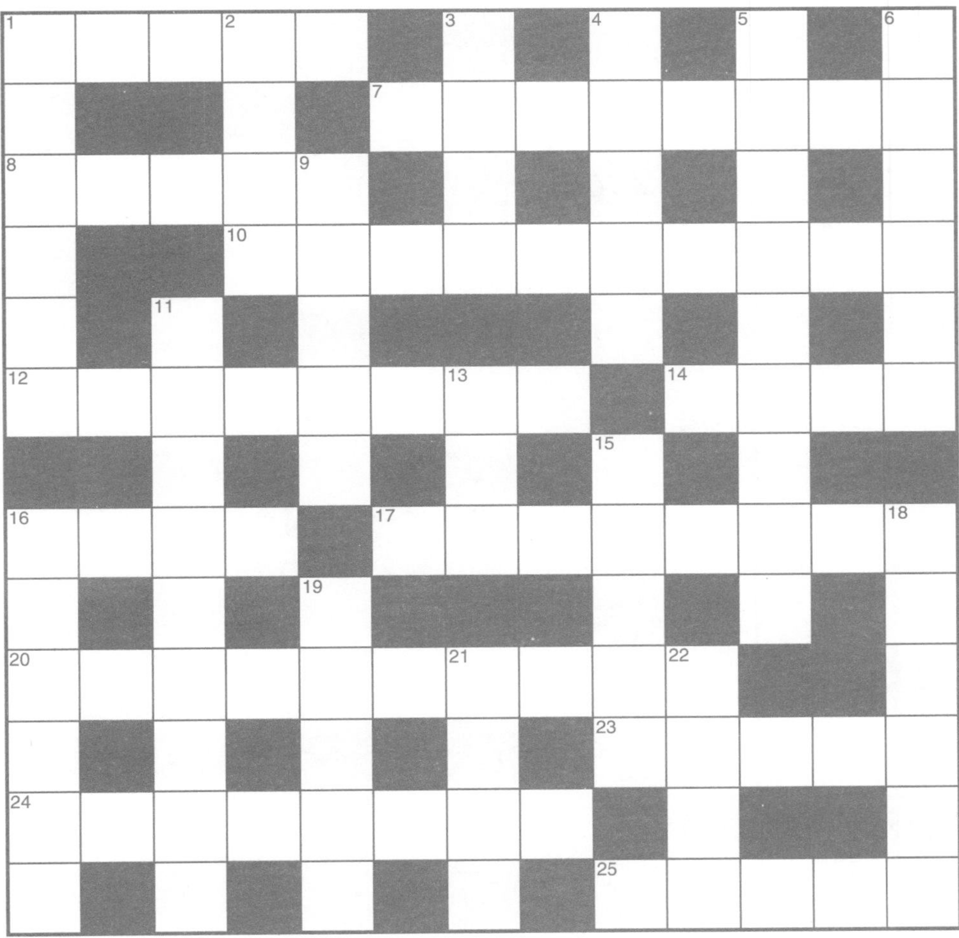

## ACROSS

1. Baked dough
7. Starter mechanism
8. Insinuating (remark)
10. Embellish
12. Eating greedily
14. Absconded
16. Irritation
17. Exerted (oneself)
20. Basking in sunshine
23. Removed
24. Informed
25. River mammal

## DOWN

1. Founding
2. Assistant
3. Highly curious
4. Wind-borne toys
5. Incapacitating
6. Certainly
9. Send abroad in disgrace
11. Vulgar comment
13. Negative adverb
15. Visit as ghost
16. Of unsound mind
18. Evening meal
19. Social blunder
21. Weeded
22. Mode of walk

# CROSSWORD 61

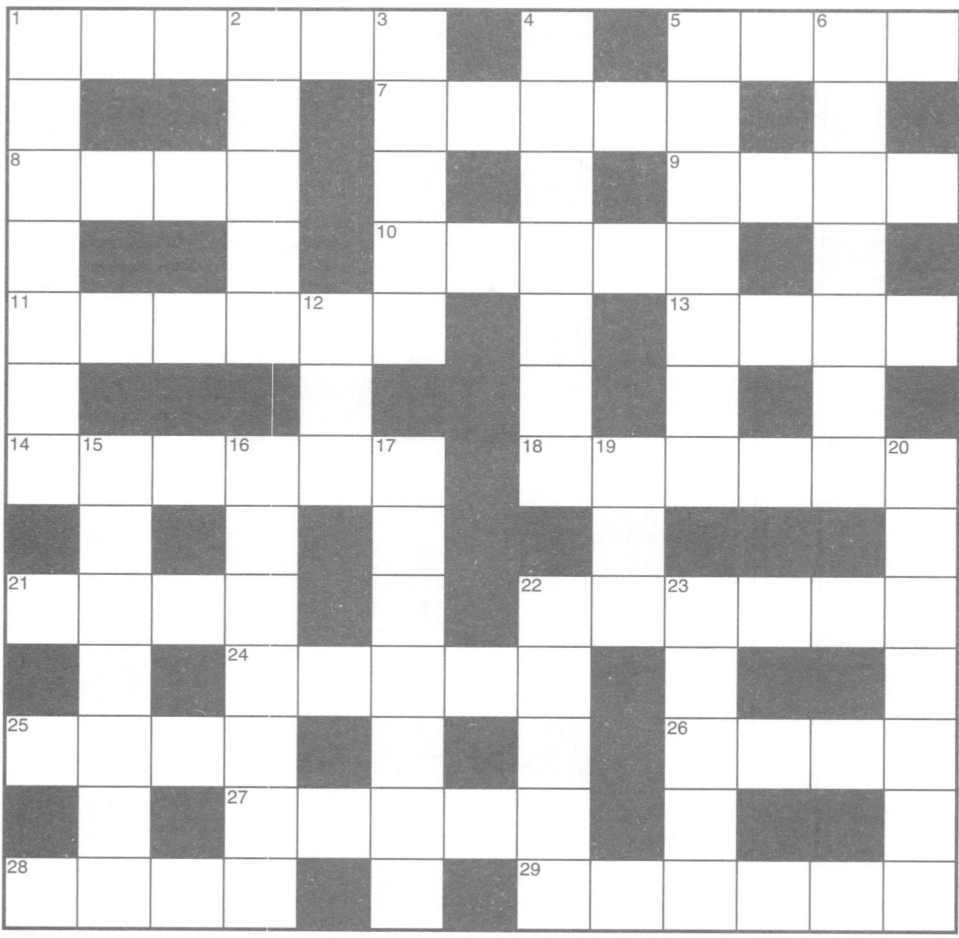

## ACROSS

1. Away from coast
5. Soil
7. Manner of treating
8. Volcano's flowing rock
9. Dissolve
10. Depart
11. Gnashes (teeth)
13. Quantity of paper
14. Portable steps
18. Patriotic song
21. Movie queen
22. Crossbreed
24. Easy pace
25. Rounded thermometer part
26. Genuine
27. Leap forward
28. Inch (along)
29. Sidesteps

## DOWN

1. Illicit
2. Once more
3. Loses shine
4. Mosquito-borne fever
5. Misconduct mark
6. Let go of
12. Scheduled to arrive
15. Amaze
16. Resistant to wear
17. Stealing
19. Negative vote
20. Standard components
22. Carved into shape
23. Revealed

# CROSSWORD 62

## ACROSS

1. Courted
5. Grass skirt dance
7. Close
8. Shuffled along
9. Degrades
12. Liberating
15. Missile's explosive section
19. Bite of food
21. Relaxed (4-4)
22. Unfeeling
23. Posterior
24. Operating doctors

## DOWN

1. Landing strip
2. Farm plot measures
3. Detective's jobs
4. Slide-out desk compartment
5. Walk lamely
6. Counting up
10. Partly open
11. Fencing sword
12. Nourished
13. Reflected sound
14. Freezes, ... over
15. Riches
16. Drove (livestock)
17. Displays
18. Spheres
19. Producer
20. Remove soap from

# CROSSWORD 63

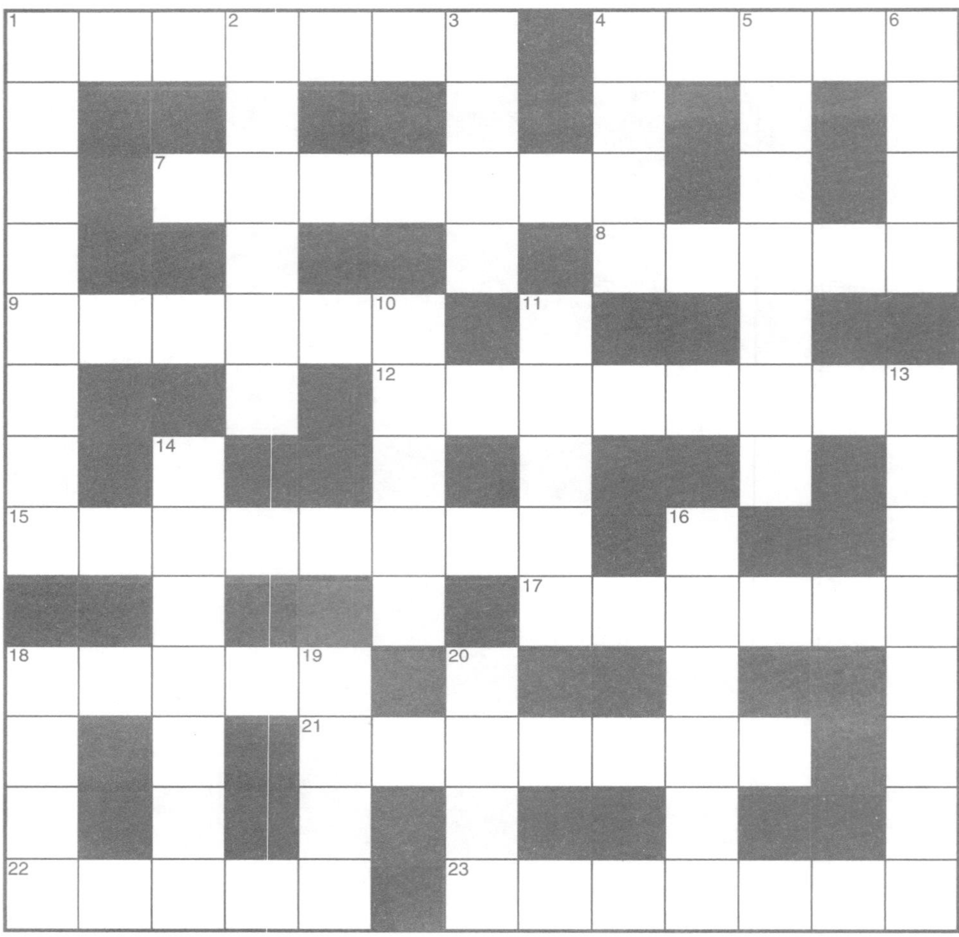

## ACROSS

1. Entangled
4. Hollywood production
7. Inundate
8. Egg-producing organ
9. Barred
12. Evilly
15. Postponement
17. Epidemic
18. Musical, The Phantom Of The ...
21. Striking with foot
22. Ascended
23. Sewer access shaft

## DOWN

1. Prisoner
2. Of cattle
3. Be brave enough
4. Single-sound source
5. Roofed deck on house
6. Glimpse
10. Old, cool star, red ...
11. Resell tickets for profit
13. Christmas season
14. Upsets
16. Middle-age spread
18. Above
19. Similar
20. Molten metal impurities

# CROSSWORD 64

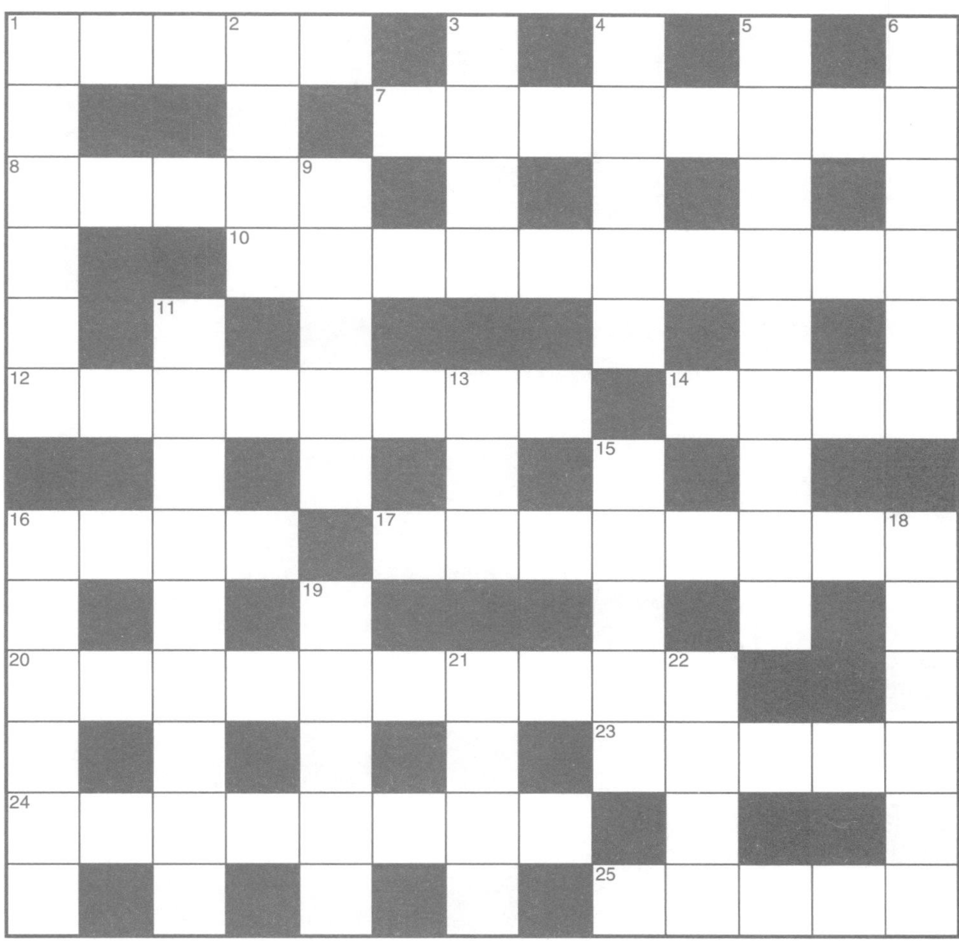

## ACROSS

1. Shaving cuts
7. Skinniest
8. Put up with
10. Consecrated
12. 12-month-old horse
14. Grain storage facility
16. Pastry case
17. Enjoyable
20. Benevolently
23. Used carpentry blade
24. Blinding by light
25. Reserve, set ...

## DOWN

1. Tidily
2. Young goats
3. Softest-known powder
4. Hank of wool
5. Having healing properties
6. Dancer's workplace
9. Ahead of time
11. Celebrity photographers
13. Nothing
15. Train tracks
16. Building's exterior
18. Plod
19. Chapter heading
21. Father's sister
22. Barks shrilly

# CROSSWORD 65

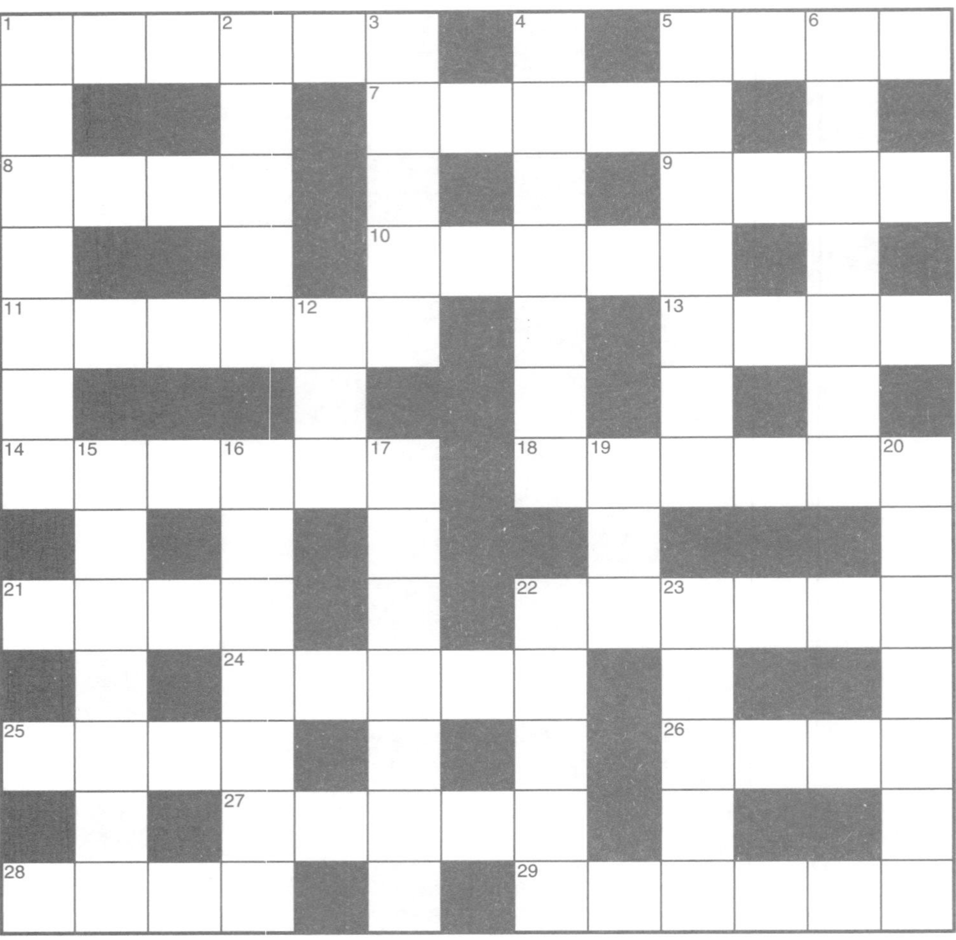

## ACROSS

1. Chatter like monkey
5. Close friend
7. Transpire
8. Sit idly
9. Hindu meditation
10. Chops in cubes
11. Principles
13. Serving platter
14. Huge star cluster
18. Seasoned (food)
21. Teen hero
22. Rang
24. Make void
25. Remain
26. Sudden plunge, ... dive
27. Correct (text)
28. Parched
29. Seductively

## DOWN

1. Bumping sharply
2. Light timber
3. Thoroughfares
4. Frozen drips
5. Clear quartz
6. Improve in quality
12. Lenient
15. Accounts examiner
16. Relieved
17. Not as old
19. Gorilla or chimpanzee
20. Feeble with age
22. Trudges
23. Attach

# CROSSWORD 66

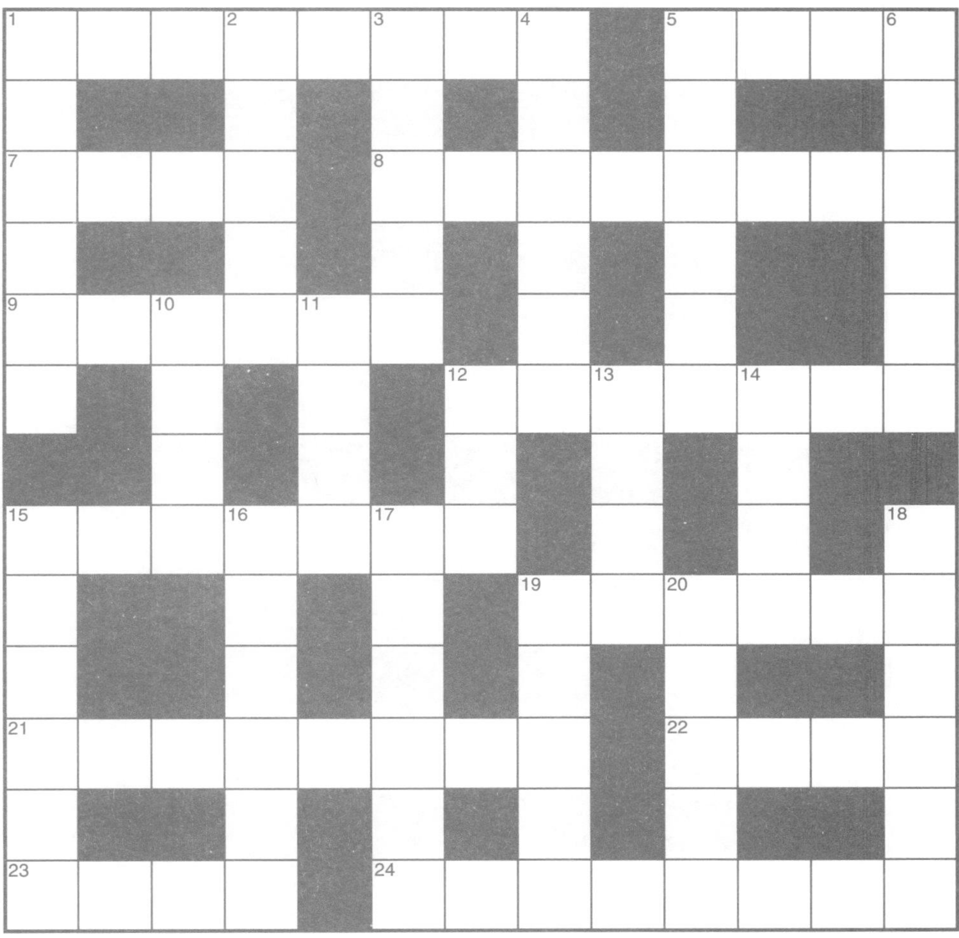

## ACROSS

1. Squid
5. Kitchen professional
7. Blocking vote
8. Questioner
9. Most pleasant
12. Goes up
15. Devotedly
19. Verbal
21. Cloudy eye condition
22. Otherwise, or ...
23. Computer input
24. Charitable gift

## DOWN

1. Exploring caverns
2. Isolated
3. Watchful
4. Mental pictures
5. Shrink (in fear)
6. Absurd comedies
10. Large town
11. Official stamp
12. Some
13. Karate blow
14. Canoodle
15. Pricked (boil)
16. Fleet of warships
17. Garden reptile
18. Trainee doctor
19. Shiny fabric
20. Open to view

# CROSSWORD 67

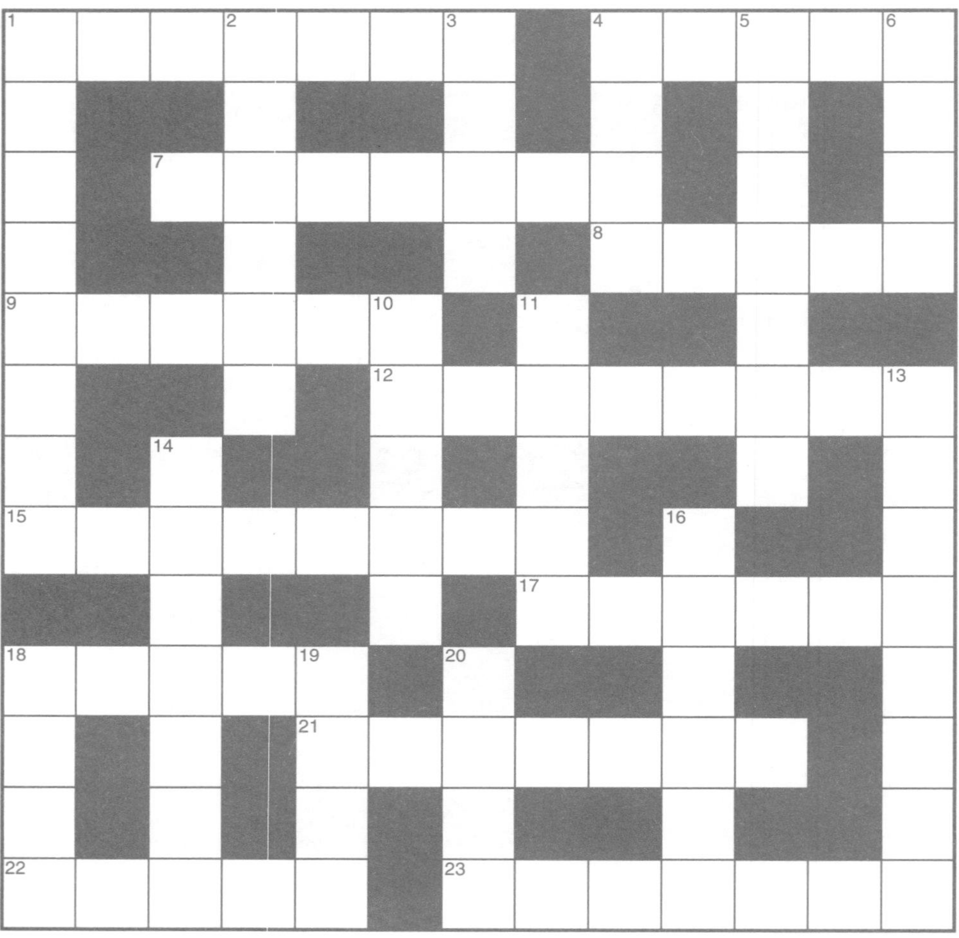

## ACROSS

1. Essentially
4. Playing card figures
7. Towards the front
8. Avoid (capture)
9. Necessitate
12. Letter jumbles
15. Examination
17. Disastrous
18. Muslim women's quarters
21. Greed
22. Snow crystal
23. Giving temporarily

## DOWN

1. Spine bone
2. Unprincipled
3. 12-month period
4. Shade of green
5. Mobile home
6. Flank
10. Cowboy's rope
11. Ribs to hips region
13. Horrifying
14. Red spice
16. Moved rhythmically
18. Six, ... a dozen
19. Female horse
20. Corridor

# CROSSWORD 68

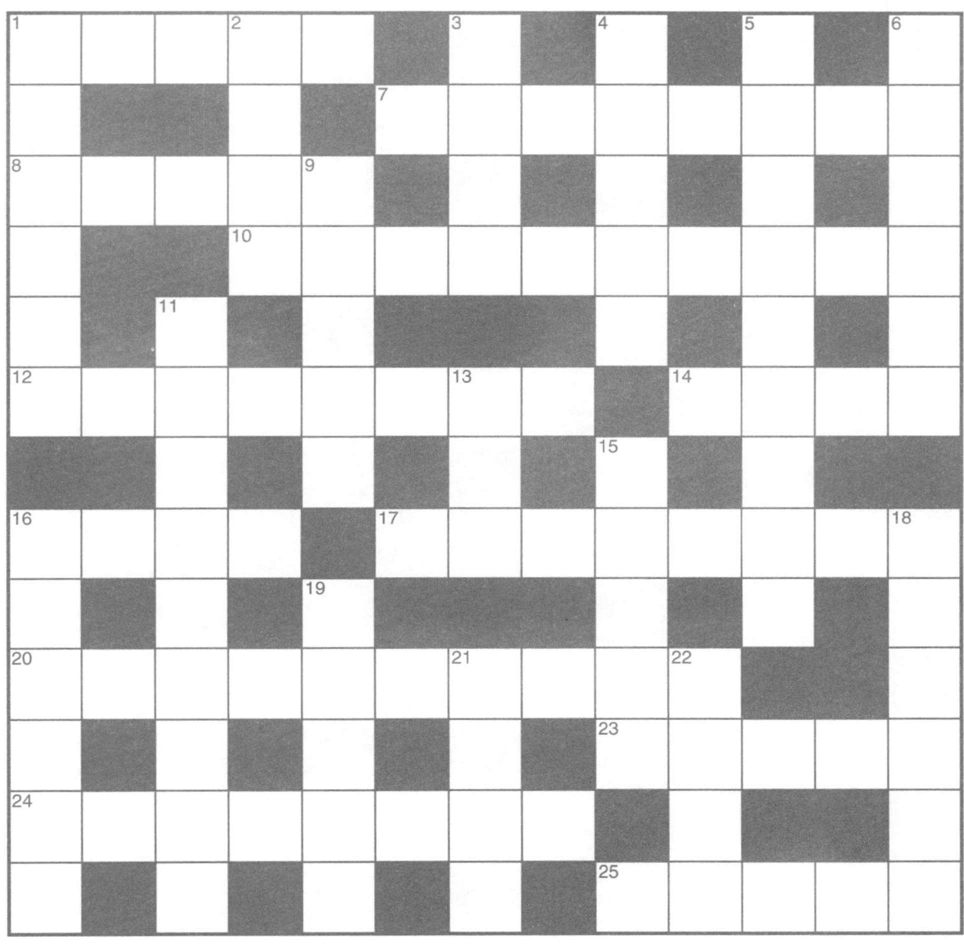

## ACROSS

1. Call on socially
7. Gives up hope
8. Senseless (comment)
10. Very tall building
12. Identify disease
14. Verbal exam
16. Contests, ... with
17. Game plan
20. Vehicle franchise
23. Grieve
24. Consecrated as priest
25. Knight's horse

## DOWN

1. Masked
2. Taverns
3. Hawaiian garlands
4. Tennis or golf
5. Dissipated
6. Stellar
9. Scraping by, ... out a living
11. Radio frequencies
13. Perched
15. Adage
16. Visual recordings
18. Sighed sleepily
19. Ancient remnant
21. Plant stalk
22. Sulky look

# CROSSWORD 69

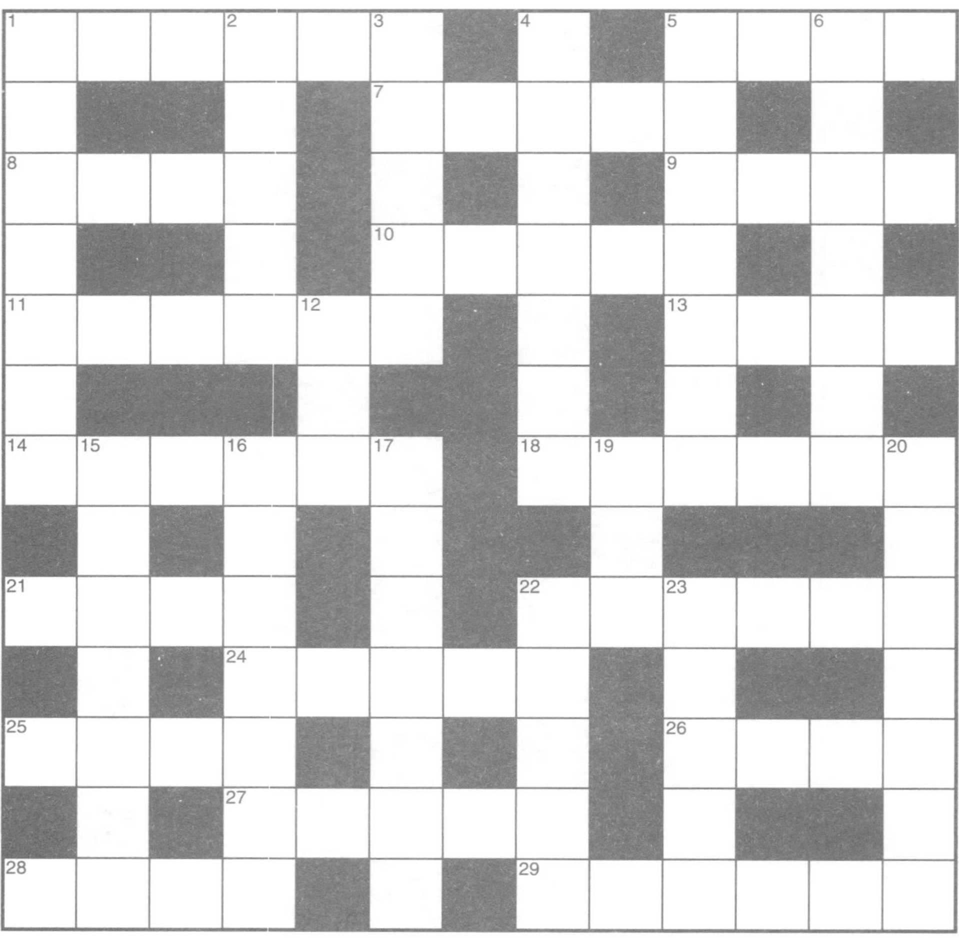

## ACROSS

1. Pines (for)
5. Unruly child
7. Shopping mall
8. Young sheep
9. Fluent & insincere
10. Being untruthful
11. Woodwind musician
13. Feel sore
14. Fierce
18. Disinclined
21. Corrosive fluid
22. Nuclear weapon, ... bomb
24. Metropolitan
25. Metal in brass
26. Festival
27. Tendency
28. Wildebeests
29. Gain by threats

## DOWN

1. Daffodil shades
2. Jewish scholar
3. Upended (drink)
4. Chocolate, strawberry or ...
5. Luggage
6. Steps from train
12. Slump
15. Sale by hammer
16. Kidnaps
17. Entitles
19. Animal physician
20. Captivate
22. Type of electrode
23. Should, ... to

# CROSSWORD 70

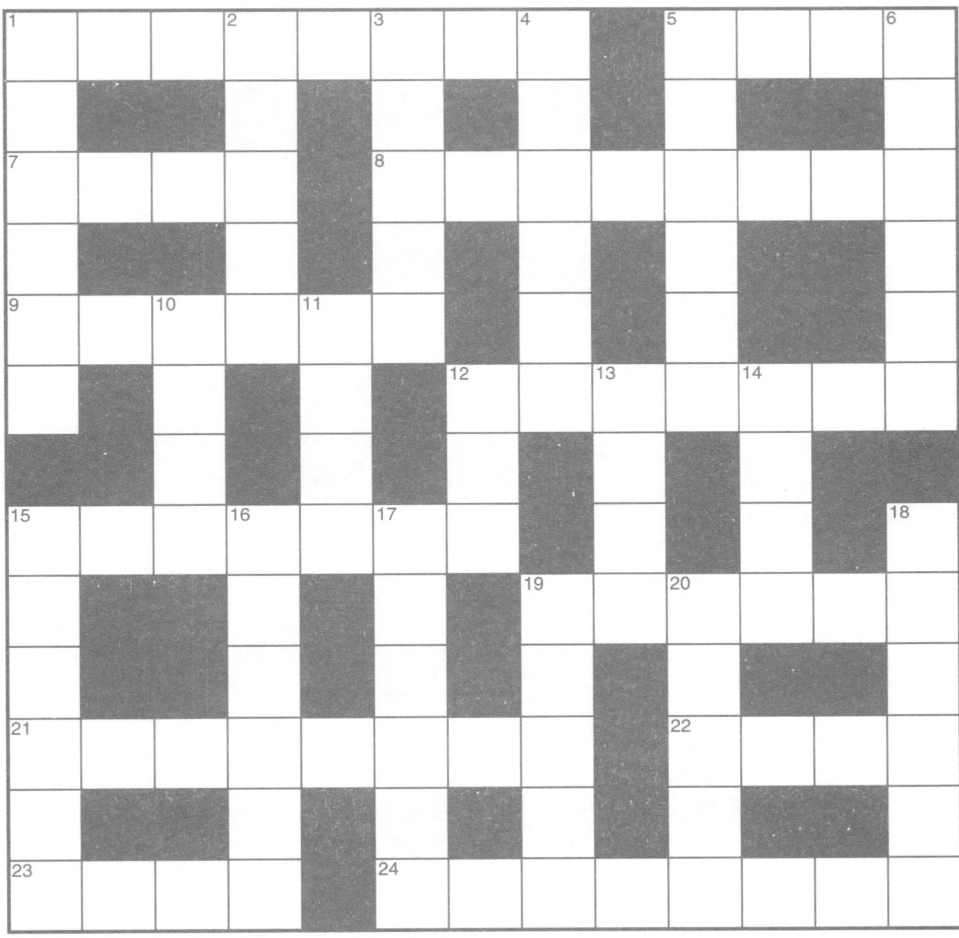

## ACROSS

1. Kitchen strainer
5. Parsley or sage
7. Belonging to you
8. Spaghetti accompaniment
9. Wanted
12. Donned clothing
15. Used nose
19. Onto terra firma
21. Supervisors
22. Recess
23. Tropical root vegetables
24. Made stable

## DOWN

1. In floods of tears
2. Ventilated
3. Curved (roof)
4. Library patron
5. Routines
6. Swelled
10. Type of sword
11. Nobleman
12. Unexploded shell
13. Shady trees
14. Alone
15. Marshy
16. Purple flowers
17. Surplus
18. Nipped with beak
19. Supermarket lane
20. Perfected (one's skills)

# CROSSWORD 71

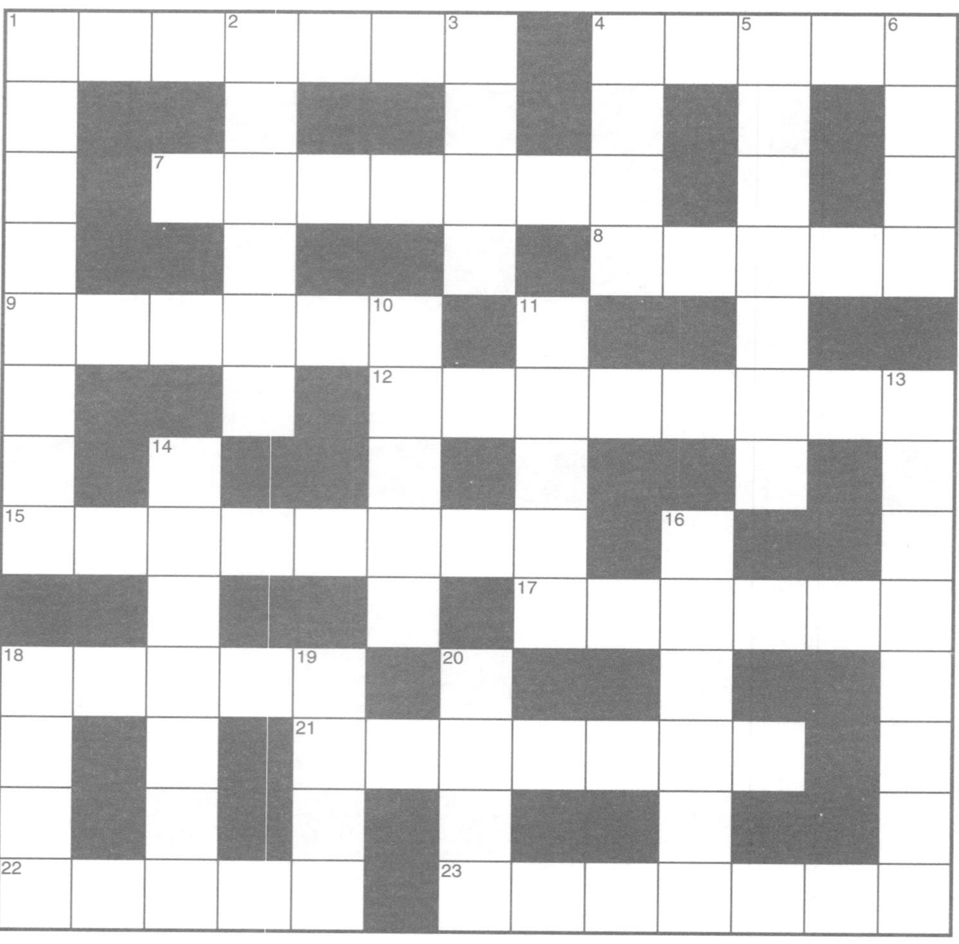

## ACROSS

1. Zealot
4. Evaporated, ... up
7. Sultan's wife
8. Sudden light
9. Stratagem
12. Slimness
15. Spanish Miss
17. Playing-card jacks
18. Restraining cord
21. Disciple
22. Move crabwise
23. Defrosting

## DOWN

1. Squashes
2. Grown-ups
3. Applaud
4. Unable to hear
5. Prisoners
6. Bowl
10. Miner's land reserve
11. Inuit canoe
13. Cutting wildly
14. Enclosed in shell
16. Candle wax
18. Spectacles glass
19. Rabbit relative
20. Nautical left

# CROSSWORD 72

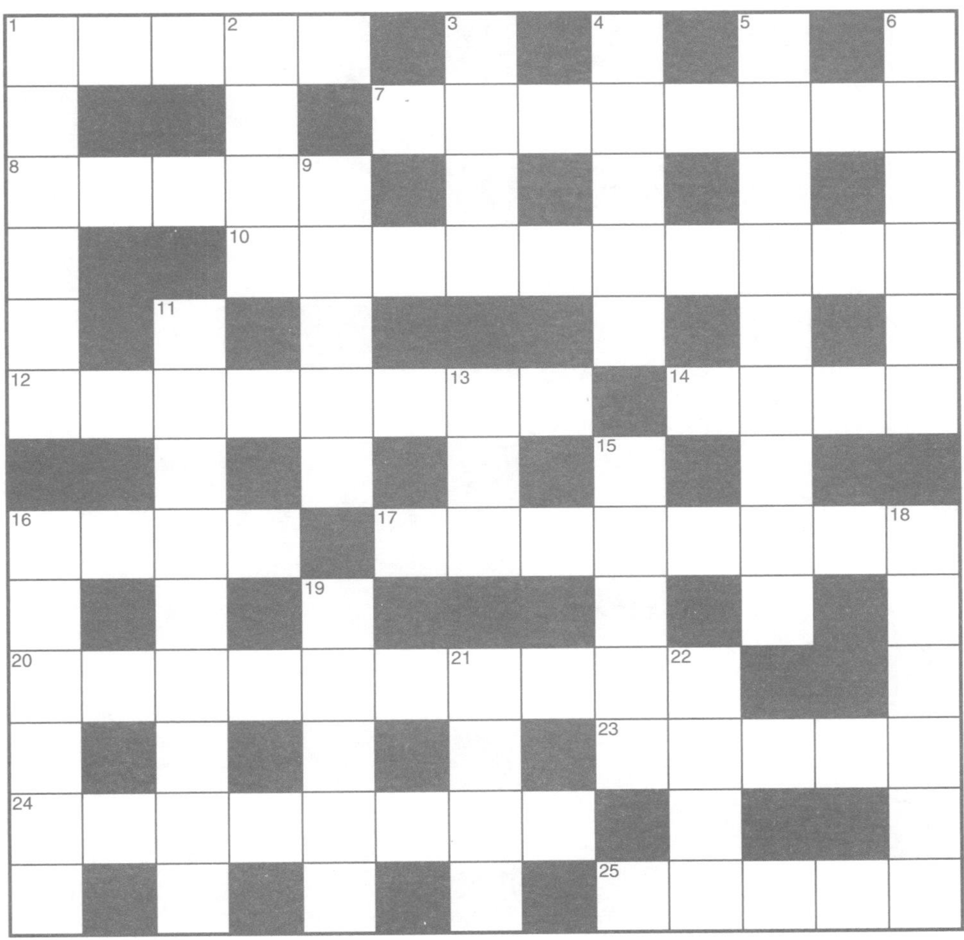

## ACROSS

1. Bluegrass instrument
7. Money matters
8. Elected
10. Put into other words
12. Insulin user
14. Pelvic joints
16. Forsake at altar
17. Reduced
20. Disbelieved
23. Light summer dish
24. Prominence
25. Glide on ice

## DOWN

1. Thundered
2. Small military vehicle
3. Travel pass
4. Washtubs
5. Instances
6. Doorkeepers
9. Stupefies
11. Weapon, ... missile
13. Fury
15. Beasts of burden
16. Hurdler
18. Lag behind
19. Instruction
21. Footwear item
22. Damp & cold

# CROSSWORD 73

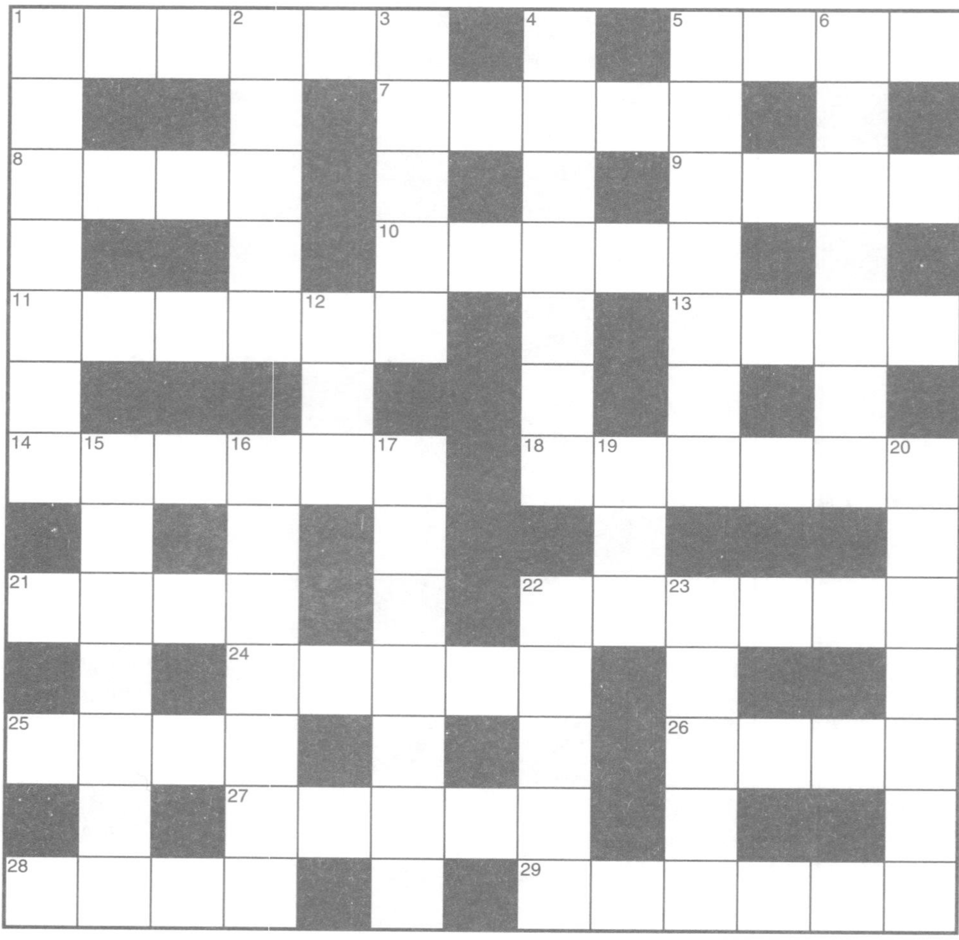

## ACROSS

1. Provoke to anger
5. Envelop
7. Greater in years
8. Sinister
9. Concludes
10. Burdens
11. Notoriety
13. Monitors, keeps ... on
14. Automobile repair shop
18. Ten, ..., twelve
21. Self-satisfied
22. Meat skewers, shish ...
24. Gain knowledge
25. Against
26. Flour factory
27. Prod
28. Sounded (of bell)
29. Indexed

## DOWN

1. Encountering
2. 4th Greek letter
3. Gallantly
4. Move ahead
5. Tussle
6. Able to be heard
12. Large cup
15. Floor-cleaning fluid
16. Fishing sport
17. Chores
19. Hide, ... low
20. Snuggled
22. Bend to pray
23. Gentle collisions

# CROSSWORD 74

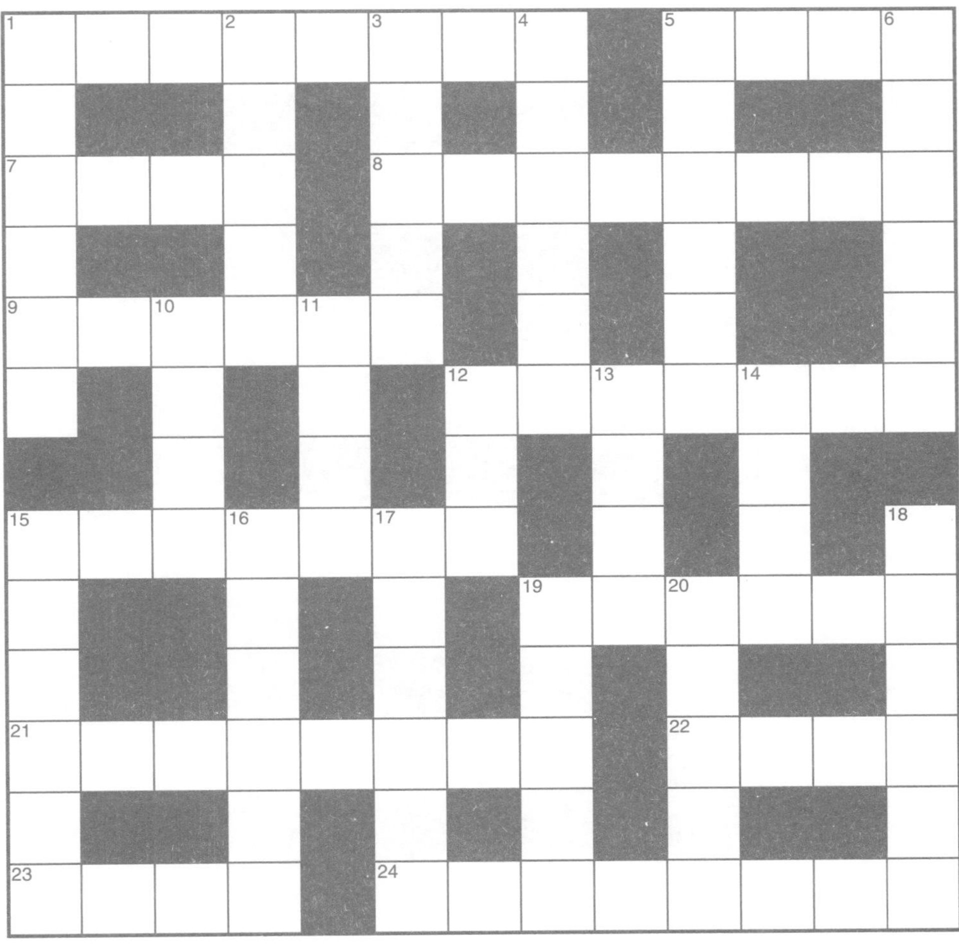

## ACROSS

1. Farm vehicles
5. Snatch
7. Money factory
8. Comprehended
9. Swirl
12. Serf
15. Brown skin mark
19. Cruises (along)
21. Sugar-refining by-product
22. Not one
23. Take nap
24. Remodels

## DOWN

1. Most docile
2. Supply food
3. Entrails
4. Parody
5. Regards smugly
6. Financial estimate
10. Small island
11. Go wild, run ...
12. Pastry dish
13. Moreover
14. Treads the boards
15. Frothed
16. Wine vessel
17. Less tight
18. Evaluate
19. Wooden barrels
20. Aggravate

# CROSSWORD 75

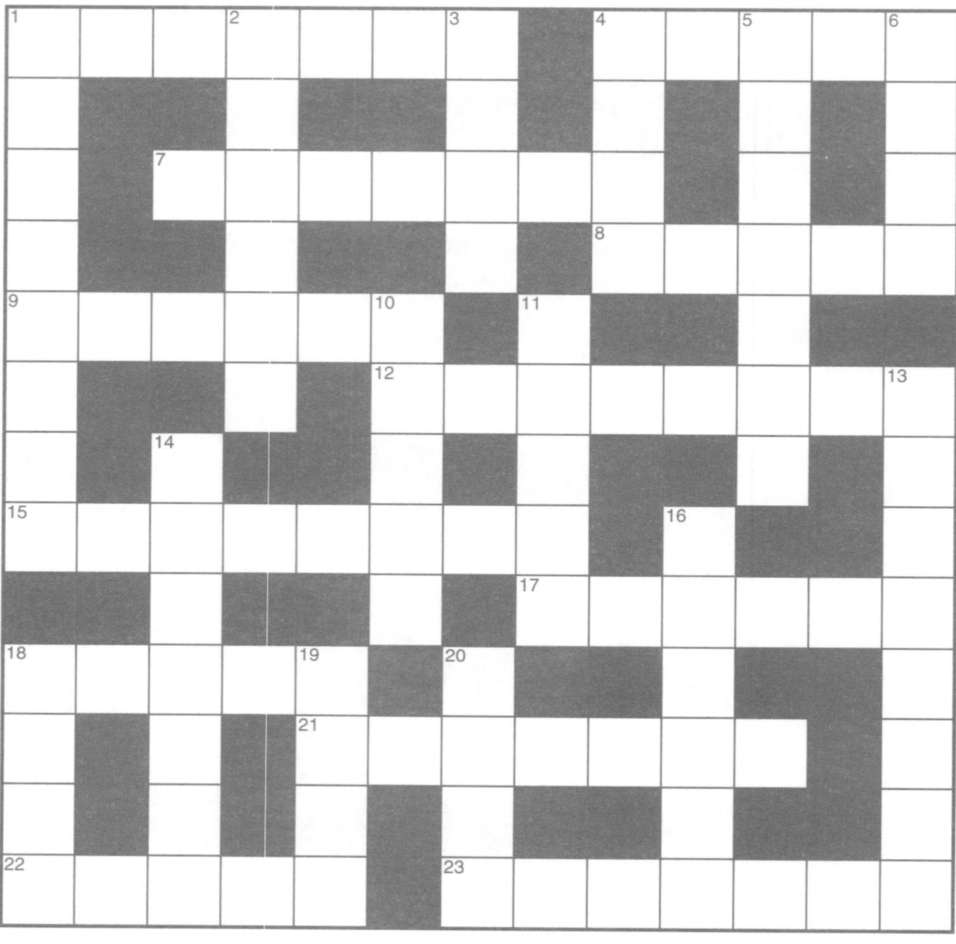

## ACROSS

1. Invalidated
4. Grant
7. Stowing space
8. Steam burn
9. Incendiary bomb material
12. Unlucky occurrence
15. Rate
17. Zigzagged (through traffic)
18. Rouse
21. In small stages
22. Helps (criminal)
23. Aggravated

## DOWN

1. Propose for office
2. Genuine
3. Control knob
4. Daunts
5. Chafes
6. Tinted
10. South American parrot
11. Wood fastener
13. Twirled (thumbs)
14. Equilibrium
16. Fairway obstacle
18. District
19. Poultry products
20. Patch (sock)

# CROSSWORD 76

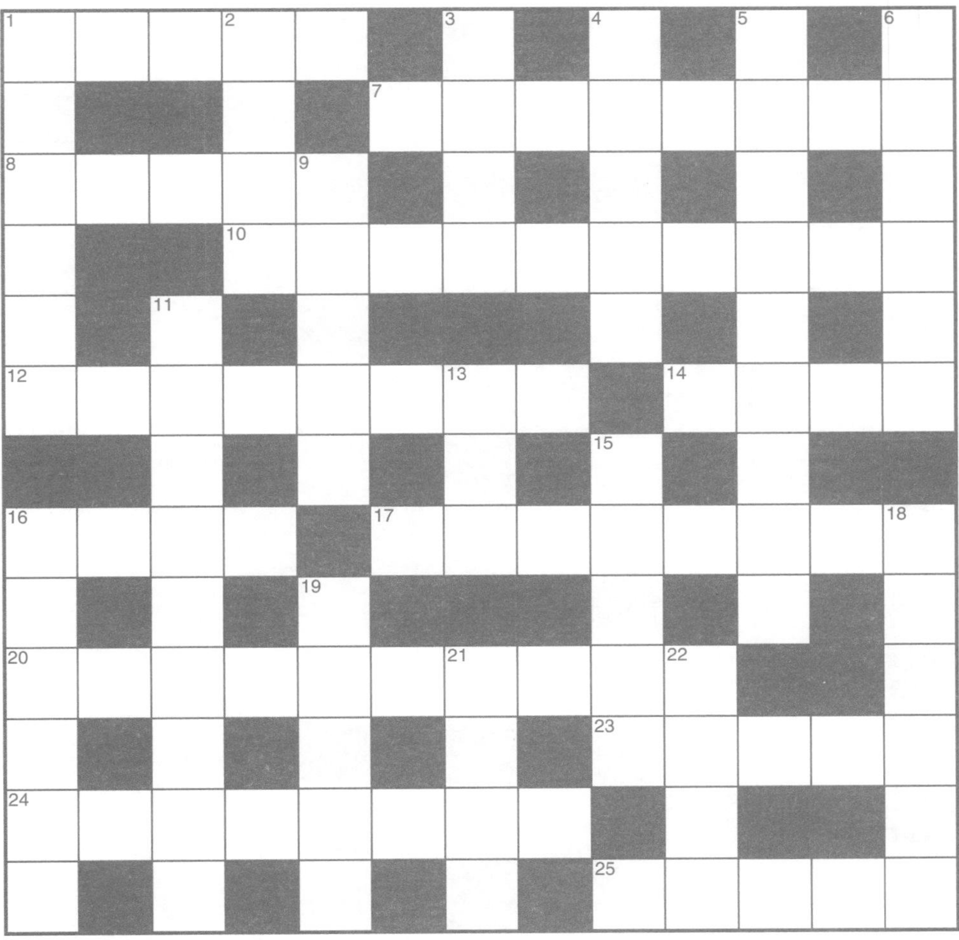

## ACROSS

1. Brass instruments
7. Divide
8. Restorative medicine
10. Mused
12. Exciting
14. Lost blood
16. Be frightened of
17. Ignored
20. Unvarying
23. Stared in awe
24. Subtracted
25. Shower

## DOWN

1. Added (up)
2. Enthusiastic
3. Obscene
4. Cooks in oven
5. Citrus preserve
6. Went (towards)
9. Suez or Panama
11. Vehicle procession
13. Charged particle
15. Person, human ...
16. Non-solids
18. Lethal
19. Sporting contest
21. Merriment
22. Breathe sharply

# CROSSWORD 77

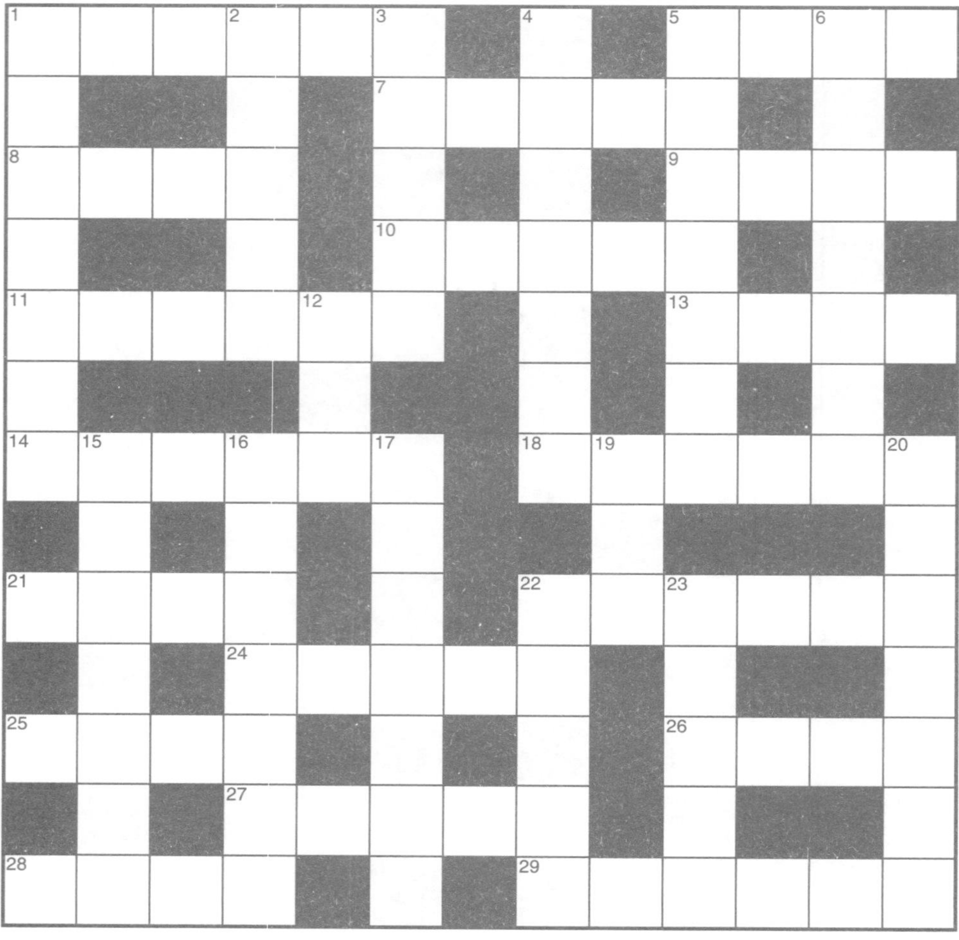

## ACROSS

1. Parish ministers
5. Prod
7. Shudder
8. Ready for picking
9. In between
10. Pale
11. Wisp
13. Single entity
14. Mental health
18. Quit job
21. Relinquish (territory)
22. More frail
24. Heartbeat
25. Actors in play
26. New Zealand bird
27. Flax cloth
28. Resist
29. Embroidering

## DOWN

1. Computer bugs
2. Stadium
3. Police group
4. Checkout operator
5. Charlie Brown cartoon
6. Injuring with dagger
12. Tennis court divider
15. Normal
16. Incompetently
17. Shouting
19. Needle hole
20. Hospital career
22. Introduces to solid food
23. Lopsided

# CROSSWORD 78

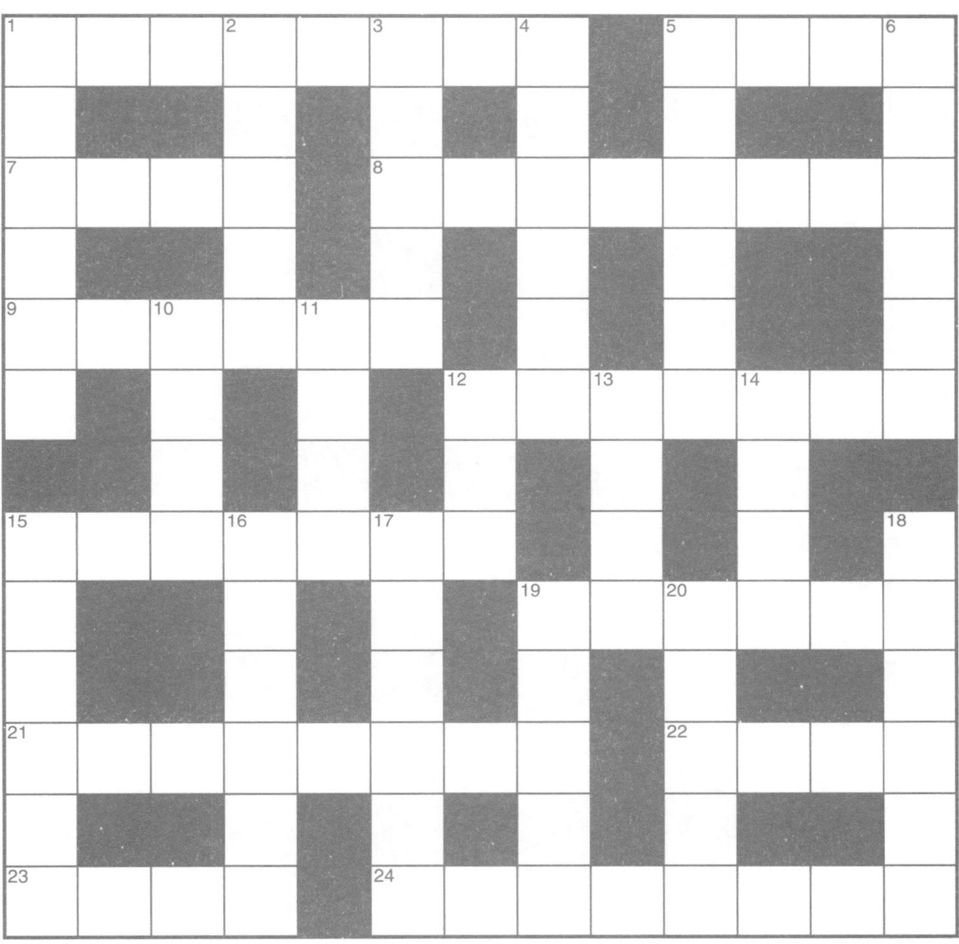

## ACROSS

1. Lacking courage
5. Touch lips
7. At a standstill
8. Askew
9. Honey base
12. Straddling
15. Most inquisitive
19. Short excursions
21. Antlered animal
22. Remove (hat)
23. Breeze
24. Invalid hearing

## DOWN

1. Customer
2. Representative
3. Furnishing scheme
4. Sailing boats
5. Zoo custodian
6. Entice
10. Male swans
11. Wheel shaft
12. Painting & sculpture
13. Canned fish
14. Cultural symbol
15. Slender
16. Pressed
17. Small river
18. Beneficial
19. Sudden tugs
20. Below

# CROSSWORD 79

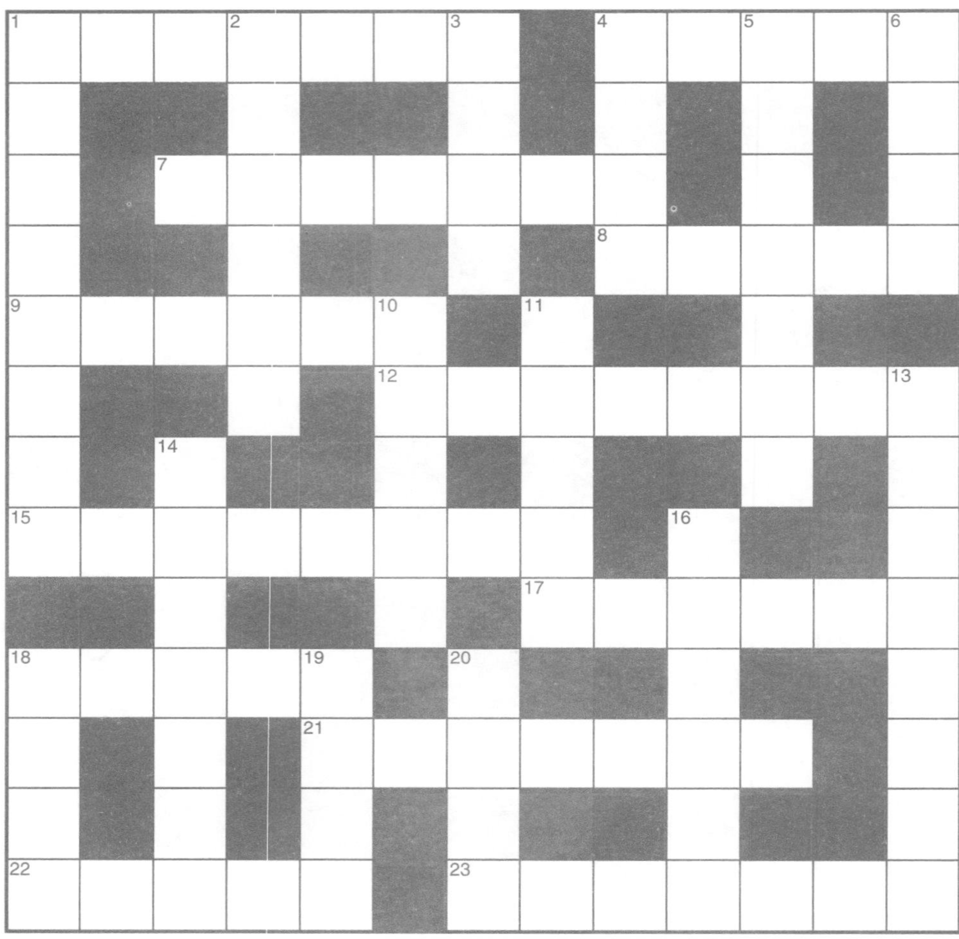

## ACROSS

1. Hard country, rough ...
4. Join (contest)
7. Nut of palm tree
8. Use razor
9. Cough mucus
12. Exaggerates
15. Slanting line
17. Capitulates
18. Lamenting
21. Dream up
22. Satellite path
23. Tour de France vehicle

## DOWN

1. Crushed underfoot
2. Unruly protester
3. Religious sisters
4. Consumes food
5. Occupancy
6. Gown
10. Pile
11. Abdomen
13. Rational
14. Transportation for hire
16. Eagerly
18. Remake
19. Birthday offering
20. Clothing

# CROSSWORD 80

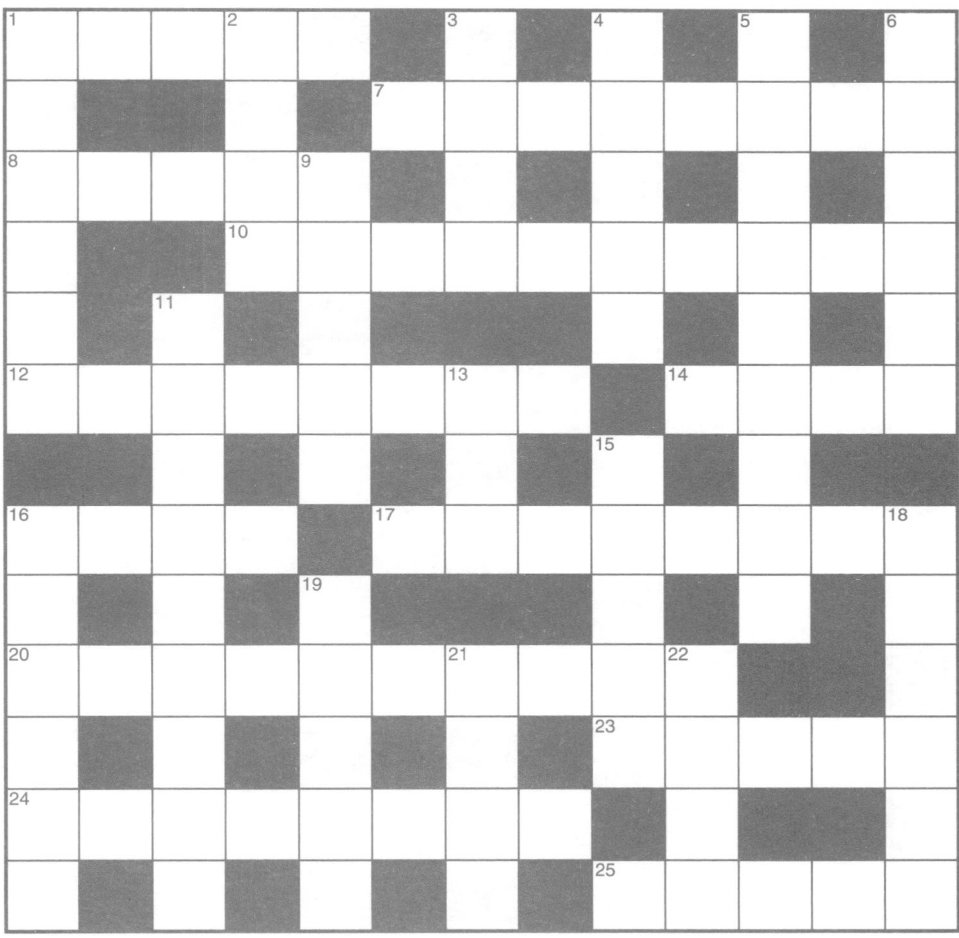

## ACROSS

1. Female person
7. Wild prank
8. Expertise
10. Feelings
12. Straw-roofed
14. Inflated promotion
16. Hidden obstacle
17. Pink wading bird
20. Strangers
23. Fate
24. Country without monarch
25. Cast ballot

## DOWN

1. Shrewdest
2. Sickens
3. Small vipers
4. Shouts, ... & raves
5. Mimicking humorously
6. Leaseholder
9. Blood-sucking worm
11. Section of writing
13. Snake-like fish
15. Smug smile
16. Game park tour
18. Ahead
19. Suspended state
21. Fixing pin
22. Pudding starch

# CROSSWORD 81

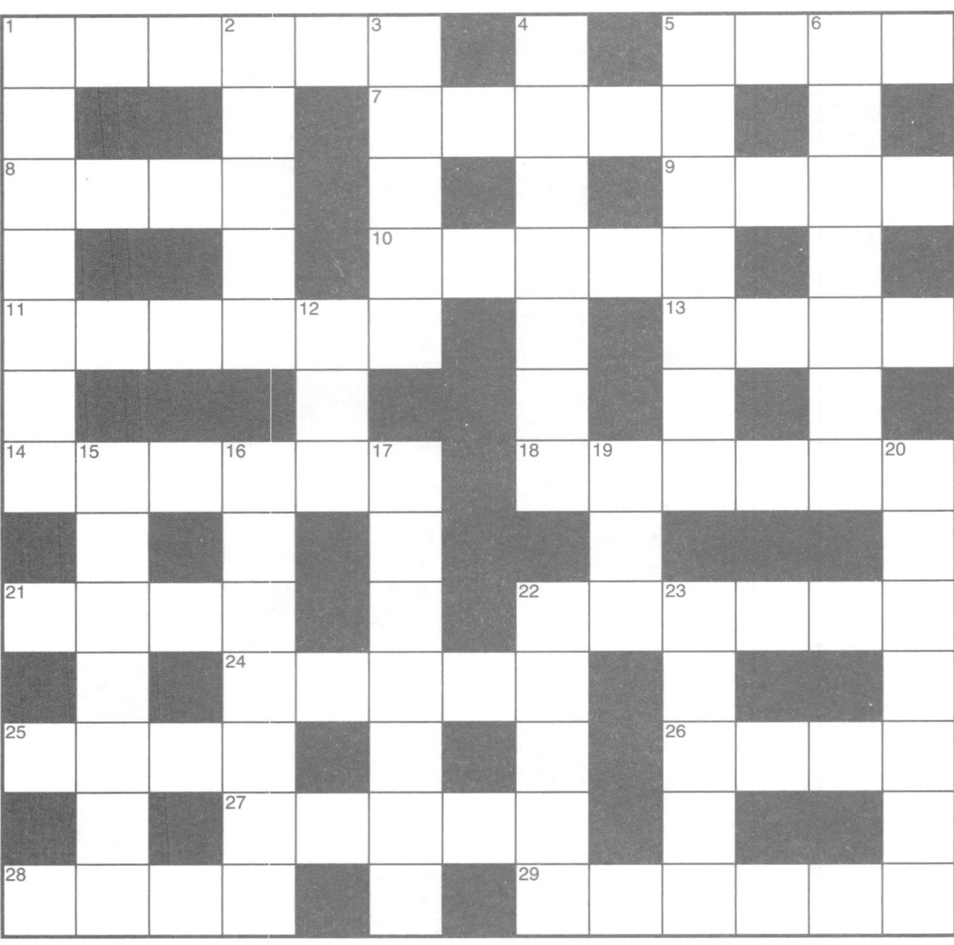

## ACROSS

1. Cited
5. Spiders' traps
7. Cousin's father
8. Tiny amount
9. Three-piece group
10. Simple
11. Evenly balances
13. Historical periods
14. Summer shoe
18. Made snug home
21. Scalp growth
22. Medium's session
24. Australian marsupial
25. She was, they ...
26. Strong wind
27. Part of play
28. Feel anxious
29. Military blockades

## DOWN

1. Trembles
2. Small crown
3. Gets rid of
4. Eight-sided figure
5. Moisture
6. Army unit
12. Meadow
15. Hobbyist
16. Blackest
17. Situated
19. Before (poetic)
20. Weight watchers
22. Auctions
23. Debate

# CROSSWORD 82

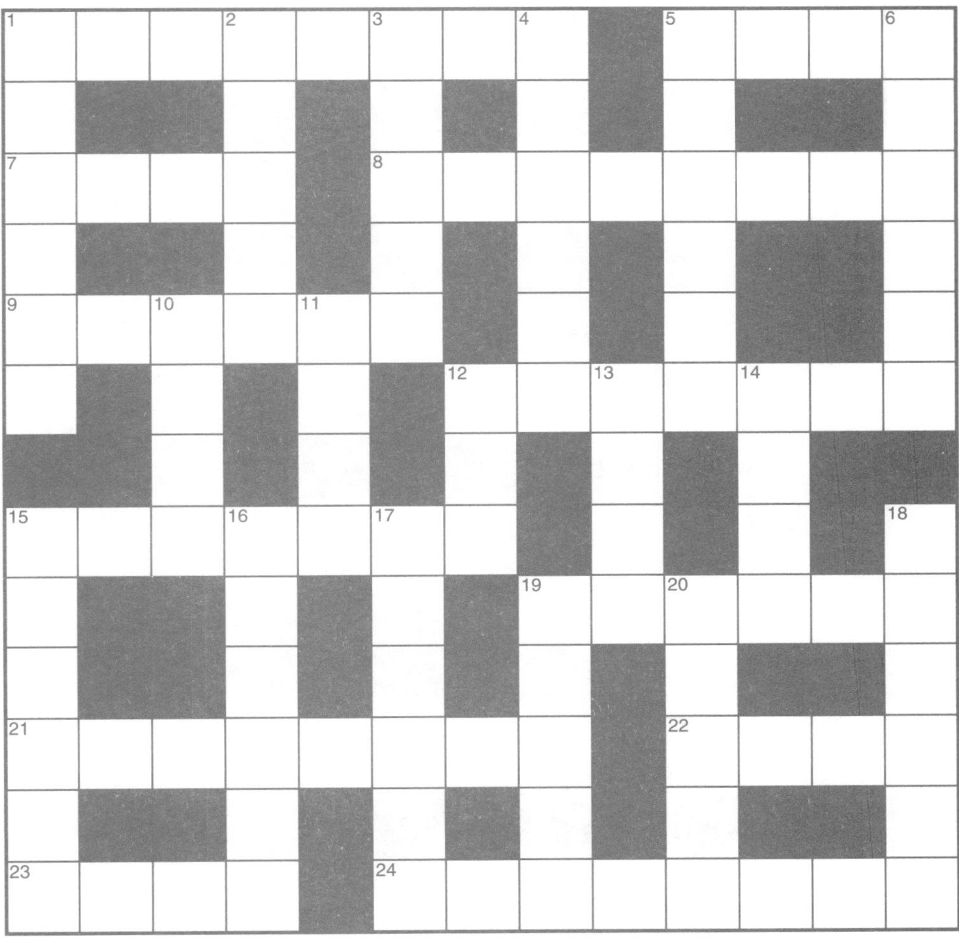

## ACROSS

1. Scout gathering
5. Voice modulation
7. Garden door
8. Party mime game
9. Bowed
12. Passionate believers
15. Armed helicopter
19. Celebratory meals
21. Crockery accident
22. Bouncing toy
23. Oxen harness
24. Recommends

## DOWN

1. Assembly puzzle
2. Tree, copper ...
3. Hurried
4. Pass (of years)
5. Ride
6. Students' written assignments
10. Metal currency
11. Engrave
12. Toothed fastener
13. Ready, willing & ...
14. Nocturnal birds
15. Grimy
16. Ferocious
17. Occupy by force
18. Bible songs
19. Liberated
20. Yellowish-brown shade

# CROSSWORD 83

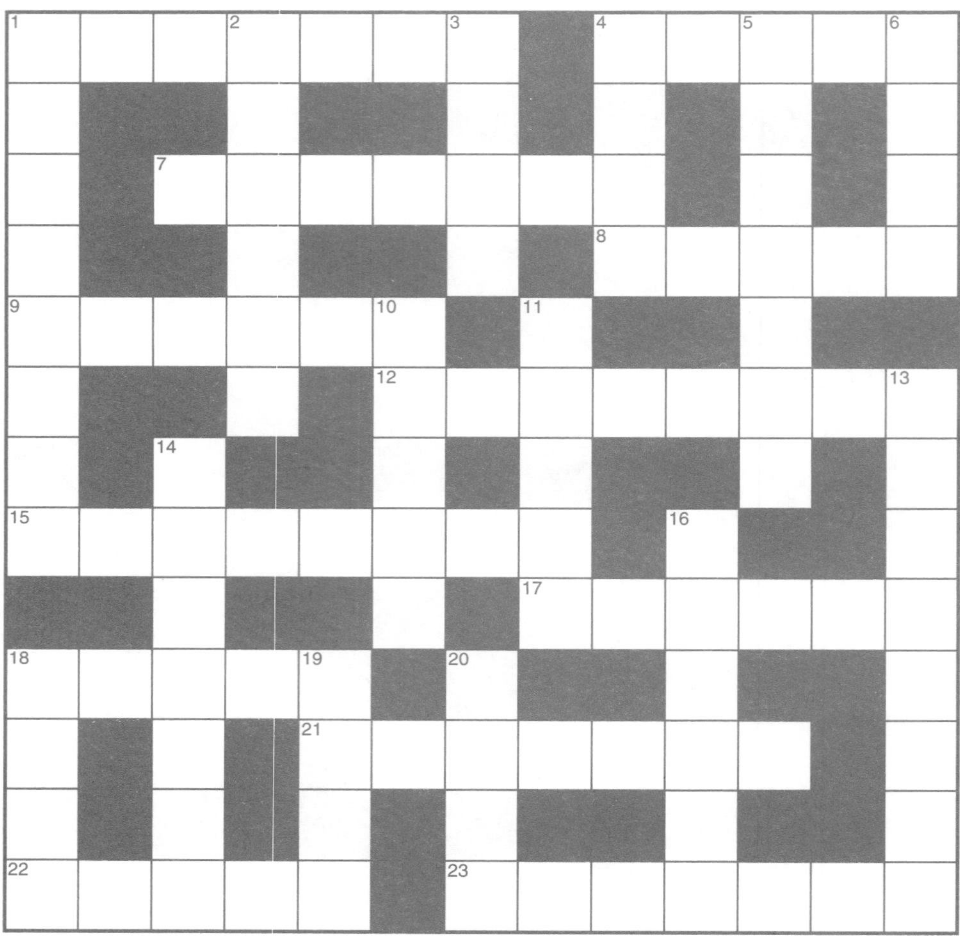

## ACROSS

1. Leftover piece
4. Torment
7. Clap
8. Precise
9. For each, per ...
12. Tough (skin)
15. Criminal underworld
17. Surrender
18. Aerial bombardment
21. Citrus fruits
22. The ones here
23. Passionate

## DOWN

1. Lessening
2. Table linen item
3. Sport squad
4. Sea phase, high ...
5. Assumed identities
6. Leave room
10. Sacrificial block
11. Nations
13. Young
14. Valuable old article
16. Missing
18. Angler's worm
19. Sector
20. Become tiresome

# CROSSWORD 84

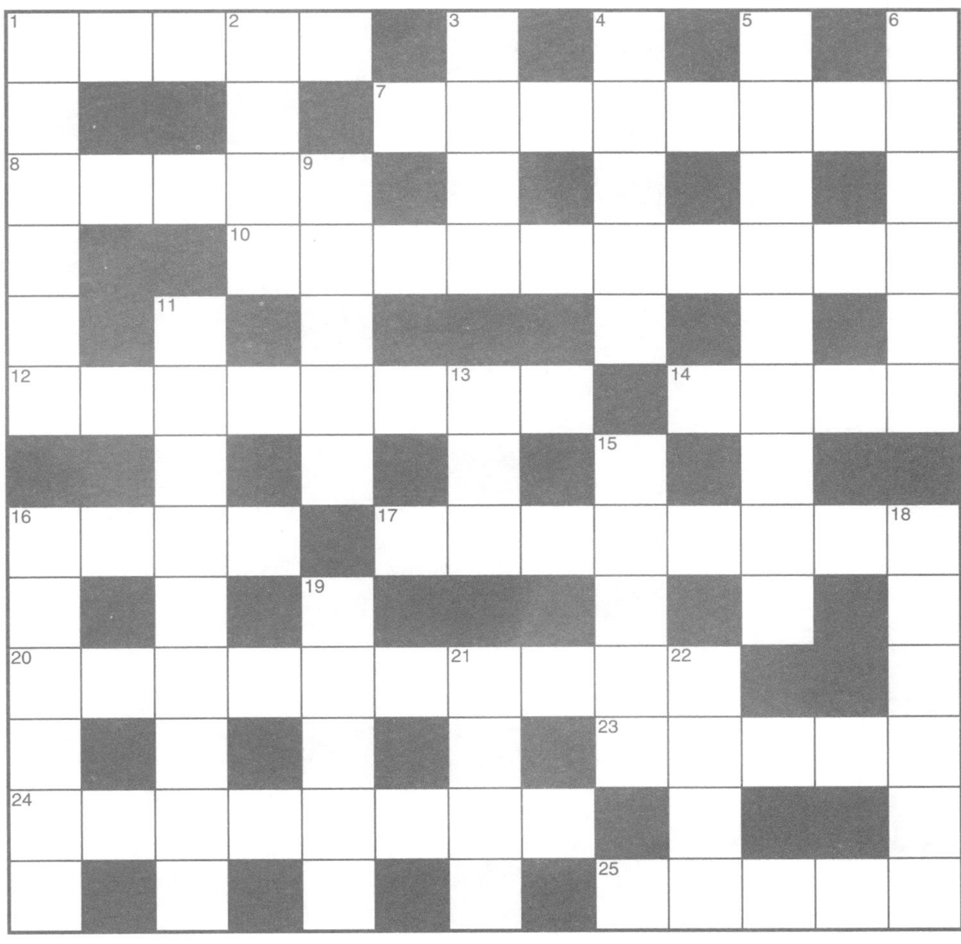

## ACROSS

1. Wall painting
7. Unlawful occupier
8. Guild
10. Ambulance officers
12. Originates (from)
14. Wound blemish
16. Young deer
17. Rejected people
20. Criminality
23. Golfer's two under par
24. Gathering bit by bit
25. Unmarried

## DOWN

1. Whipped dessert
2. On the summit of
3. Water
4. Went on rampage
5. Flight of steps
6. Pencil-mark remover
9. Concerning ships
11. Careless pedestrian
13. Flightless bird
15. Excruciating (pain)
16. Food chiller
18. Scatter
19. Great suffering
21. Wrinkle
22. Fanciful story

# CROSSWORD 85

## ACROSS

1. Bores holes
5. Utensil
7. Flinch
8. Sob
9. Not at home
10. Paris landmark, The Eiffel ...
11. Propels
13. Fleur-de-lis plant
14. Merriment
18. Inching (toward)
21. Supporting beam
22. Bordered
24. Brown pigment
25. Orange-peel lining
26. Be an omen of
27. Weight measure
28. Membranous sac
29. Pouted

## DOWN

1. Breaking (of day)
2. Minor transgression
3. Crushes (fly)
4. Weave around
5. Rupturing (muscle)
6. Speech
12. Ignited
15. Boost (sound)
16. Listening range
17. Barking in pain
19. Perish
20. Boon
22. Windmill blades
23. Freedom fighter

# CROSSWORD 86

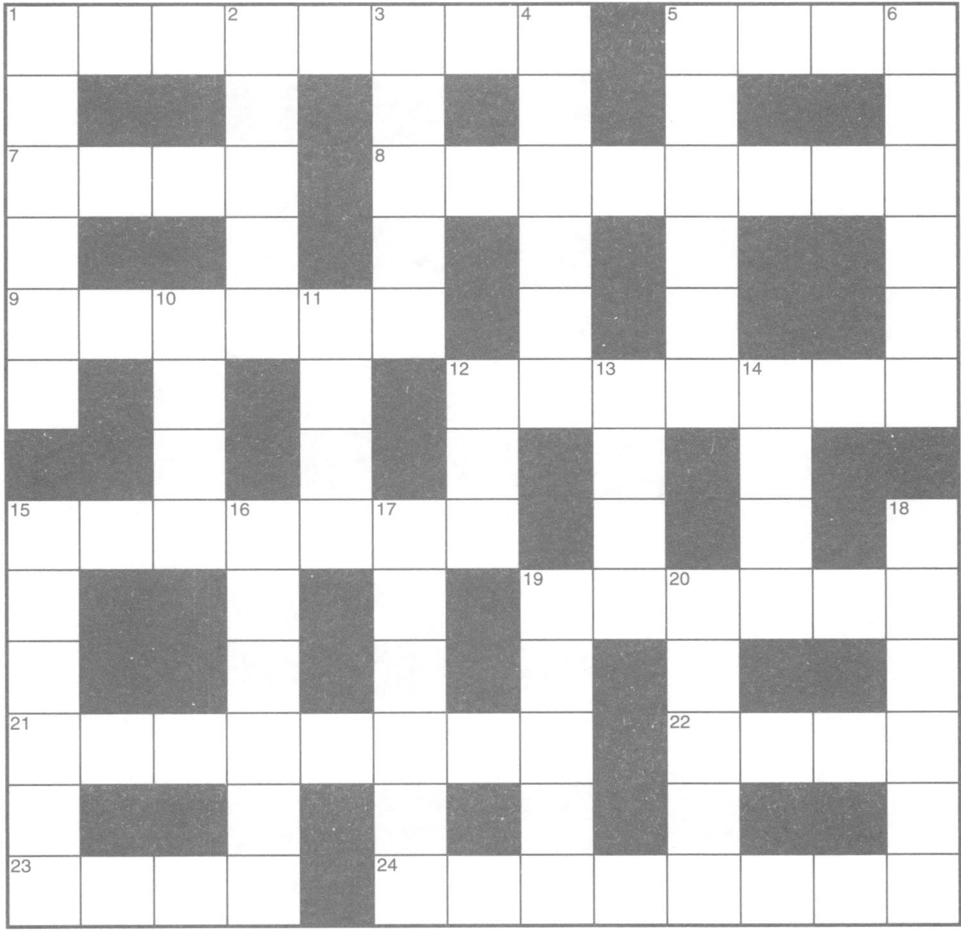

## ACROSS

1. Waste
5. Several moose
7. Trick
8. Wanders aimlessly
9. Tenderly
12. Buyers & sellers
15. Preserving liquid
19. Holds tightly
21. Glue
22. Arm bone
23. Sodium bicarbonate, baking ...
24. Edge-of-your-seat anticipation

## DOWN

1. Small branches
2. Skilled
3. Mannequin
4. Harvester
5. Curled (of smoke)
6. Silk bands
10. Subject of a verb
11. Lengthy
12. Sticky coal by-product
13. At a great distance
14. Flows away
15. Singing parts
16. Allergic inflammation
17. Military forces
18. Get-out (clause)
19. Estimate
20. Mistreat

# CROSSWORD 87

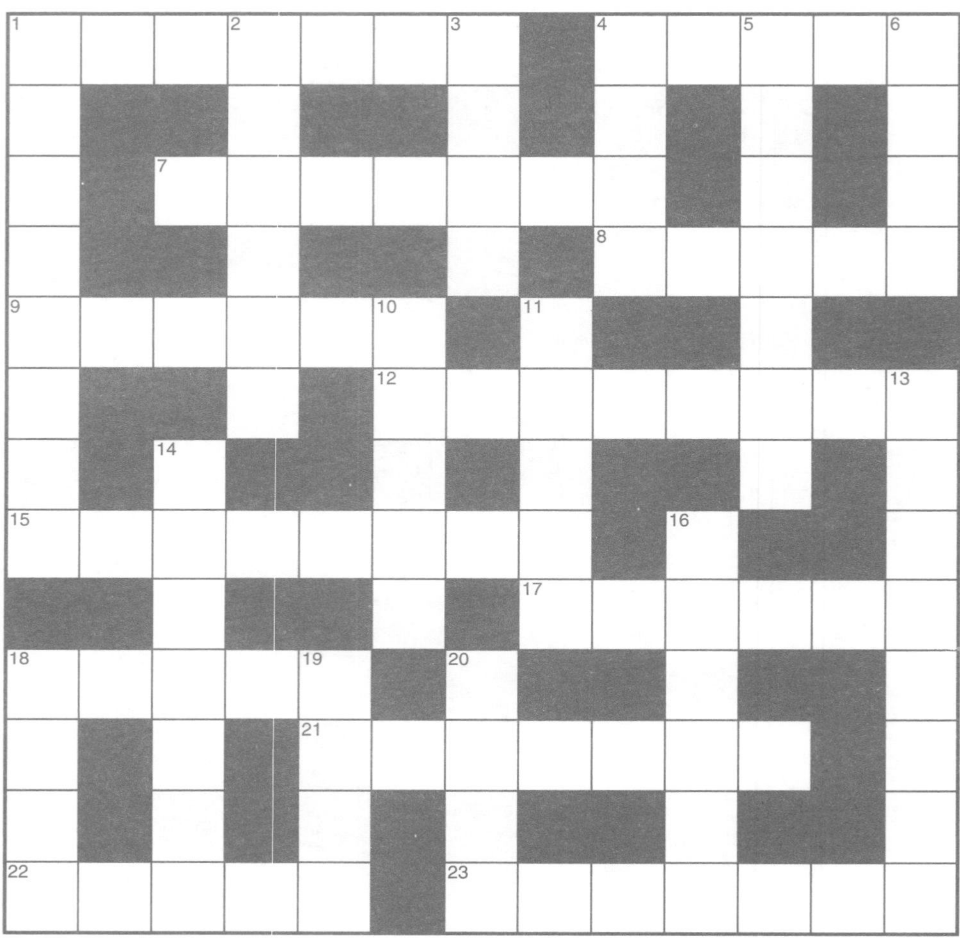

## ACROSS

1. Cared for medically
4. Lunches or dinners
7. Clashing instruments
8. Add-on
9. Transgressed
12. Most fatigued
15. Surprised
17. Unchanging
18. Intended
21. Sweltered
22. Gnat-like fly
23. Authoritarian rule

## DOWN

1. Pants
2. Unspecified person
3. University faculty head
4. Ruminate
5. Second (one)
6. Couch
10. Lived
11. Incursions
13. Deceit
14. Marched
16. Cinematographer's apparatus
18. Cripple
19. Loyal
20. Discretion

# CROSSWORD 88

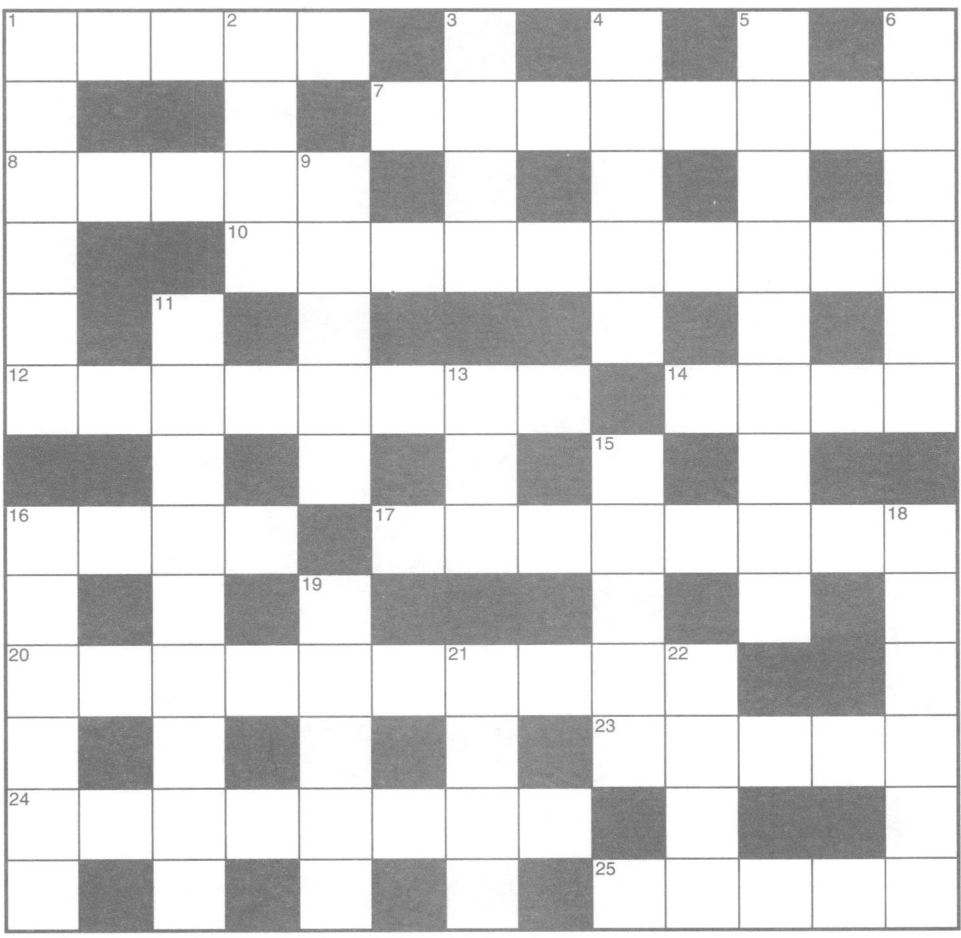

## ACROSS

1. Doorposts
7. Flight industry
8. Keep afloat, ... water
10. Strolling
12. Lack of generosity
14. Metal depression
16. Consumer
17. Imaginary
20. Calmly
23. Beetle grub
24. Frozen shipping hazards
25. Creative thoughts

## DOWN

1. Flotsam & ...
2. Lingerie items
3. Equal
4. Surfaced with concrete
5. Industrious quality
6. Horse-head chess piece
9. Intimidate
11. Curator
13. Bashful
15. Oyster casing
16. Overdue (bill)
18. Village's population
19. Control handle
21. Beseech
22. Enclosed area

# CROSSWORD 89

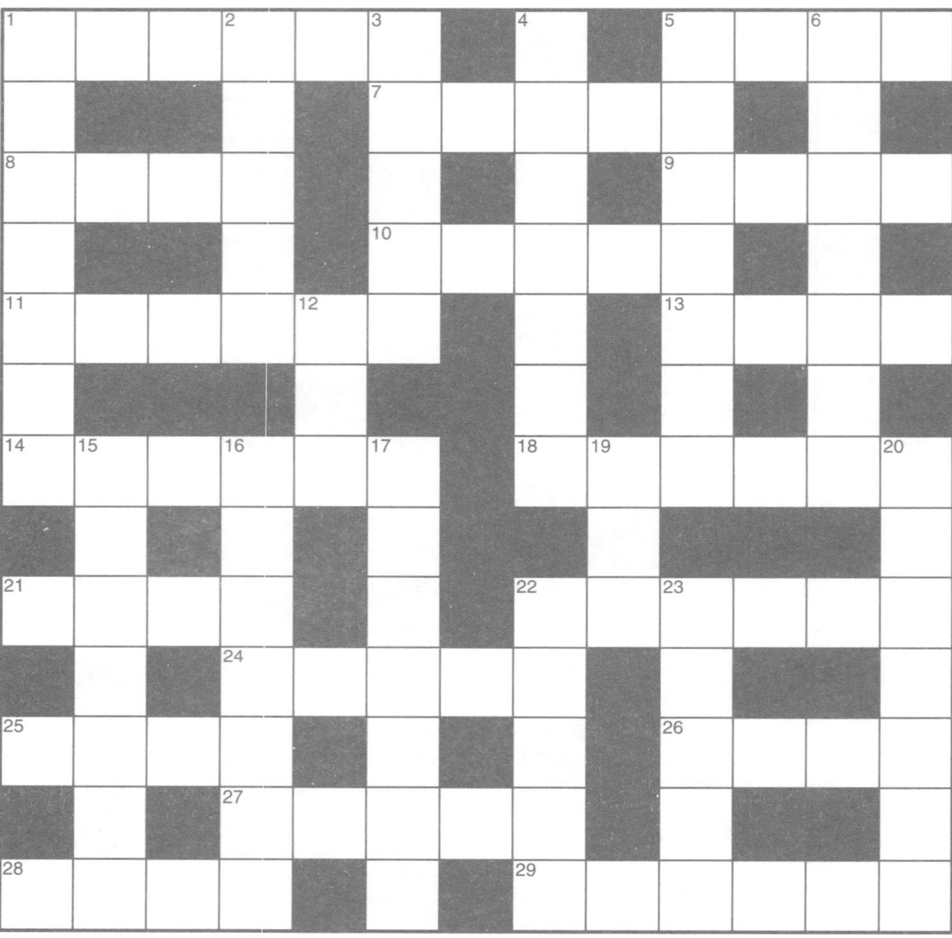

## ACROSS

1. Musical composition
5. Candle string
7. Wooden packing case
8. Coarse file
9. Scrapes by, ... out a living
10. Mad (dog)
11. Recent
13. Niggles
14. Spiced sausage
18. Excessively sweet
21. Pimply condition
22. Raps
24. Huge
25. Trifling
26. Clip
27. Hard iron alloy
28. Inquires
29. Delivered (blow)

## DOWN

1. Small prawns
2. Abundant
3. Squirrel nut
4. Sings like canary
5. Removing unwanted plants
6. Twist pioneer, Chubby ...
12. Male sheep
15. Arrow marksmen
16. Eternally youthful
17. Piano keys
19. Hot drink dispenser
20. Eastern veil
22. Ships' spines
23. External

# CROSSWORD 90

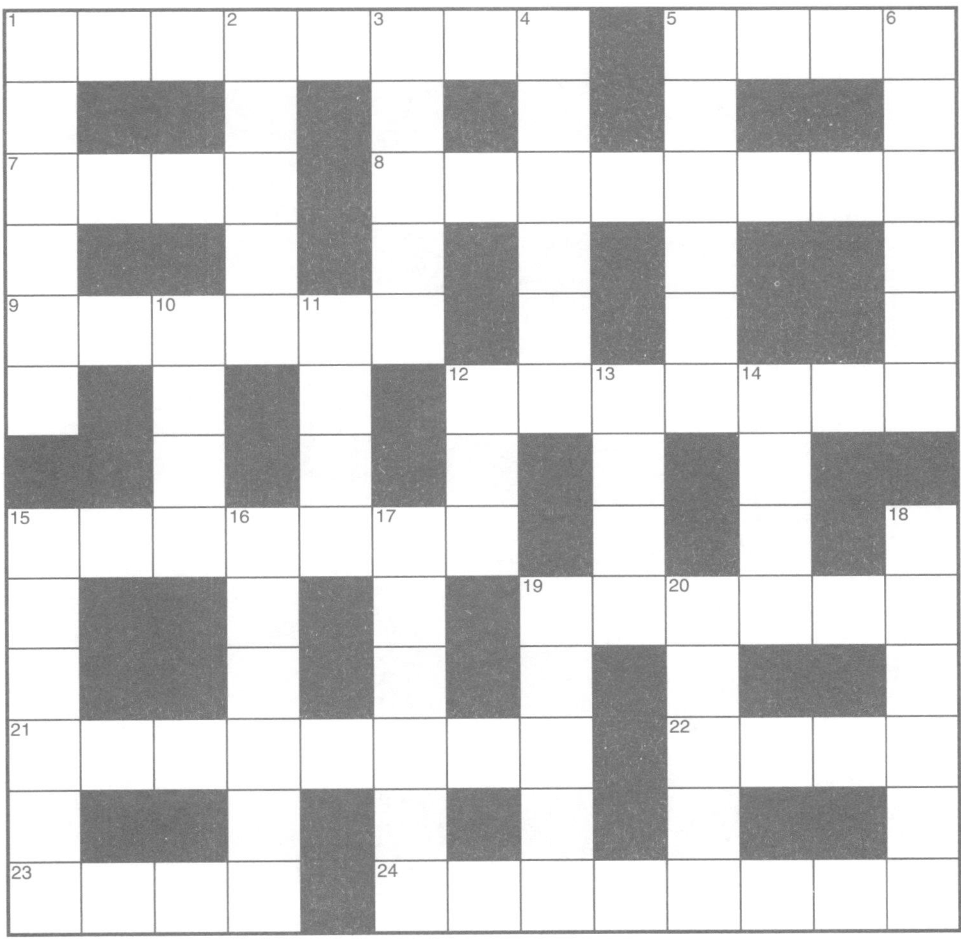

## ACROSS

1. Brazenness
5. Fill (with tears)
7. Polish
8. Mariner
9. Change over time
12. Genetic mixes
15. Increases threefold
19. Small-necked bottles
21. Native American hatchet
22. Set down
23. Ride waves
24. Ribbon awards

## DOWN

1. Strolled
2. Abysmal
3. Subject up for discussion
4. Twelve-monthly
5. Sportsman's jacket
6. Principles
10. Leak slowly
11. Calf meat
12. Belonging to him
13. Invoice
14. Printing fluids
15. Samples (food)
16. Representing, on ... of
17. Chocolate choux pastry
18. Stage whispers
19. Forgeries
20. Apportion

# CROSSWORD 91

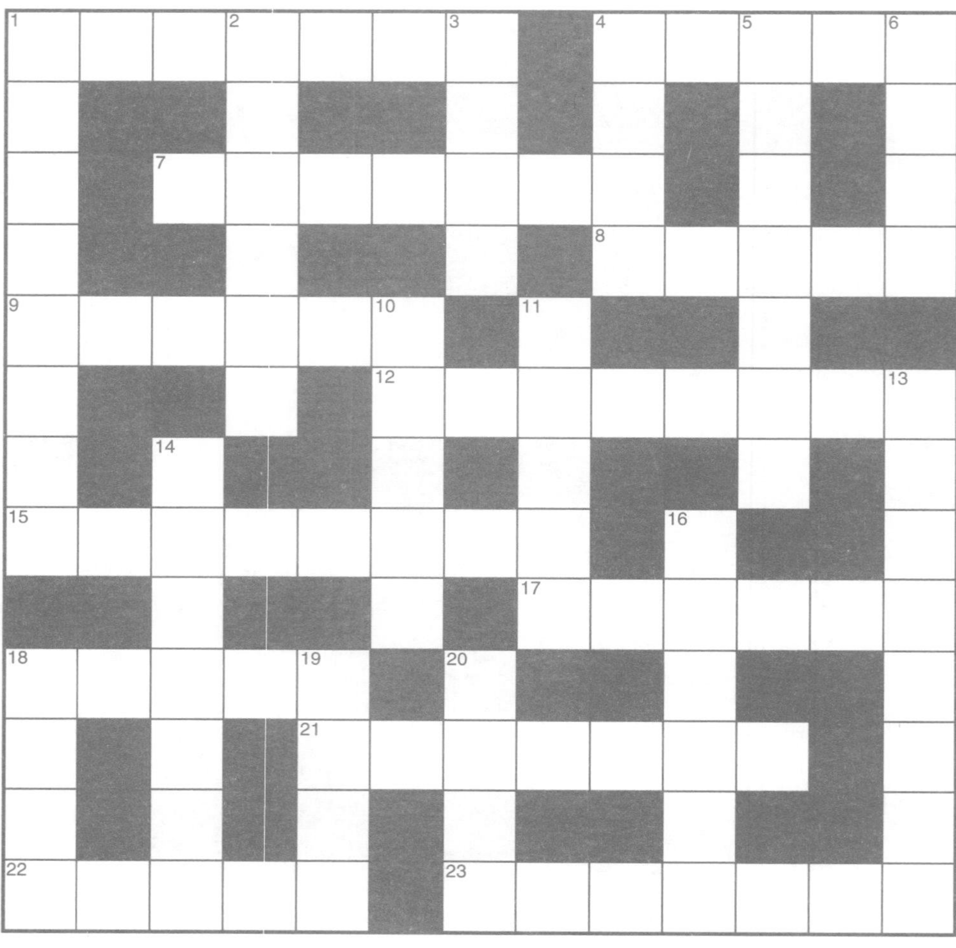

## ACROSS

1. Grumbled
4. Whiskers
7. Sealed with bung
8. Sedate
9. Spread of eight notes
12. Drawings
15. Regional speeches
17. Eluded
18. Sawn-off tree trunk
21. Refugee
22. Pales
23. Peeked

## DOWN

1. Rode quickly
2. Not submerged
3. Canines
4. Auction offers
5. Yearly book of events
6. Act
10. Decree
11. Pay increase
13. Followed secretly
14. Came of age
16. Cave
18. Individual identity
19. Domestic animals
20. Hoodlum group

# CROSSWORD 92

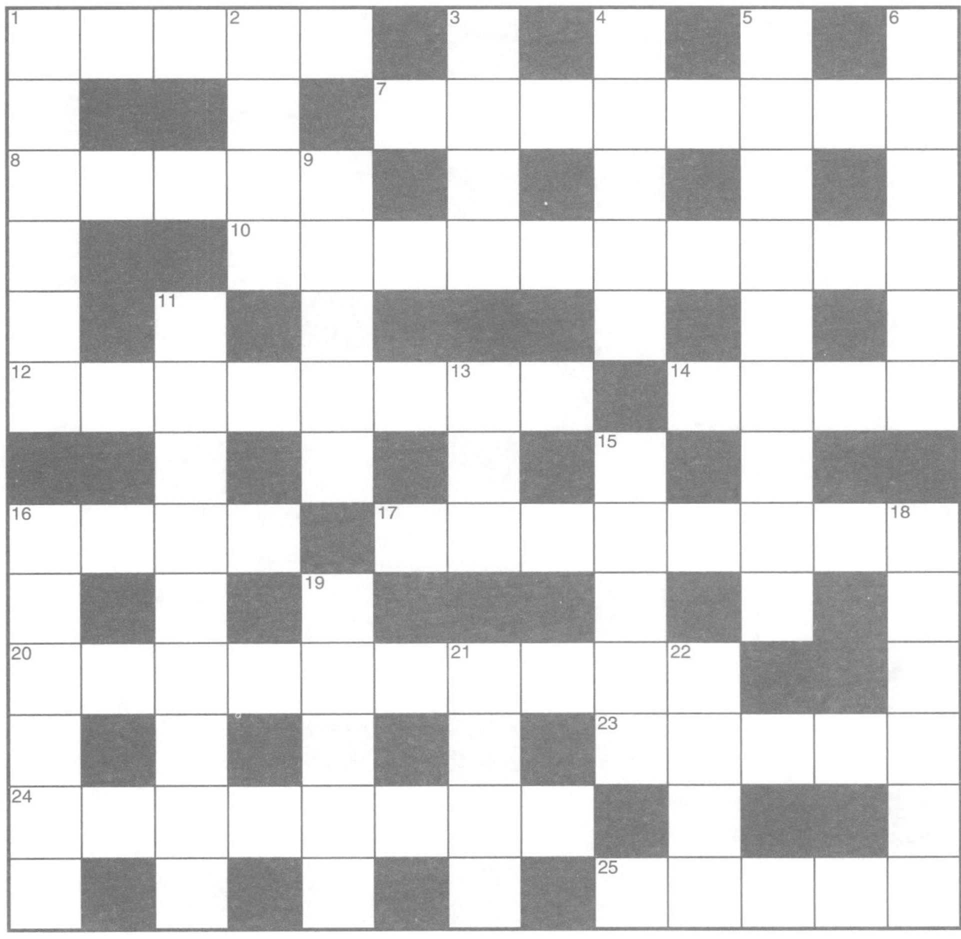

## ACROSS

1. Shoo!
7. Undressed
8. Earlier
10. Tornado geyser
12. Circus swings
14. Coffin stand
16. Make hazy
17. Leave homeland
20. Transformation
23. Lubricated
24. Heard, ... to
25. Distributed, ... out

## DOWN

1. Group of seven
2. Affirm
3. Tiny spider
4. Collision
5. Of the stomach
6. Magazine chief
9. Shouted, ranted & ...
11. Indistinctness
13. Disease-prone tree
15. Snow shelter
16. Shoe fastener
18. Worn away
19. High temperature
21. Prosecutes
22. Eight, ..., ten

# CROSSWORD 93

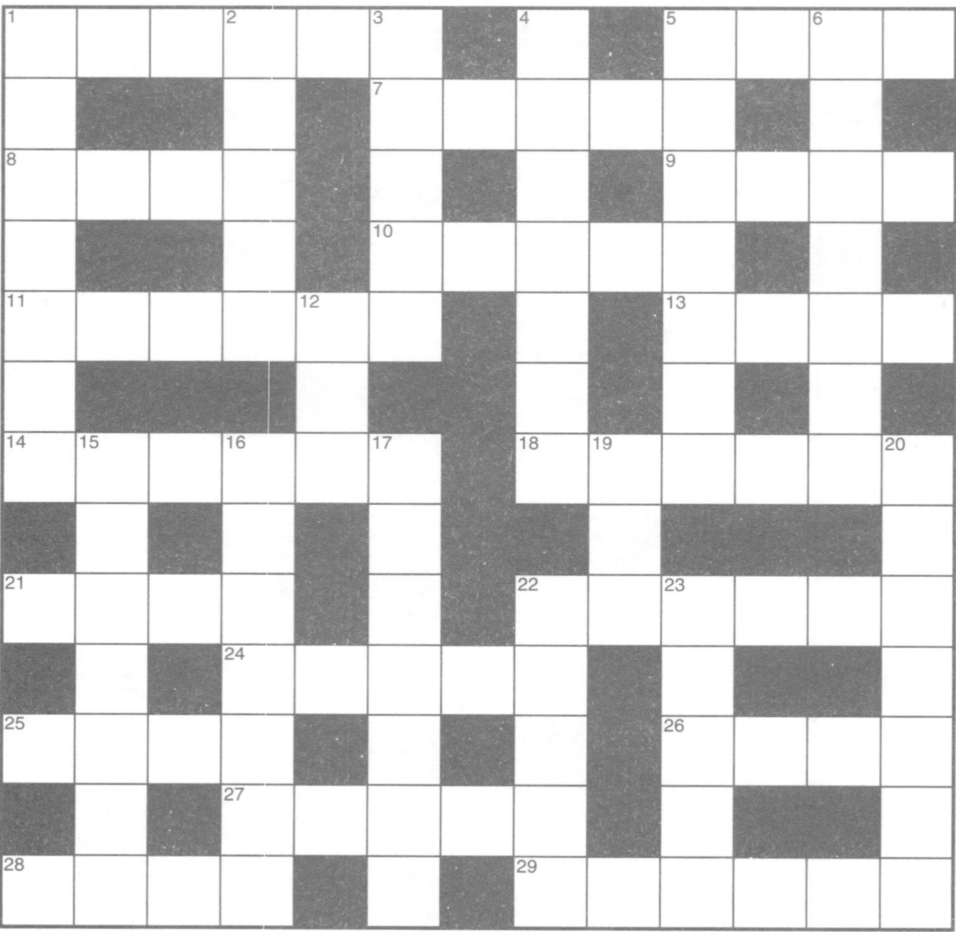

## ACROSS

1. 14-line poem
5. Puts on (hat)
7. Lift with effort
8. Require
9. Cajole
10. Praise highly
11. Teeter
13. Chilled
14. Weekly earnings
18. Casts out
21. Smartly-groomed
22. Wanted badly
24. Possessor
25. Spurts of water
26. Scuba descent
27. Uniform
28. Honey makers
29. Rests on knees

## DOWN

1. Nasal cavities
2. Nodules
3. Tossed
4. Ecstatic joy
5. Decrease
6. Closest
12. House cooler, ... conditioner
15. Gain
16. Approaches boldly
17. Gaping
19. Glass pot
20. Sorrow
22. Fissure
23. Confuse

# CROSSWORD 94

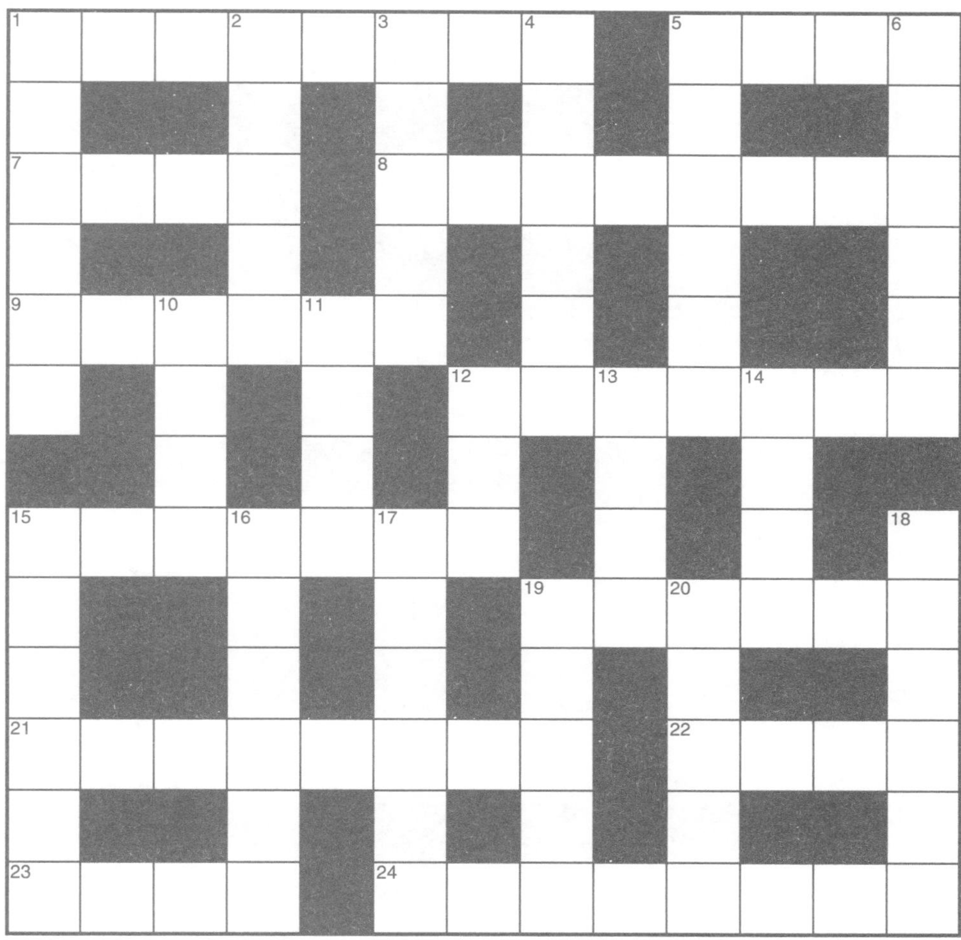

## ACROSS

1. Mountainous (region)
5. Chore
7. 007 agent, James ...
8. Aged (of paper)
9. Proposals
12. Set of 3 books
15. Specimen
19. Respect
21. Naughtiness
22. Political power group
23. Shipment
24. Miscellaneous items

## DOWN

1. Keep company (with)
2. Clipped plant border
3. Gulf
4. Unit of money
5. Bricklayer's tool
6. Renal organ
10. Pet's parasite
11. Sloped walkway
12. Foot digit
13. Tropical wading bird
14. Storybook monster
15. Tooth covering
16. Finely chopped (garlic)
17. Pond flowers
18. Spanks
19. Pointy-featured
20. Underground stem

# CROSSWORD 95

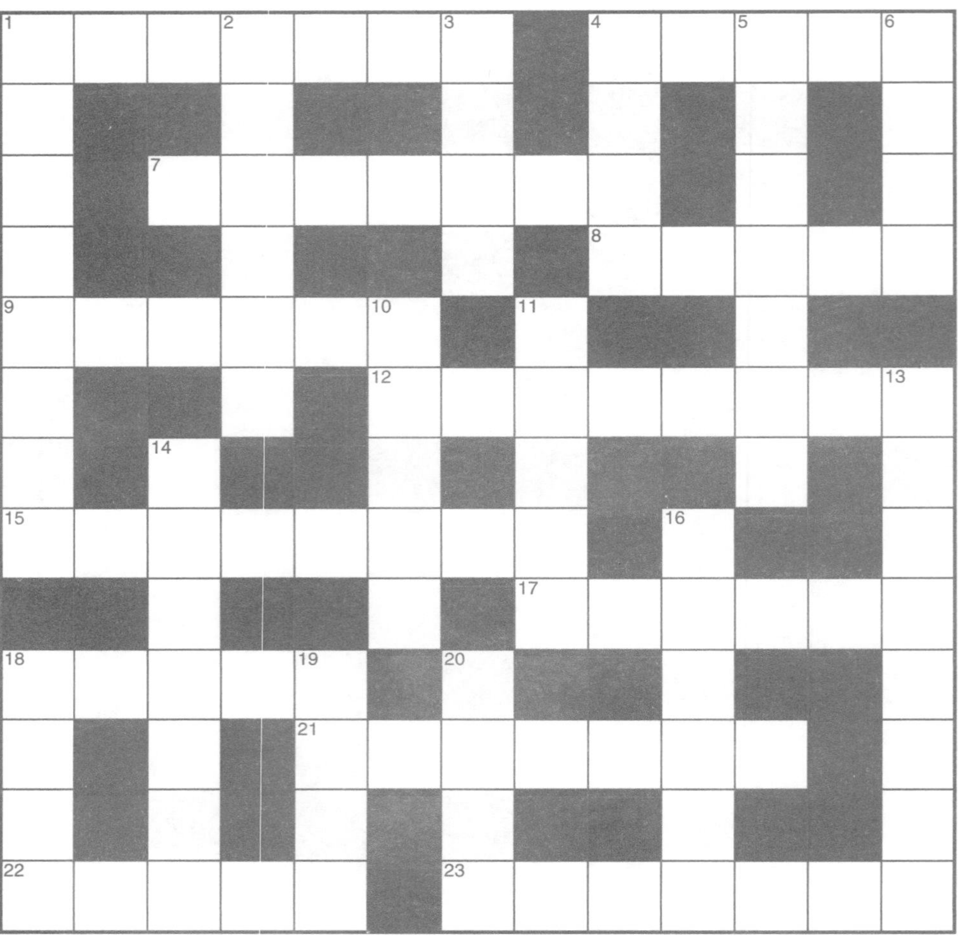

## ACROSS

1. Slow worker
4. Duckling's dad
7. Dairy/egg dessert
8. Clever
9. Struck with foot
12. Re-emerge
15. Gain degree
17. Place of worship
18. Slaked one's thirst
21. Most orderly
22. Separated
23. Asian food items

## DOWN

1. Removing feathers from
2. Alcoholics
3. Scan
4. Failures
5. Displayed
6. Compass point
10. Imagine
11. Trainee journalist
13. Sets free
14. Burnt sugar
16. Entertained
18. Confers knighthood on
19. Mend (of bones)
20. Chessman

# CROSSWORD 96

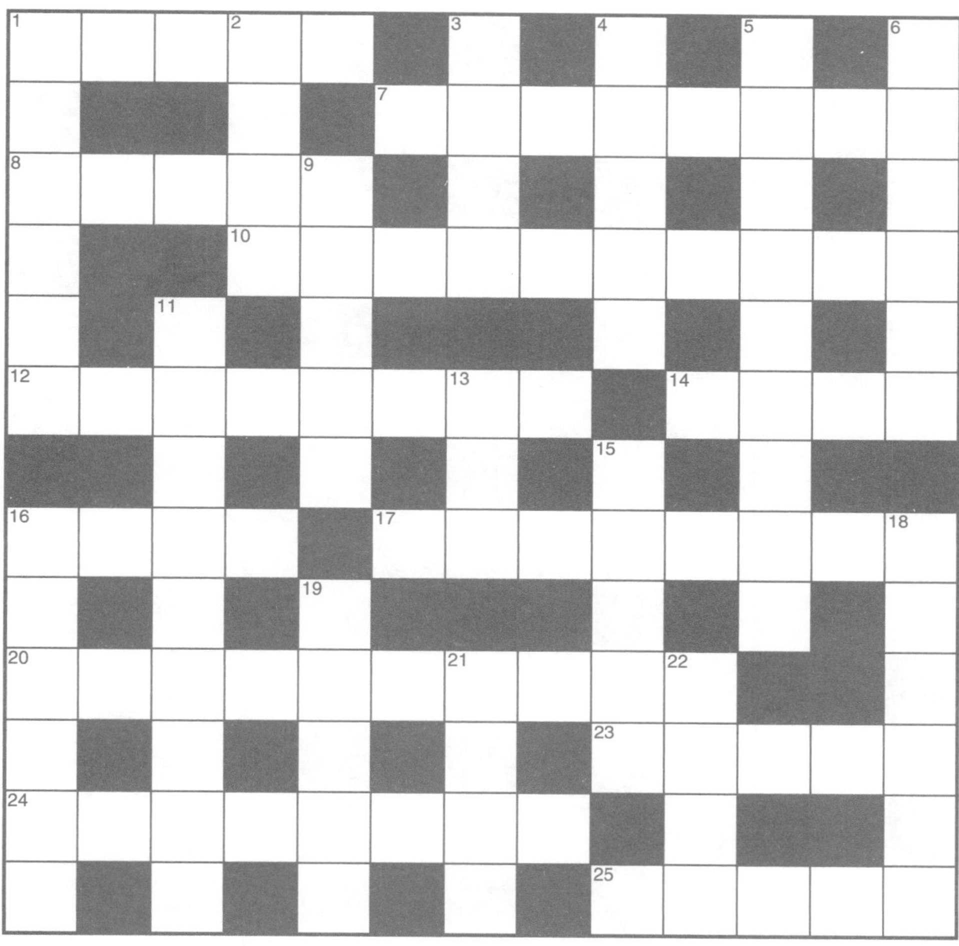

## ACROSS

1. Garlic segment
7. Even if
8. Dock
10. Children
12. Grabbed quickly
14. ... & duchess
16. Peel
17. Of metal
20. Unavoidably
23. Of sound
24. Clumsy
25. Cranium

## DOWN

1. Cringes
2. Fluctuate
3. Large family
4. Which person's?
5. Musically
6. Pure
9. Strength
11. Washed (clothes)
13. Night before
15. Yacht canvases
16. Dried grape
18. Invalidate
19. Bitingly cool
21. Crooked
22. Nucleus of egg

# CROSSWORD 97

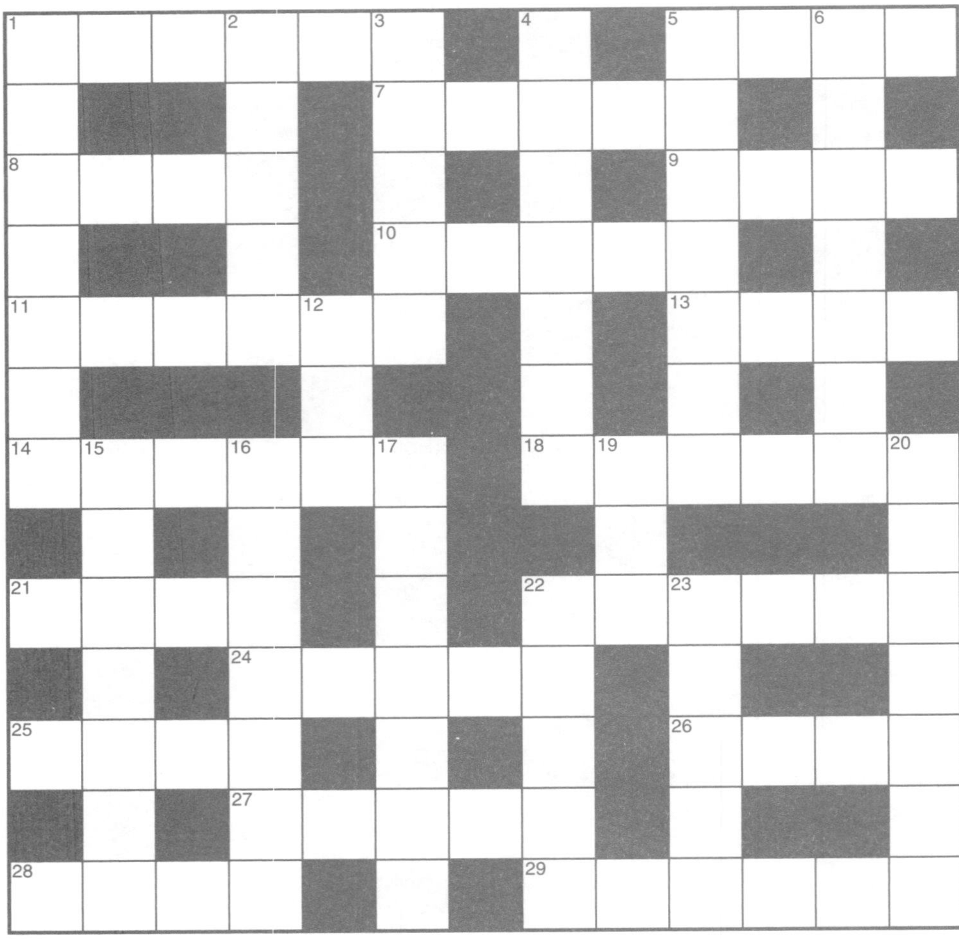

## ACROSS

1. Deliver sermon
5. Weight measure
7. Song of the Swiss
8. Soprano's solo
9. Yell of pain
10. T-shirt openings
11. Biliousness
13. Narrow aperture
14. Wild river waters
18. Naval flag
21. Beach crustacean
22. Clergyman
24. Public profile
25. Infant's bed
26. Very short skirt
27. Do well (at)
28. Filled with wonder
29. Four-door cars

## DOWN

1. Strategist
2. Accumulate
3. African scavenger
4. Teach
5. Shiny paints
6. Raising (eyebrows)
12. Terminate
15. Flight staff
16. Partook of liquor
17. Scrape
19. Formerly known as
20. Female goats
22. Distributes playing cards
23. Pointed (gun)

# CROSSWORD 98

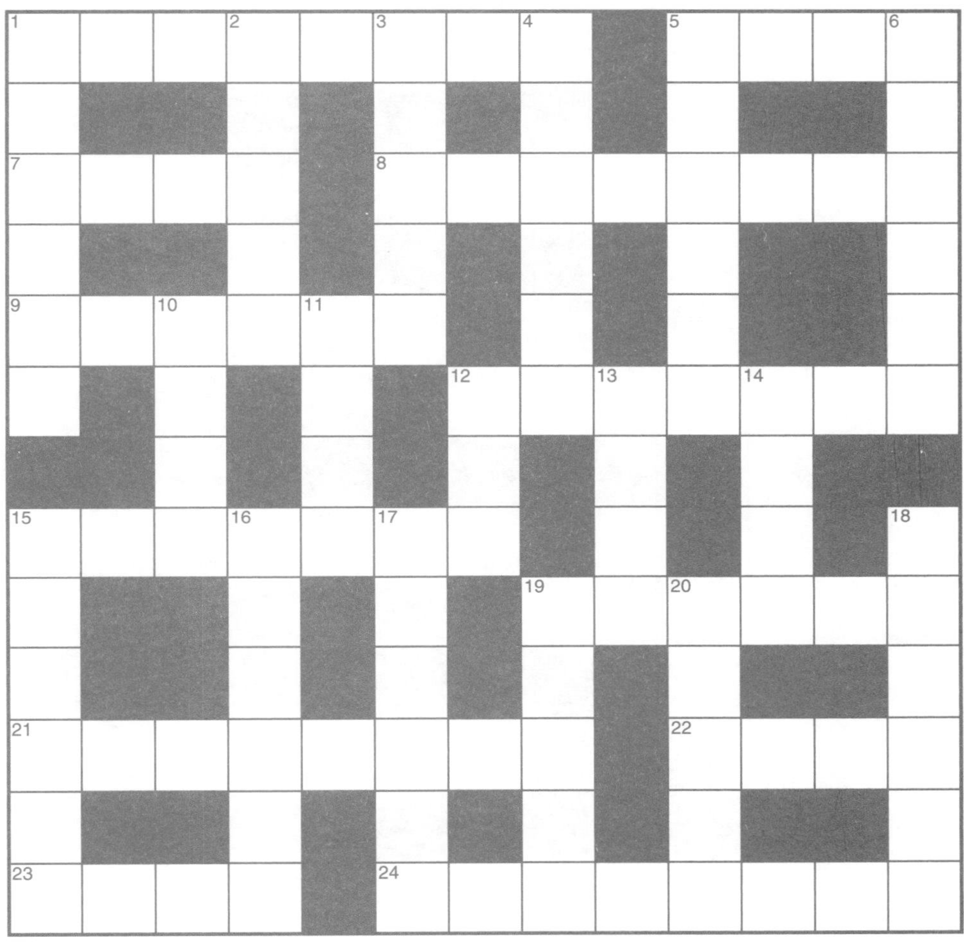

## ACROSS

1. Entranceway chime
5. Recited
7. Skating arena
8. Evacuating
9. Gorges
12. Negative (criticism)
15. Tampered (with)
19. Stuck down (envelope)
21. Acting properly
22. Thick slice
23. Stared at
24. Be uncertain

## DOWN

1. Straight (route)
2. Scrapes (leaves)
3. Large jugs
4. Pruned
5. Reaping tool
6. Temperature unit
10. Discontinued
11. Shopping complex
12. Charitable funding
13. Flower container
14. Music style, rock and ...
15. Frail
16. Insist on
17. Improve (soil)
18. Able to be eaten
19. Long tales
20. Valuable possession

# CROSSWORD 99

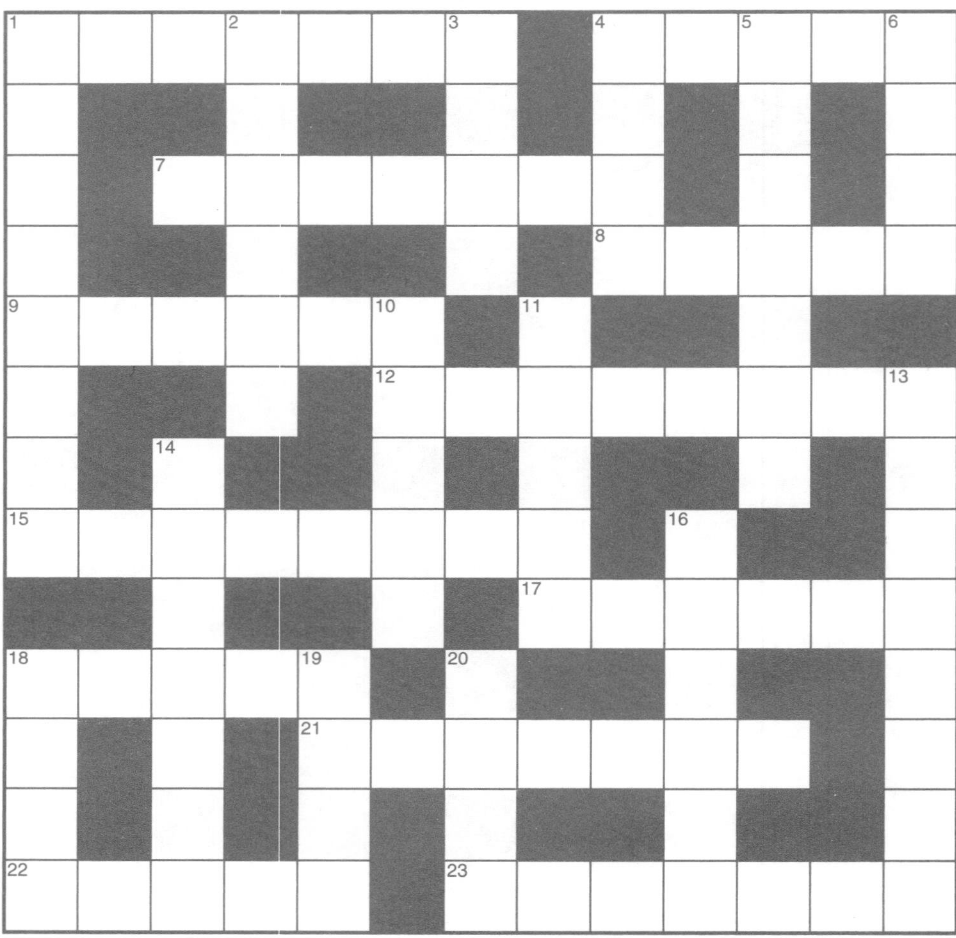

## ACROSS

1. Long-necked animal
4. Sentimental
7. Arch over eye
8. Of birth
9. Synthetic fabrics
12. Name
15. Lack of hearing
17. Of family group
18. Bronze medal position
21. Furiously
22. Stone overhang
23. Emitting

## DOWN

1. Banned from flying
2. In any case
3. Makes slip-up
4. Milled (timber)
5. Plait of hair
6. Shout
10. Flanks
11. Minimum amount
13. Capitulating
14. Relayed on air
16. Searched through
18. Above average height
19. Paris cathedral, Notre ...
20. Gape at

# CROSSWORD 100

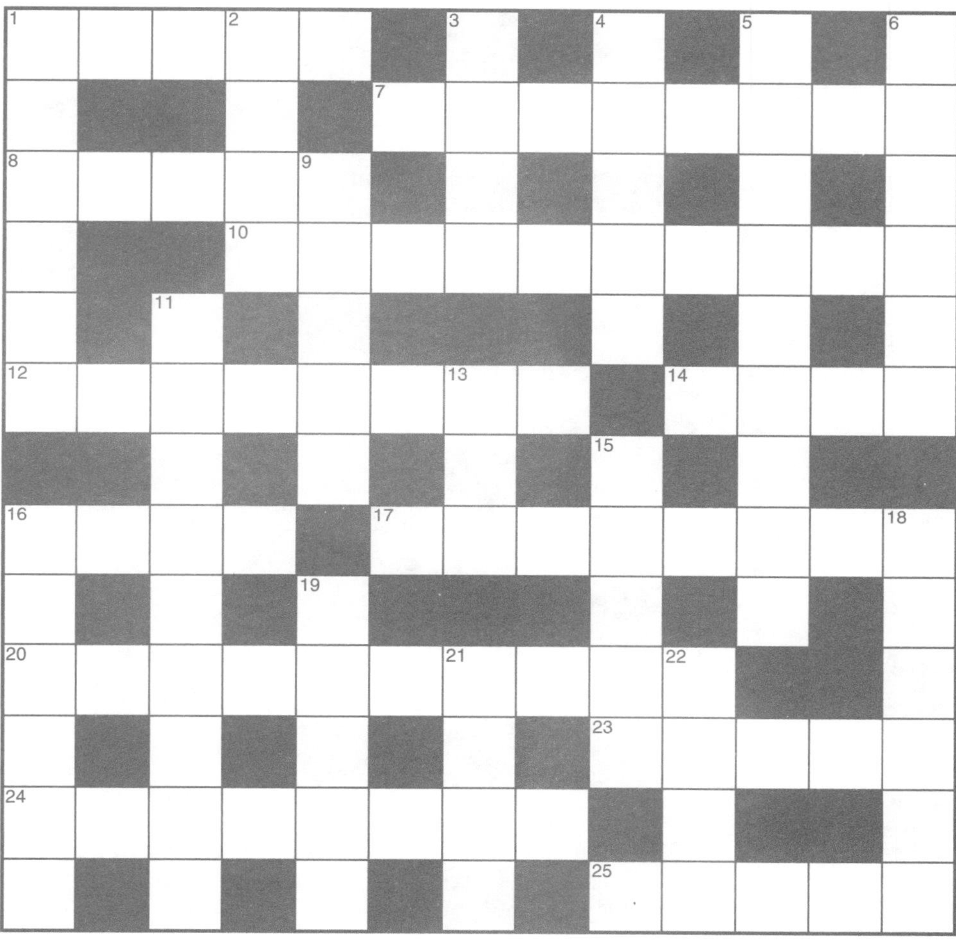

## ACROSS

1. World map book
7. Sliding out of control
8. Fundamental
10. Hot season
12. Dingier
14. Body-piercing adornment
16. Sect
17. Prepare for performance
20. Two-week periods
23. Steam bath
24. Studies closely
25. Got up from chair

## DOWN

1. Soundtrack CDs
2. Line of rotation
3. Pass lightly (over)
4. Love deeply
5. Clergymen
6. Reached an understanding
9. Keeps in check
11. Prison escape
13. Female sheep
15. Makes joke
16. Bean drink
18. Message to run
19. Remove (brooch)
21. Departs
22. ... & pepper

# CROSSWORD 101

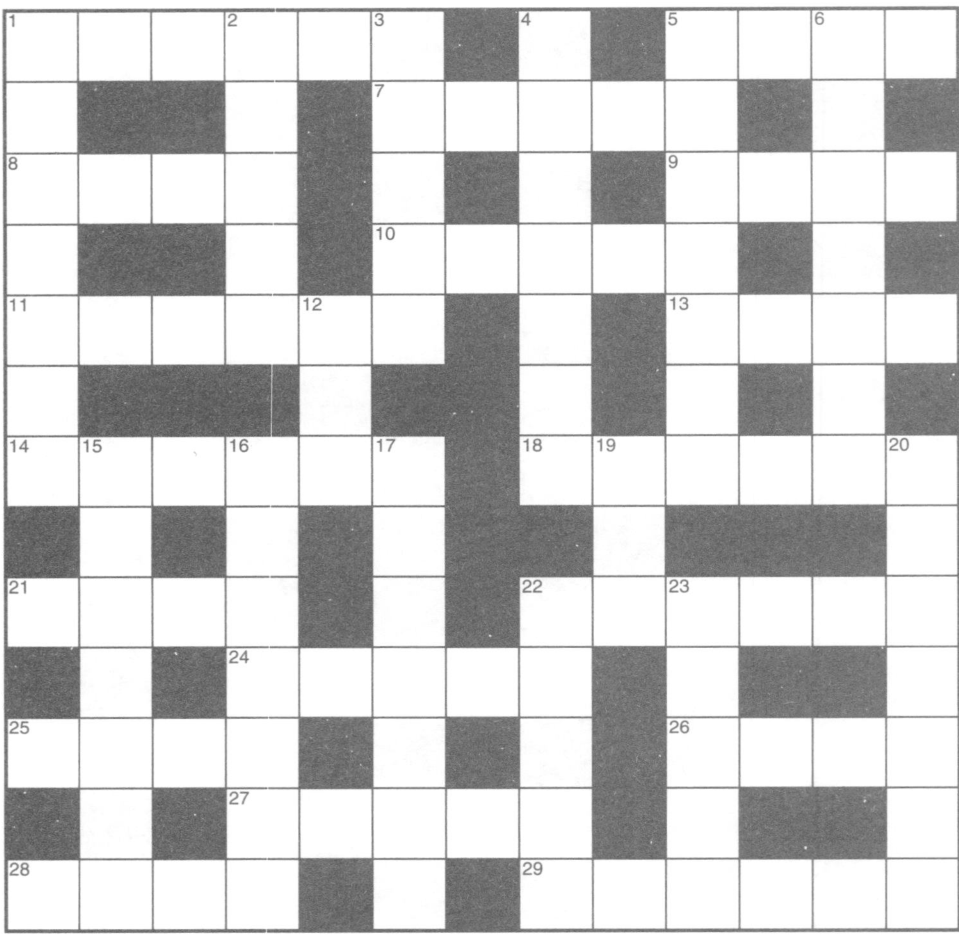

## ACROSS

1. Decorated with set-in design
5. Sadly
7. Implant
8. Not binding
9. Molecule part
10. Titleholder
11. Sewing tool
13. Very small
14. Lettuce dishes
18. Cruelty
21. Body's outer layer
22. Halts
24. Live coal
25. Farm reservoirs
26. Earnest request
27. Nails
28. Offhandedly
29. Horse shed

## DOWN

1. Baseball game sessions
2. Suffered
3. Tennis score
4. Acquires
5. Adjusted
6. Numbers
12. Pot top
15. Ungainly
16. Human rights group, ... International
17. Relapse in recovery
19. Positive vote
20. Error
22. Rude
23. First Greek letter

# CROSSWORD 102

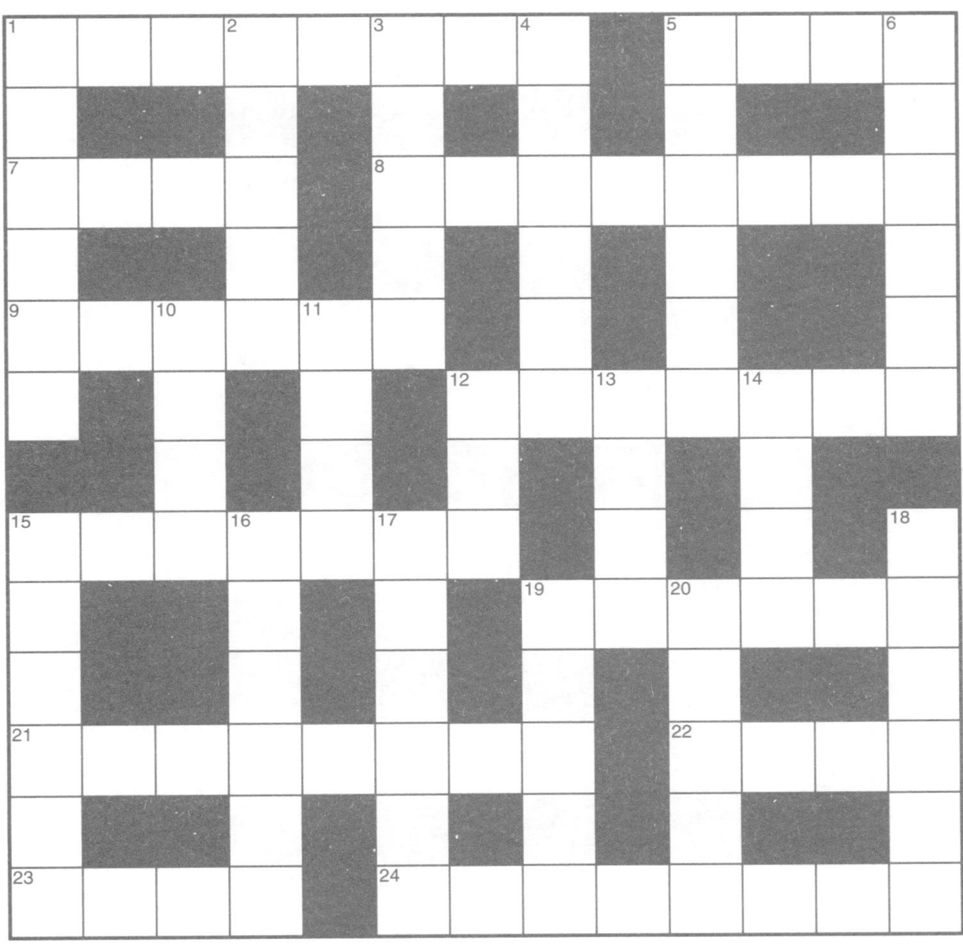

## ACROSS

1. Game fowl
5. Rob during riot
7. Cougar
8. Mineral reserves
9. Sent in high arc
12. Expedition porters
15. Every evening
19. Sounds
21. Foreword
22. Stare fixedly
23. Nickel & ...
24. Vigorous action

## DOWN

1. Eyeball circles
2. Not joined
3. Stated further
4. Overbalance
5. Smaller
6. Mixes (salad)
10. Whip
11. Utter (cry)
12. Male child
13. Singing pitch
14. Immense time spans
15. Slept briefly
16. Compassionate
17. Accountable
18. Aft
19. Nephew and ...
20. Brick of precious metal

# CROSSWORD 103

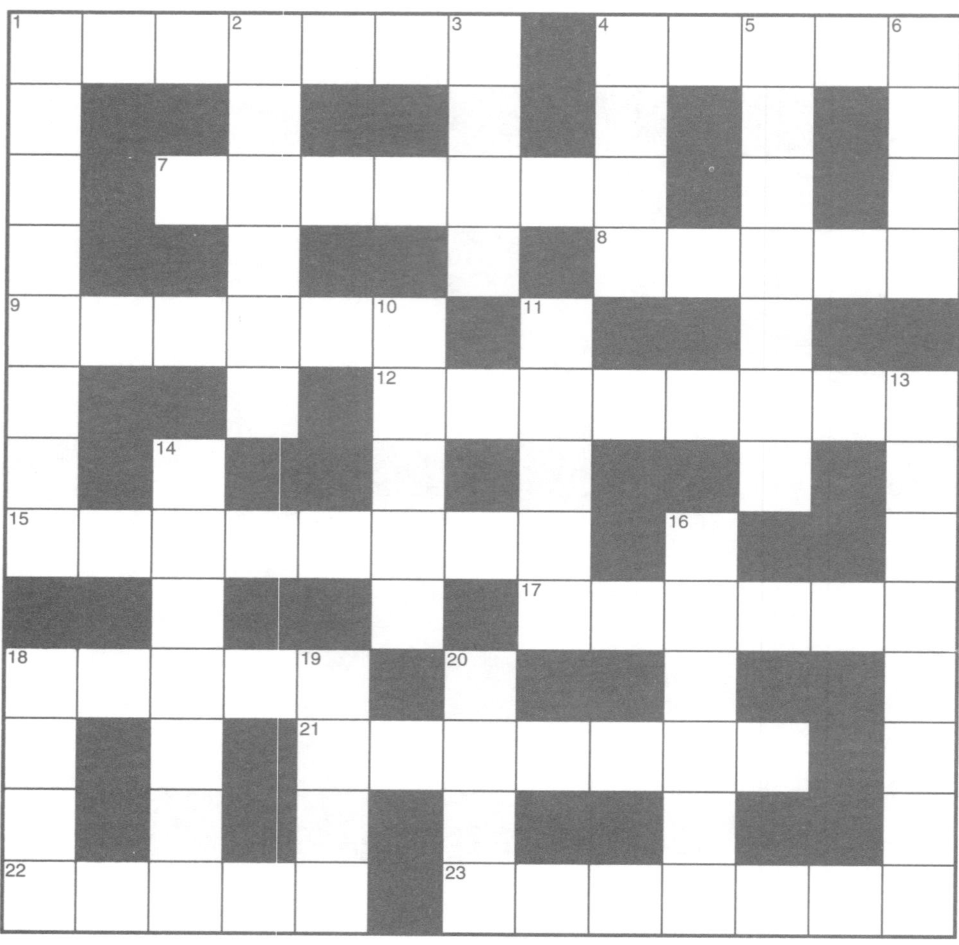

## ACROSS

1. Tense
4. Reject
7. Principled
8. Touches with tongue
9. Mean
12. High-ranking soldiers
15. Switch
17. Subtle difference
18. Forgery
21. Ignorant
22. Male rabbits
23. Infected sore

## DOWN

1. Lacy bed robe
2. Refused consent
3. Potato bag
4. Auction off
5. Untwist (jar lid)
6. Pecans or almonds
10. Ups & ...
11. Frequently
13. Church spires
14. Of the Pacific or Atlantic
16. Woven material
18. Unwanted fat
19. Membership fees
20. Mother

# CROSSWORD 104

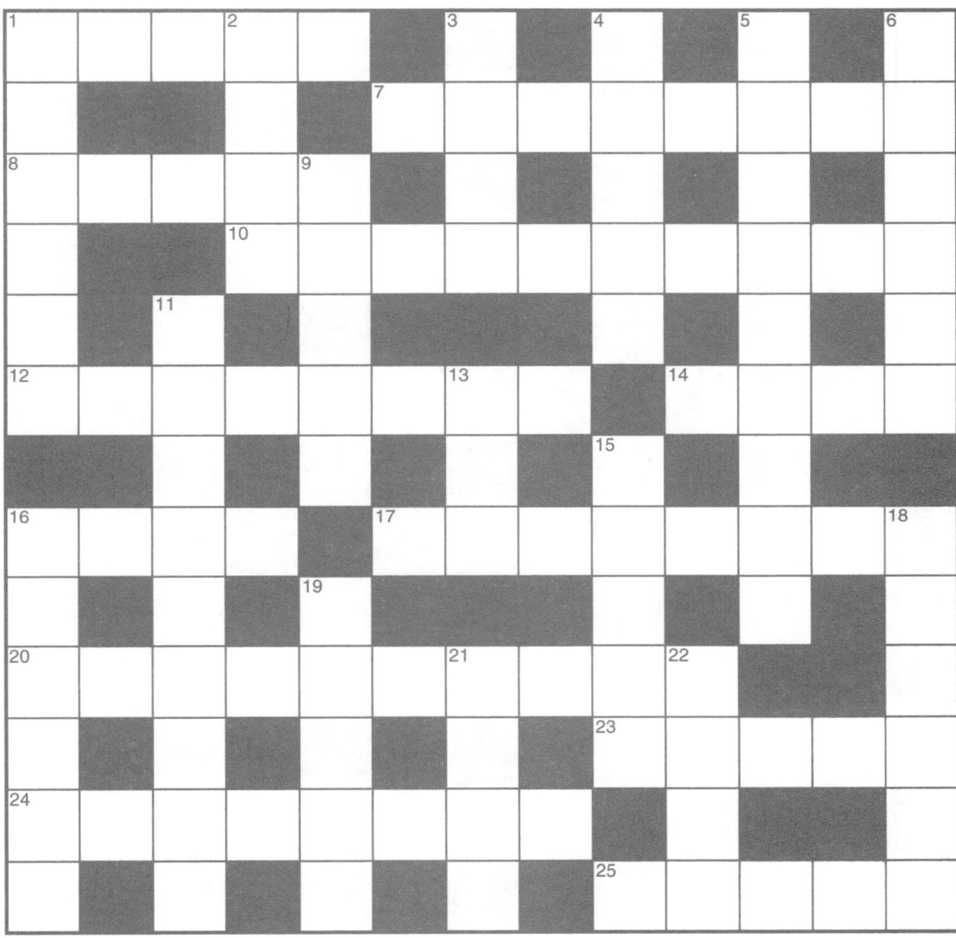

## ACROSS

1. Female title
7. Jumble (letters)
8. 3rd month
10. German cabbage dish
12. Hiking
14. Discover
16. Make (profit)
17. Unsightliness
20. Rituals
23. Cattle farm
24. Tourist's greeting note
25. Small isle

## DOWN

1. Instant
2. Curves over
3. Unit of land
4. Woofs
5. Polishing substances
6. Thawed
9. Chops wildly
11. Violent activist
13. Old horse
15. Renter
16. Apart from
18. Tiny food packet
19. Artist's coat
21. Standard
22. Sinks in middle

# CROSSWORD 105

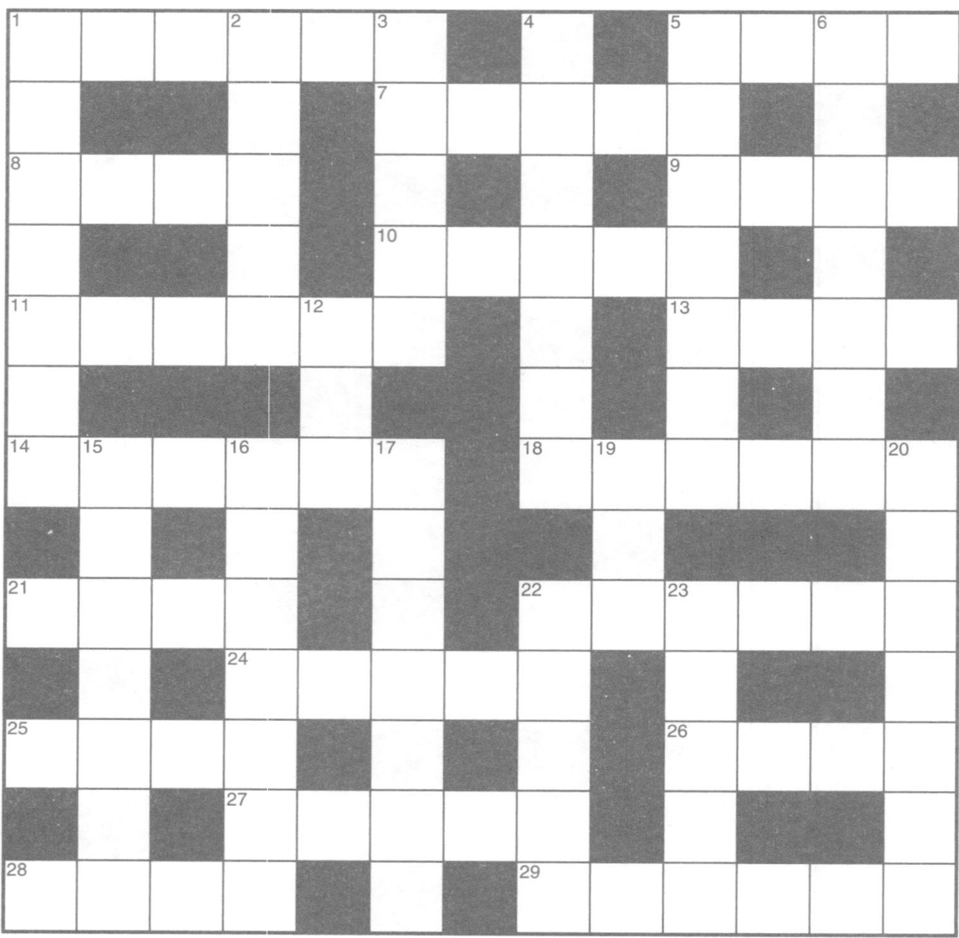

## ACROSS

1. Prodded
5. Move (wings)
7. Snake, death ...
8. Temper
9. Measure of length
10. Chivalrous
11. Tags
13. Intrusive
14. Holy people
18. Cutting beams
21. Squalid district
22. Insect antenna
24. Hold responsible
25. Independent
26. Roman dress
27. Sharp crest
28. Pigments
29. Scoff at

## DOWN

1. Muddles
2. Dislodge
3. Condemns
4. Peculiar person
5. Acquaintances
6. One who points the finger
12. Tennis call on serve
15. Sensitivity to substances
16. Quantities
17. Threads
19. Beer
20. Family title
22. Entertained lavishly
23. Carnivore, meat ...

# CROSSWORD 106

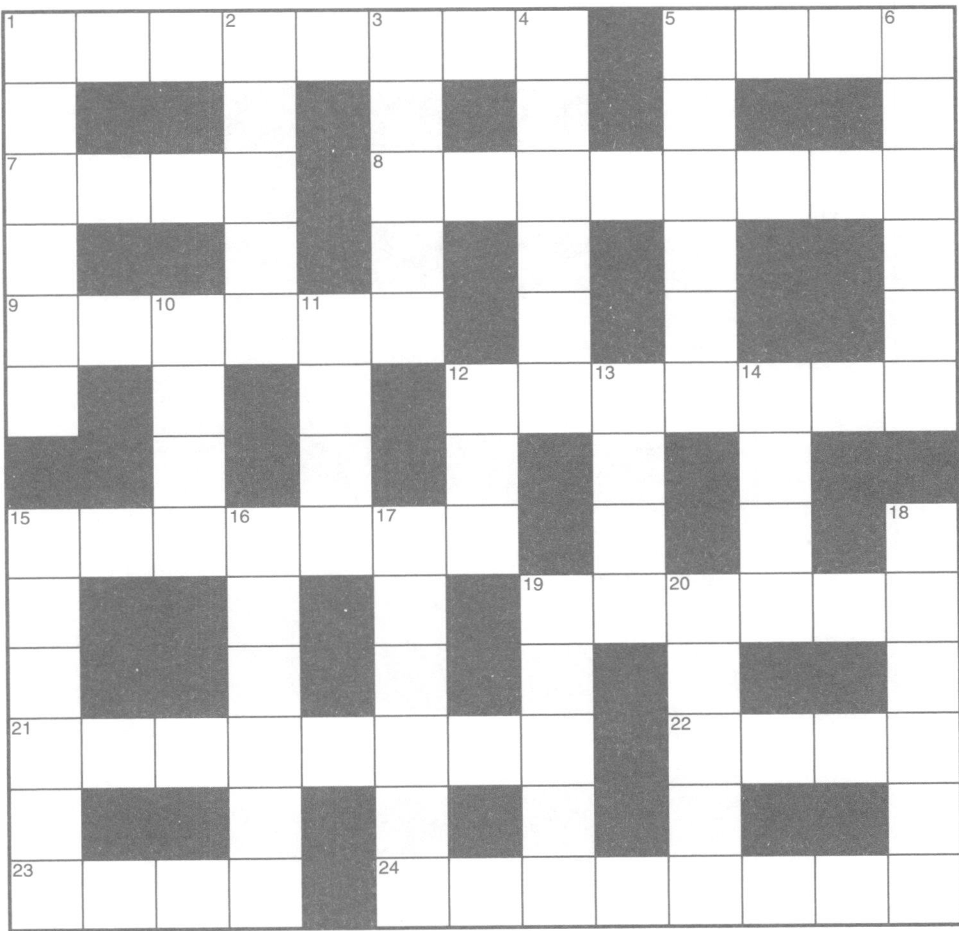

## ACROSS

1. Moved forward
5. Resentful desire
7. Organs of hearing
8. Special event
9. Hypnotic state
12. Banqueted
15. Peppered (with holes)
19. Near-sighted
21. Perverts
22. Charismatic glow
23. Large Australian birds
24. Prison term

## DOWN

1. Prevents (disaster)
2. Incendiary crime
3. Old woman
4. Resolve
5. Comes next
6. Tugged sharply
10. Copied
11. Summon
12. Trend
13. Wartime friend
14. Stumble
15. Save
16. Snow White's seven companions
17. Flees to wed
18. Fuel energy rating
19. Stone builder
20. Speak to crowd

# CROSSWORD 107

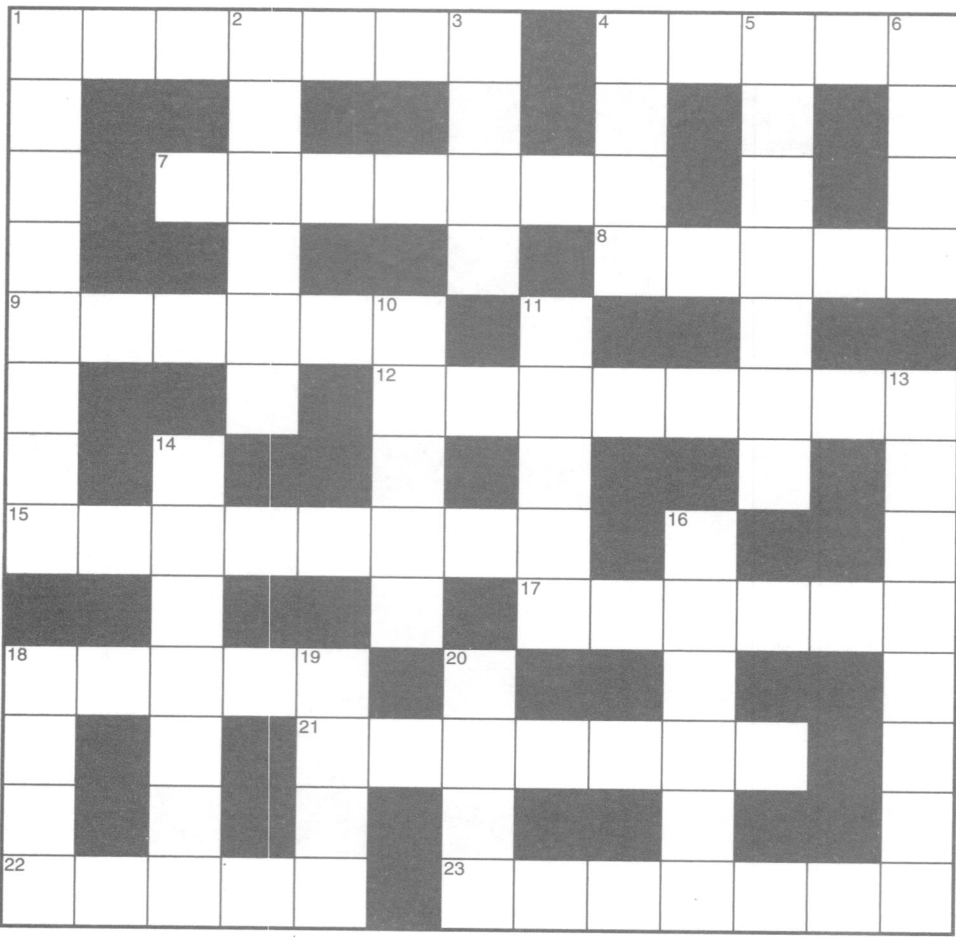

## ACROSS

1. Chatters like monkey
4. Nook
7. Precious stone
8. Apportion
9. Part of sentence
12. Baby's enclosures
15. Cattle charge
17. Flipped (through book)
18. More considerate
21. Endorsing
22. Naked models
23. Teasing

## DOWN

1. Riding breeches
2. Bewail
3. Swing to & fro
4. Indicates consent
5. Less contaminated
6. Alleviate
10. Fencing swords
11. Ring-shaped bun
13. Clarifying, ... light on
14. Deprived of water
16. Sieved (for gold)
18. Midday
19. Decays
20. Bird of prey

# CROSSWORD 108

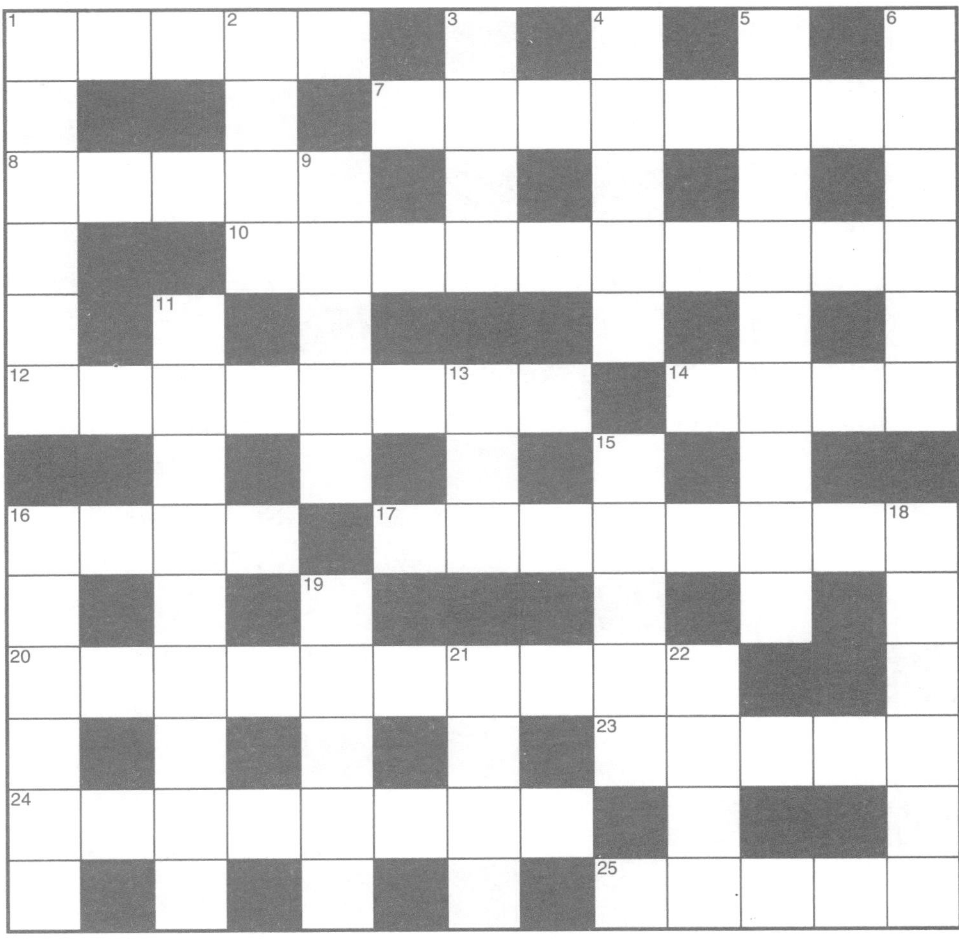

## ACROSS

1. Embalmed Egyptian relic
7. Weasel-like animals
8. Snaking dance
10. Female pupil
12. Disgraces
14. Crash (into)
16. Card below queen
17. Ocean-liner waiters
20. Meteorologist
23. Ignited again
24. Stayed around
25. Meat jelly

## DOWN

1. South American parrots
2. Earthenware cups
3. Company symbol
4. Shoe parts
5. Thin blood vessel
6. Political refuge
9. Corrosive fluids
11. Artificial sweetener
13. Load
15. Vow
16. Sapphires & diamonds
18. Festering
19. Main
21. Regrets
22. Tennis court barriers

# CROSSWORD 109

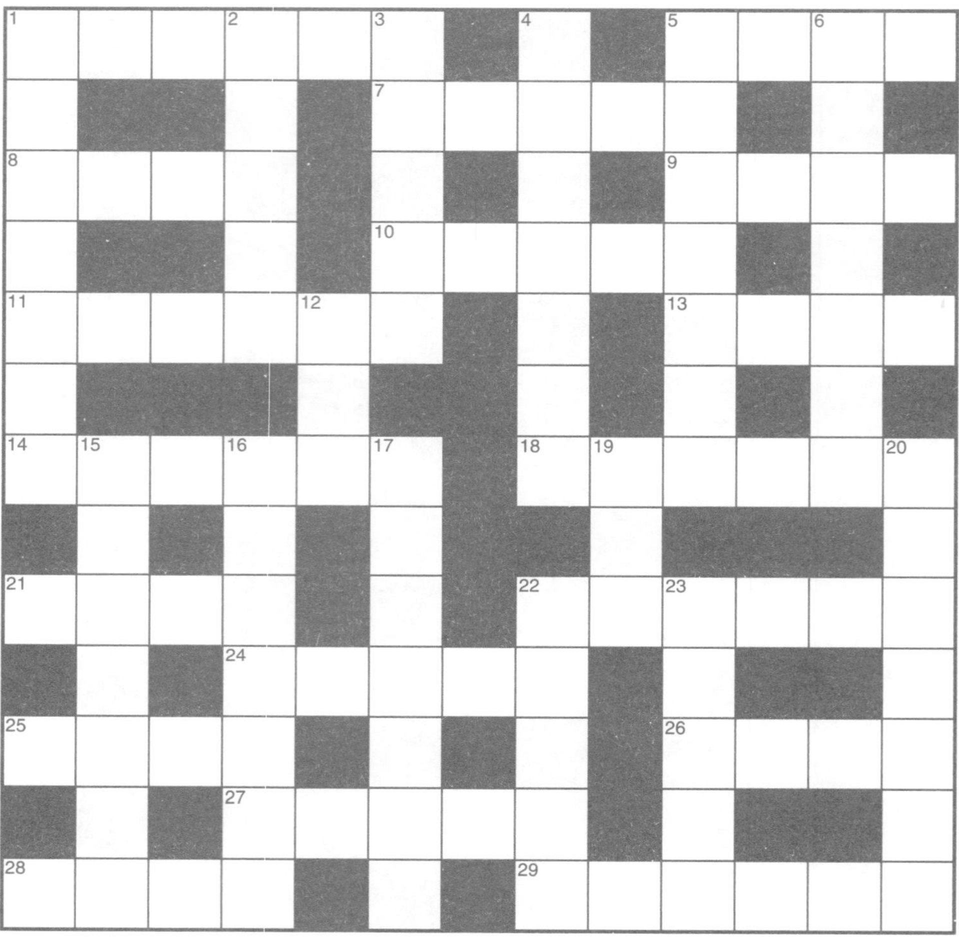

## ACROSS

1. Move in circles
5. Open (parcel)
7. Odds or ...
8. Mexican snack
9. Restore to health
10. Angry
11. Squirm in agony
13. Fishing spool
14. Howled shrilly
18. Calm
21. Accustomed (to)
22. Whinnies
24. Hang in folds
25. Lamenting cry
26. Level
27. Opt
28. Plant embryo
29. Inclined

## DOWN

1. Passage through a fence
2. Assume ownership of
3. Spooky
4. Mars
5. Showed (to seat)
6. Most beloved
12. Garden tool
15. Entrap
16. Propelled canoe
17. Postponed
19. Supplement, ... out
20. Made certain
22. Baby bird shelters
23. Lead-in

# CROSSWORD 110

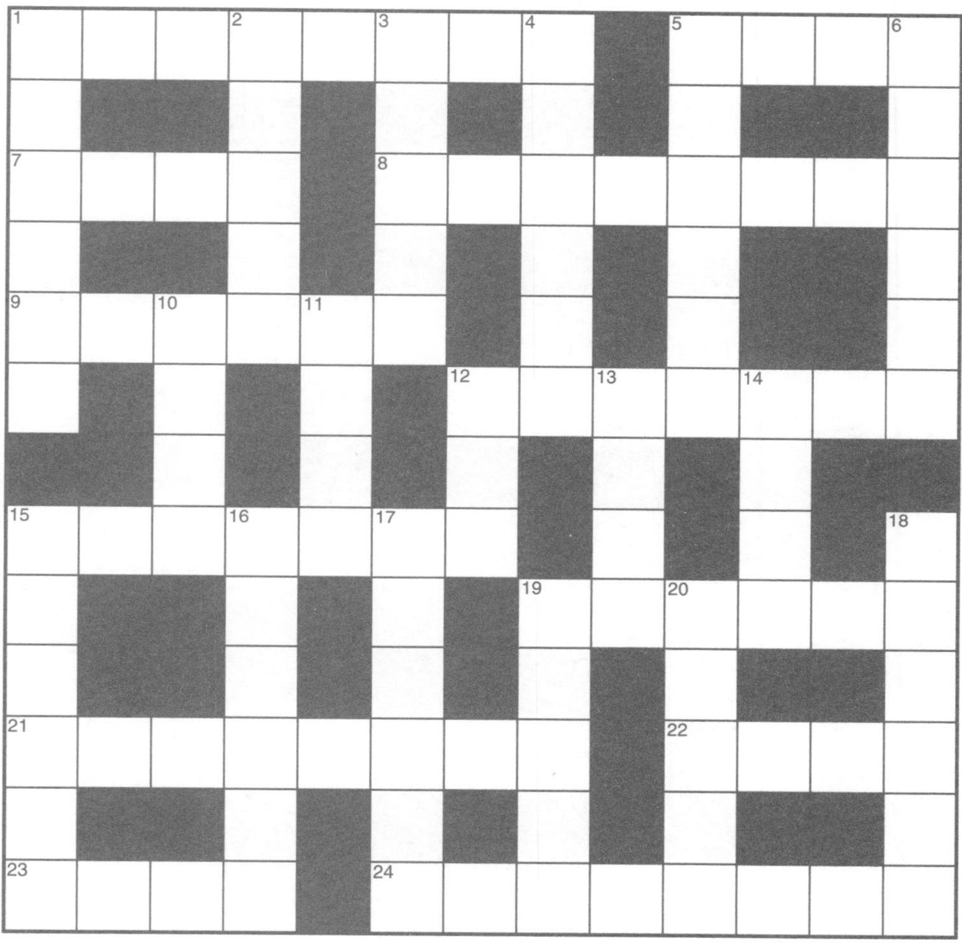

## ACROSS

1. Resumed (investigation)
5. Atop
7. Acidic
8. Highlighted
9. Exclusively
12. Puts clothes on
15. Soft leather
19. Powerful businessman
21. Small decorative object
22. Musician's sample tape or CD
23. Woodwind instrument
24. Magnifies

## DOWN

1. Oppose
2. Money pouch
3. Nimble
4. Desk compartment
5. Steals (power)
6. Light pushes
10. Cooking fat
11. Take a peek
12. Lair
13. Ill at ease
14. Japanese wrestling style
15. Geisha's robe
16. Geometric shape
17. Obstruct
18. Pungent bulbs
19. Add up to
20. Fermented apple juice

# CROSSWORD 111

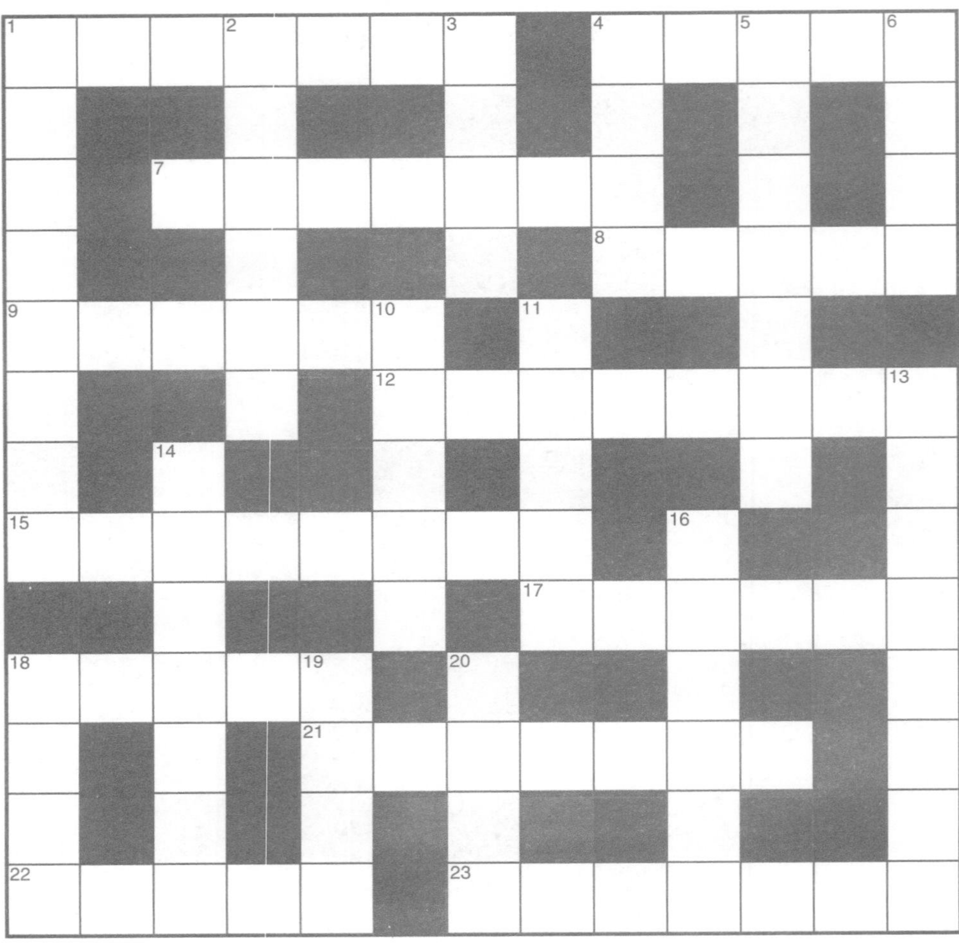

## ACROSS

1. Walked heavily
4. Pit worker
7. Hug
8. Do business
9. Fiction books
12. Scaremonger
15. Bread grillers
17. Warmed up
18. Get on (ship)
21. Reactor fuel
22. Supporting beam
23. Ignites

## DOWN

1. Skinniest
2. Club participant
3. Lug
4. Be introduced to
5. Always on the move
6. Part played
10. Rescued
11. Low wetland
13. Twirls (thumbs)
14. Card game
16. Treasured
18. Shapeless mass
19. Sand hill
20. Wolf group

# CROSSWORD 112

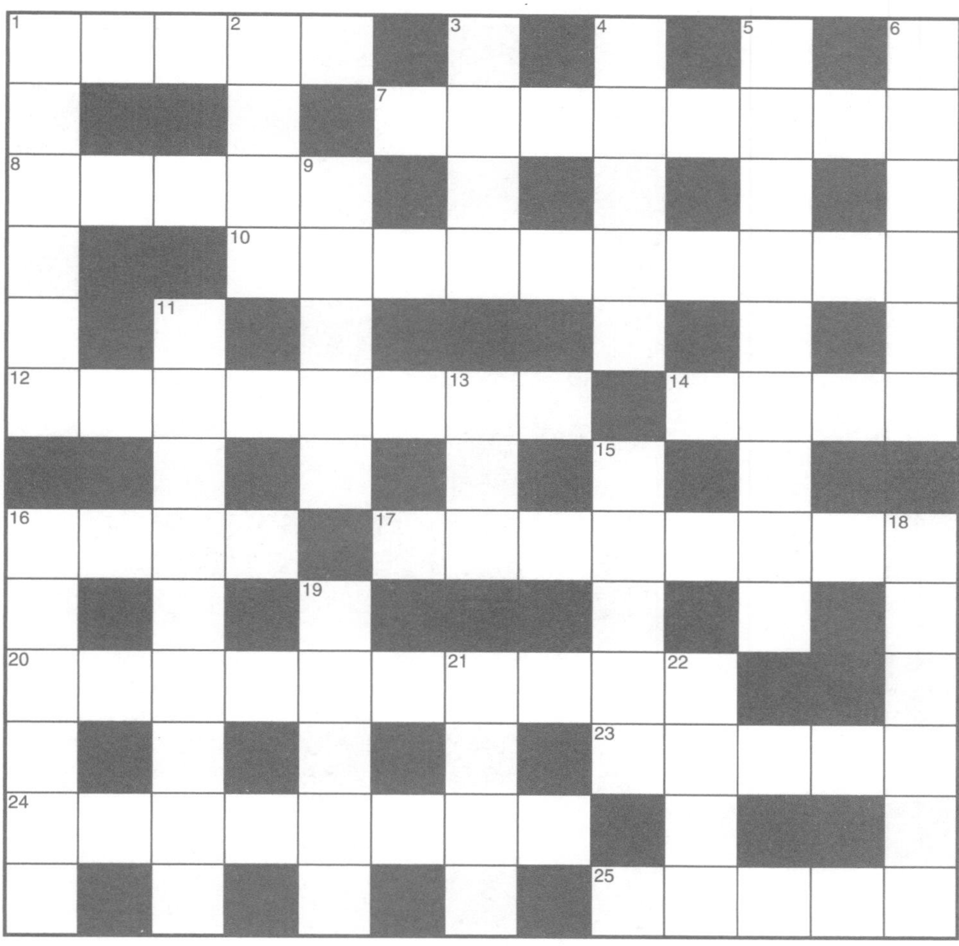

## ACROSS

1. Loft
7. Overseas trader
8. Quickly, in a ...
10. Attaching (horse to cart)
12. Male astronaut
14. Stupefy
16. Pod vegetables
17. Spotted for a second
20. Stalactite & ...
23. Paintbrush hair
24. Issued (from)
25. Printed (text)

## DOWN

1. Modifies
2. Flea bite irritation
3. Yoked beasts
4. Timid
5. Most stern
6. Root
9. Roof overhangs
11. Twin-hulled boat
13. Entirely
15. Overlooks
16. Shoved
18. Rely
19. Air traffic monitoring system
21. Humble, ... & mild
22. Effortless

# CROSSWORD 113

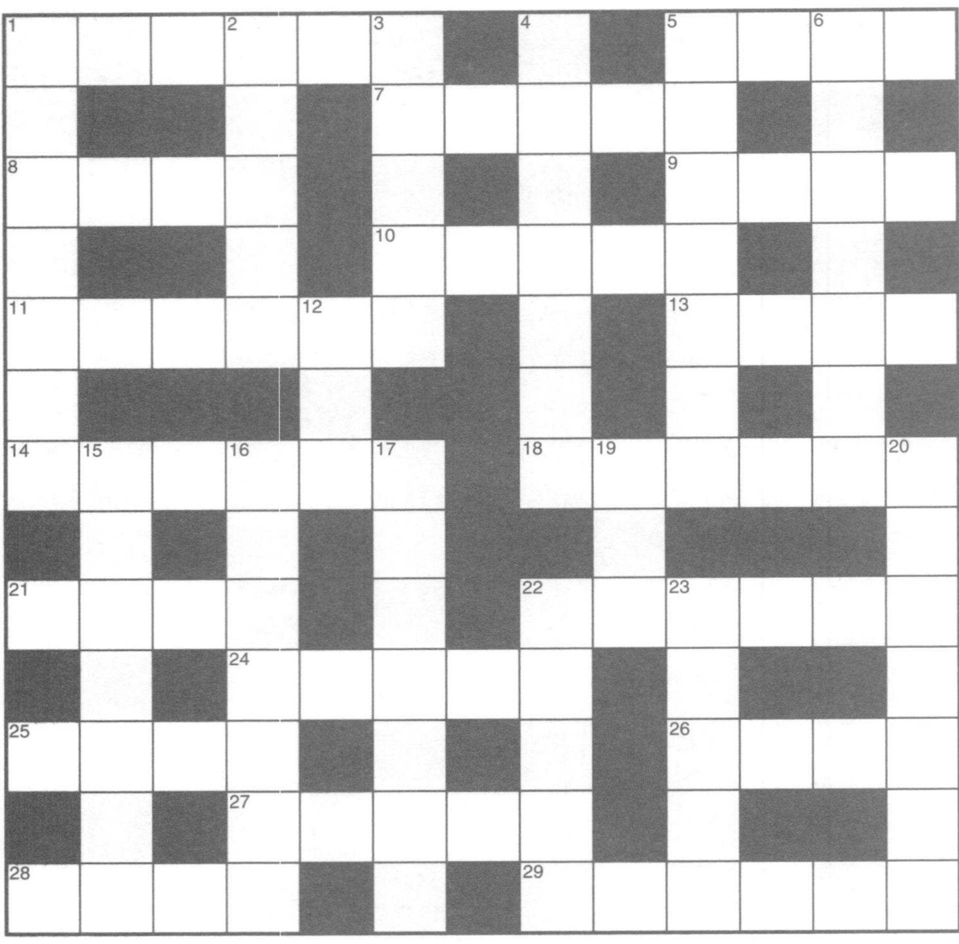

## ACROSS

1. Strictly conventional
5. Listen to
7. Astonish
8. Notch
9. Rock hollow
10. Talent
11. Becomes informed
13. Traditional knowledge
14. Bold
18. First-born
21. Animal den
22. USSR flag emblem, hammer & ...
24. Bygone (days)
25. Creative thought
26. Goods trucks
27. Horror
28. Dedicatory poems
29. Inscribes

## DOWN

1. Touched affectionately
2. Fabricator
3. Is deficient in
4. Ghoulish
5. Harassed with questions
6. Verb modifiers
12. Convent sister
15. Granted
16. Encroachments
17. Foundation garments
19. Hawaiian garland
20. Locks of hair
22. Insinuating (remark)
23. Municipal

# CROSSWORD 114

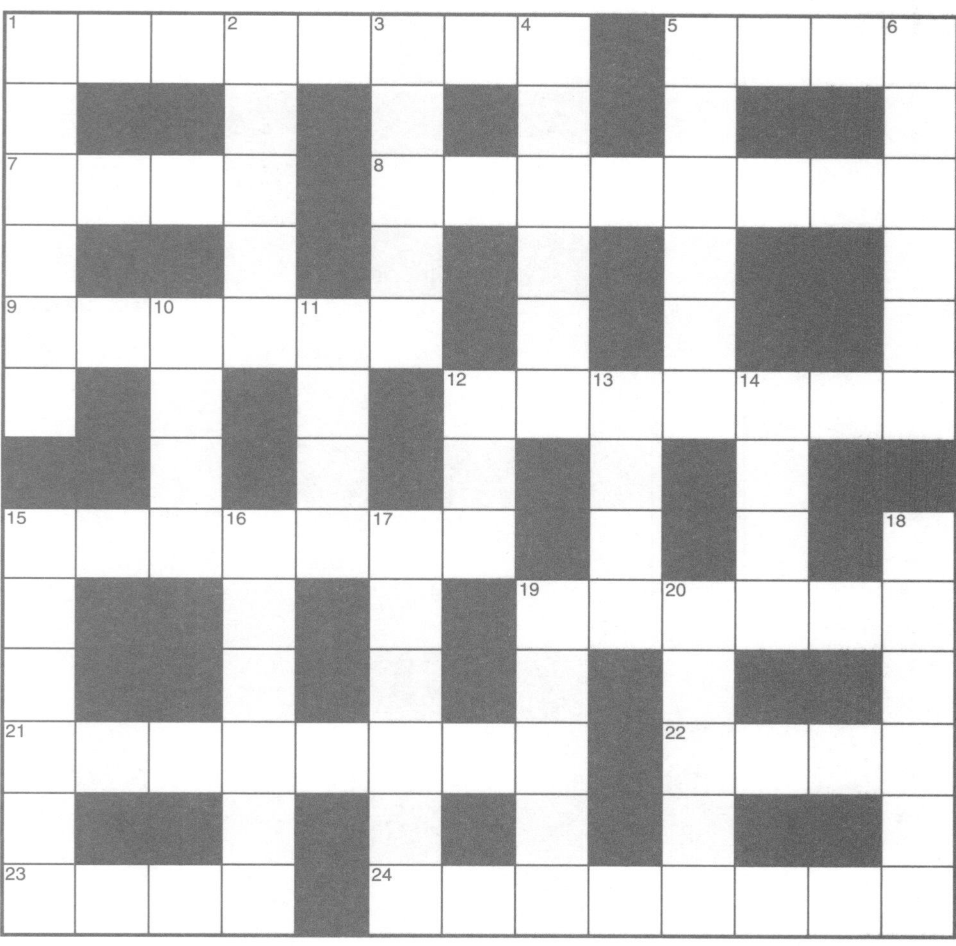

## ACROSS

1. Teetering
5. Doorpost
7. Stare awkwardly
8. Mentally conjured up
9. Ruler
12. Stiff whisker
15. Assistant priests
19. Husky-voiced
21. College lessons
22. Paint roughly
23. Extent
24. Perspiring

## DOWN

1. Move (toes)
2. Cooked (cake)
3. Chillier
4. Shredder
5. Flooring supports
6. Dress top
10. Half-open
11. Reword
12. Commuter vehicle
13. Towards the inside of
14. Cry, shed a ...
15. Large violins
16. Female relative
17. Accessories
18. Mattress pest
19. Hurriedness
20. Examine (accounts)

# CROSSWORD 115

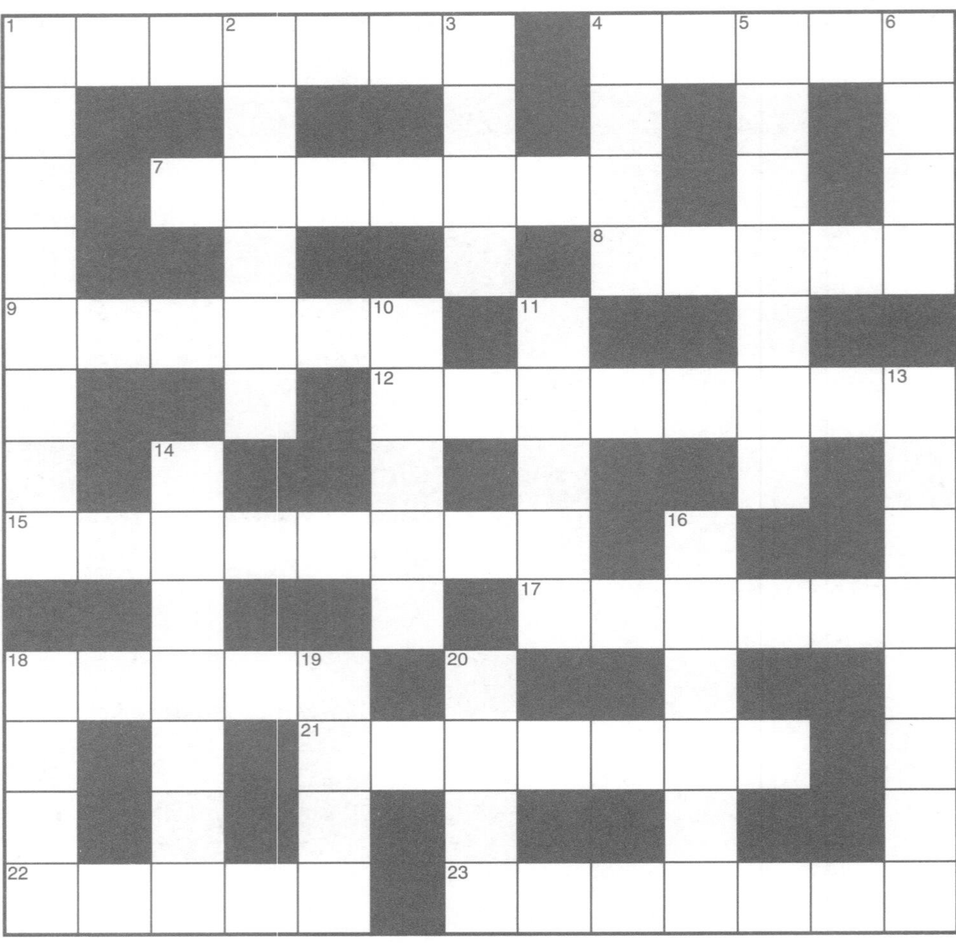

## ACROSS

1. Amazon river fish
4. Metal links
7. Female thespian
8. Shrimp relative
9. Pleated
12. Meat plant
15. Most terrifying
17. Pink-eyed rabbit
18. Fabled giant
21. Without weapons
22. Pulsate
23. Clattered

## DOWN

1. Decontaminates
2. Shopping walkway
3. Tip of triangle
4. Zodiac crossover
5. Pilot
6. Sign-light gas
10. Valleys
11. Italian food
13. Rotated
14. More delicious
16. Thing
18. The one there
19. Lacking sensation
20. Twosome

# CROSSWORD 116

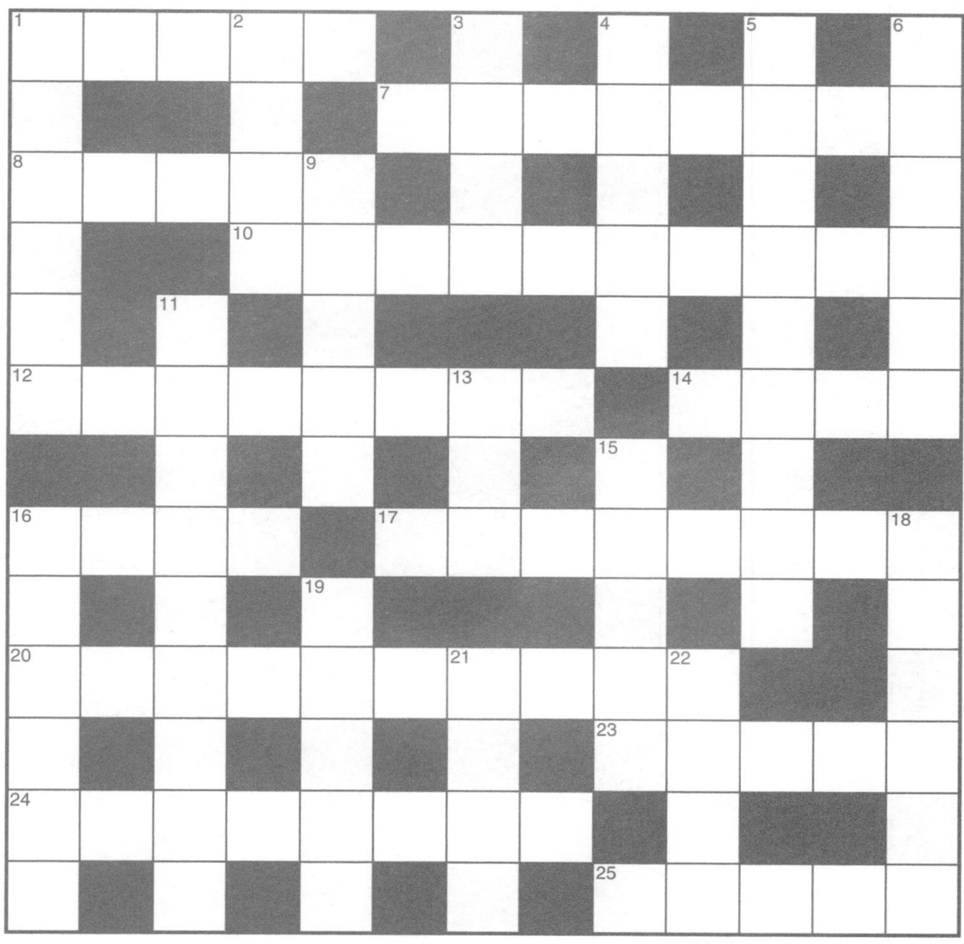

## ACROSS

1. Leisure-time activity
7. Courted
8. Fruit liquid
10. Abducting
12. Given honorary title
14. Chooses
16. Strike with foot
17. United
20. Alpine landslides
23. Estimated age of
24. Drug-dependent
25. Knife's cutting edge

## DOWN

1. Seize (aircraft)
2. Reverse
3. Small city
4. Buckles
5. Being frugal
6. Maxims
9. Number of spider's legs
11. Herring-like fish
13. Self-regard
15. Receded
16. Australian marsupials
18. Trawl (riverbed)
19. Impertinent
21. Musical symbol
22. Voyage

# CROSSWORD 117

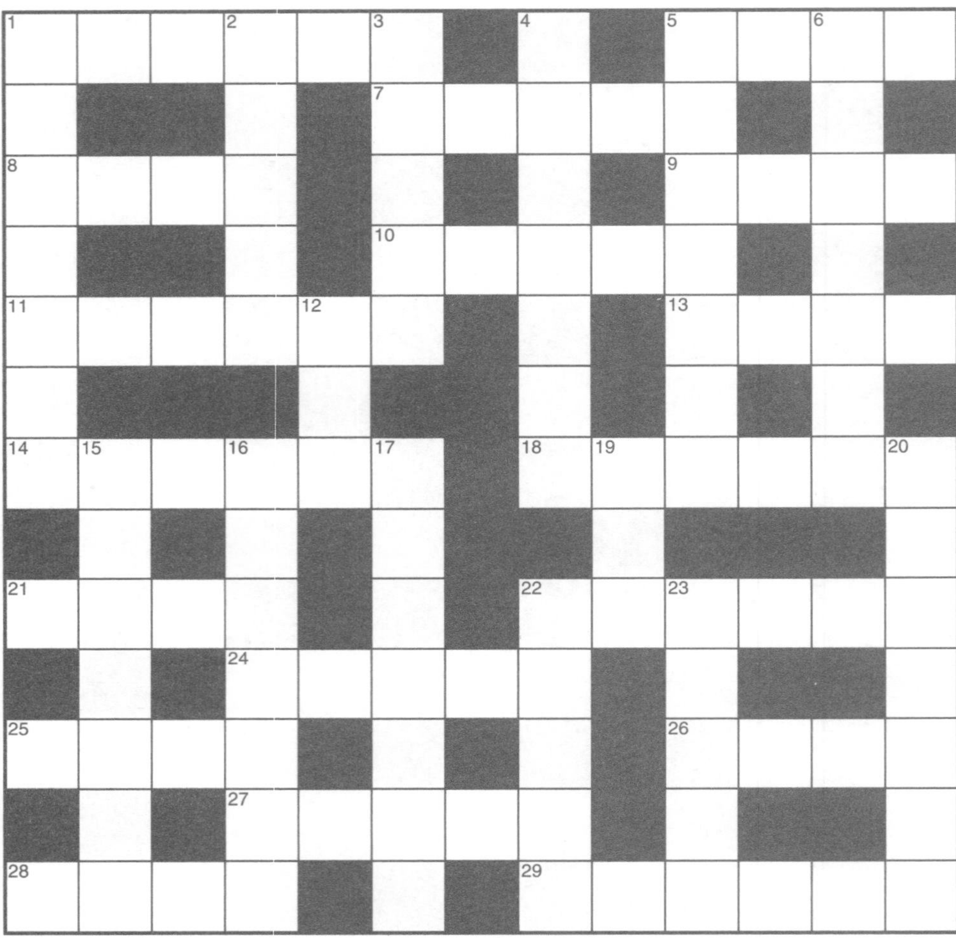

## ACROSS

1. Yellow fruit
5. A lot of
7. Book leaf
8. Young horse
9. Spellbound
10. Ill-suited
11. Voice box
13. Single article
14. Security
18. Most bashful
21. Washtub
22. Hipbone structure
24. Great artery
25. After that
26. Melt together
27. Set of beliefs
28. Brink
29. Gangways

## DOWN

1. Comes to pass
2. Narrow lane
3. Attach (to)
4. Gladdens
5. Humiliate
6. Codes
12. Louse egg
15. Made ashamed
16. Increase in attractiveness
17. Hankered
19. Shade
20. Perfume samplers
22. Bamboo-munching mammal
23. Elevates

# CROSSWORD 118

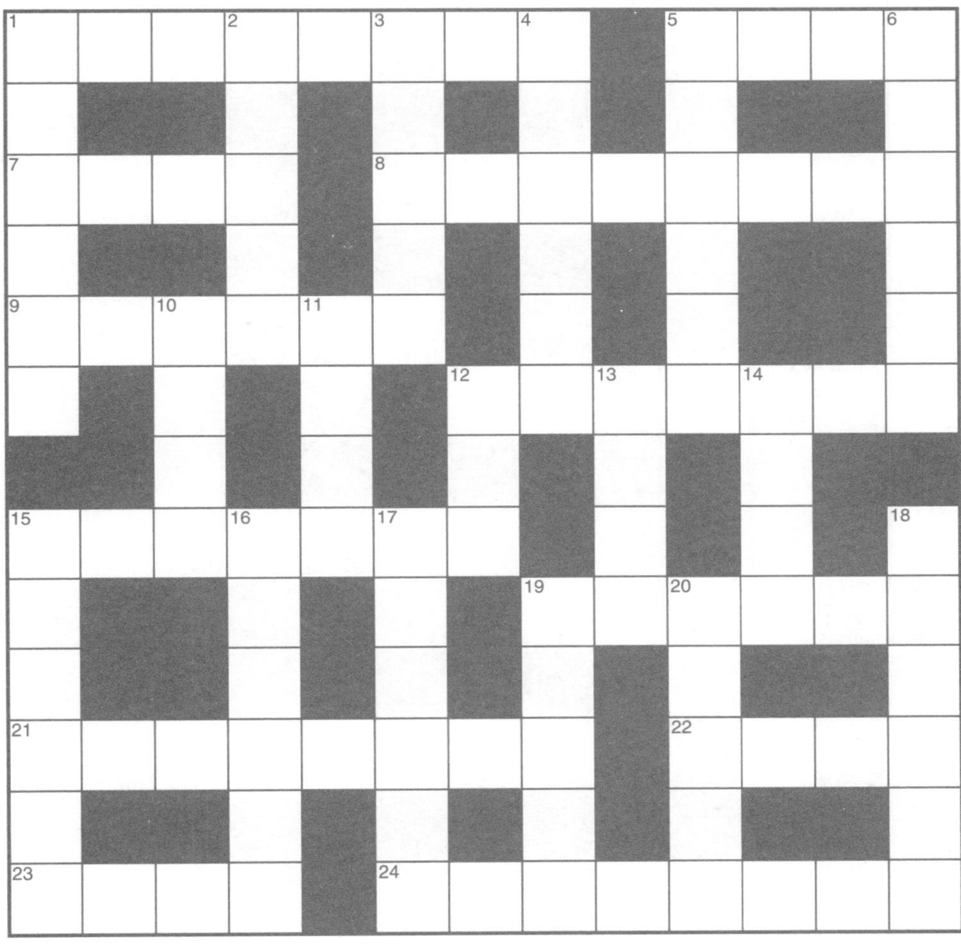

## ACROSS

1. Falling heavily
5. Empty space
7. Carry-cases
8. 1000 watts
9. World best (time)
12. Male journalist
15. Hunter-gatherer
19. Taunted
21. Throw (jockey)
22. Climbing plant
23. Bass brass instrument
24. Tennis court marking

## DOWN

1. Underground stems
2. 70s dance music
3. Irritated
4. Aplenty
5. Non-consonants
6. Keep in custody
10. Blacken
11. Ladder step
12. Neither here ... there
13. Farewell gesture
14. Sponges
15. Display boldly
16. Spanish fleet
17. Evades (capture)
18. Cling (to)
19. Twill weave
20. Blacksmith's block

# CROSSWORD 119

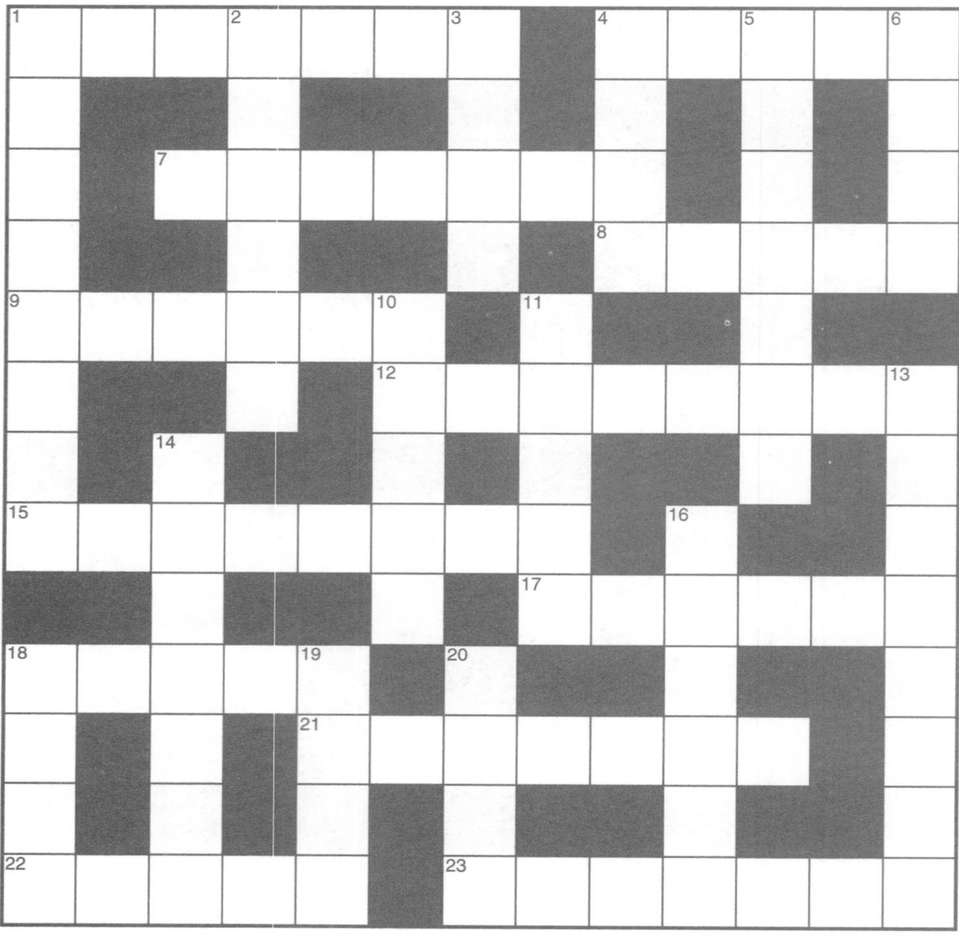

## ACROSS

1. Flawless
4. Public square
7. Stir
8. Unpaid servant
9. Go back on deal
12. Strategists
15. Orbit
17. Alcoholic spirits
18. Furry fruit
21. Makes as one
22. Fashion flair
23. Peeling (of paint)

## DOWN

1. Evening ... oil
2. Steamed up
3. Serving platter
4. Pastry meals
5. Soothed
6. Dull throb
10. Long tales
11. Type of orange
13. Disfiguring
14. Bony
16. Mouse noise
18. Helicopter landing areas
19. Immense
20. Petty quarrel

# CROSSWORD 120

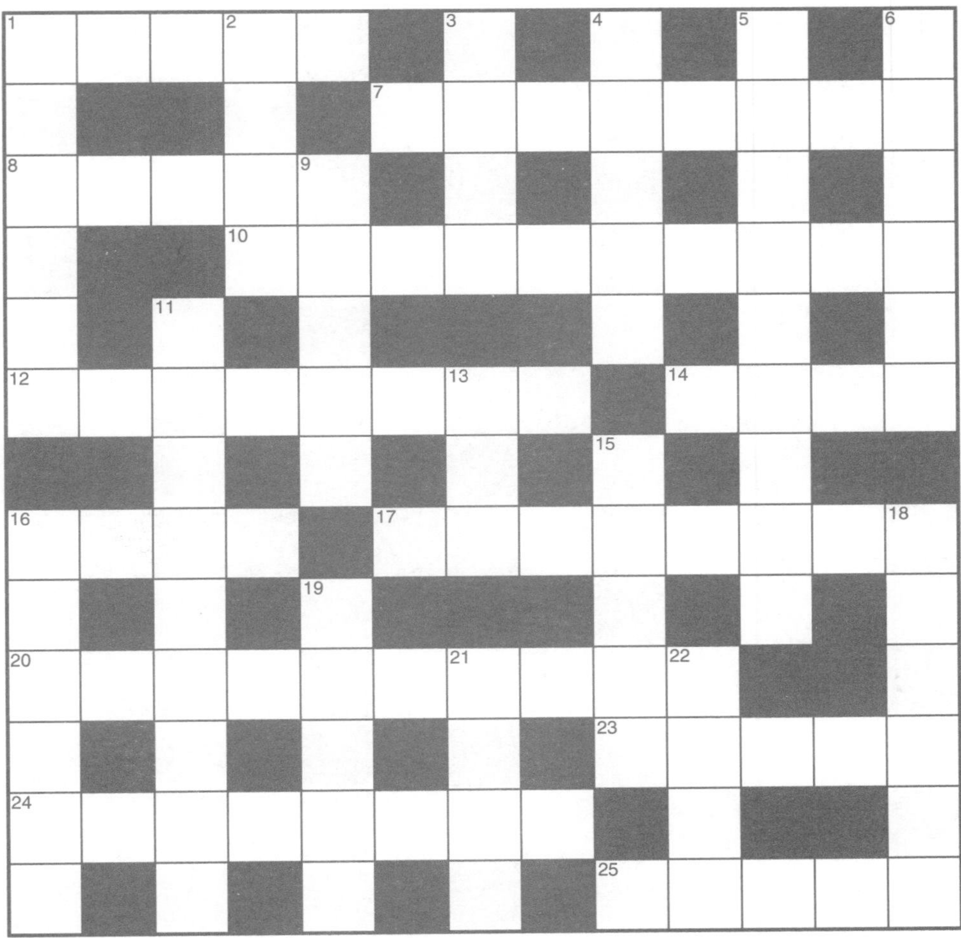

## ACROSS

1. Moves listlessly
7. Fuse switches, circuit ...
8. Incensed
10. Sixtieth, ..., eightieth
12. Rained lightly
14. Prolonged unconsciousness
16. Grecian vases
17. Waste discharge
20. Mariner's skill
23. Ballet
24. Young children
25. Invited

## DOWN

1. Warrants
2. Lambs' mothers
3. Forest plant
4. Doesn't eat
5. Building company owner
6. Respiratory ailment
9. Postpone
11. Towards ground
13. Fairy
15. Liquid
16. Distresses
18. Sewing yarn
19. Gymnastics event
21. Indian gown
22. Gently touches

# CROSSWORD 121

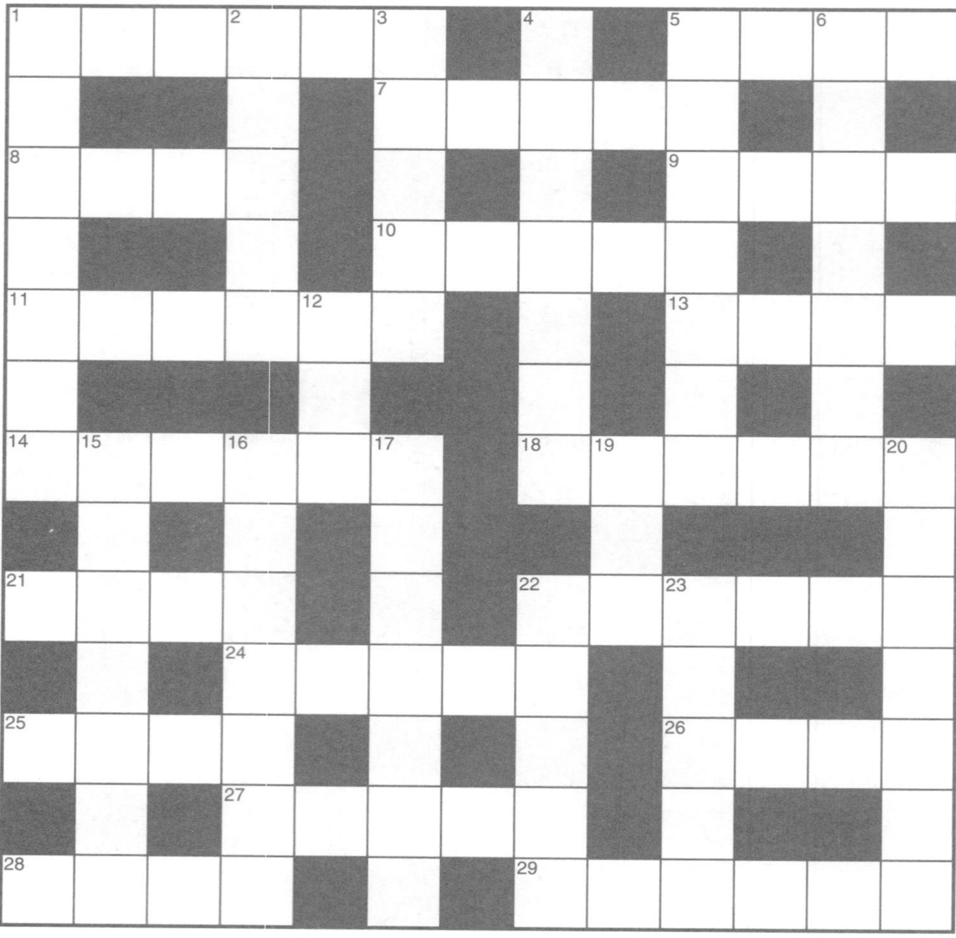

## ACROSS

1. Respect, ... highly
5. Child's play objects
7. Covered with water
8. Ward (off)
9. Unwanted plant
10. Shinbone
11. Digging tools
13. Cycled
14. Impair
18. Stay
21. Match before final
22. Talked to God
24. Saunter
25. Puncture with knife
26. If not, or ...
27. Light purple
28. Whirlpool
29. Bestows

## DOWN

1. Turned down (offer)
2. Assisted
3. Blowpipe missiles
4. Casino regular
5. Foils
6. Bowed to the inevitable
12. Free-range or barn-laid product
15. Given warning
16. Good-naturedly
17. Optic orb
19. Slip up
20. Infinite
22. Absence of war
23. Reform

# CROSSWORD 122

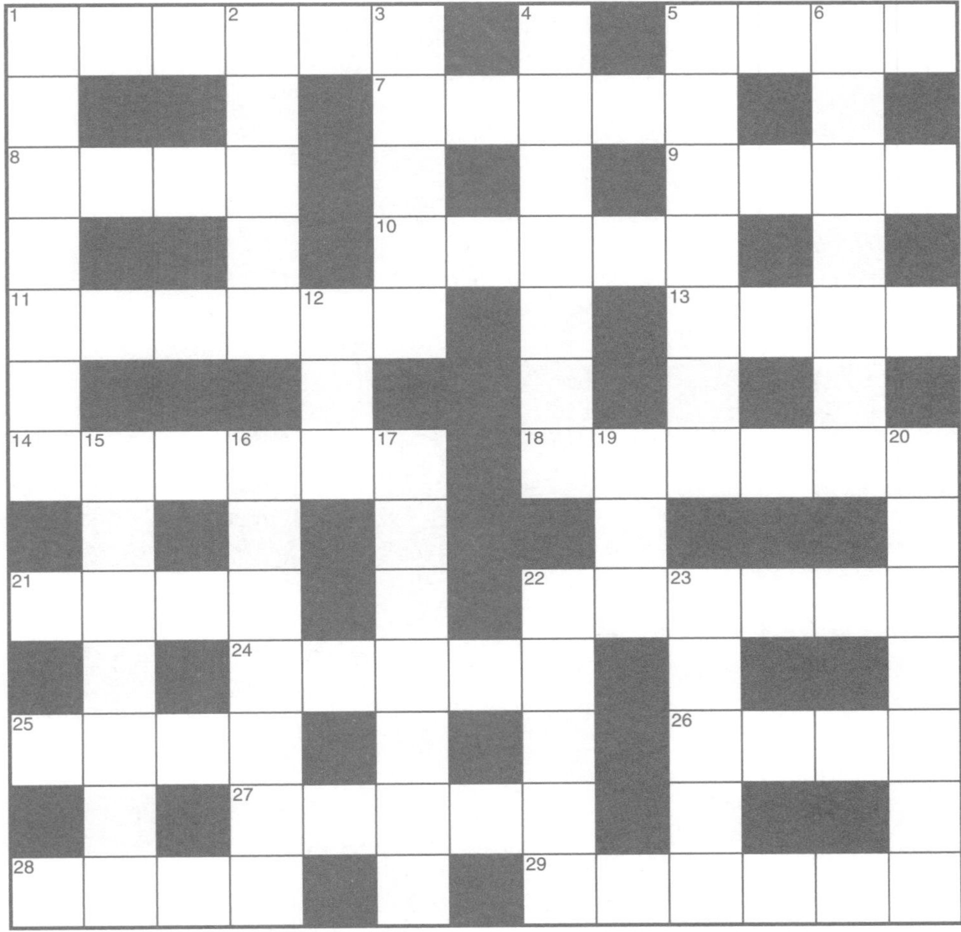

## ACROSS

1. Public disturbance
5. Take rudely
7. Fill with joy
8. Insincere (of speech)
9. Research rooms
10. Appeal earnestly
11. Shades, Venetian ...
13. Wading bird
14. Dwellings
18. Involve (in)
21. Imitated
22. Crossbred (animal)
24. Tropical fruit
25. Tiny (version)
26. Injure with horns
27. Alcove
28. Keenly excited
29. Sister's daughters

## DOWN

1. Branch of mathematics
2. Batman's partner
3. Shrill barks
4. Paint-mix board
5. Castrated horse
6. Sauntering
12. Scheduled to arrive
15. Hitting quickly
16. Avoiding
17. Superficial cut
19. Negative vote
20. Infinite
22. Shelter
23. Small trumpet

# CROSSWORD 123

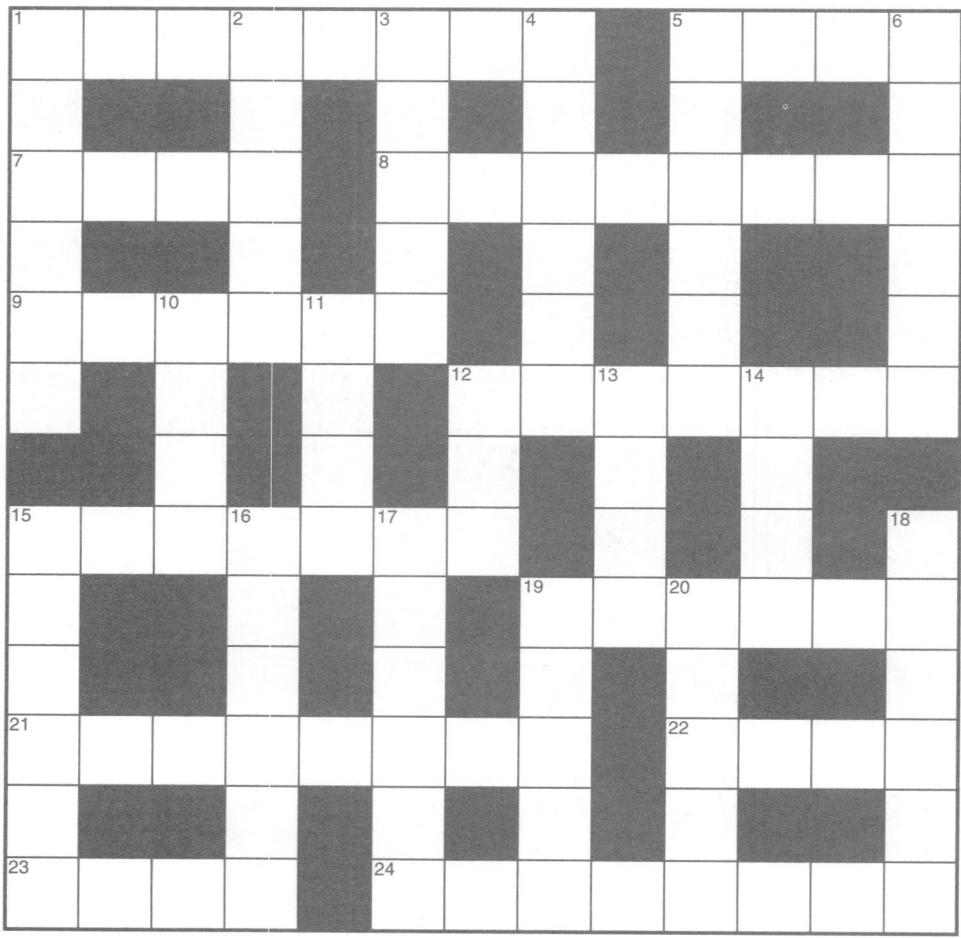

## ACROSS

1. Money matters
5. Downpour, heavy ...
7. Viewed
8. Debatable
9. Most submissive
12. Shutdown
15. Embedding
19. Monarch's seat
21. Single strand
22. Jumping parasite
23. Ascend
24. Wavered (on edge)

## DOWN

1. Spanish festival
2. Muddle
3. Sing monotonously
4. Indicator
5. Cooks in oven
6. Hypodermic syringe
10. Bland
11. Half
12. Gearwheel tooth
13. Yell of pain
14. Unbutton
15. Lazy person
16. Vehicle depot
17. Freshest
18. Refunded
19. Name of book
20. Long firearm

# CROSSWORD 124

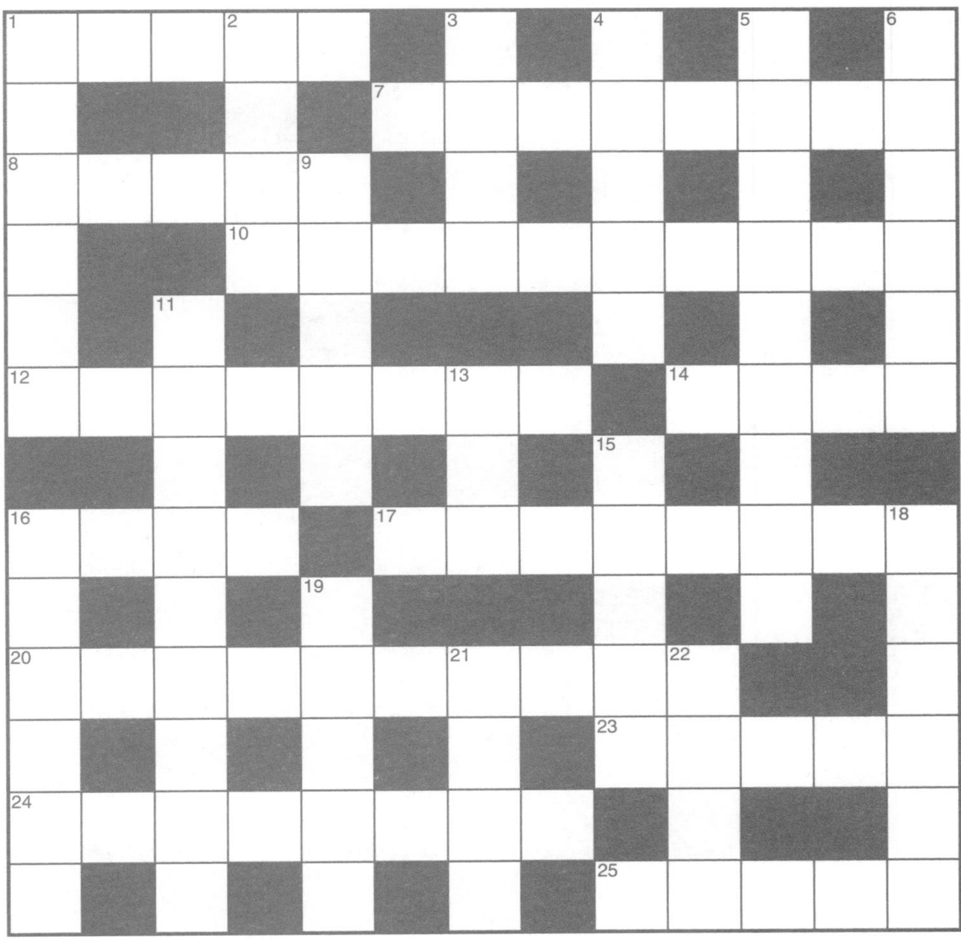

## ACROSS

1. Bread-raising agent
7. Small army units
8. Rugged peaks
10. Lightning (storm)
12. Dingier
14. Troubles
16. Outlays money
17. Wide Mexican hat
20. Got rid of
23. Brazilian dance
24. Placed
25. Observed covertly

## DOWN

1. Boats
2. Wise person
3. Political power group
4. Tale
5. Became pregnant
6. Sacred songs
9. Mortuary tables
11. Network of tunnels
13. Self-regard
15. Reed instruments
16. Polite request word
18. Ahead
19. Competitor
21. Filled with wonder
22. Slightly wet

# CROSSWORD 125

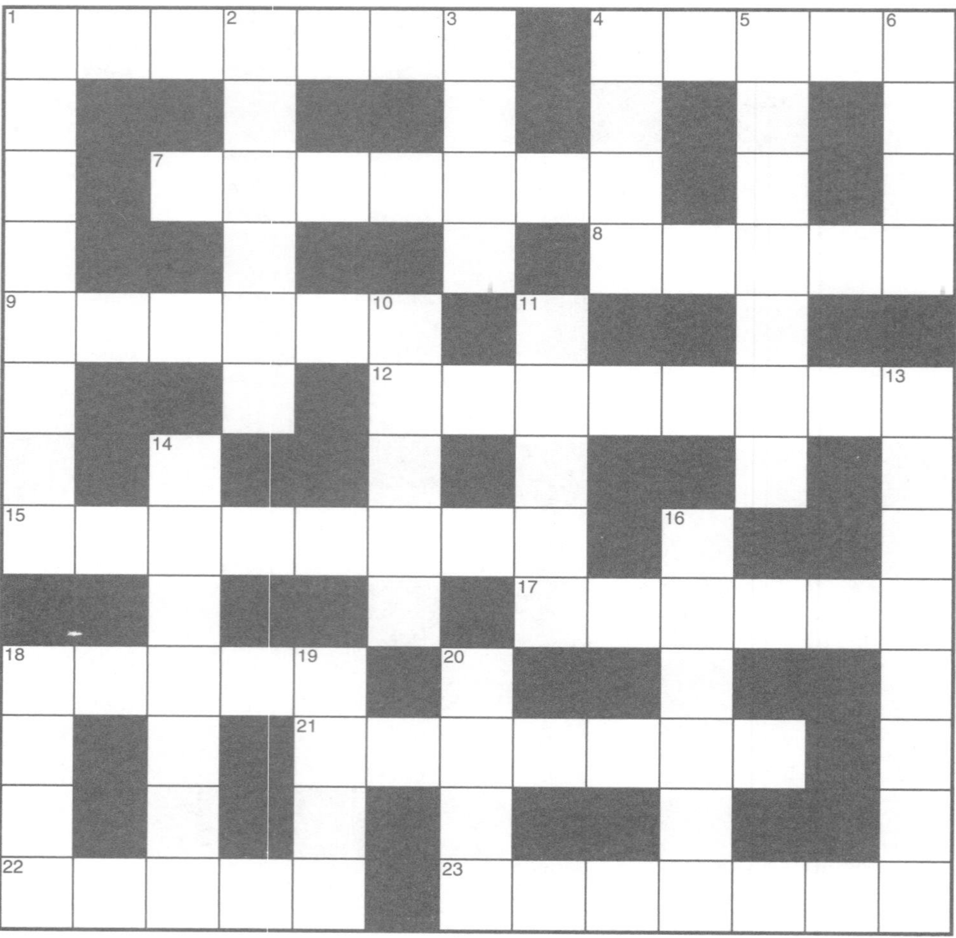

## ACROSS

1. Drifted on water
4. Singer, Buddy ...
7. Impart knowledge
8. Ocean predator
9. Chest spasm
12. Episode
15. Task-completion date
17. Zigzagged (through traffic)
18. Informal language
21. Craved
22. Parsley & mint
23. Harasses

## DOWN

1. Tennis stroke
2. Habitual user
3. Beloved
4. Shades
5. Situated
6. Pull with a jerk
10. Fairy
11. Wood fastener
13. Fiddles with thumbs
14. Bullfighter
16. Juries
18. Moan sadly
19. Fitness clubs
20. Speed of sound measure

# CROSSWORD 126

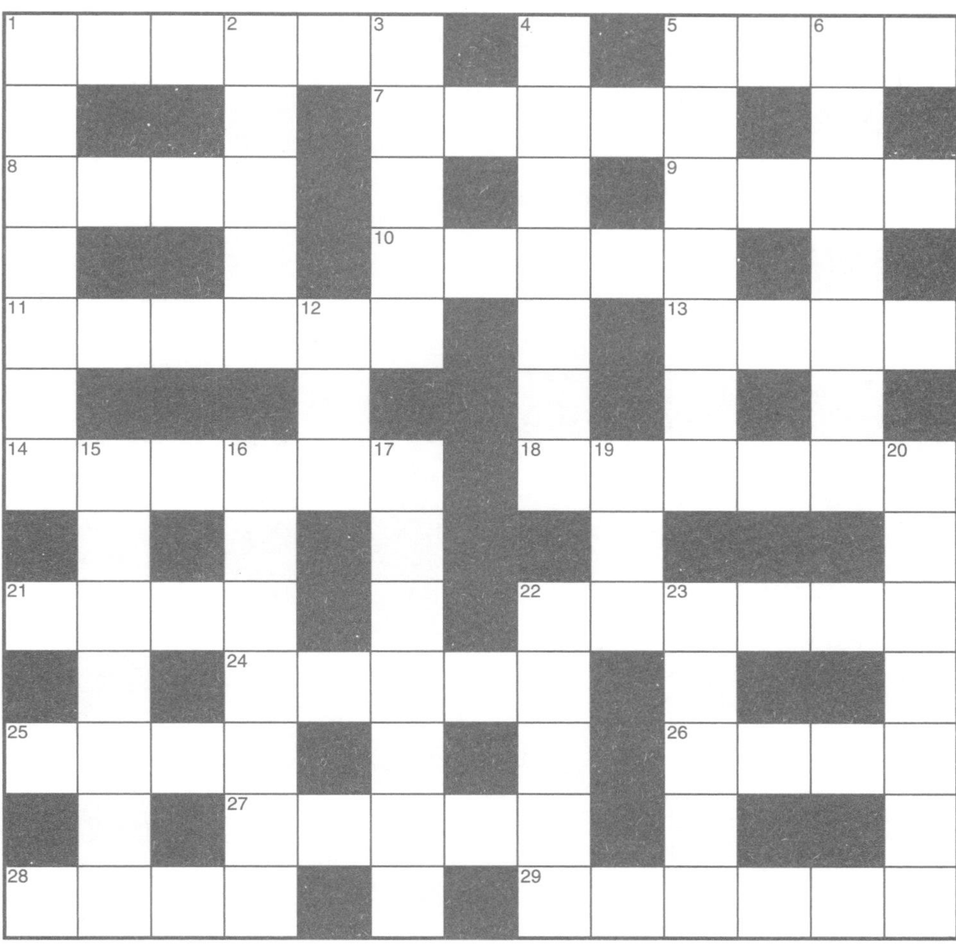

## ACROSS

1. Red salad fruit
5. Globes
7. Truncheon
8. Be dressed in
9. Every single
10. Unintoxicated
11. Puzzle
13. Follow orders
14. Strongly-built
18. Abstain (from)
21. Travel pass
22. Coarse
24. Probe
25. New Zealand bird
26. Highway fee
27. Knight's spear
28. Stratagem
29. Hopes

## DOWN

1. Foils
2. Ventilated
3. Unhealthily overweight
4. Banged (toe)
5. Burdensome
6. Supporters
12. Jar top
15. Minor (detail)
16. Easily
17. Shouting
19. Ostrich relative
20. Fills with excitement
22. Troubled
23. Wood-turning machine

# CROSSWORD 127

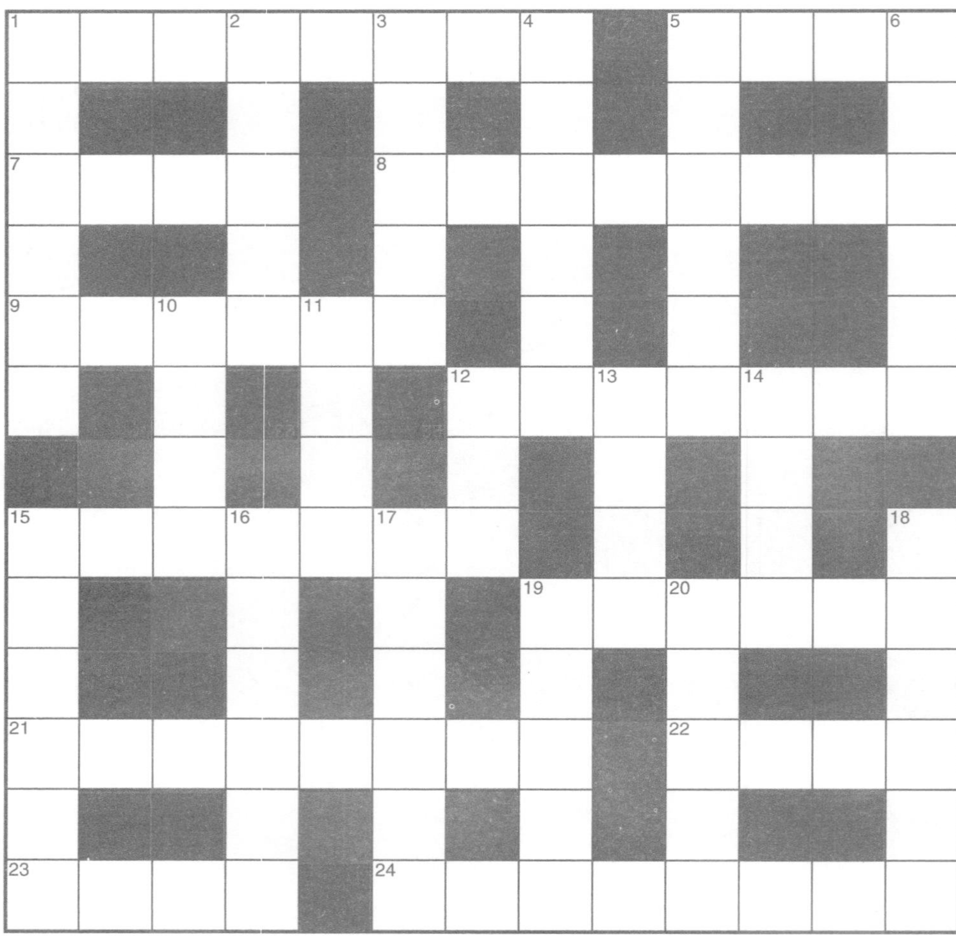

## ACROSS

1. Purgative
5. Margin
7. Insect larva
8. Warm (eggs) to hatch
9. Trusted adviser
12. Movie classifiers
15. Competition
19. Buyer & seller
21. Small aquarium
22. Earth
23. Bellow
24. Denied ownership of

## DOWN

1. Bean or pea
2. Head monk
3. Chillier
4. Enclose in box
5. Arm joints
6. Brings to bear
10. Midday
11. Formerly
12. Carve
13. Snout
14. Spoken test
15. Consult together
16. Attach with rope
17. Moment in time
18. Swapped
19. Dress-up toys
20. Entitle

# CROSSWORD 128

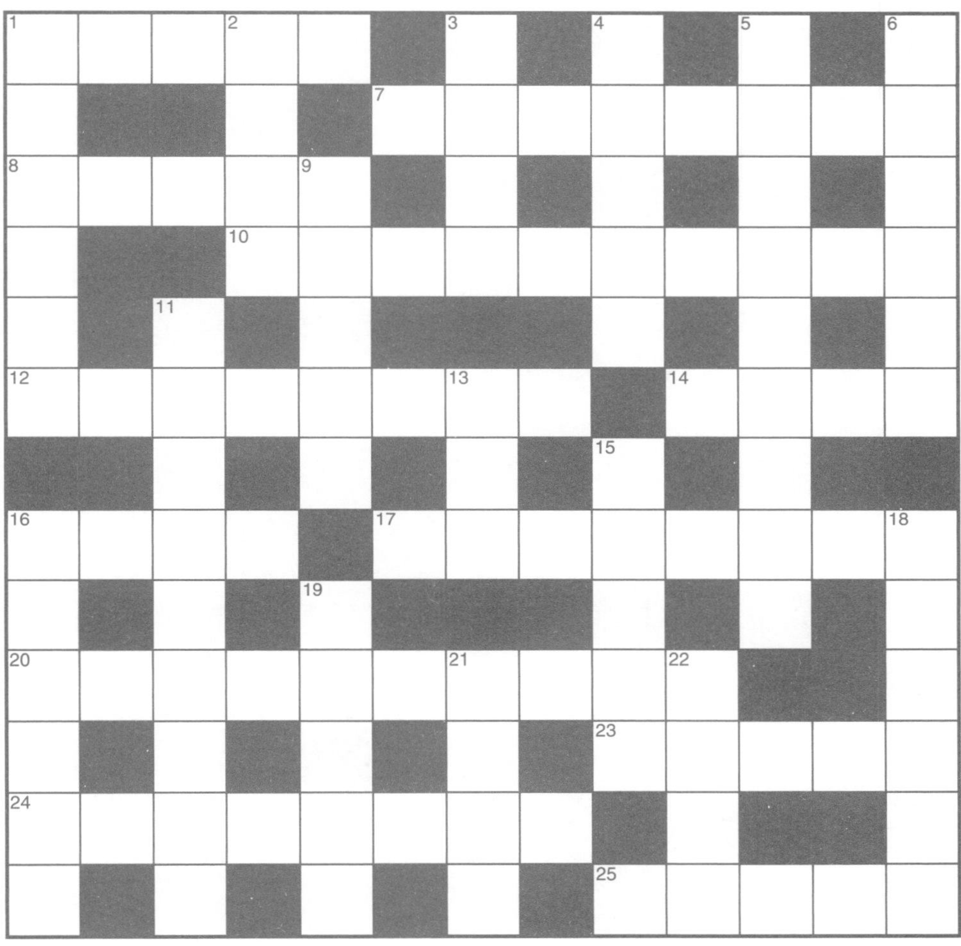

## ACROSS

1. Vocal sound
7. Fellow employee (2-6)
8. Fissure
10. Citrus fruits
12. People of no consequence
14. King cat
16. Yacht
17. Utterly preoccupied
20. Reproductions
23. Sharp (pain)
24. Resting on knees
25. Clumsy

## DOWN

1. Sight
2. Voucher
3. Melodic refrain
4. Serves from bottle
5. Most slender
6. Correctional institution
9. Late arriving
11. Polishing substances
13. Outgoing flow, ... tide
15. Hair dye
16. Eyelid movements
18. Conquer
19. Rains ice
21. Hotels
22. Read quickly

# CROSSWORD 129

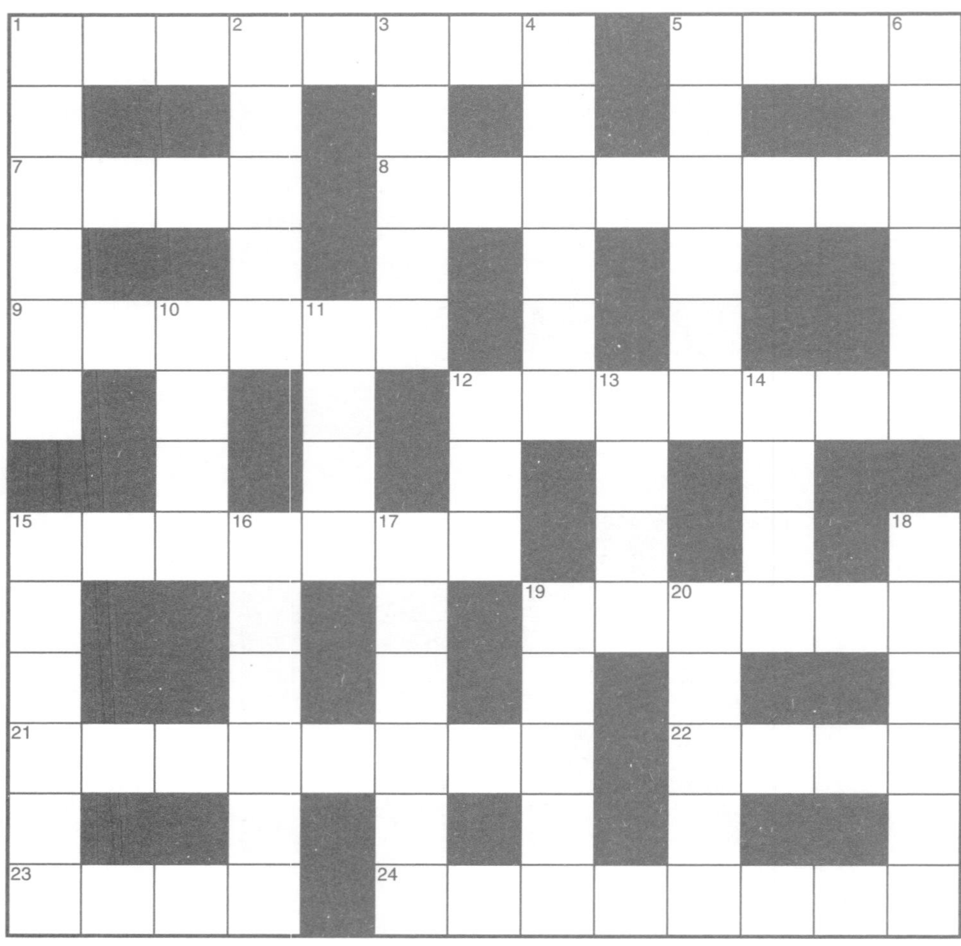

## ACROSS

1. Pessimistic
5. Fish-landing pole
7. Sponges lightly
8. Contract killer
9. Movie collie dog
12. Put in quarantine
15. Loosely-woven material
19. More orderly
21. Tend (to)
22. Single sound system
23. Tired reflex
24. Imaginative

## DOWN

1. Small lump
2. Donkeys
3. Foolish
4. Painting stands
5. Biblical text
6. Melted cheese dish
10. Asian sauce bean
11. Pressing appliance
12. Unwell
13. On an occasion
14. Touch at one end
15. Rigidly
16. Country
17. Sensual
18. Channel
19. Skin sensor
20. Let in

# CROSSWORD 130

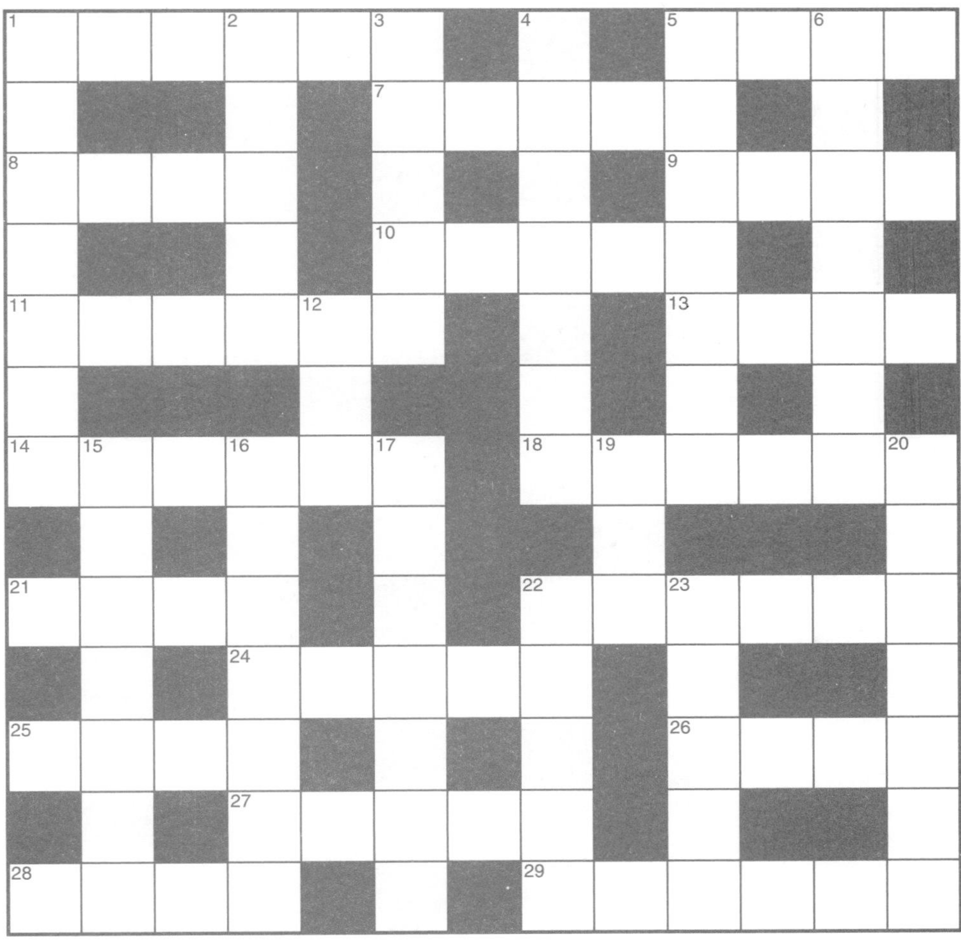

## ACROSS

1. Sedative drug
5. Period of time
7. Dull brownish-yellow
8. Arm or leg
9. Not hard
10. Flu symptom, ... congestion
11. Aromatic spice
13. Unfathomable
14. Game park tour
18. Neatened
21. Essential part
22. Discontinued
24. Snow house
25. Bullock team harness
26. Half
27. Pushes (shirt in)
28. Reside
29. Adjusting pitch

## DOWN

1. Rectangles
2. Photo book
3. Supplementing, ... out
4. Legal action
5. Bowed to the inevitable
6. Harsh
12. Wheat tip
15. Airline hub
16. Nervous tension
17. Sloping letters
19. Frozen water
20. Avoiding
22. Ocean fringe
23. Fire crime

# CROSSWORD 131

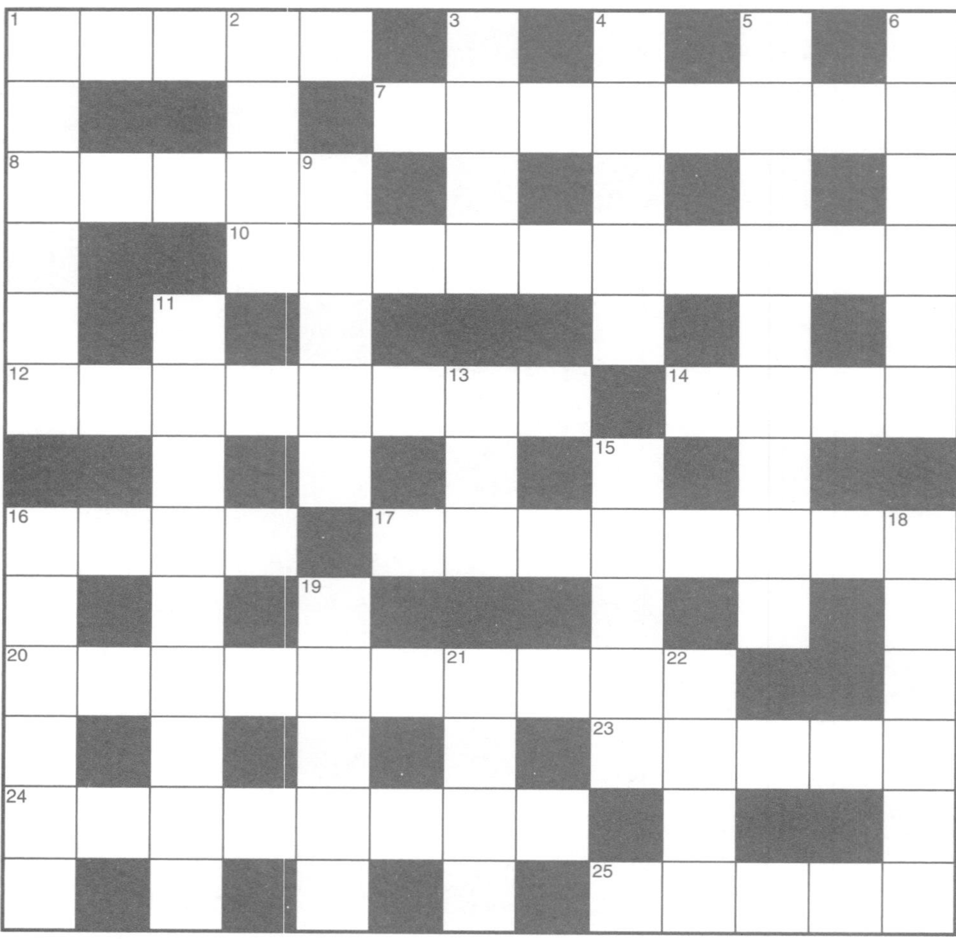

## ACROSS

1. Imperfections
7. Fugitives
8. Staple crop
10. Insignificant
12. Illustrations
14. Shallow river crossing
16. Multiple-birth child
17. Spread out
20. Dumping
23. Three-foot lengths
24. Growing up
25. In a state of activity

## DOWN

1. Bowed & scraped
2. Take (baby) off bottle
3. Unexciting
4. Emblem
5. Bewilder
6. Climb (stairs)
9. Lukewarm
11. Waterfalls
13. Rift
15. Wet (weather)
16. Pangs of doubt
18. More compressed
19. Beautify
21. No part
22. Gallivants (about)

# CROSSWORD 132

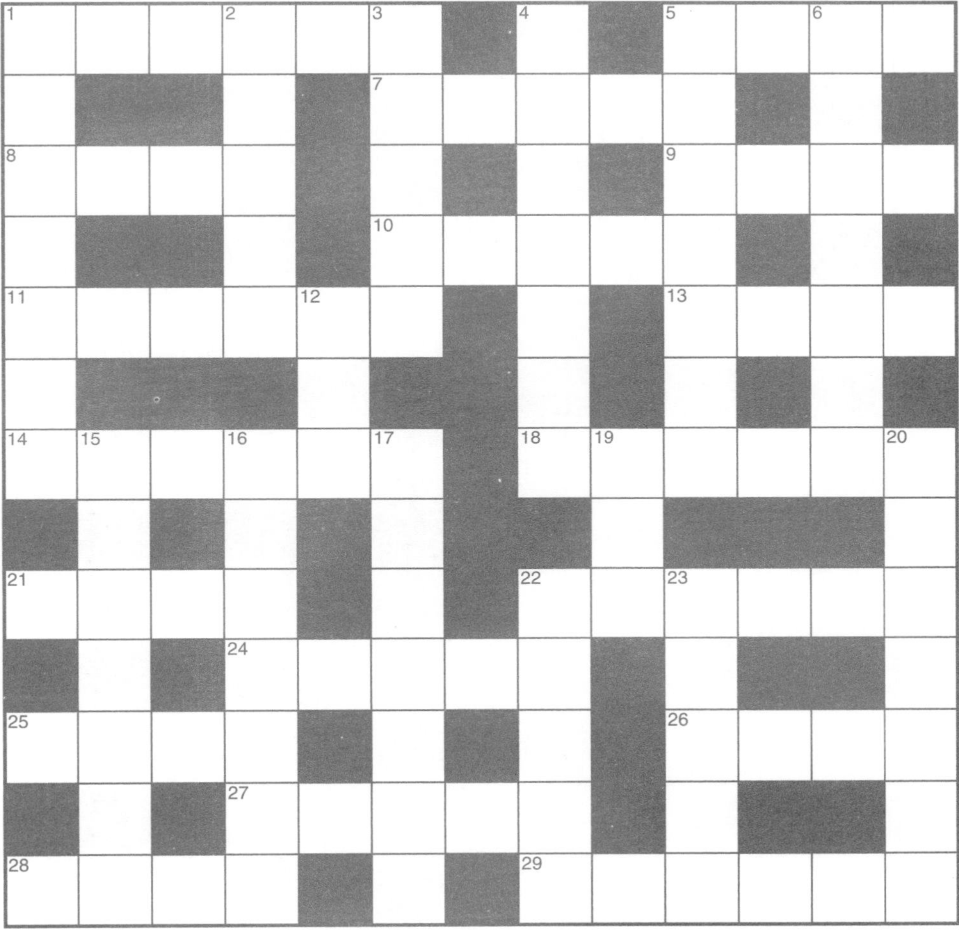

## ACROSS

1. Spoof
5. Atlas pictures
7. Monks' home
8. Adopt a stance
9. Exchange
10. Cardiac organ
11. Counterbalance
13. Megastar
14. Nonagenarian's age
18. Uttering
21. ... of Capri
22. Laughed sneeringly
24. Italian country house
25. Expelled magma
26. Lively dance
27. Drying cloth
28. Chimney duct
29. Computer tablet pen

## DOWN

1. Cinema snack
2. Follows directives
3. Sailing boat
4. Scrapes
5. Bewilder
6. Military subdivision
12. Consume
15. Place in position
16. Lift
17. Golden hues
19. Top pilot
20. Mechanical devices
22. Imprisons
23. Relish

# CROSSWORD 133

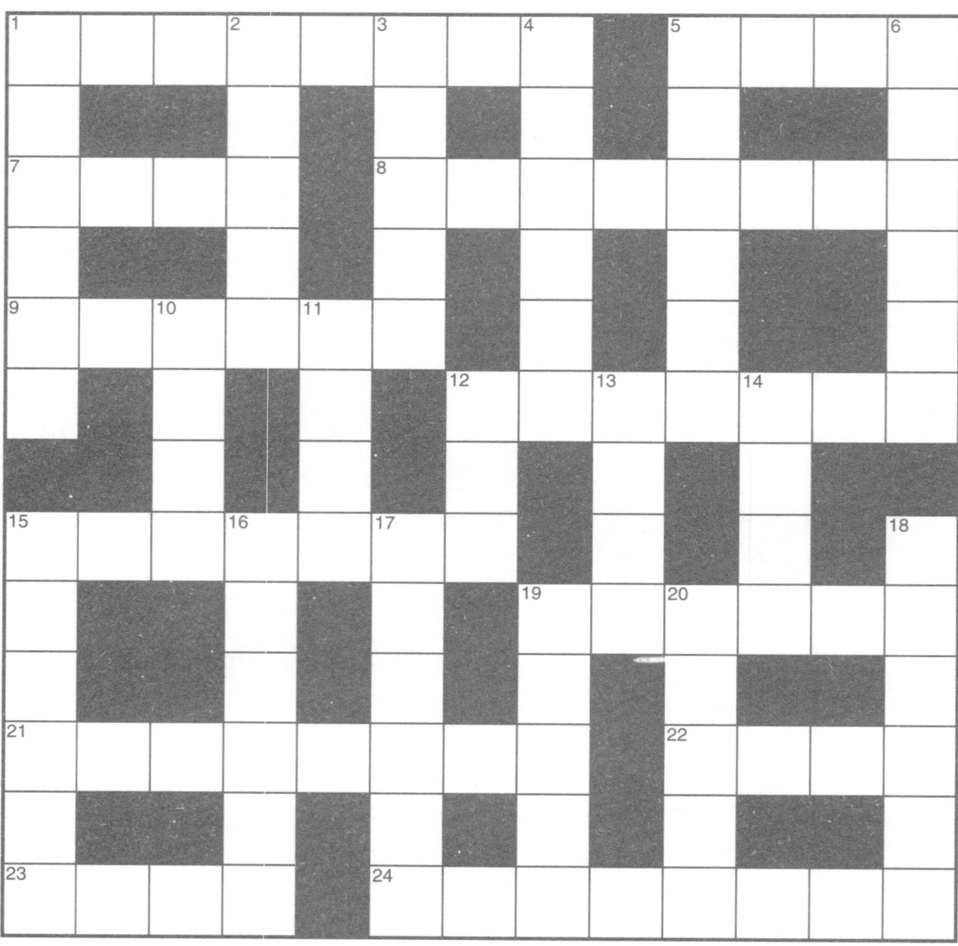

## ACROSS

1. Pamphlets
5. Unaccompanied
7. Meal list
8. Speeches
9. Tortoise relative
12. Livestock farmer
15. Auburn-haired person
19. Loose (of muscle)
21. Affixed
22. Deep wound
23. Wooden barrels
24. Human frame

## DOWN

1. Boundaries
2. Shortcoming
3. Wear away
4. Beard trimmer
5. Repress
6. Shellfish
10. Sudden invasion
11. Disabled
12. Unopened bloom
13. Noble rank
14. Dull
15. Make mention of
16. Pester
17. Curved structures
18. Punctuation mark
19. Soft confection
20. Journalist's slant

# CROSSWORD 134

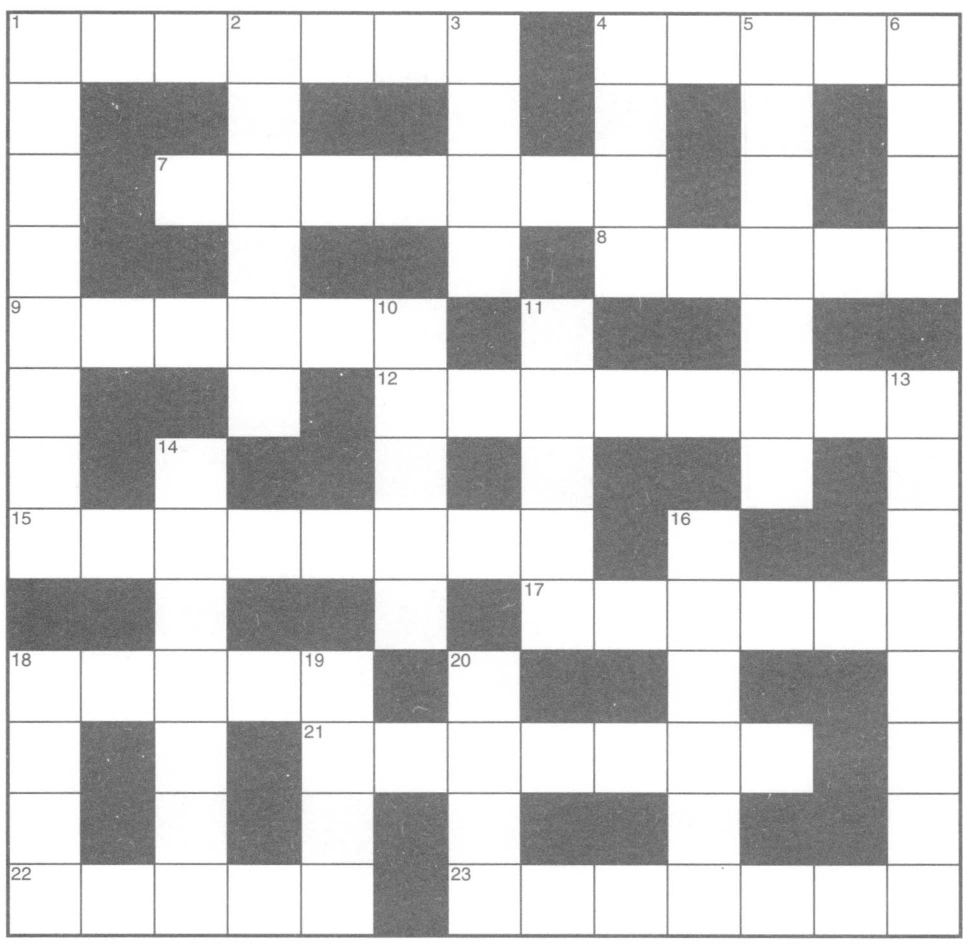

## ACROSS

1. Of fired clay
4. Intends
7. Illegal
8. Copy outline of
9. Stares angrily
12. South American snake
15. Standing sentry duty at
17. Funeral vehicle
18. Complains
21. Word conundrum
22. Door pivot
23. Medical emergency, ... arrest

## DOWN

1. Blocking (drain)
2. Attraction
3. Male fowl
4. Actor, ... Damon
5. Reaches
6. Location
10. Glossy fabric
11. Giggle
13. Sensitive (to substance)
14. Movable dwelling
16. Peril
18. Legend
19. Japanese rice wine
20. Perfumed powder

# CROSSWORD 135

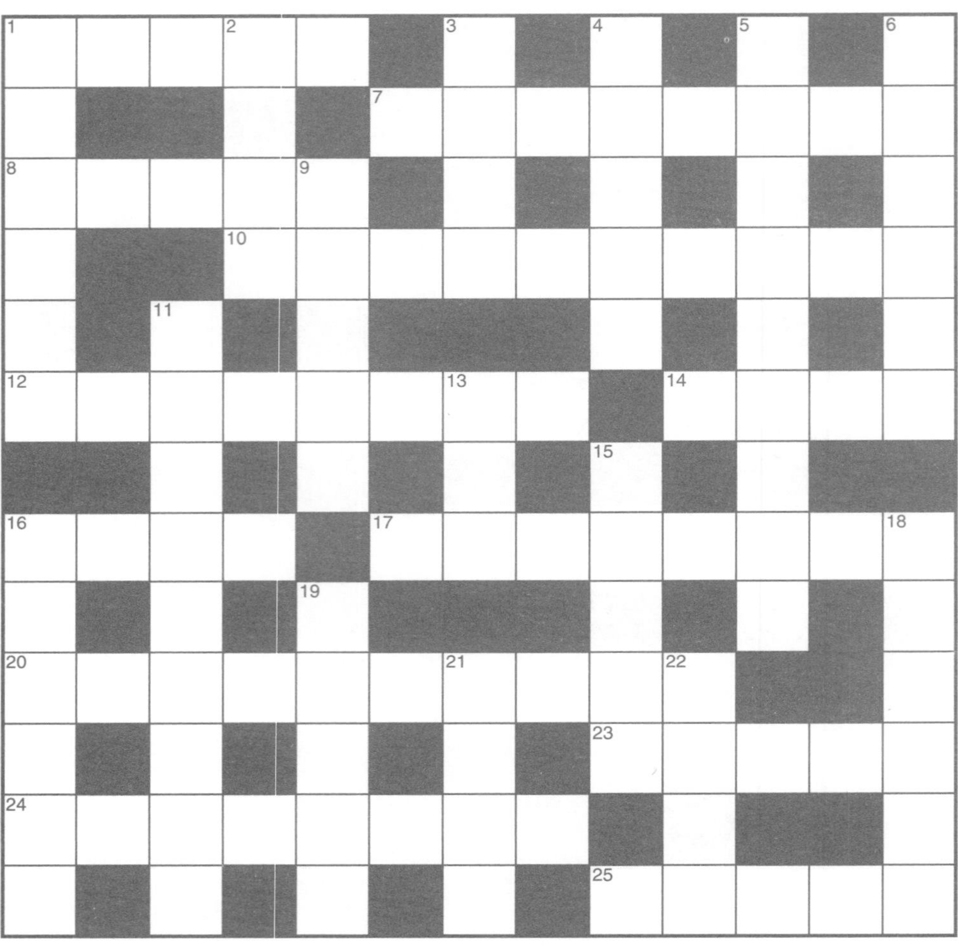

## ACROSS

1. Trophy
7. Most obvious
8. Regional
10. Designed garden
12. Roofs with straw
14. Blocking vote
16. Not imagined
17. Frying pans
20. Meteorologists
23. This 24 hours
24. Poorest
25. Fatigued

## DOWN

1. Curtain-rail cover
2. Enthusiasm
3. Gratified
4. Trapdoor
5. Bewilders
6. Film production company
9. Spear
11. Information banks
13. Moose
15. Group of warships
16. Using oars
18. Nimbly
19. Table & ...
21. Ascend
22. Snout

# CROSSWORD 136

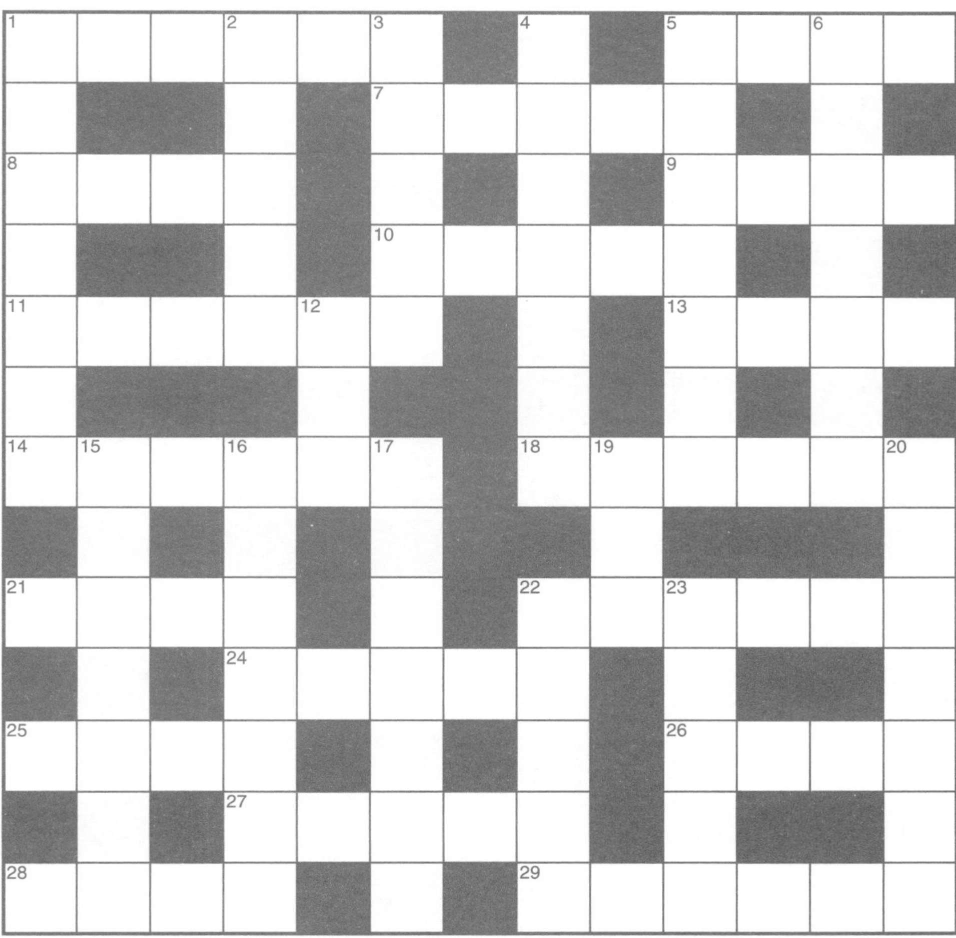

## ACROSS

1. Pattern of small tiles
5. Operates
7. Kingdom
8. Festive occasion
9. Mountain top
10. Card game
11. Insult
13. Fencing sword
14. Mental health
18. Expel from country
21. Raced
22. Support (broken bone)
24. In darkness
25. Spoken test
26. Medicine amount
27. Magic lamp spirit
28. AM, ... meridiem
29. Feel aggrieved by

## DOWN

1. Fly larvae
2. Conscious
3. Large gathering
4. Passenger vehicle
5. Countless
6. Pencil rubbers
12. After tax
15. Common analgesic
16. Luxuriate
17. Shouting
19. Rock band's sound booster
20. Most heated
22. Guide (boat)
23. Ore veins

# CROSSWORD 137

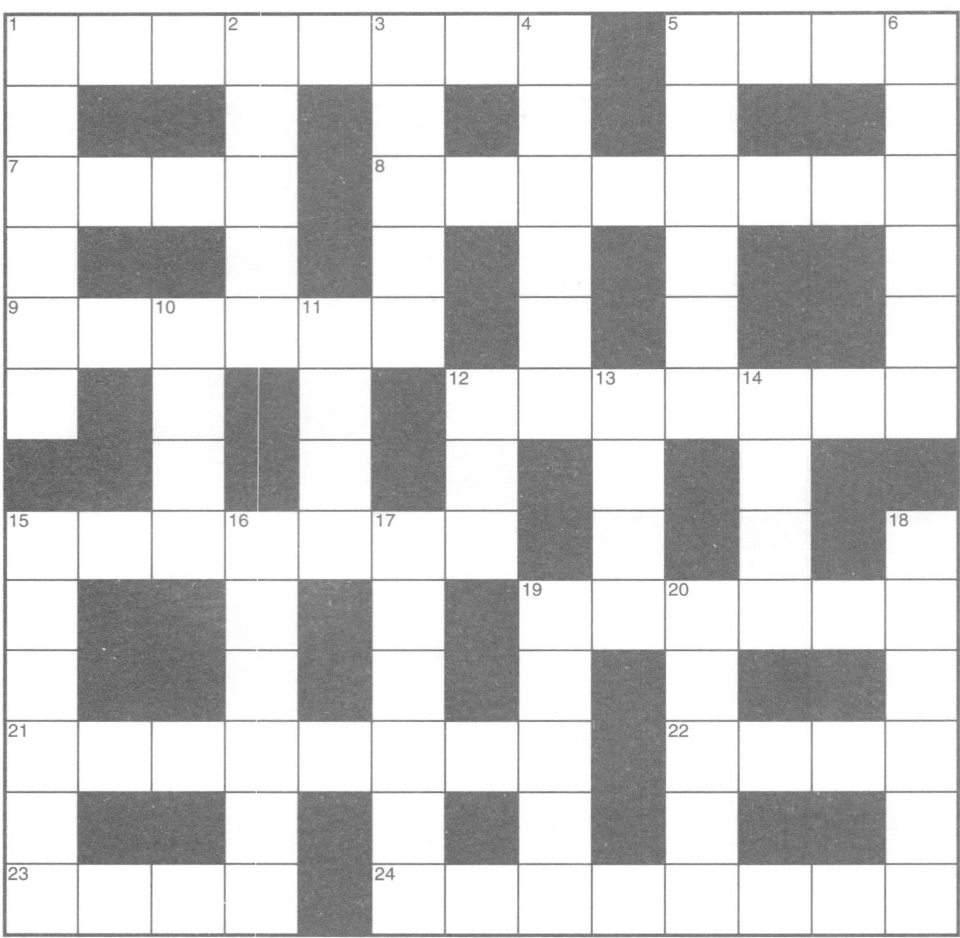

## ACROSS

1. Was worthy of
5. Green gemstone
7. Arrive
8. Shaved with knife
9. Ransacked
12. Liquid-filled sac
15. Pupil
19. Sachet
21. Cruel
22. ... & queen
23. Force of troops
24. Abstained (from)

## DOWN

1. Placid
2. Hurl out
3. Pledged
4. Nonsense
5. Wrote quickly
6. Make beloved
10. Sworn promise
11. Diabolical
12. Forbid entry
13. Region
14. Ship's floor
15. Drool
16. Reside in
17. On train
18. Presented (play)
19. Equals
20. Baked treats

# CROSSWORD 138

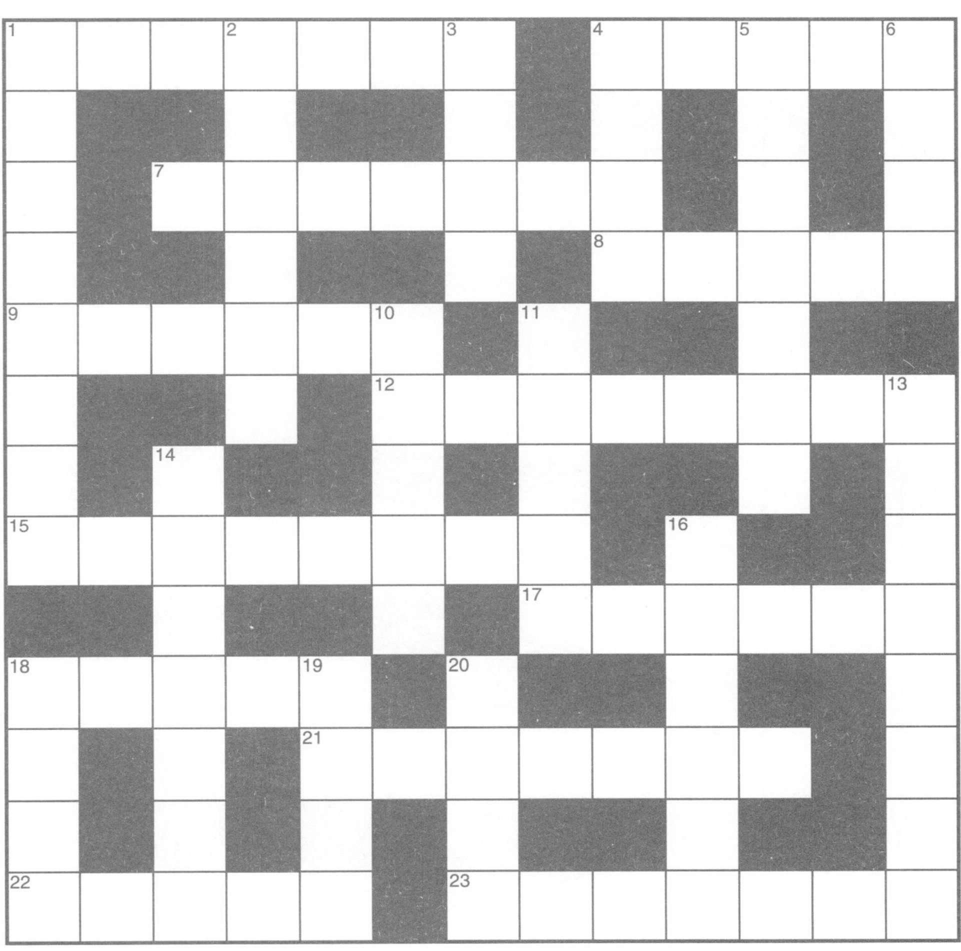

## ACROSS

1. Packed tightly
4. Gallantly
7. Eternally youthful
8. Furnish with supplies
9. Matched
12. Parasol
15. Ignition mechanisms
17. Allow
18. Hate
21. Greed
22. Ravine
23. Lit

## DOWN

1. Boats, pleasure ...
2. Powerful
3. Eat to slim
4. Facial feature
5. Bewitch
6. Dog's shrill howl
10. Beach formations
11. Humble (oneself)
13. Had an impact on
14. Coy
16. Spoiled (of butter)
18. Eagerly expectant
19. Sporty
20. Blemish

# CROSSWORD 139

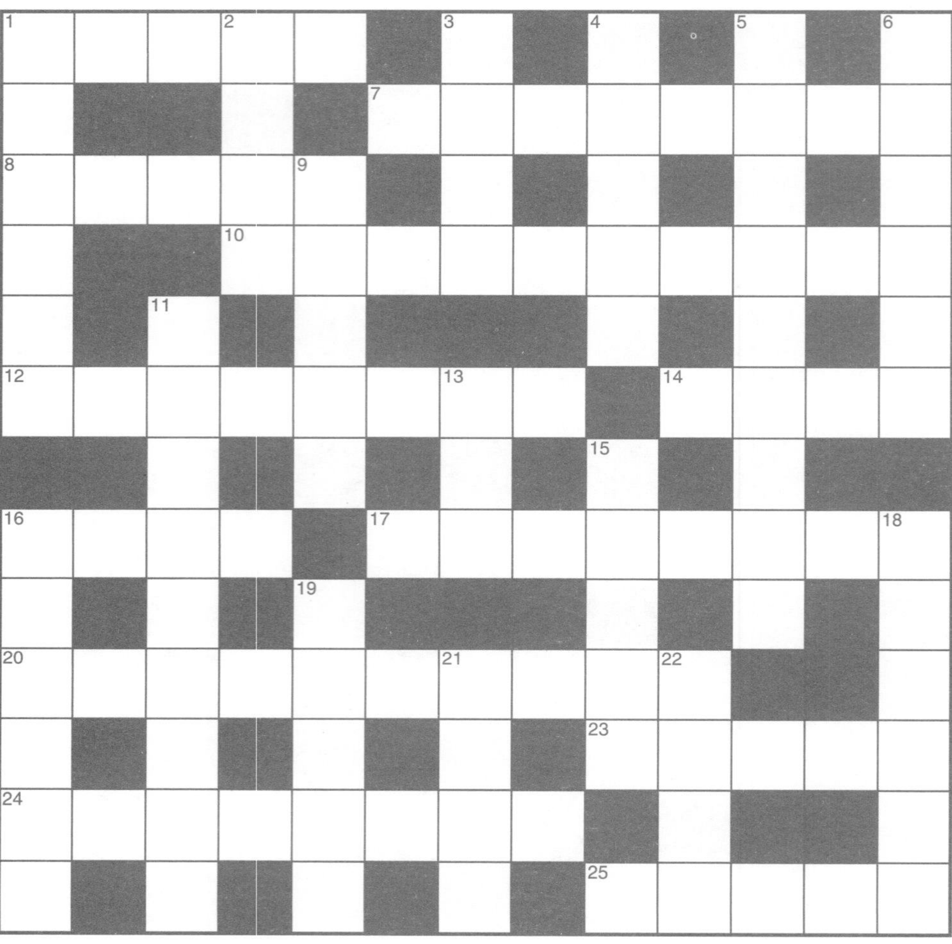

## ACROSS

1. Elsewhere excuse
7. Marooned
8. Wide
10. Record player
12. Chewing
14. Dog's feet
16. Fall suddenly
17. Canines
20. Delicate quality
23. Mayhem
24. Witch's pot
25. Supply sparingly

## DOWN

1. Reddish-brown
2. Boast
3. Derive (from)
4. Hornet relatives
5. Supports (cause)
6. Cows' mammary glands
9. Dental tool
11. Objectionable
13. Negative vote
15. Stow away
16. Conclude
18. Chest spasm
19. Collar fasteners
21. ... & cranny
22. Cloth bag

# CROSSWORD 140

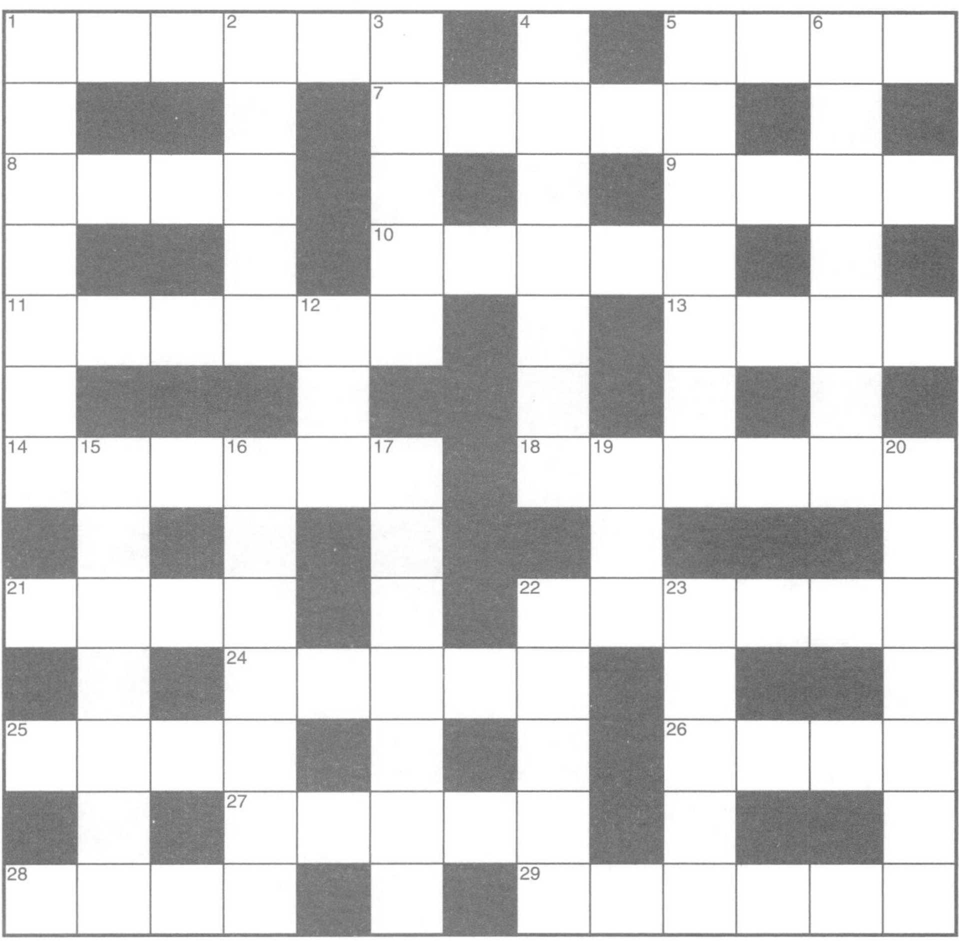

## ACROSS

1. Secondary route
5. Stupefy
7. Aunt & ...
8. Porridge cereal
9. Frolic
10. Light olive-brown
11. Extinguishes
13. Fall in drops
14. Join in sporadically
18. Red salad root
21. King cat
22. Joked
24. Push
25. Broad
26. Elliptic
27. Ceasefire agreement
28. Becomes mature
29. Spooned (out)

## DOWN

1. Sat on (eggs)
2. Fertile desert spot
3. Dips into drink
4. Paint-removing tool
5. Scorned
6. Walking corpses
12. Conger
15. Emerging
16. Baby's hats
17. Hearing membrane
19. I am, you ...
20. Crowded together
22. Precious stone
23. Rebuke

# CROSSWORD 141

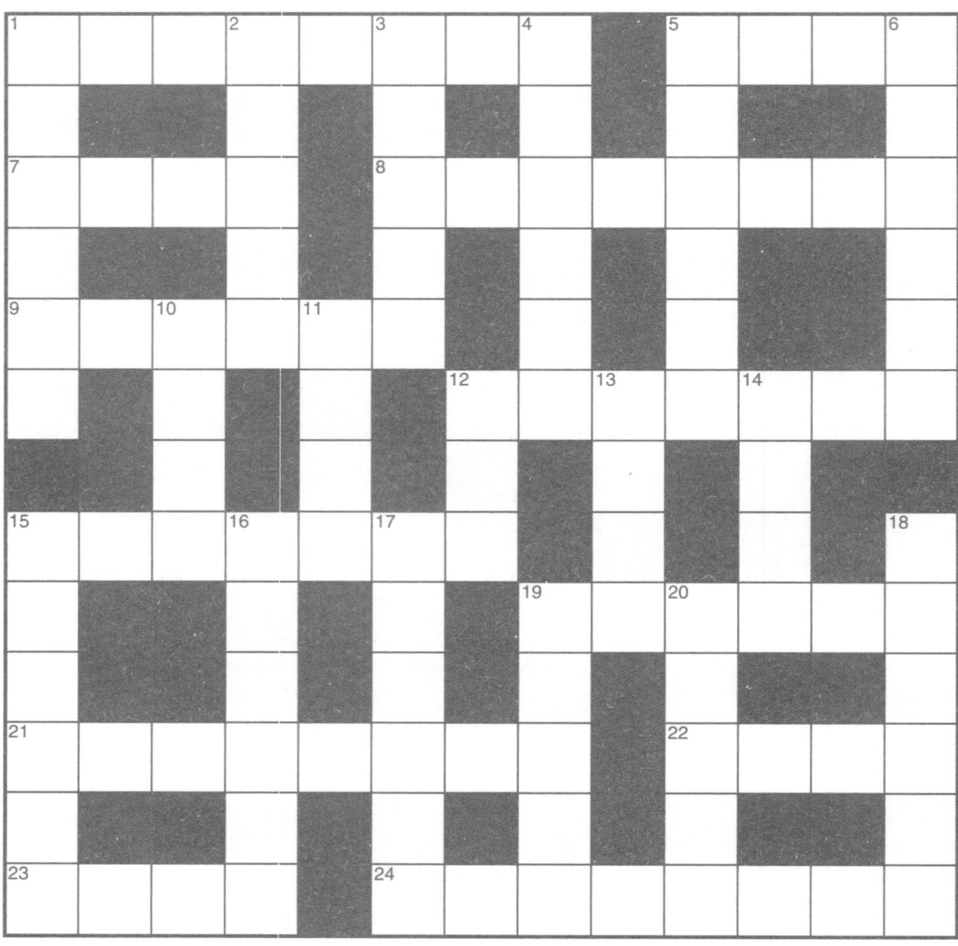

## ACROSS

1. On the inside
5. Military subdivision
7. Dinner chime
8. Leaping
9. Striped big cats
12. Regards highly
15. Immature frog
19. Four-sided shape
21. Raiders
22. Trim
23. Ablaze, on ...
24. Colonists

## DOWN

1. Gold bars
2. Quarrel
3. Sums owing
4. Teenage people
5. Untied
6. Leggings
10. Criss-cross structure
11. Refashion
12. Poet's word for before
13. Pharaoh's resting place
14. Resounding noise
15. Import tax
16. Royal residence
17. Tiers
18. Reaches an understanding
19. Beginning (of illness)
20. Collar fold

# CROSSWORD 142

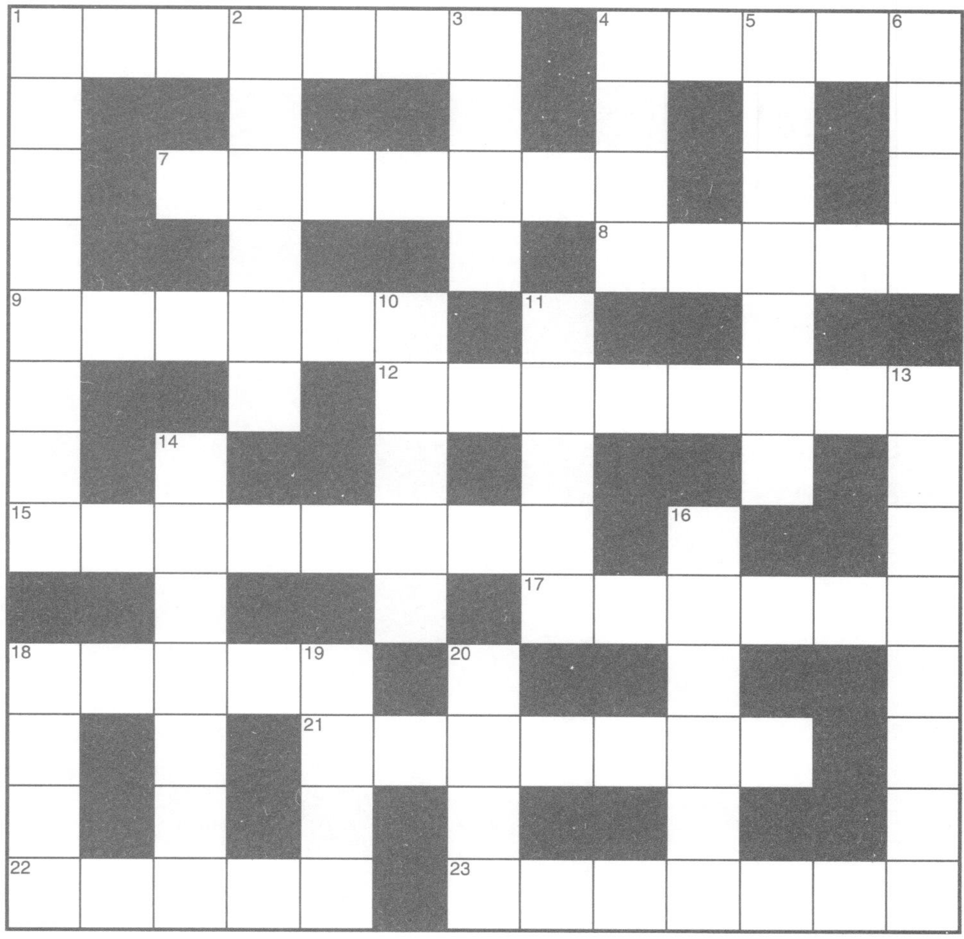

## ACROSS

1. Encroach
4. Cheerfully
7. Tight corner, ... bend
8. Bird of prey
9. Painter or sculptor
12. Closely inspected
15. Specimens
17. Looks forward to
18. Open sore
21. Military school
22. Dough-raising agent
23. Stowing space

## DOWN

1. Occasion
2. Sloping (font)
3. Catch sight of
4. No longer here
5. Envision
6. Bullock team harness
10. Recounts
11. Model-plane wood
13. Deter
14. Eyelash cosmetic
16. More sedate
18. Hideous
19. Floating log platform
20. Rowing aids

# CROSSWORD 143

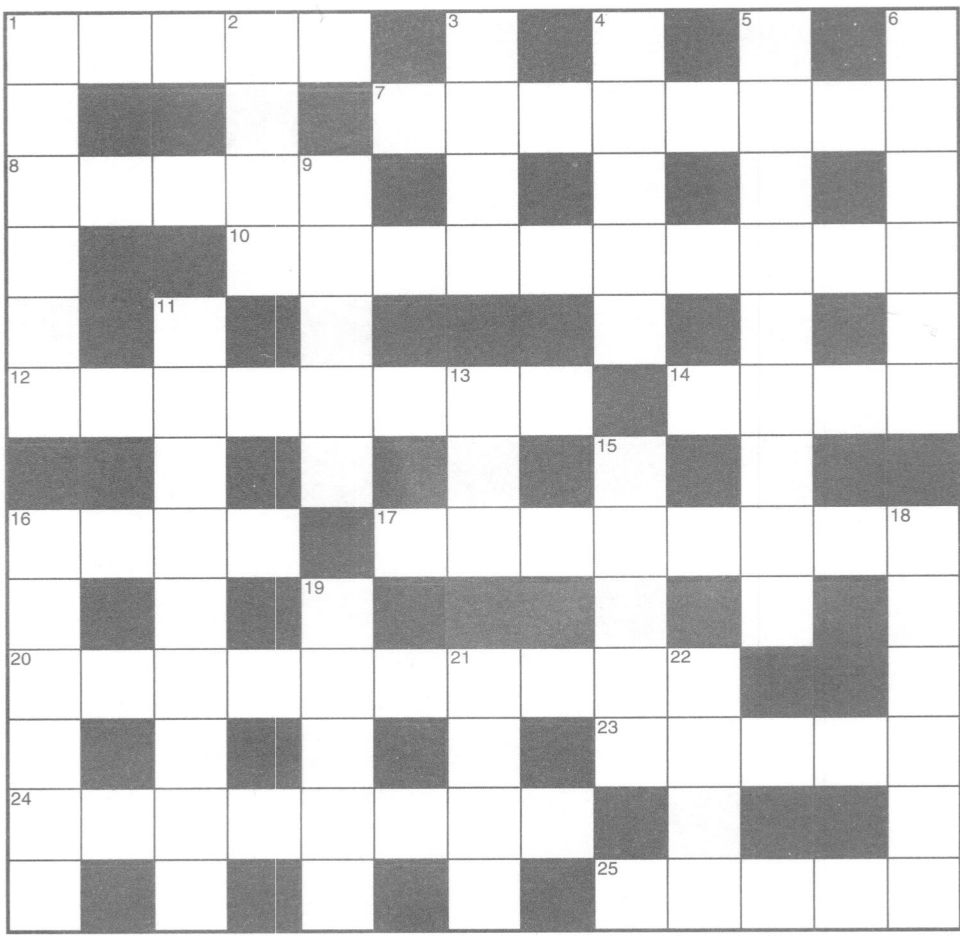

## ACROSS

1. Shroud
7. Comes undone
8. To the fore
10. Horseracing track
12. Edge of highway
14. Short-term worker
16. Pen tips
17. Pullovers
20. Strategically
23. Soil
24. Of musical drama
25. Unnourished

## DOWN

1. Lunar landform
2. A great way off
3. Respectfully, on bended ...
4. Fortune-telling card
5. Dog, golden ...
6. Slumbering
9. Flower necklace, ... chain
11. Outdoor grills
13. Dawn moisture
15. Roof end
16. Idea
18. Moaned sadly
19. Of sea phases
21. Amongst
22. Knitting thread

# CROSSWORD 144

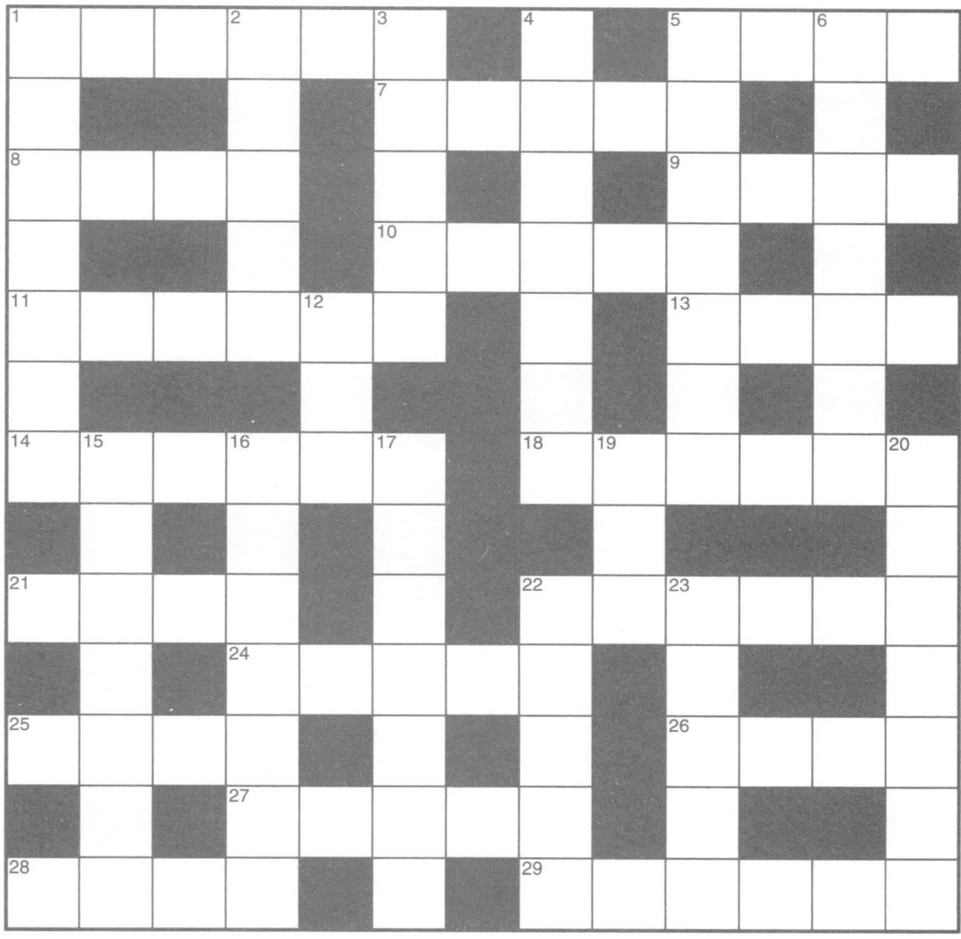

## ACROSS

1. Stifle
5. Group of workers
7. Put
8. Cow excrement
9. Snare
10. Discord
11. Grab
13. On any occasion
14. Desires greatly
18. Guarantee
21. Non-alkali
22. Roof tiles
24. Just right
25. Long upholstered seat
26. Horse restraint
27. Plucked string sound
28. Festival
29. Entice

## DOWN

1. Humility
2. Boxing match
3. Geological time unit
4. Flair
5. Ties up
6. Nonprofessional
12. Is able to
15. Wrap
16. Give out (energy)
17. Quite a few
19. No score
20. Concentrated solution
22. Snail relatives
23. Screened on TV

# CROSSWORD 145

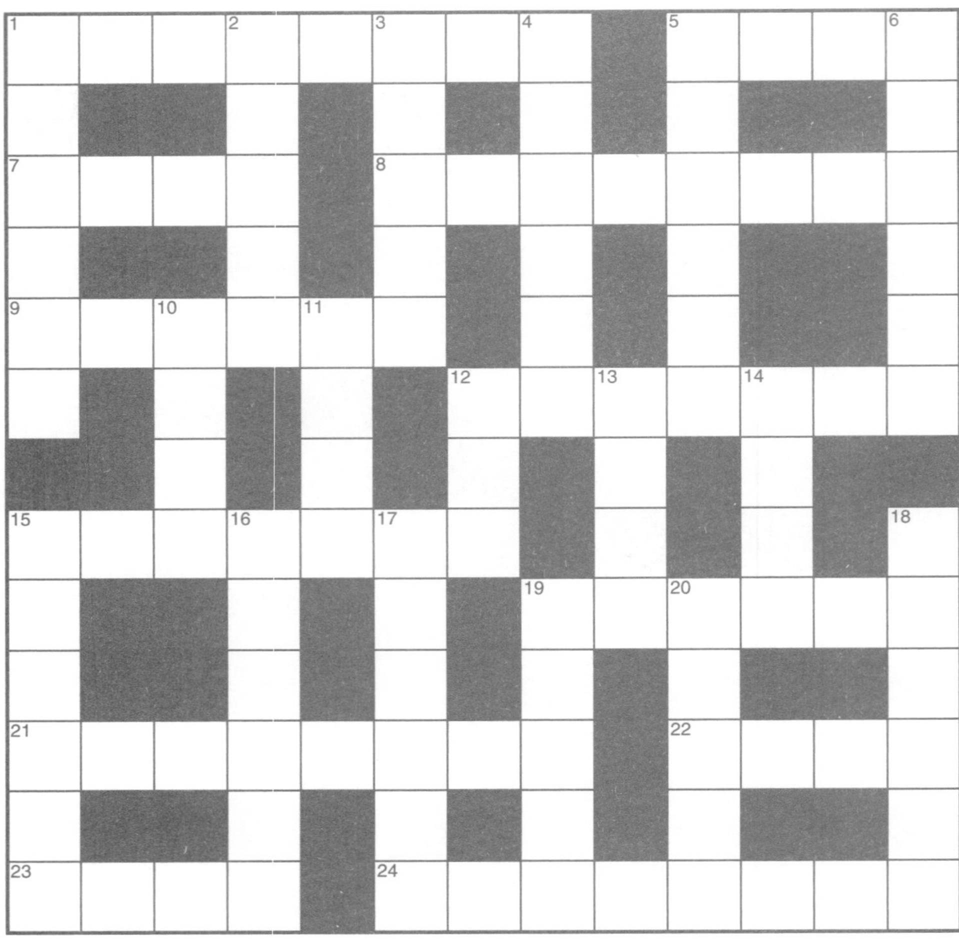

## ACROSS

1. Illicit
5. Skin irritation
7. Leaf-scraping tool
8. Government levy
9. Lessens in severity
12. Water-main outlet
15. Soiled
19. Goods thrown overboard
21. Dates chart
22. Circus arena
23. Lamented
24. Operating doctors

## DOWN

1. Commotion
2. Publicist, press ...
3. Destinies
4. Indulgence
5. Prefer to
6. Trusty
10. Shade of blue
11. Smooth
12. Concealed
13. Small cubes
14. Pub brews
15. Cup & ...
16. Certainly
17. Mass departure
18. Reflections
19. Trial panel member
20. Number in trio

# CROSSWORD 146

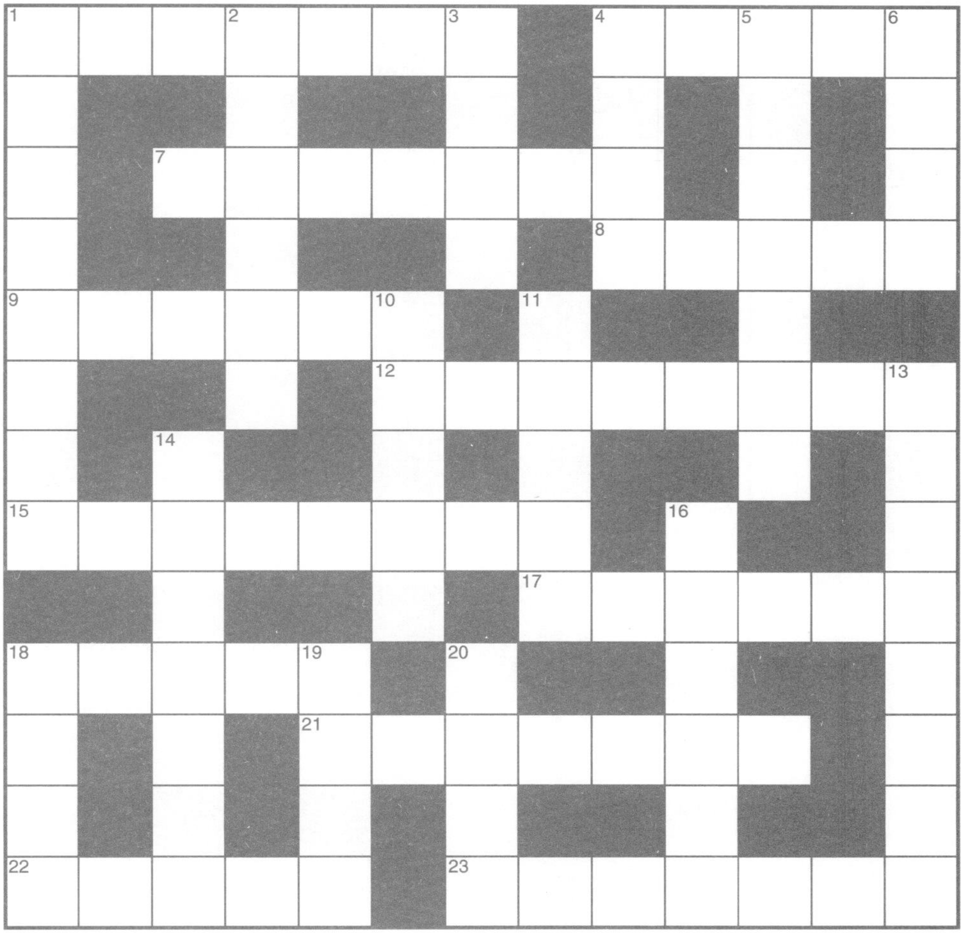

## ACROSS

1. Competent
4. Tongue of fire
7. Coin disc-player
8. Pulls sharply
9. Detain during wartime
12. Unlucky occurrence
15. Intensify (war)
17. Formal argument
18. Camera light
21. Partakes of liquor
22. Thus
23. Less full

## DOWN

1. Persist
2. Maltreats
3. Wanes
4. Crafty
5. Retaliates for
6. Just manages, ... out a living
10. Concerning ships
11. Was painful
13. In unison
14. Eight-sided figure
16. Missing
18. Scaly aquatic animal
19. Rent
20. Skilled

# CROSSWORD 147

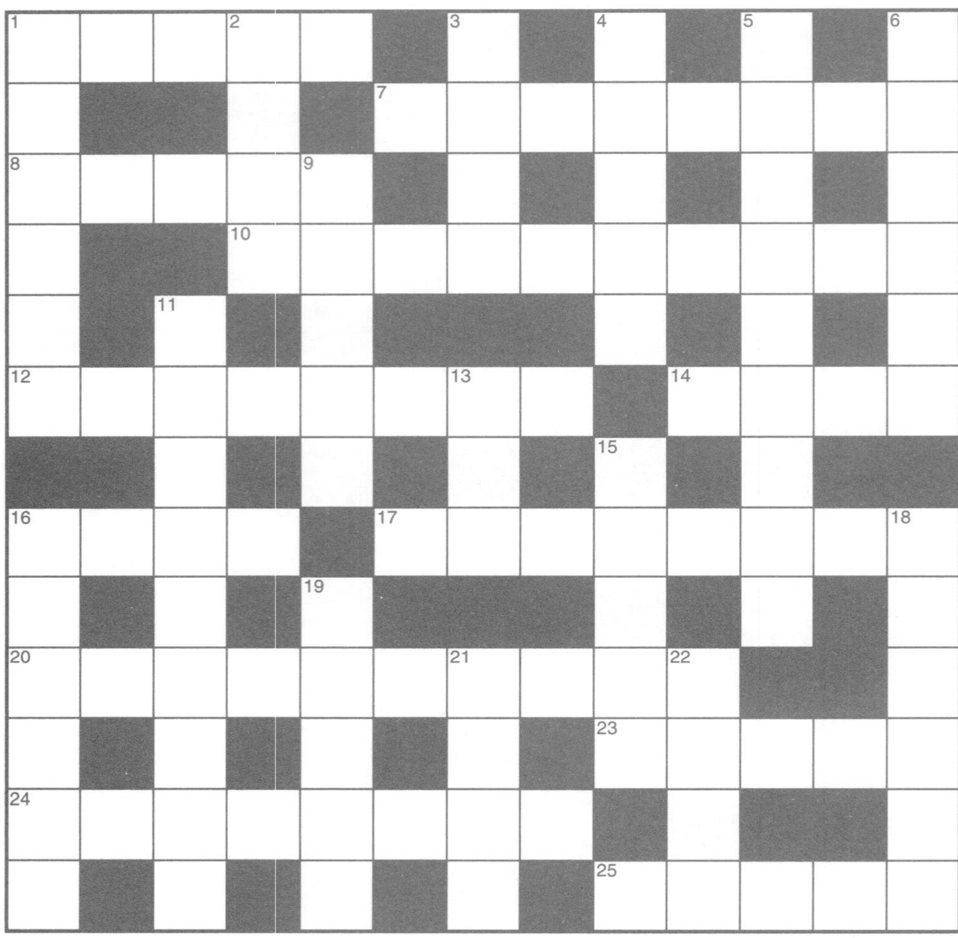

## ACROSS

1. Body part
7. Mercifully
8. Tolerate
10. Reinforce
12. Engraved artworks
14. Globes
16. Rugged peak
17. Genetically altering
20. Triumphantly
23. Not hollow
24. Viewing platforms
25. Cooked in oil

## DOWN

1. Frosted (glass)
2. Tallies
3. Donkey/horse cross
4. Lanky
5. Apathetic
6. Laughing scavengers
9. Moral standard
11. Keepsakes album
13. African antelope
15. Train tracks
16. Flatter
18. Provoked
19. Inundate
21. Quick letter
22. Thy

# CROSSWORD 148

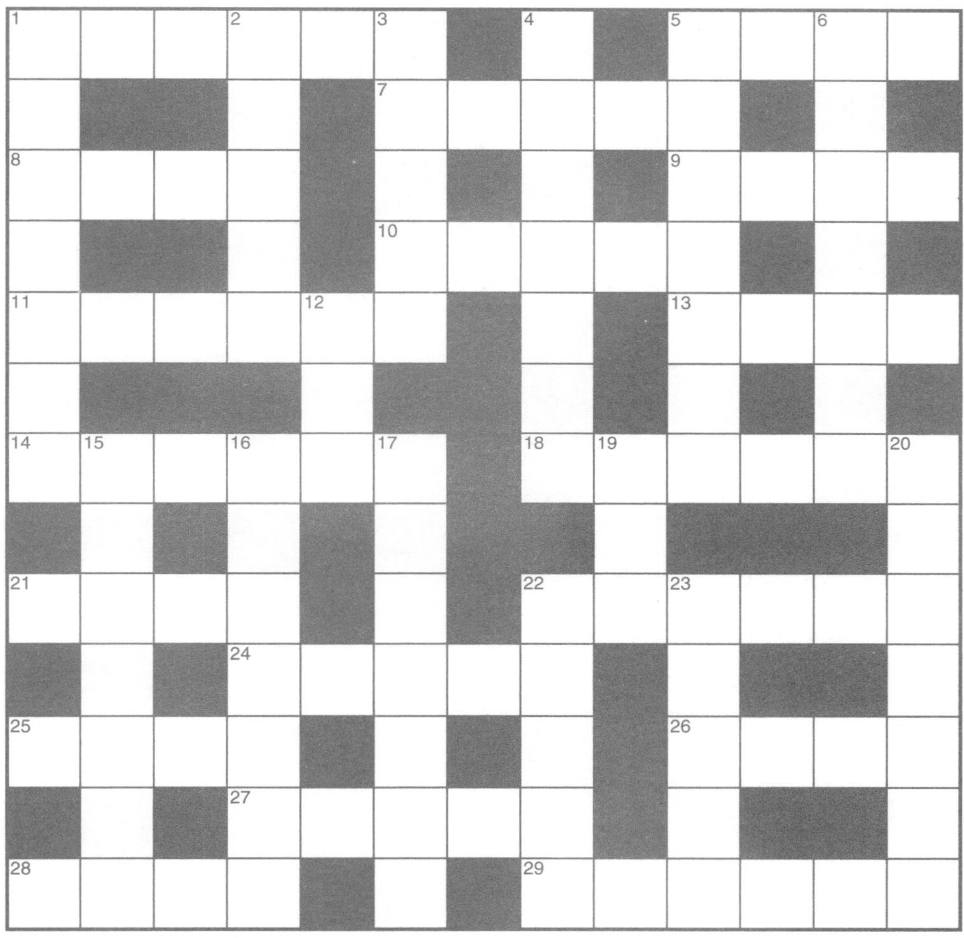

## ACROSS

1. Large Galápagos lizard
5. Hindu exercise routine
7. Fast European dance
8. Repair
9. Chair
10. Belt hole
11. Horde
13. Paw roughly
14. Military greeting
18. Maintenance
21. Makes request
22. Crowded in upon
24. Royal headwear
25. Forearm bone
26. Knitting stitch
27. Shine
28. Present
29. Edged (towards)

## DOWN

1. Prisoners
2. Of hearing
3. Imitating
4. High plain
5. Muslim veil
6. Small grain
12. Kernel
15. Clear of blame
16. Outshine
17. Involves (in)
19. Full-time golfer
20. Sold on street
22. Incapacitates
23. Two-footed creature

# CROSSWORD 149

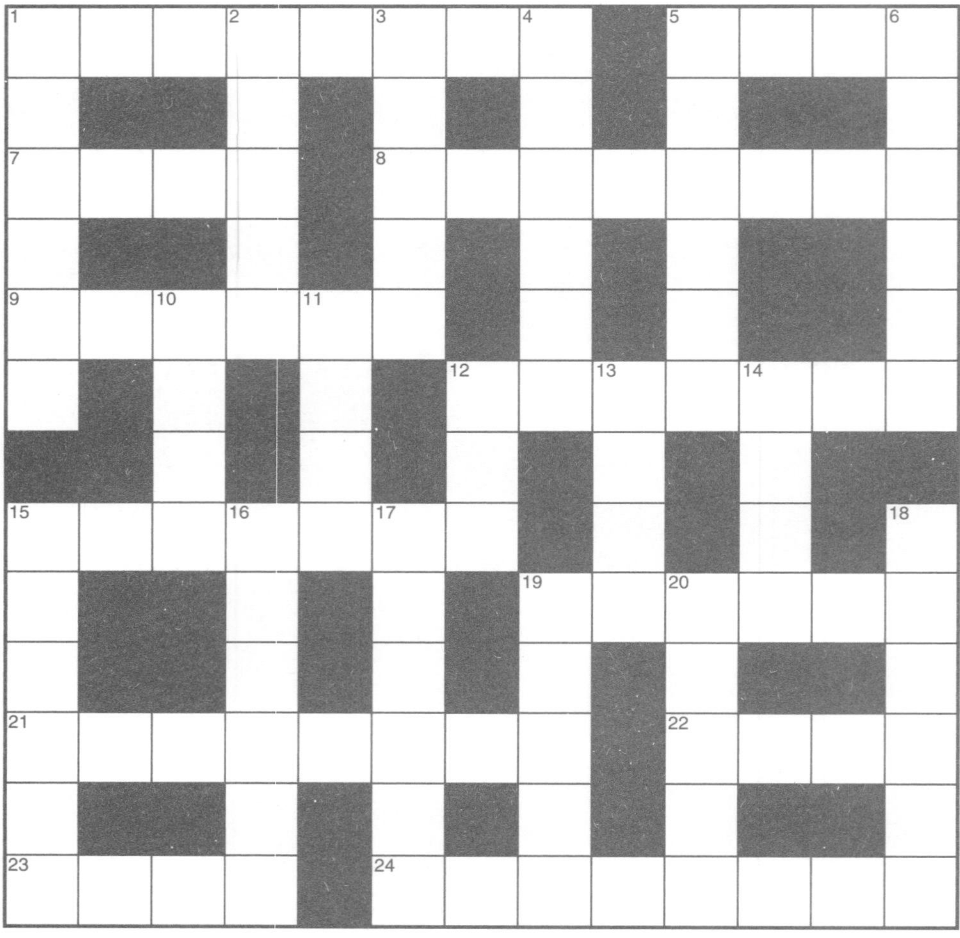

## ACROSS

1. More nauseous
5. Lump of earth
7. Jot
8. Tidiness
9. Gentler
12. Danced (of horse)
15. Nasal opening
19. Made unlucky
21. Concerning, in ... to
22. Sit lazily
23. Clean
24. Simplicity

## DOWN

1. Eccentric mannerisms
2. Trophy
3. Inside
4. Magazine subscriber
5. Artillery gun
6. Hurried
10. Crab pinches
11. Large jug
12. Buddy
13. Opposed to
14. Vital part
15. Slender
16. Trounce
17. Set fire to
18. Grown-ups
19. Chinese sail boats
20. Synthetic fabric

# CROSSWORD 150

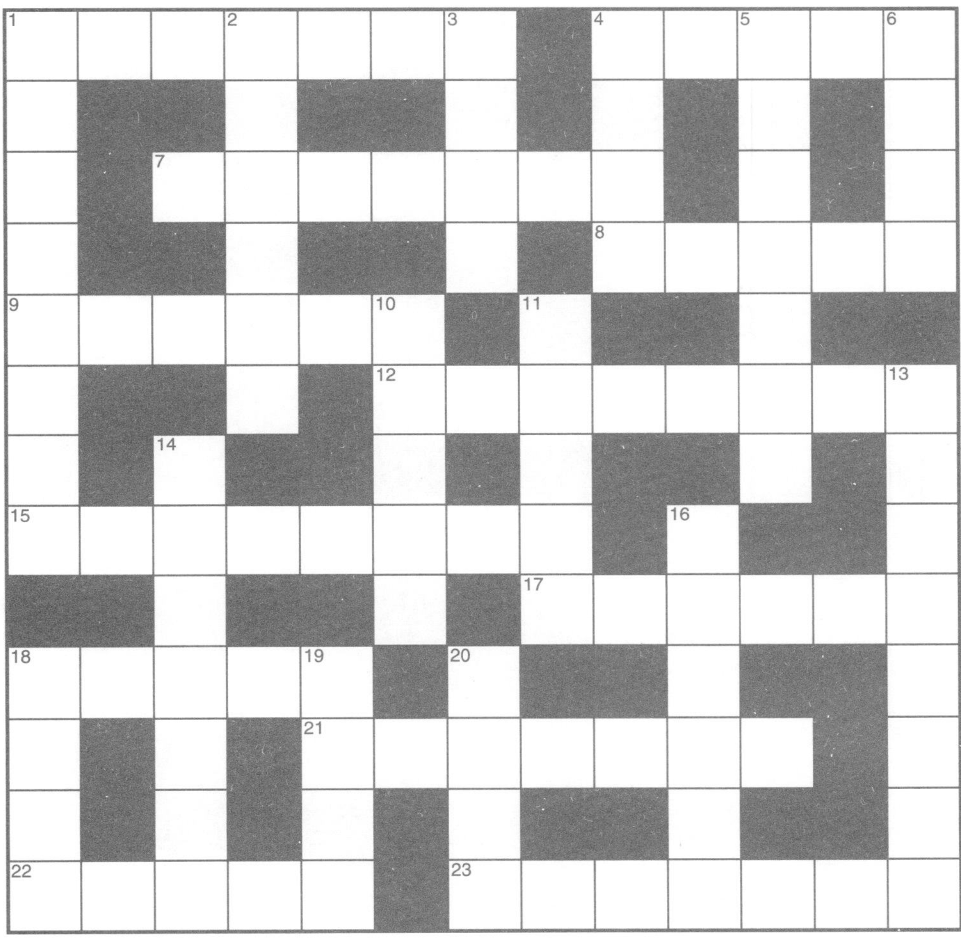

## ACROSS

1. Steals plane
4. Hang limply
7. Grape variety
8. Governed
9. Form of dermatitis
12. Travel document
15. Identify disease
17. Riches
18. Older person
21. Citrus fruits
22. Military blockade
23. Announces

## DOWN

1. Toughened
2. Entertains
3. Tarry
4. Beloved
5. Future prospect
6. Walk with heavy steps
10. Chef's garment
11. Crooked
13. Fastens (bolt)
14. Young pilchard
16. Photographer's tool
18. Terminates
19. Fragrant flower
20. Payment for goods

# CROSSWORD 151

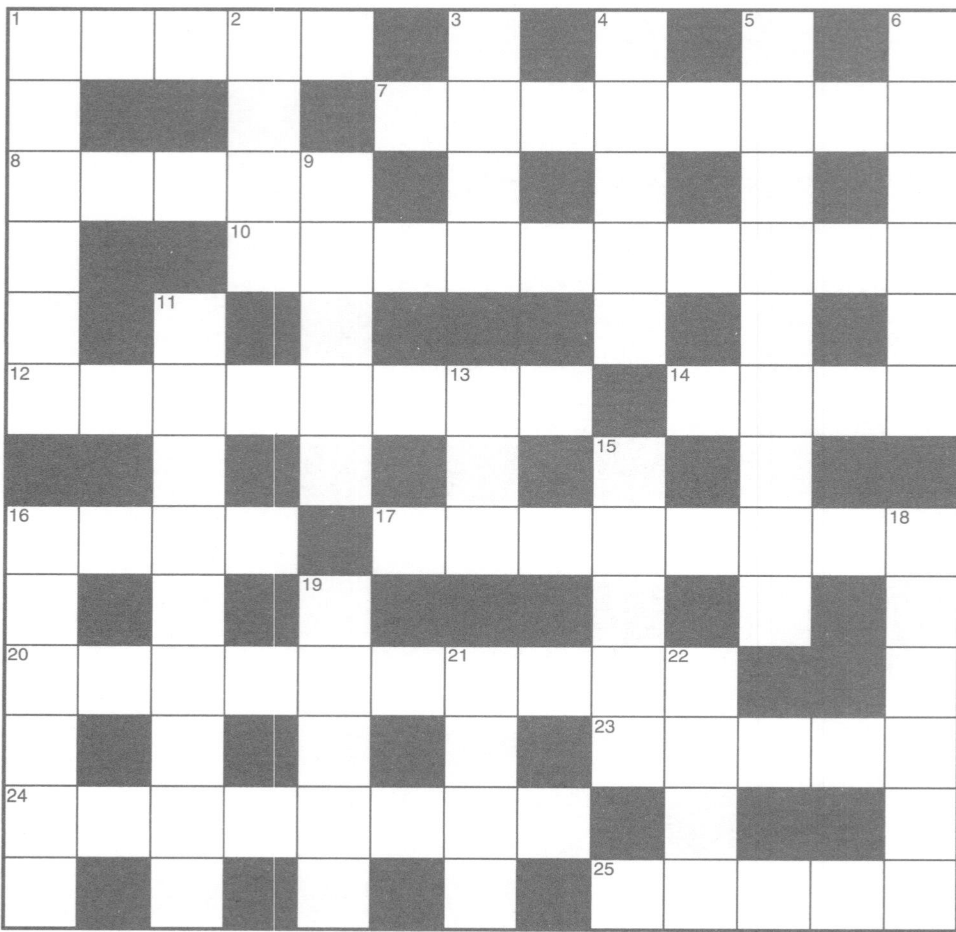

## ACROSS

1. Dental caries, tooth ...
7. Cleaning (ship's deck)
8. Pushed for
10. Obedience
12. Speaking lazily
14. Long narrative
16. Seedy fruit
17. Deeply shocked
20. Mix together
23. Inuit snow shelter
24. Pre-dinner drink
25. Magazine edition

## DOWN

1. Painted roughly
2. Cancels (TV show)
3. Move through water
4. Chasm
5. Likewise
6. Meeting schedule
9. Loses shine
11. Linguist's studies
13. Short sleep
15. Spiny succulents
16. Noisy brawl
18. Signify
19. A second time
21. Domestic helper
22. Henhouse produce

# CROSSWORD 152

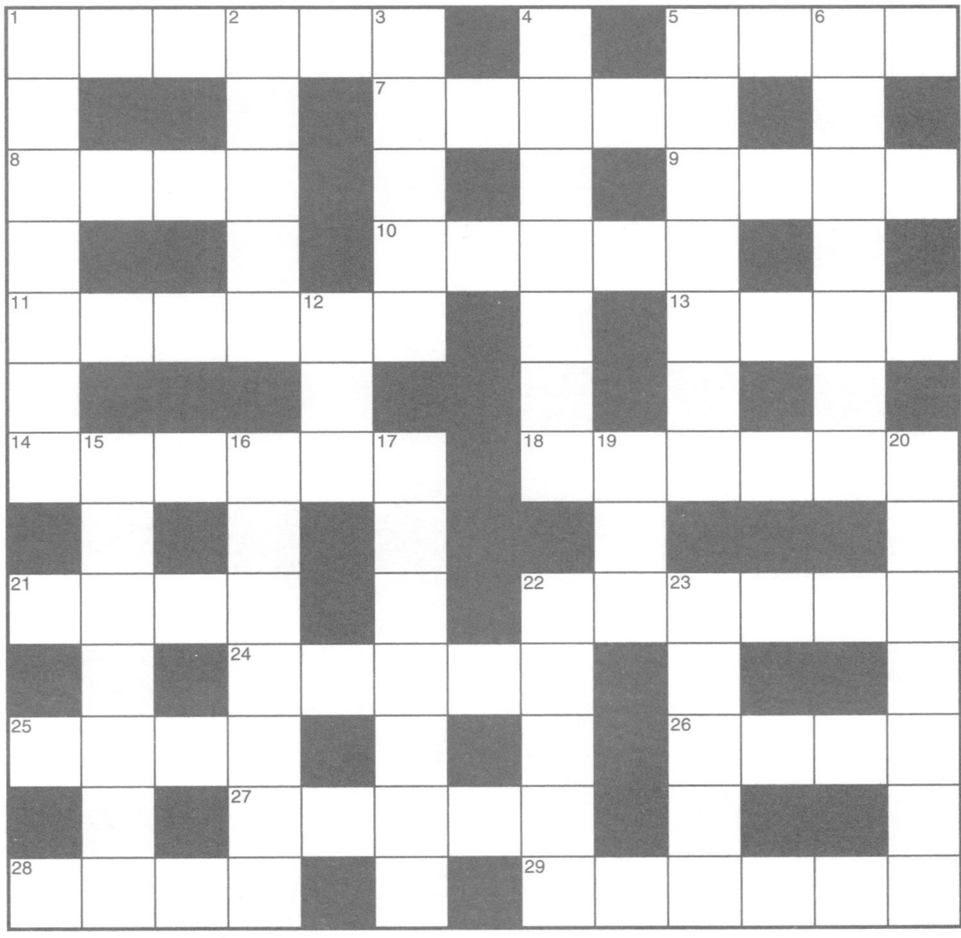

## ACROSS

1. Detect
5. Frail
7. Foolishly idealistic
8. Social group
9. Optic organs
10. Rattle (like chain)
11. Excused
13. Clock face
14. Ferocious
18. Fashioned
21. Departure
22. Stinging weed
24. Hospital worker
25. He was, they ...
26. Paper quantity
27. Triangle or circle
28. Colorants
29. Smelled strongly

## DOWN

1. Lewd men
2. Photo book
3. Pass (legislation)
4. Drumming insects
5. Tuesday or Friday
6. Par
12. Snub-nosed dog
15. Worry
16. Suitability
17. Endless
19. Knot
20. Indulged in reverie
22. Not ever
23. Concise

# CROSSWORD 153

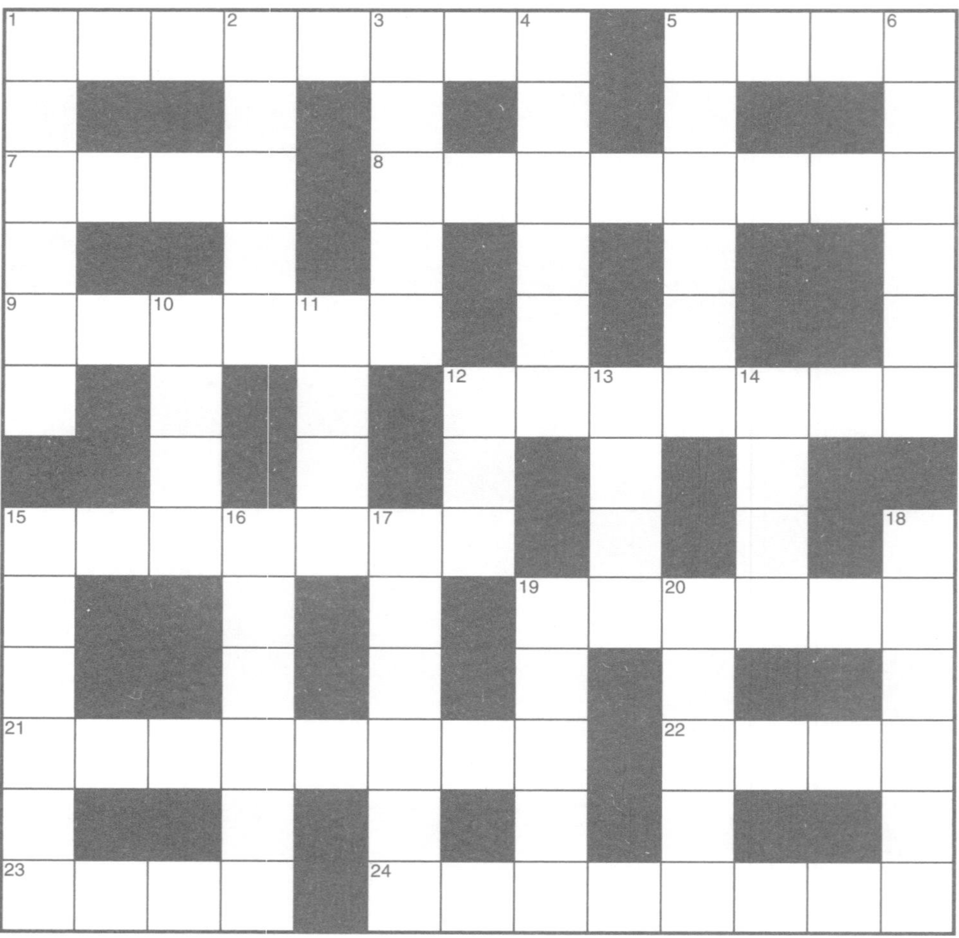

## ACROSS

1. Keep apart
5. Very eager
7. Waterless
8. By surprise
9. Escorts
12. Sewing spikes
15. Cried (of lamb)
19. (The) rest
21. Highest
22. Uterus
23. Sinewy and lean
24. Crop-beating machine

## DOWN

1. Social standing
2. Muddle
3. Touches at one end
4. Go by (of time)
5. Astonished
6. Dance clubs
10. Long walk
11. Talk wildly
12. Doze, ... off
13. North, south, ..., west
14. Scalp parasites
15. Swell (of sails)
16. Lack of interest
17. Limit
18. Pressure line on map
19. Exterior
20. Birds of prey

# CROSSWORD 154

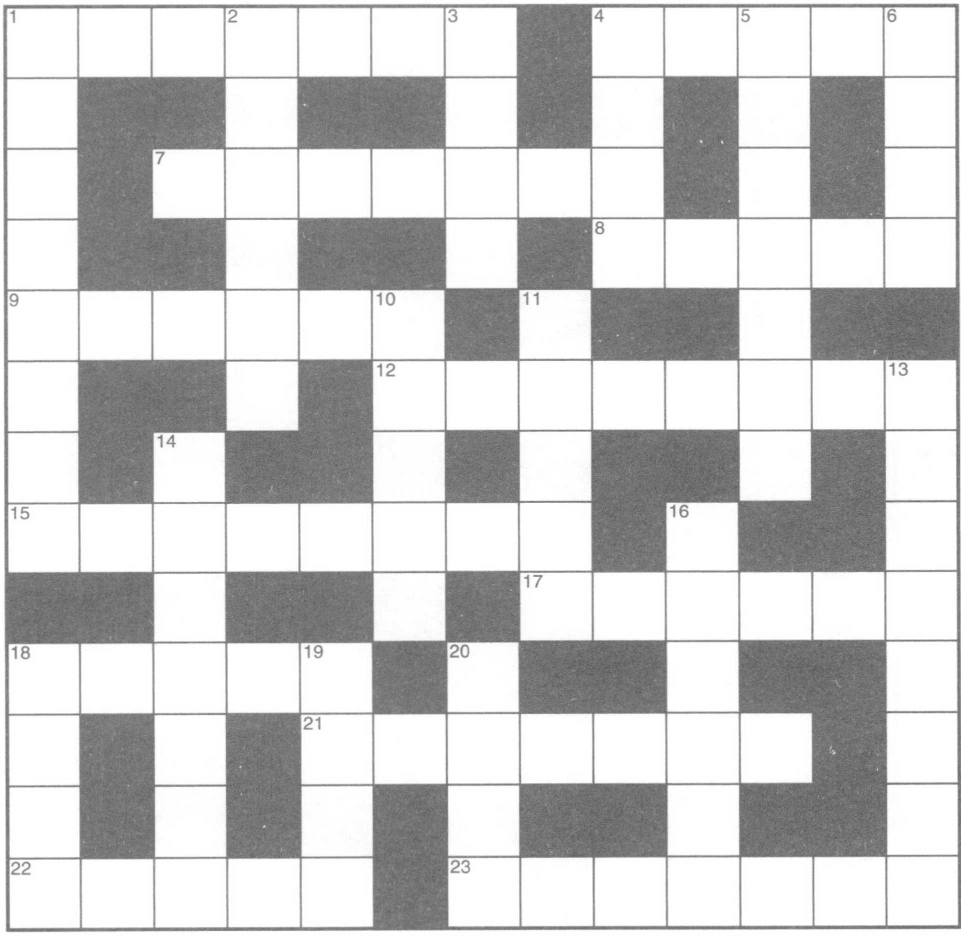

## ACROSS

1. Assistant at childbirth
4. Animate
7. Moved lightly (over)
8. 52-week intervals
9. Panoramic
12. Flying around (planet)
15. Gets in touch with
17. Plant seed part
18. Outspoken
21. Independently
22. Wield (influence)
23. Chatters idly

## DOWN

1. Magnificent
2. Stirring from sleep
3. Spreading trees
4. Musical, My Fair ...
5. Thiamine or riboflavin
6. Religious sisters
10. Large seashell
11. Overweight
13. Rubber overshoes
14. Finger joint
16. Miserable (poverty)
18. Cast ballot
19. Strong desire
20. Sport, ... tennis

# CROSSWORD 155

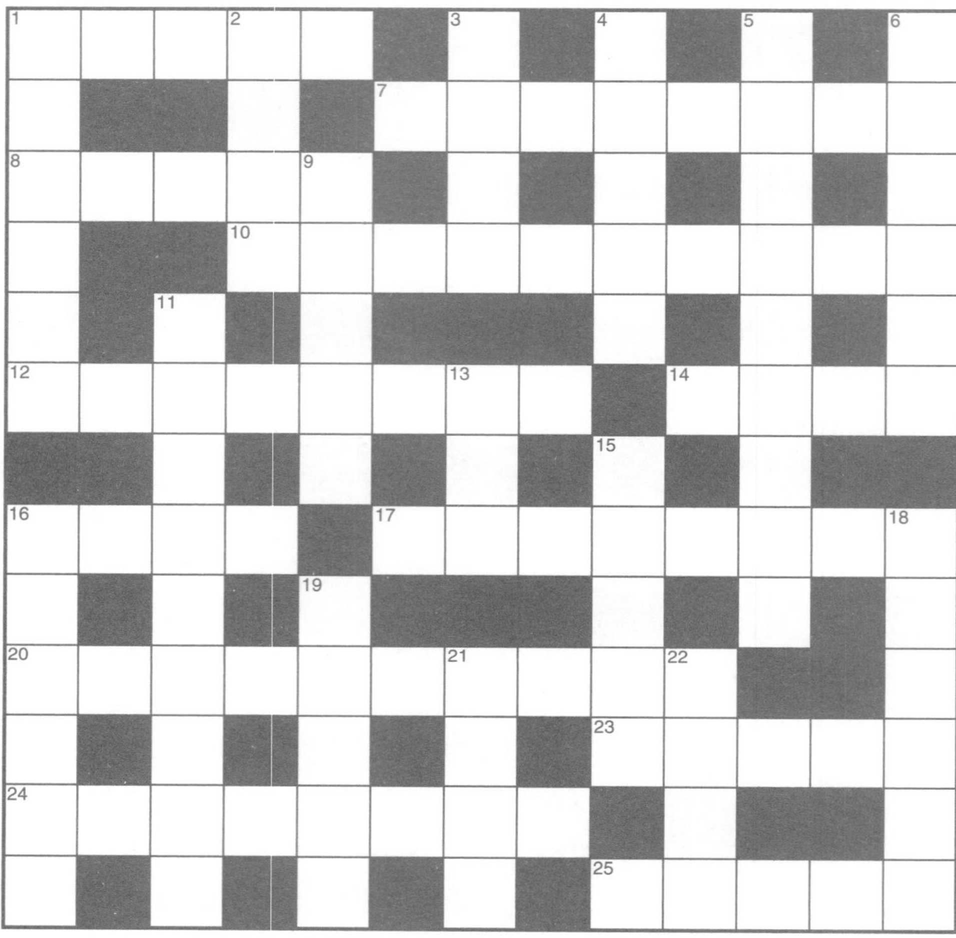

## ACROSS

1. Traditional
7. More sordid
8. Flinch
10. Persistent annoyance
12. Gaining knowledge
14. Celestial body
16. Naming word
17. Got
20. Assured
23. Painter's tripod
24. Style
25. Less risky

## DOWN

1. Sick
2. Curved foot part
3. Hopping insect
4. Stringent
5. Redirecting
6. Author
9. Deserves
11. Drenched
13. Capture (criminal)
15. Wage recipient
16. Gold lump
18. Card server
19. Lacking originality
21. Stitched fold
22. Scientific information

# CROSSWORD 156

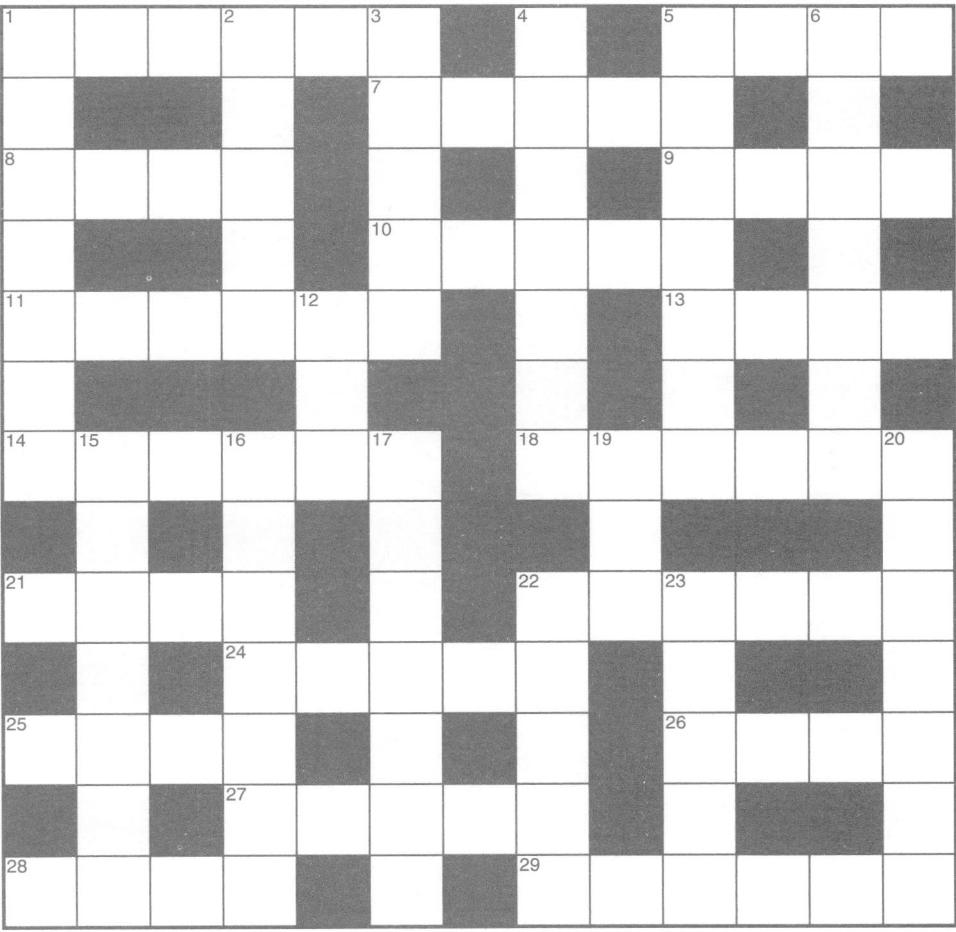

## ACROSS

1. Attractiveness
5. Door handle
7. Wipe out
8. Want
9. Plant stem lump
10. Heavily loaded
11. Urges into motion
13. Is mistaken
14. Desexed
18. Compositions
21. Forehead
22. Filled (suitcase)
24. Horse's cry
25. Flightless New Zealand bird
26. Title
27. Fixes with hammer
28. Warm & protected
29. Surfeit

## DOWN

1. Outlaws
2. Unwarranted
3. Screams
4. Wound wrapping
5. Dogs' homes
6. Neat
12. Recline
15. Segment
16. Sighing sleepily
17. Shortfall
19. Bubbling bath
20. Depresses
22. Stage
23. Doubter

# CROSSWORD 157

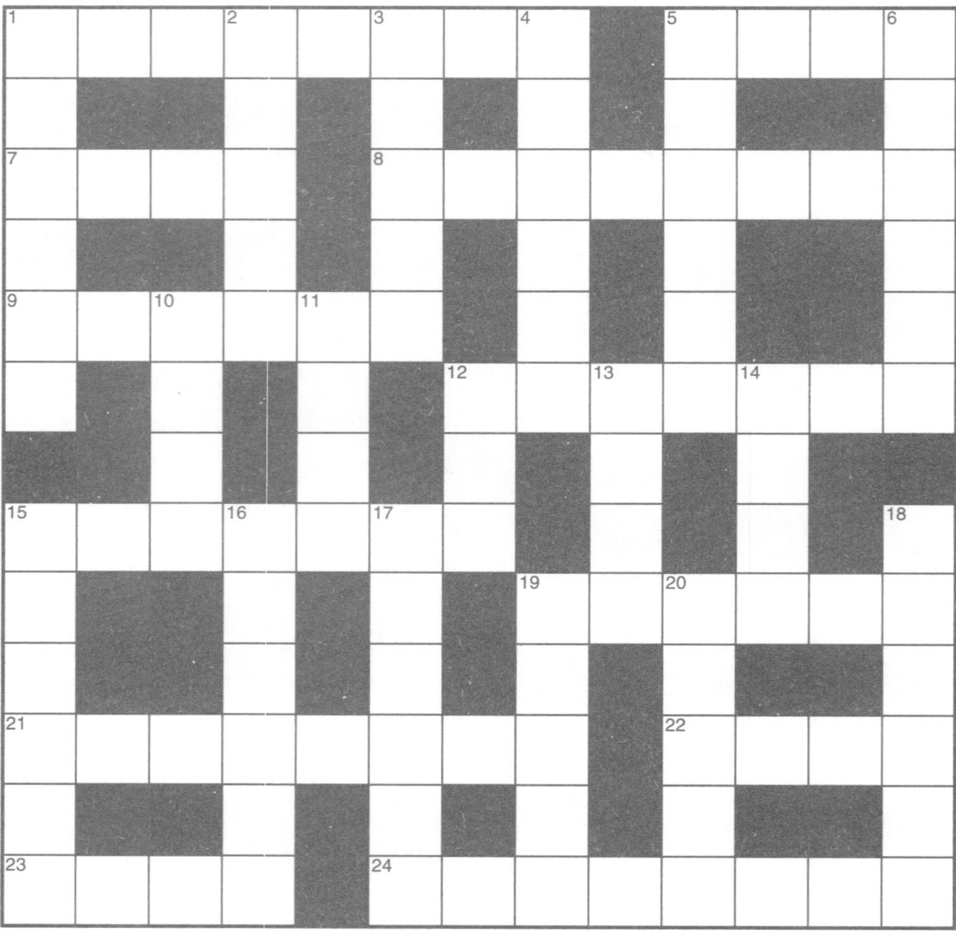


## ACROSS

1. Supplied capital
5. Chamber
7. Swamp
8. More reliable
9. Rented
12. Japanese hostesses
15. Happy
19. Made airtight
21. Boxer's winning punch
22. Insincere (of speech)
23. Polishes
24. Consecrate

## DOWN

1. Close relatives
2. Sectors
3. Mentioned as example
4. Tennis score, ... fault
5. Helicopter blades
6. Standards of behaviour
10. Wheel spindle
11. Consumes
12. Deity
13. Indolent
14. Ship's frame
15. Purse up (mouth)
16. Early counting instrument
17. Put into cipher
18. Fit for consumption
19. Situates
20. Fury

# CROSSWORD 158

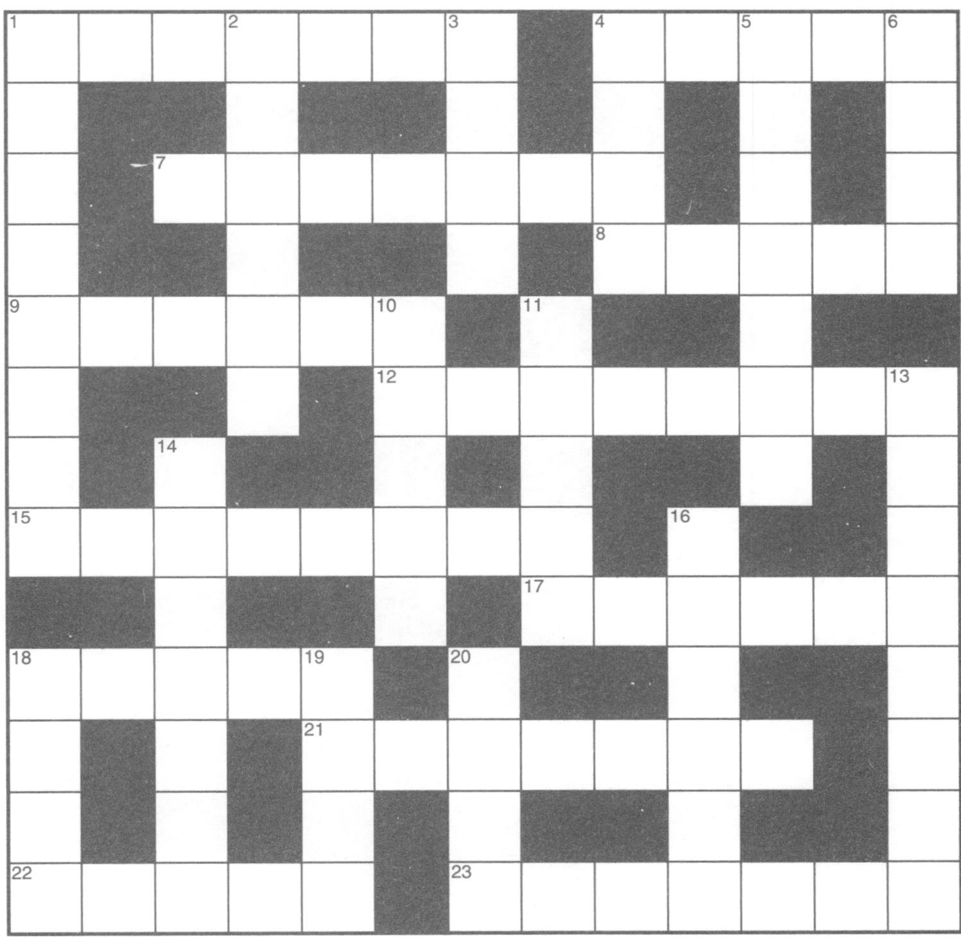

## ACROSS

1. Diabolic
4. Dinners or lunches
7. Hair soap
8. Contact
9. Escape vent
12. Resurface
15. Sword holder
17. Sloops or ketches
18. Compass point
21. Angrily
22. Fathered
23. Conveying

## DOWN

1. Props up
2. For some time
3. Manage
4. Anchor (boat)
5. Shopping walkways
6. Beauty queen's ribbon
10. Court hearing
11. Late arriving
13. Perching
14. Obstacle
16. Reduced, ... down
18. Persistently scolds
19. Rear (legs)
20. Methods

# CROSSWORD 159

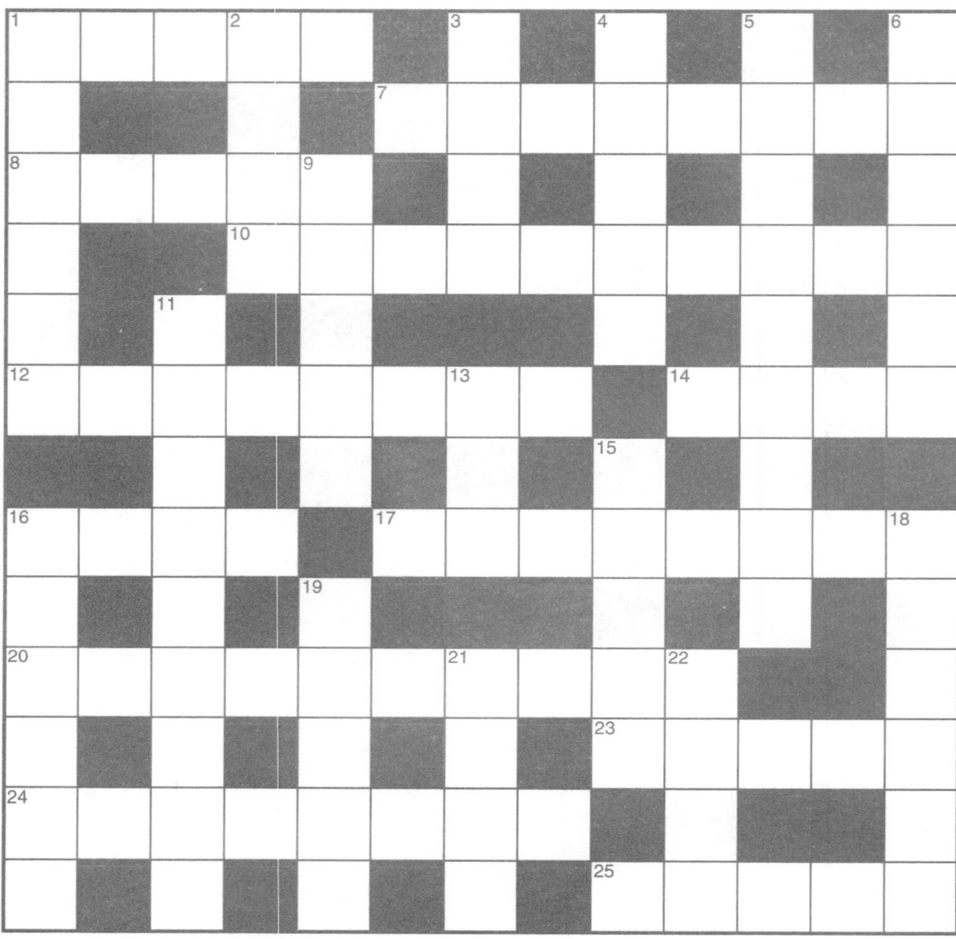

## ACROSS

1. Unaffected by alcohol
7. Crystal wine server
8. Foul-smelling
10. Woven wall-hangings
12. Aristocrat
14. Gyrate
16. Seep
17. Domestic employees
20. Maliciously
23. Brazilian dance
24. Last teenage year
25. Pale-faced

## DOWN

1. Become less hard
2. Let out (shriek)
3. Insignificant
4. Sample
5. Getting undressed
6. Correctional institution
9. Calendar entries
11. Flesh wounds
13. Affirmative vote
15. Wicked wrongs
16. Shedding (weight)
18. Wrench (ankle)
19. Warms
21. Operator
22. Shrill barks

# CROSSWORD 160

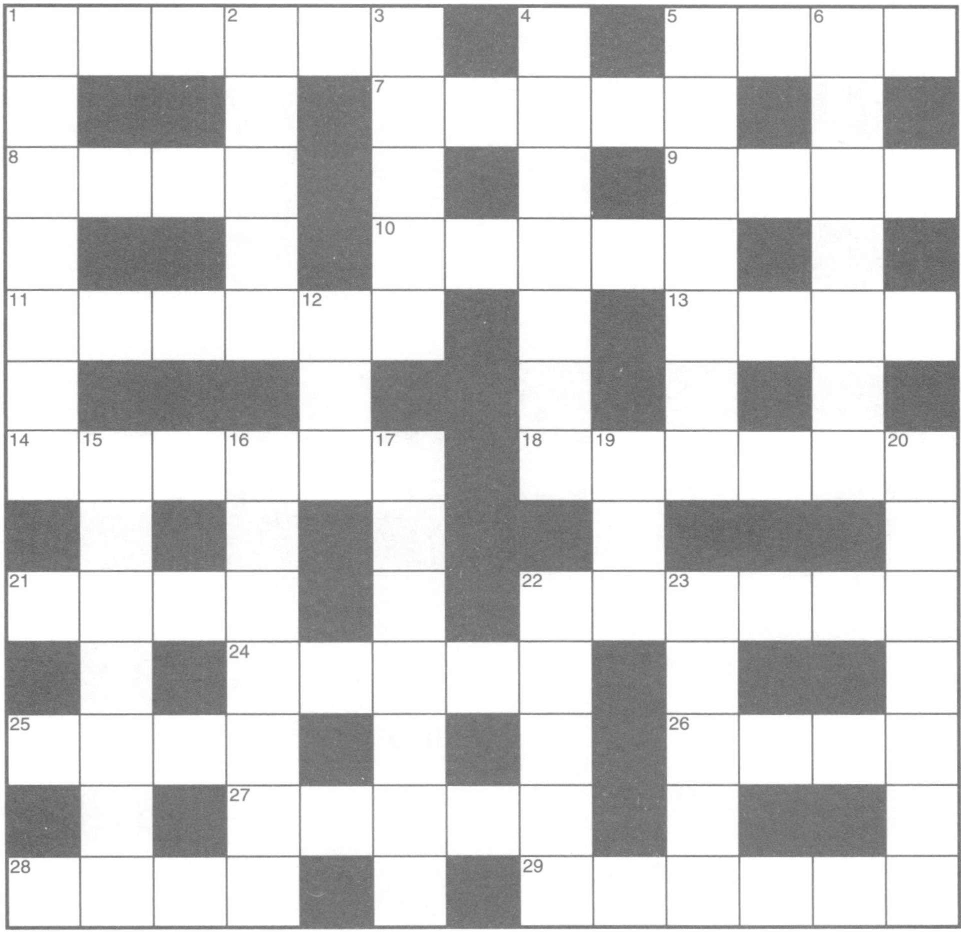

## ACROSS

1. Leave without a trace
5. Calf flesh
7. Improper (influence)
8. Tailor's ... measure
9. Horse's gait
10. Skirt fold
11. Washes soap from
13. Pigmented eye membrane
14. Sick feeling
18. Absorb (food)
21. Air pollution
22. Oyster treasures
24. Ultra-virile
25. Honest
26. Grow weary
27. Sister's girl
28. Legal order
29. Hurries

## DOWN

1. Former soldier
2. Single entities
3. Camel's mounds
4. Stuck (to)
5. Critically examining
6. Great pains
12. Lamb's mother
15. Devotee
16. Part
17. In-flight attendants
19. Glacial material
20. Fringed cords
22. Difficult question
23. Types of saxophones

# CROSSWORD 161

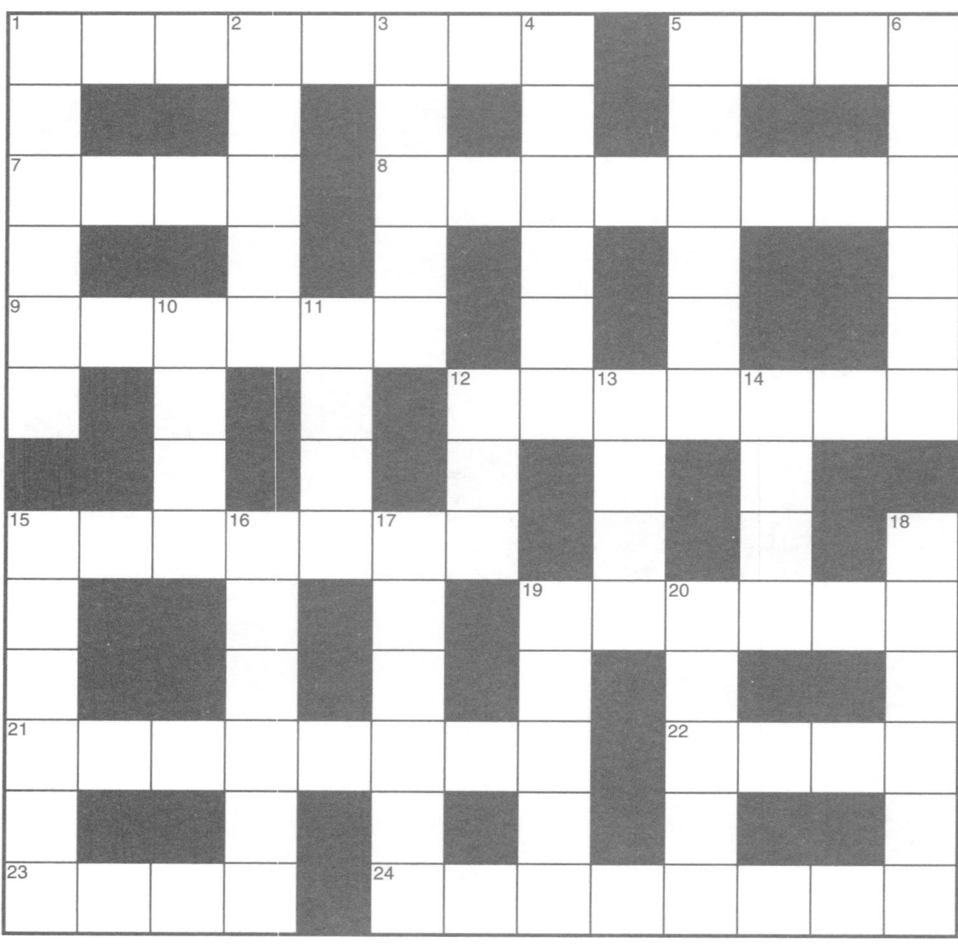

## ACROSS

1. Muddling
5. Troubles
7. Throw (dice)
8. Idle
9. Apart from
12. Weirdness
15. Most eager
19. Population count
21. Massaging
22. Was in arrears to
23. Completed
24. Accentuates

## DOWN

1. Dairy cattle breed
2. Prettiest girl, ... of the ball
3. Simpleton
4. Classified
5. At rear of vessel
6. Navigates
10. Travel bag
11. Drainage tube
12. Not at home
13. Springboard descent
14. Morays
15. Twisted
16. Annul
17. Fissures
18. Incidental comments
19. Tobacco product
20. Alcoves

# CROSSWORD 162

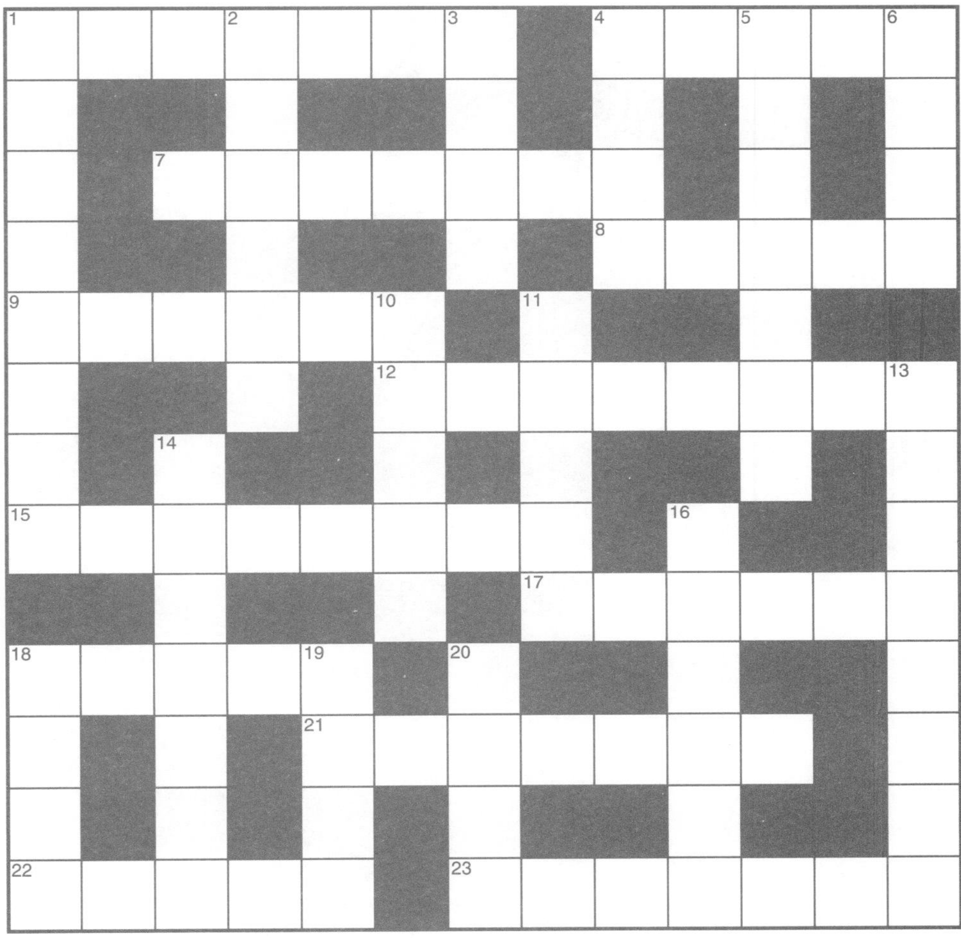

## ACROSS

1. Exposes
4. Allude
7. No longer operative
8. Fill with joy
9. Insist
12. Year-old animal
15. Leadership
17. Cherishing
18. Australian marsupial
21. Moving closer to
22. Stares suggestively
23. Paint-mix board

## DOWN

1. Constant
2. Rinks
3. Pop chart hit
4. Social custom
5. Extremist
6. Travel by bike
10. Expiring
11. Desert beast
13. Decay of body tissue
14. Habitable
16. Wide street
18. Ship's spine
19. Tiny insects
20. Inhale audibly

# CROSSWORD 163

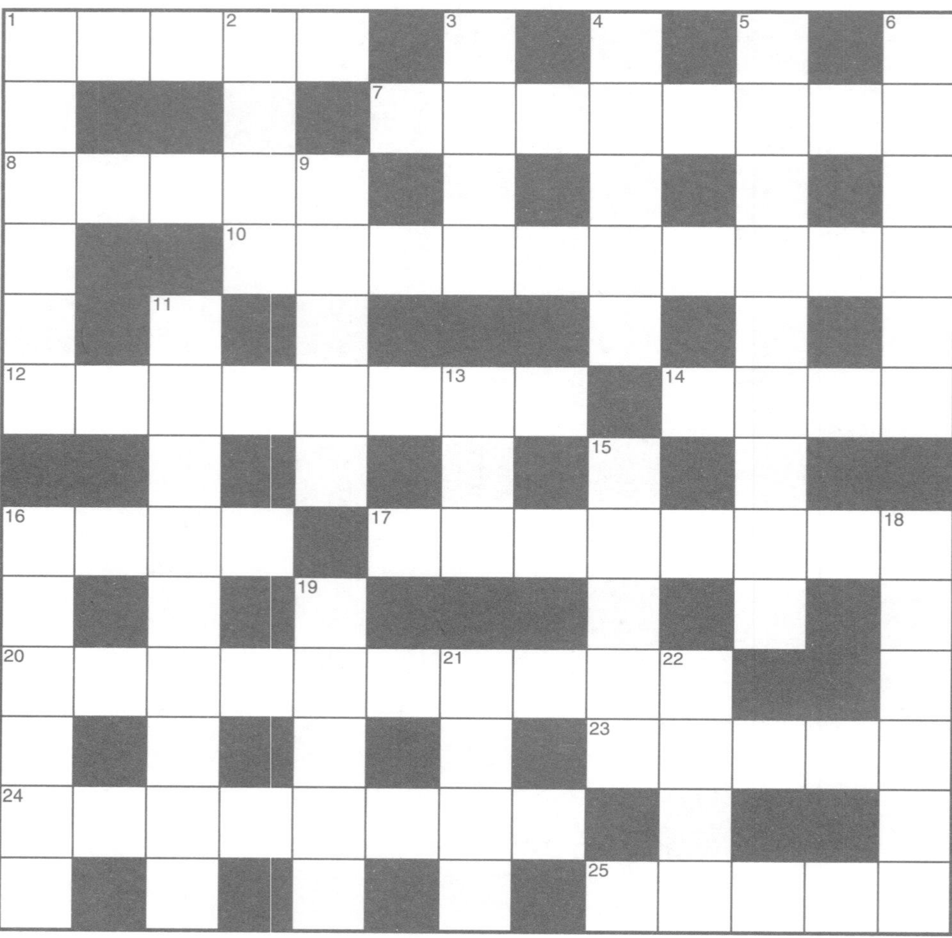

## ACROSS

1. Small mythical creature
7. Fracture
8. Female
10. Huge spiders
12. Insulin-deficient person
14. Feel sympathy for
16. Mouse relatives
17. Punch to chin
20. Liquor factory
23. Stupefied
24. Aggravating
25. Love

## DOWN

1. Stared stupidly
2. Castle ditch
3. Opera solo
4. Enticements
5. Rear part
6. Paltry
9. Nude
11. Dreams
13. Small demon
15. Facial hair
16. Gnawing mammal
18. Walk wearily
19. Low mountains
21. Chain loop
22. Enclosure

# CROSSWORD 164

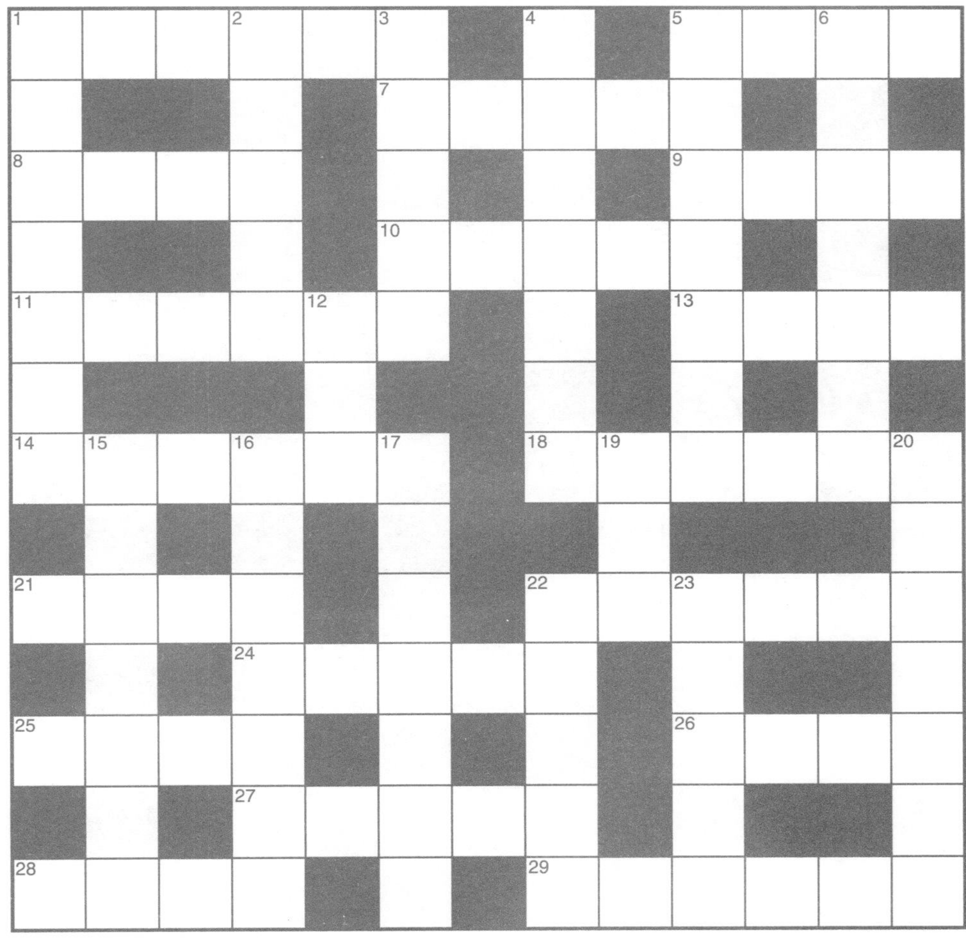

## ACROSS

1. Prodded sharply
5. Evil habit
7. Ocean giant
8. Holy statue
9. Shadow-box
10. Company emblems
11. Result
13. Periods of time
14. Raw vegetable dishes
18. Tried
21. Vipers
22. Packed for transport
24. Yellow shade
25. Move for take-off
26. Pleasant
27. Comprehensible
28. Individuals
29. Speech of praise

## DOWN

1. Furniture makers
2. Drinking spree
3. Resided
4. Most extensive
5. Arteries, blood ...
6. False pretence
12. Ruminant's food
15. Refrain (from)
16. Besieges
17. Reversal in progress
19. Head of corn
20. Frail with age
22. Rough
23. Declare void

# CROSSWORD 165

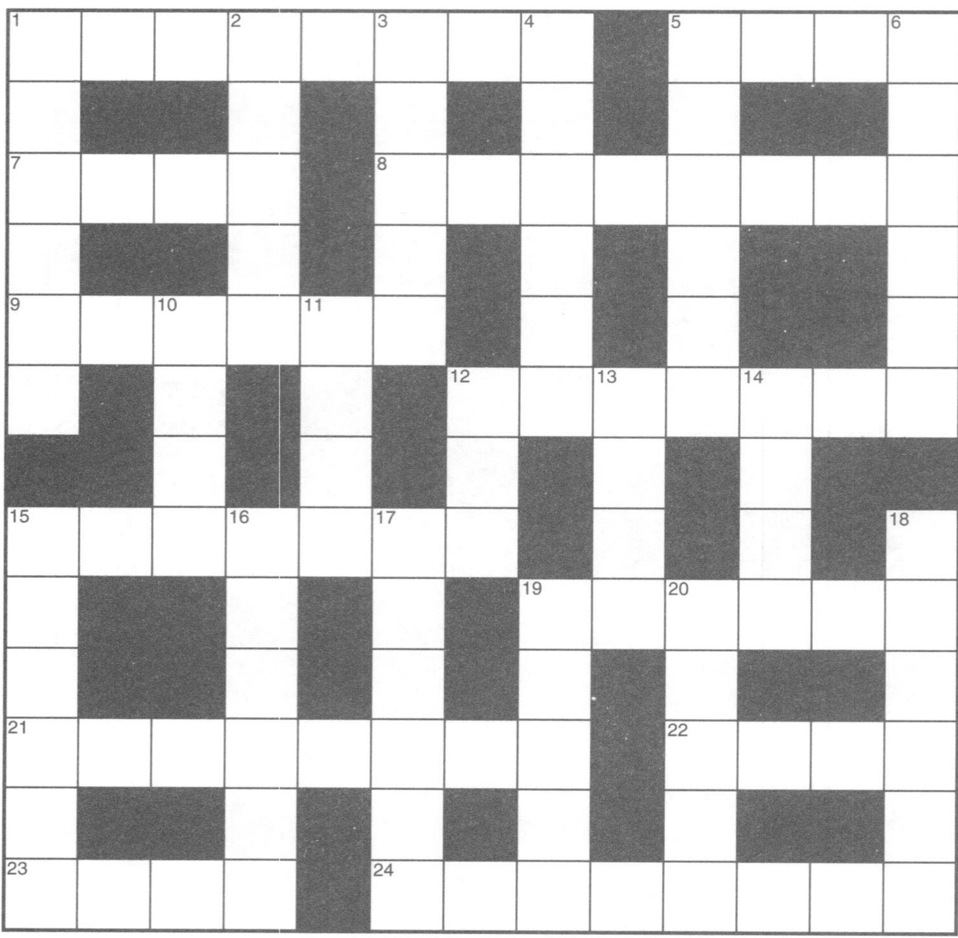

## ACROSS

1. Lozenge
5. Single combat
7. Chinese dog breed
8. Tolerable
9. Stamina
12. Hugh Hefner publication
15. Red pepper spice
19. Resistant to infection
21. Thin slices (of wood)
22. Radiance
23. Tilt
24. Allowed

## DOWN

1. Trouser pouch
2. Paris landmark, The Eiffel ...
3. Hotel foyer
4. Vitreous coating
5. Drearily
6. Margin of safety
10. Jealousy
11. Acquire
12. Pastry meal
13. Molecule particle
14. Actor, ... Bridges
15. Sculptor's tool
16. Roman XI
17. Nicety
18. Money for good deed
19. Map within map
20. Aimed

# CROSSWORD 166

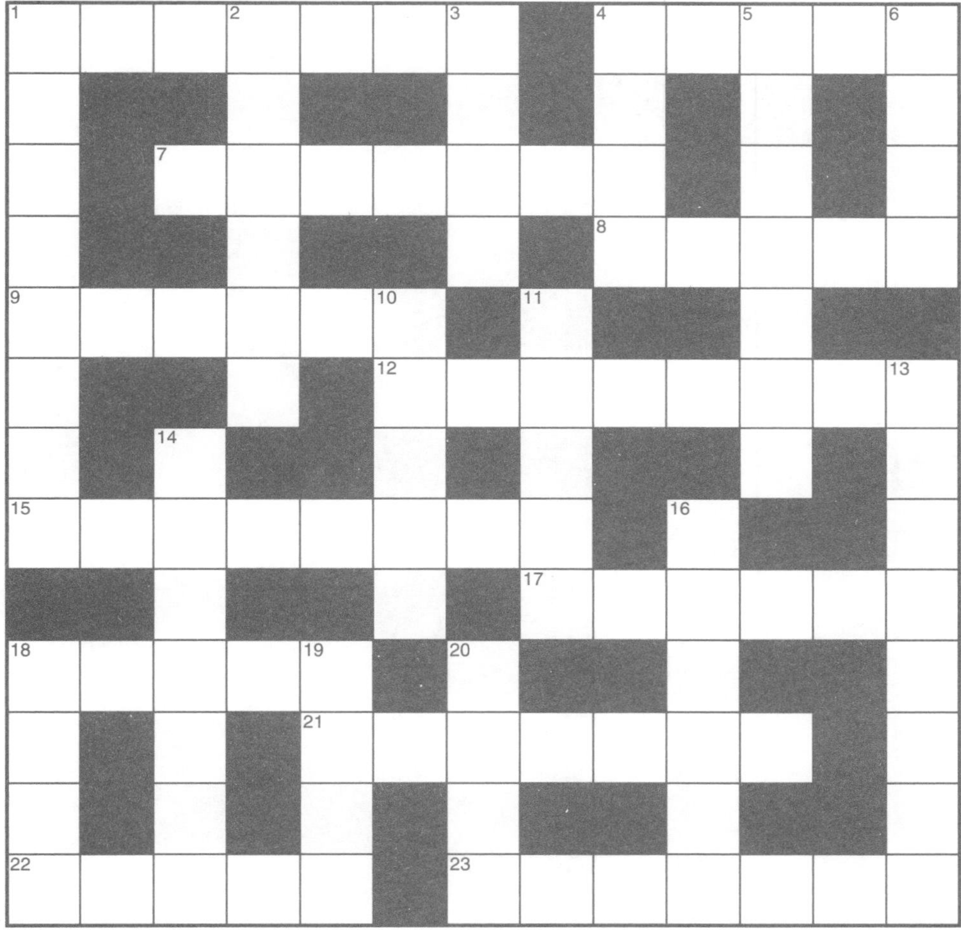

## ACROSS

1. Chilliest
4. Alpaca relative
7. Worship
8. Scoundrel
9. Looked upon
12. Not scared
15. Rescued disaster victims
17. Flowing away
18. Dog lead
21. Unfastens (door)
22. Dirt
23. Fidget, ... one's thumbs

## DOWN

1. Sexually chaste
2. Becomes embedded
3. Durable timber
4. Emblem of Wales
5. Yearbook
6. Area measurement
10. Cons
11. Reason
13. Vomit
14. Sunshade
16. Lessened
18. Bread quantity
19. Peace & quiet
20. Illegally help

# CROSSWORD 167

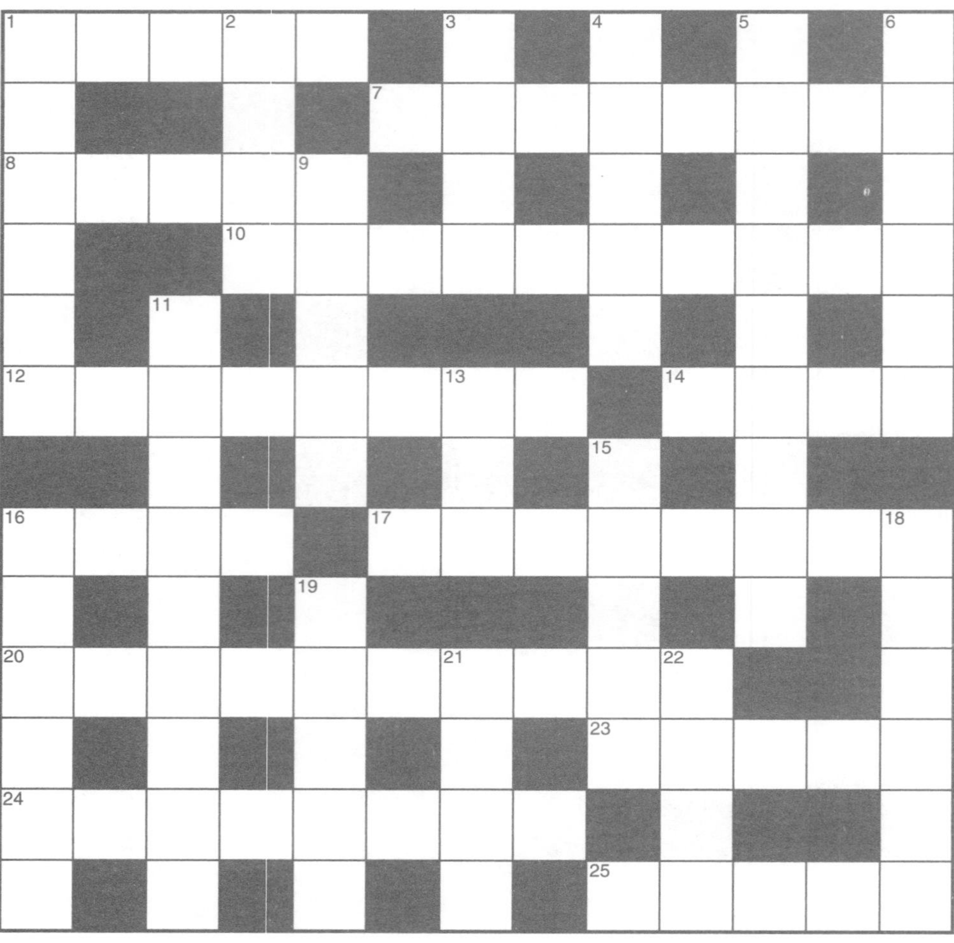

## ACROSS

1. Shout for joy
7. Precious rock
8. Room base
10. Specially tagging
12. Complete disorder
14. Magician's rod
16. As well
17. Epidemic
20. Appraisal
23. Dining bench
24. Coup
25. Church songs

## DOWN

1. Thin biscuits
2. Double-reed instrument
3. Presidential duration
4. Wrongfully seize (power)
5. Stimulates interest
6. Beseeched
9. Jewish pastor
11. Dried grass piles
13. Australian bird
15. Head monk
16. Warns
18. Rests on knees
19. Personal glory
21. Swarm
22. Armed fleet

# CROSSWORD 168

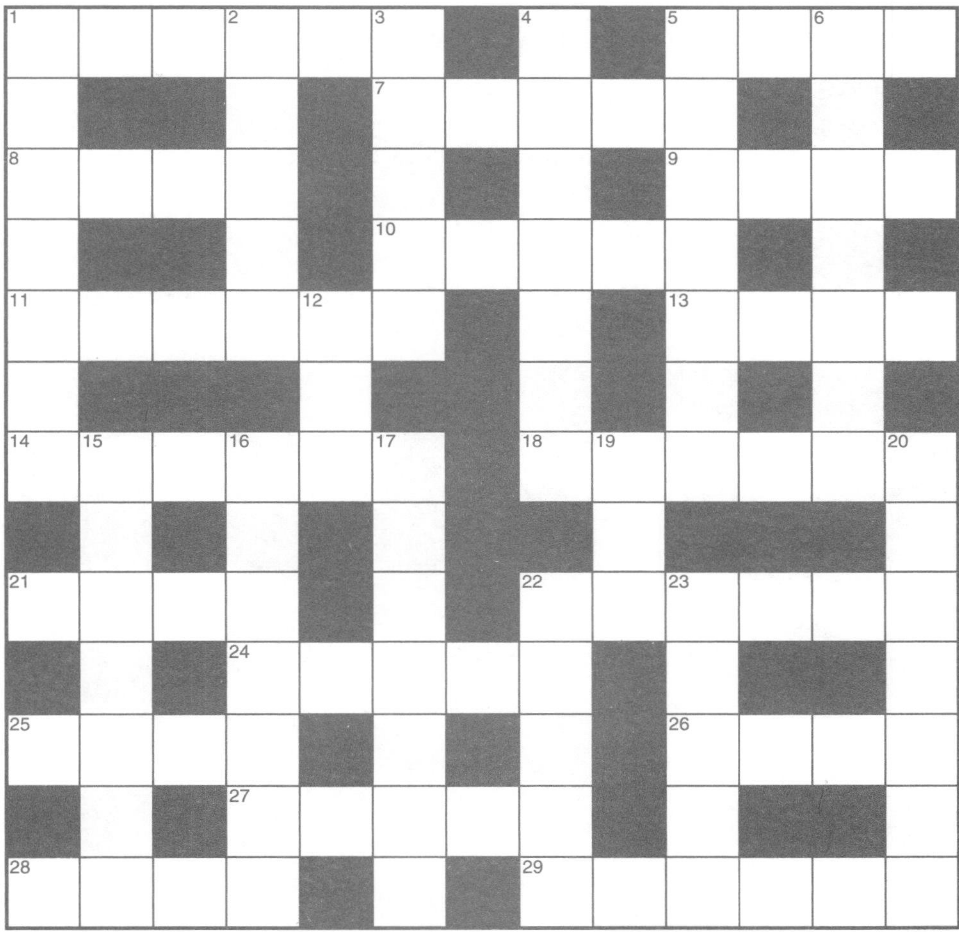

## ACROSS

1. Duck calls
5. Glass pots
7. Surpass
8. College test
9. Shipment
10. Cook in oven
11. Opponents
13. Wading bird
14. Succumbs
18. Numbers
21. Open valley
22. Not in a position (to)
24. Hold firmly
25. Net fabric
26. Upon
27. Summon up
28. Tints
29. Butted

## DOWN

1. Oddly
2. Punctuation mark
3. Goes rancid
4. Wandered off course
5. Jogging (memory)
6. Practical person
12. Youngster
15. Visual symbolism
16. Blood-sucking worms
17. Sordid conditions
19. Tavern
20. Trod
22. Capital letters, ... case
23. Danger alert

# CROSSWORD 169

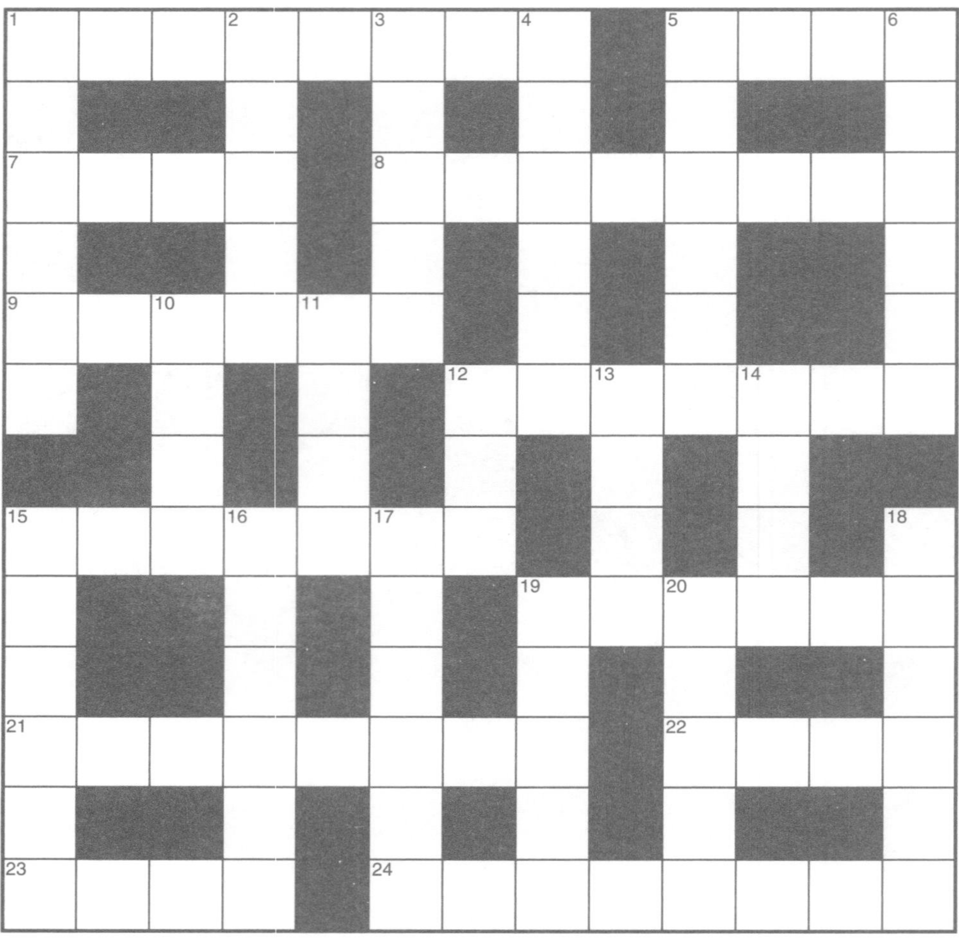

## ACROSS

1. Gravely
5. Potter's oven
7. River sediment
8. Accumulates
9. Sheathe
12. Whirled
15. Outlay too much
19. Rubbed until sore
21. Dangerously
22. Greek liquor
23. Moan sadly
24. Rifle blades

## DOWN

1. Sibling
2. Surplus
3. Recess
4. Cowardly
5. Zoo custodian
6. Made home in tree
10. Hint
11. Leak slowly
12. Plaything
13. Mosquito bite irritation
14. Frond
15. Transpires
16. Rework (old material)
17. Verb modifier
18. Horrid
19. Shyly
20. Oak kernel

# CROSSWORD 170

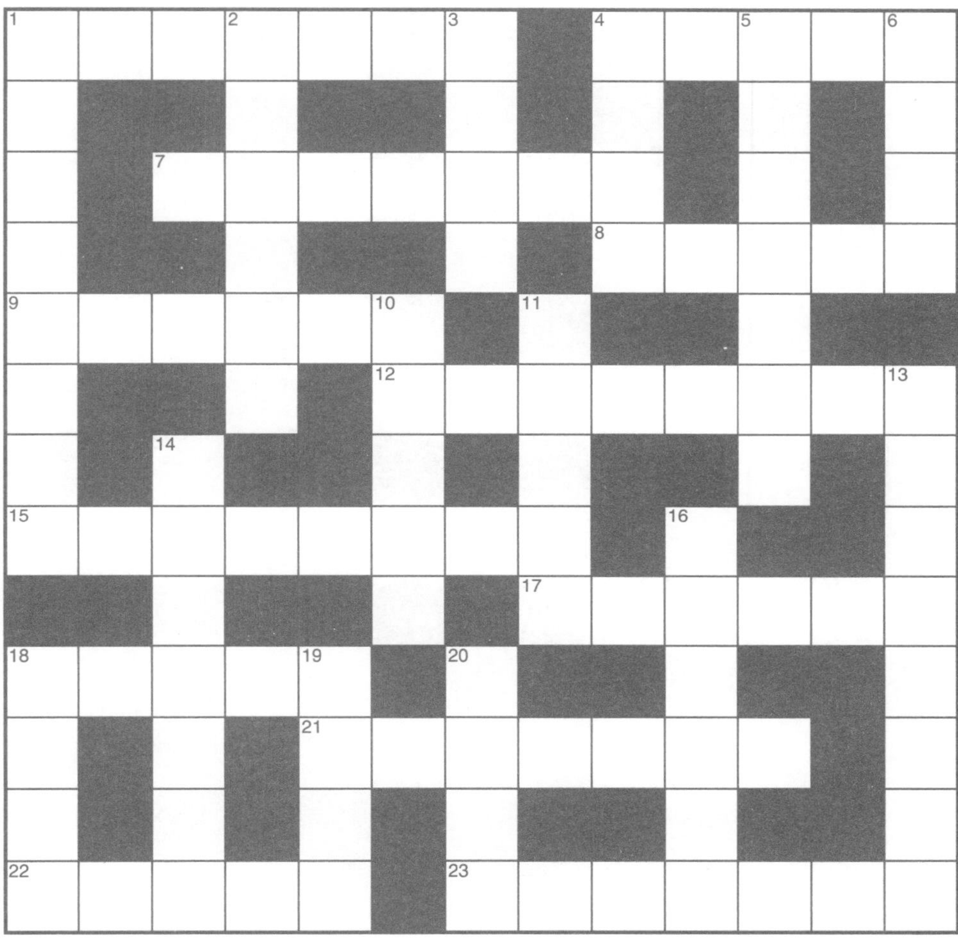

## ACROSS

1. Oiled
4. Exit
7. Official trade ban
8. Flat dish
9. Propose
12. Re-evaluate
15. Entitling
17. Radio interference
18. Address crowd
21. Diminish, ... from
22. Sordid
23. Athletic jumper

## DOWN

1. Naive
2. Military forces
3. Blowpipe missile
4. Rope circle
5. Pen names
6. Simplicity
10. Empty (glass)
11. Hooligan groups
13. Perfectionist
14. Card game
16. Pricked (boil)
18. Unprocessed minerals
19. Anxious
20. Cut (design) with acid

# CROSSWORD 171

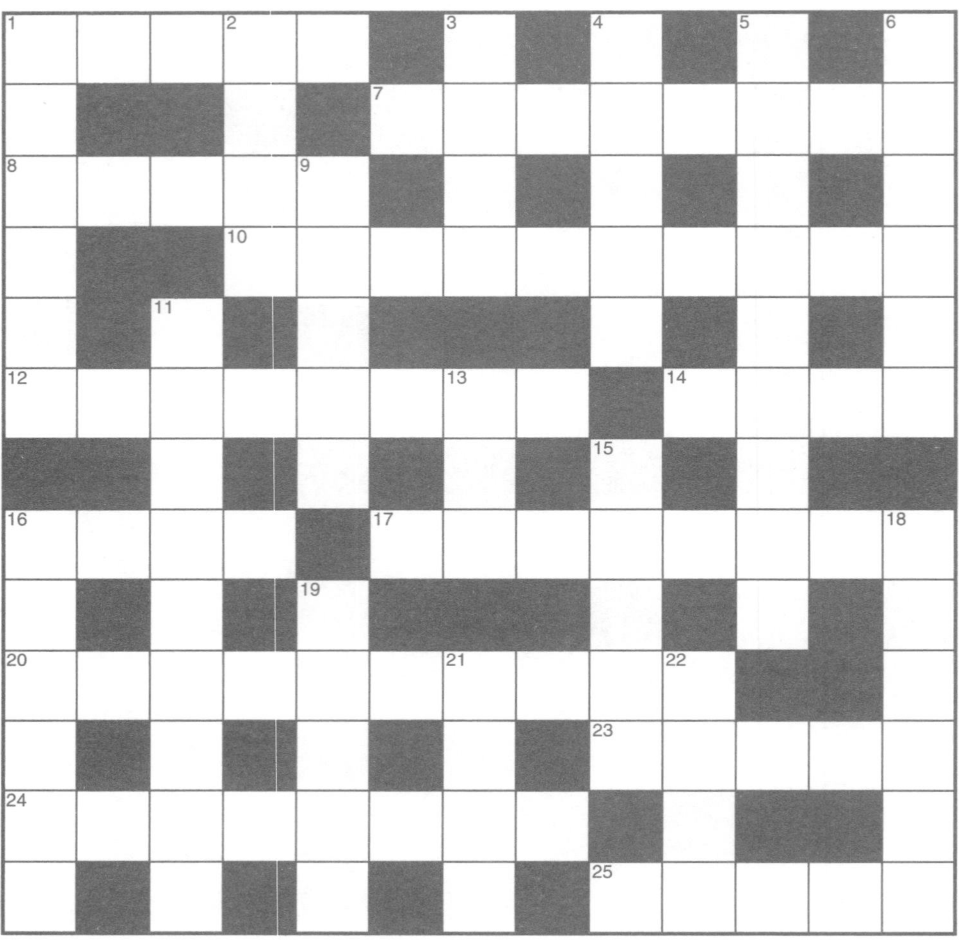

## ACROSS

1. Hostile frown
7. Climb hurriedly
8. Faithful
10. Soft-cover books
12. Occasion
14. Raised (cattle)
16. Whistle balls
17. Of metal
20. Machine-like
23. Undeveloped insect
24. Exaggerates
25. Endure

## DOWN

1. Italian sausage
2. Enclose
3. Pimples
4. Brindled feline
5. Hazily
6. Stiffened
9. Exalts
11. Superficial cuts
13. Named before marriage
15. Waterway
16. Cheerleader's accessory
18. Faint-hearted person
19. Inuit canoe
21. Towards interior of
22. Concluding

# CROSSWORD 172

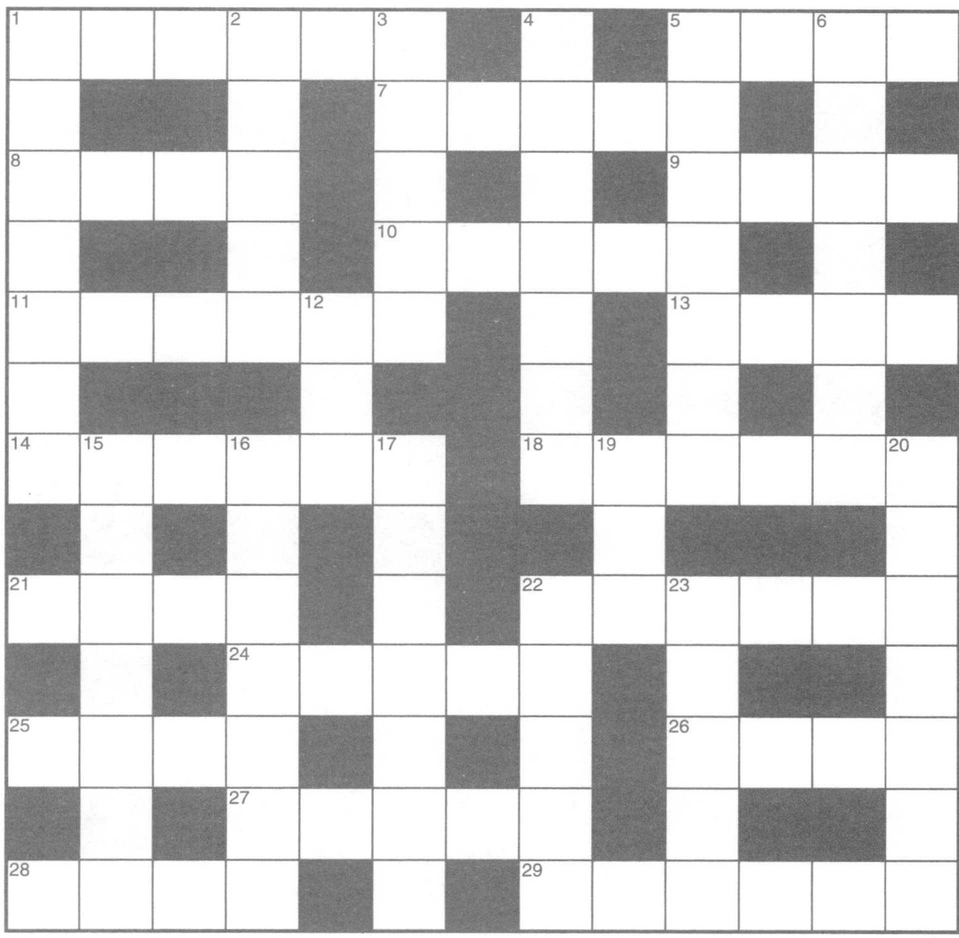


## ACROSS

1. Mainly
5. Calm (sea)
7. Terrible
8. Talk indiscreetly
9. Remove wrapping from
10. Din
11. Soldiers
13. Shaving cut
14. Lay waste
18. Sneakiest
21. Power group
22. Pulled sharply
24. Greeting word
25. Evil giant
26. Risotto ingredient
27. Mountain range top
28. Lyrical verses
29. Page format

## DOWN

1. Crime syndicate member
2. Socially unacceptable
3. Threads
4. Agencies
5. Smoothness of speech
6. Kidnaps
12. Boundary marker
15. Claimed
16. Arrow marksmen
17. Optic covers
19. Meadow
20. Neatest
22. Alpine song
23. Jittery

# CROSSWORD 173

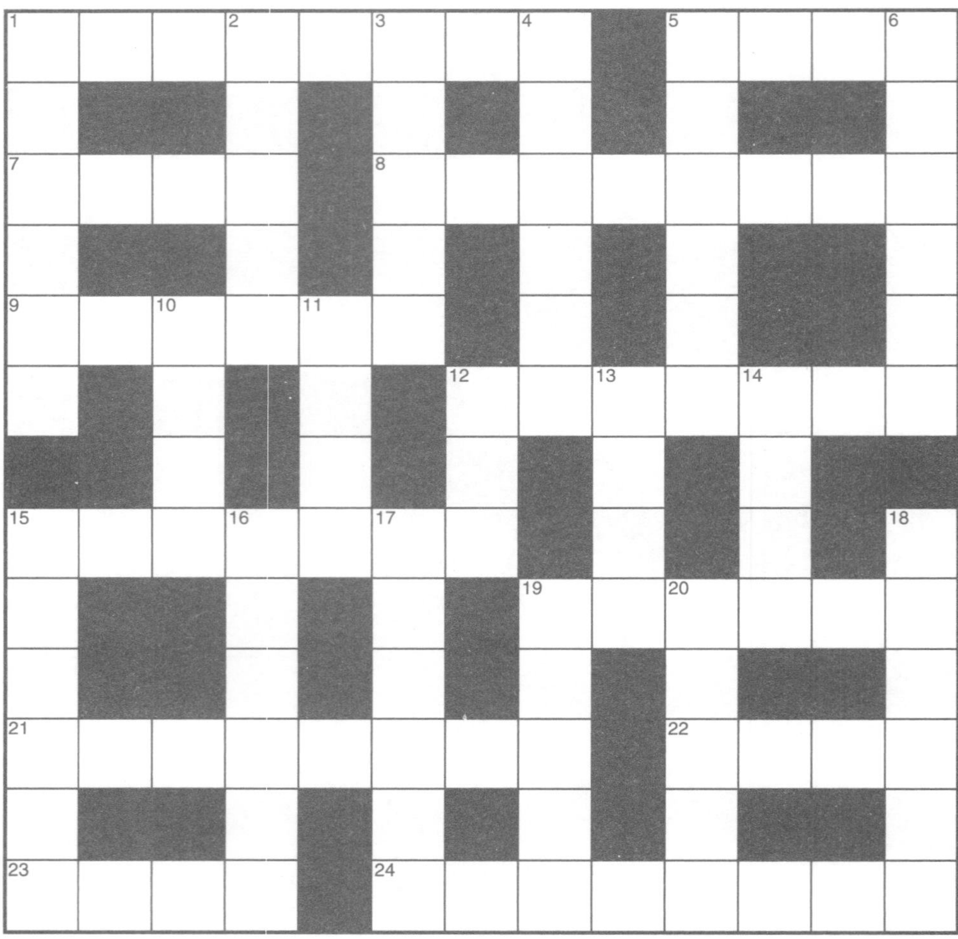

## ACROSS

1. Visionaries
5. Strong desire
7. Stylish
8. Piercing with knife
9. Asian food item
12. Numbs
15. Least cold (climate)
19. Fortified
21. Comes before
22. Parent's sister
23. Light sleeps
24. Greatly enjoyed

## DOWN

1. Wholesome
2. Formed a curve
3. Happen next
4. Posture
5. Become less formal
6. Predatory birds
10. On top of
11. Solo
12. Small spot
13. Not fully shut
14. Long movie
15. Fighting instrument
16. Finely chops (garlic)
17. Join (metal parts)
18. Prepared (manuscript)
19. Sweet herb
20. Collect

# CROSSWORD 174

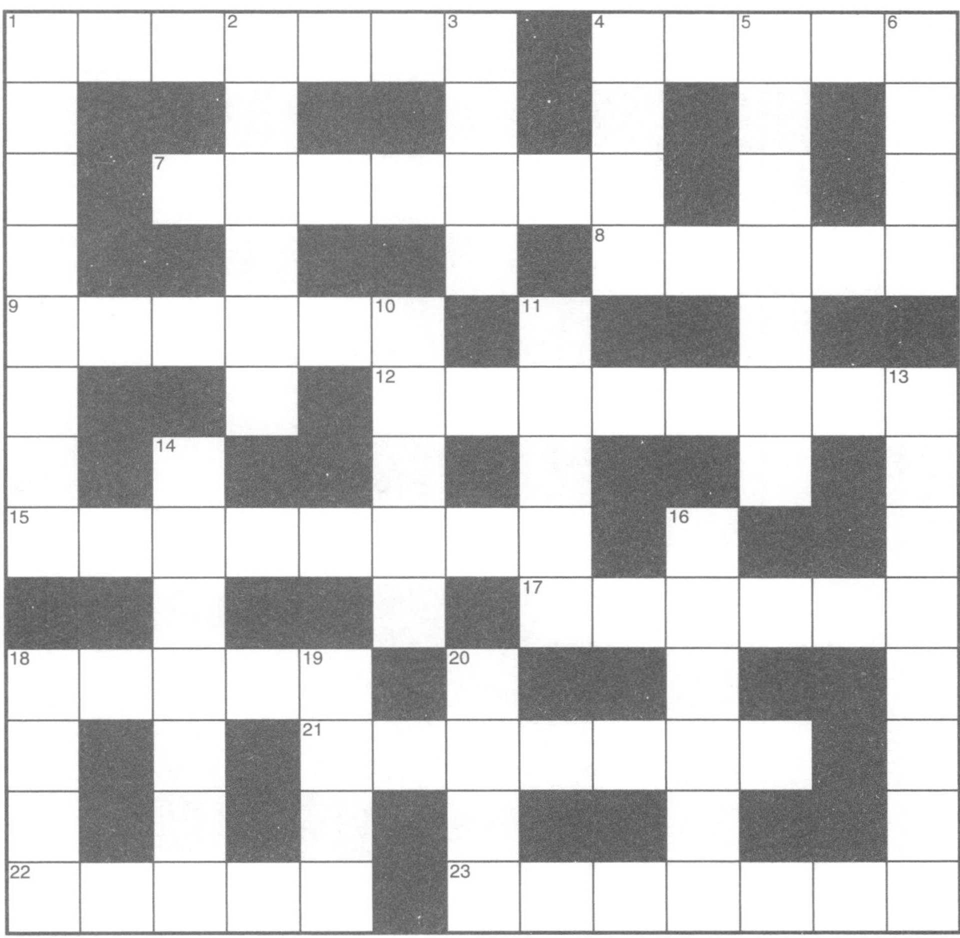

## ACROSS

1. Single eyeglass
4. Heavy goods vehicle
7. Took large swallows
8. Accurate
9. Amass
12. Lost strength
15. Happened repeatedly
17. Gazed fixedly
18. Simmer (eggs)
21. Stretchy tape
22. Walked back & forth
23. Return to health

## DOWN

1. Impartial negotiator
2. Forward
3. Verge
4. Sea phase, low ...
5. Strangely unexpected
6. Mend (of bones)
10. Washstand jugs
11. Delivers, ... over
13. More poisonous
14. Marine
16. Unbleached cotton
18. Inflate, ... up
19. Chief
20. Wig material

# CROSSWORD 175

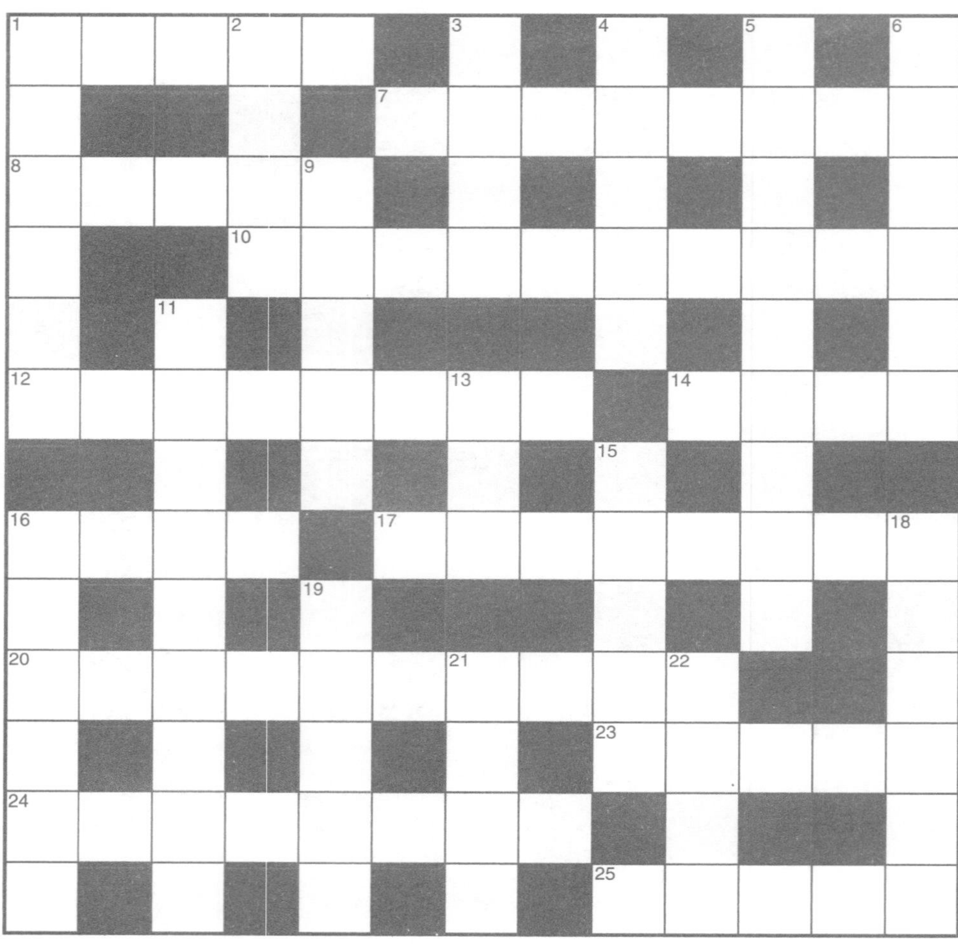

## ACROSS

1. Person, ... being
7. Circus performers
8. Garden tool
10. Superior quality
12. Slipshod
14. Communal bedroom
16. Professions
17. Unclogs
20. Sites
23. Diversity
24. Physical activity
25. Advantage

## DOWN

1. Snake sounds
2. Helper
3. Govern
4. Sprightly
5. Strengthen
6. High regard
9. Secrete
11. Cooked outdoors
13. Male child
15. Adjust
16. Abandoned (lover)
18. Noiseless
19. Strike with fingernail
21. Elephant ivory
22. Utters

# CROSSWORD 176

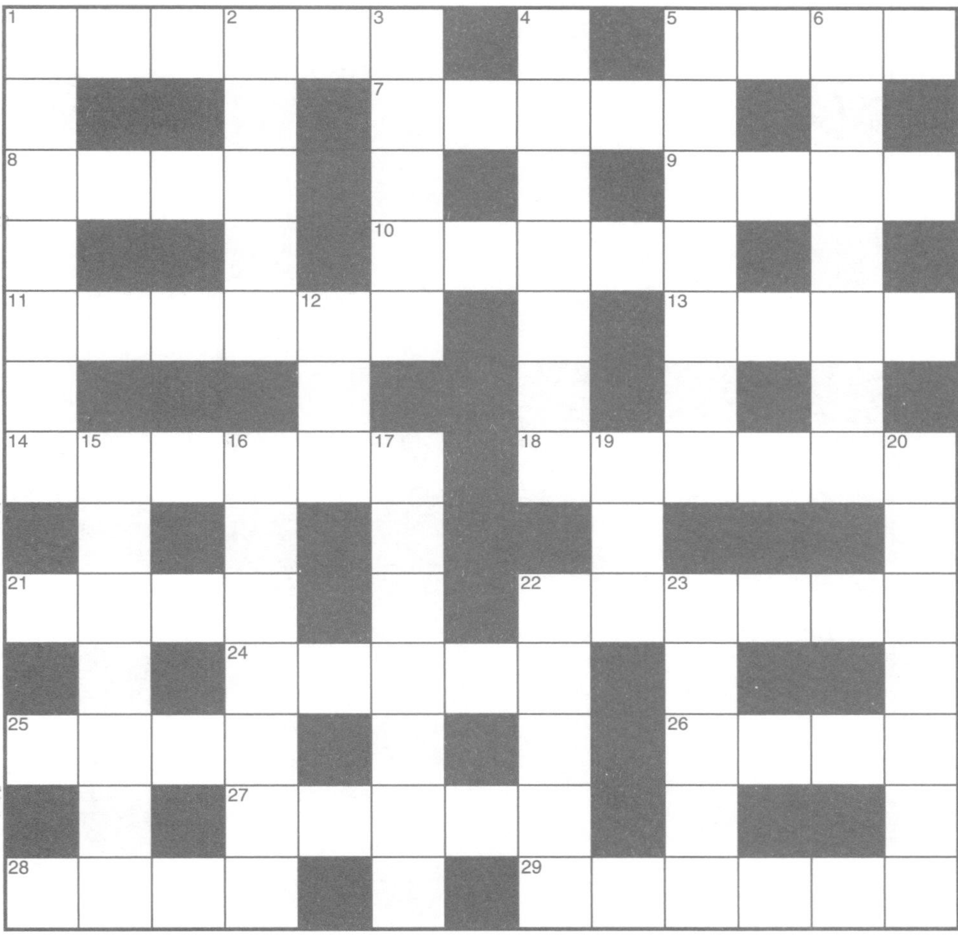

## ACROSS

1. Pigment, ... blue
5. Nourish
7. Walk through the door
8. Shout
9. To ... her own
10. Cooking herb
11. Throws
13. Musical instrument
14. Groomed (hair)
18. Clogged (up)
21. Bang (toe)
22. Ovation call
24. Crowd fight
25. Travel by sea
26. Chinese pans
27. Banishment
28. Slip sideways
29. More sorrowful

## DOWN

1. Deliberately confusing
2. Geography reference volume
3. Written passages
4. Remaining
5. Liberty
6. Omit
12. Use frugally, ... out
15. Be senior in command to
16. Boiled
17. Energetic
19. Decorative garden pot
20. Wardrobe assistant
22. Fairies
23. Sounded like crow

# CROSSWORD 177

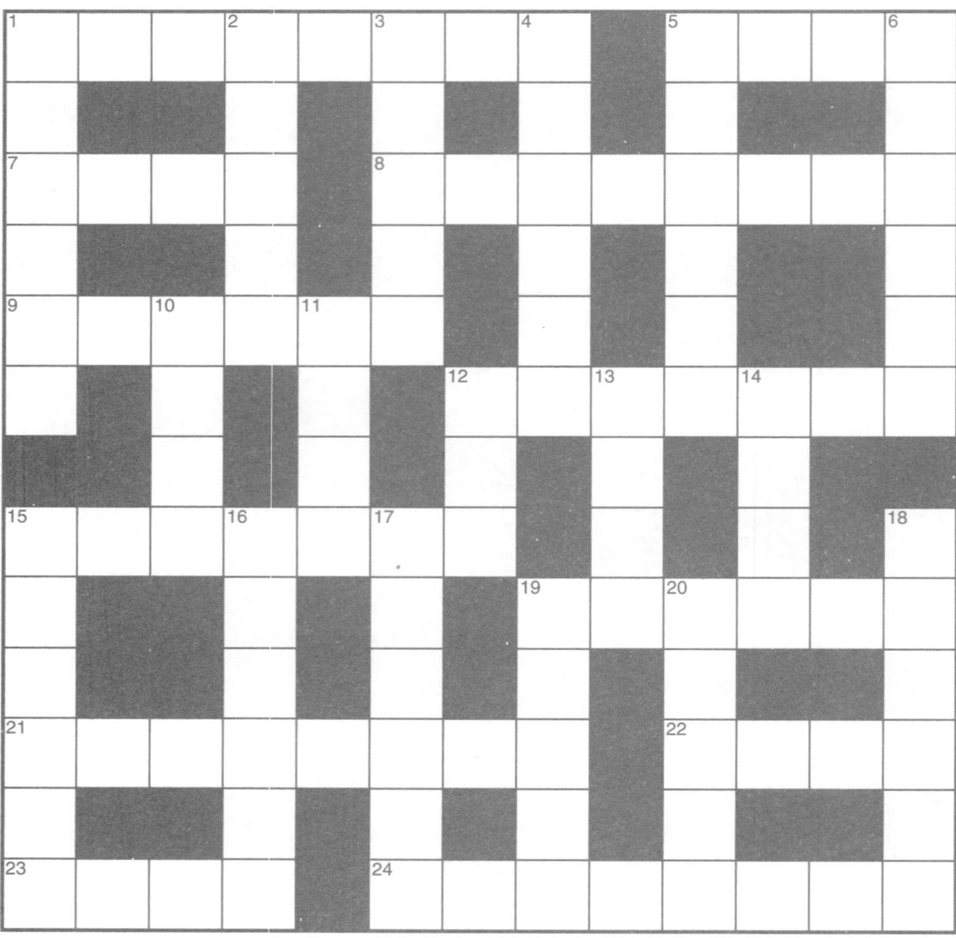

## ACROSS

1. Infants
5. Excess weight
7. Take off (hat)
8. One who remains alive
9. Obliterates
12. Frugal
15. Line of hereditary rulers
19. Pervert
21. Courted
22. Look at
23. Root vegetables
24. Unforested

## DOWN

1. Prods with elbow
2. Enthusiasts
3. Goes upwards
4. Be thrifty
5. More just
6. Uncovering
10. Nameless author
11. Moose
12. Pig enclosure
13. Suffer pain
14. Creep (towards)
15. Earnestly
16. Soothes (fears)
17. Male feline
18. Asphyxiates in water
19. Rock shelf
20. Courteous

# CROSSWORD 178

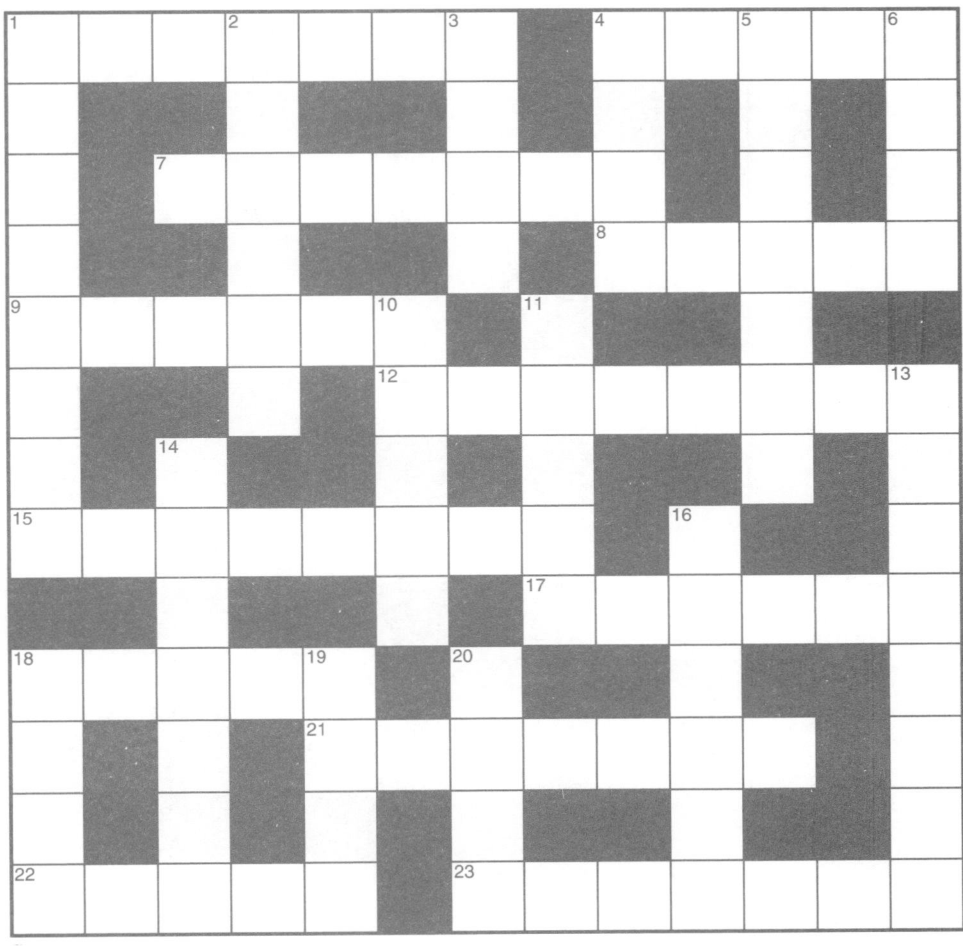

## ACROSS

1. Slicing
4. Narrow straits
7. Boosts morale of
8. Long (for)
9. Strength
12. Restate (position)
15. Front teeth
17. Shocking ordeal
18. Requirements
21. Male rowers
22. Standards
23. Springs up again

## DOWN

1. Squid
2. Subjects
3. Donation
4. Intrusive
5. Wine vessels
6. Graceful bird
10. Boo-boo
11. Girth measurement
13. Pacts
14. Conspirator
16. Subterranean chamber
18. Midday
19. Scatters (seeds)
20. Take rudely

# CROSSWORD 179

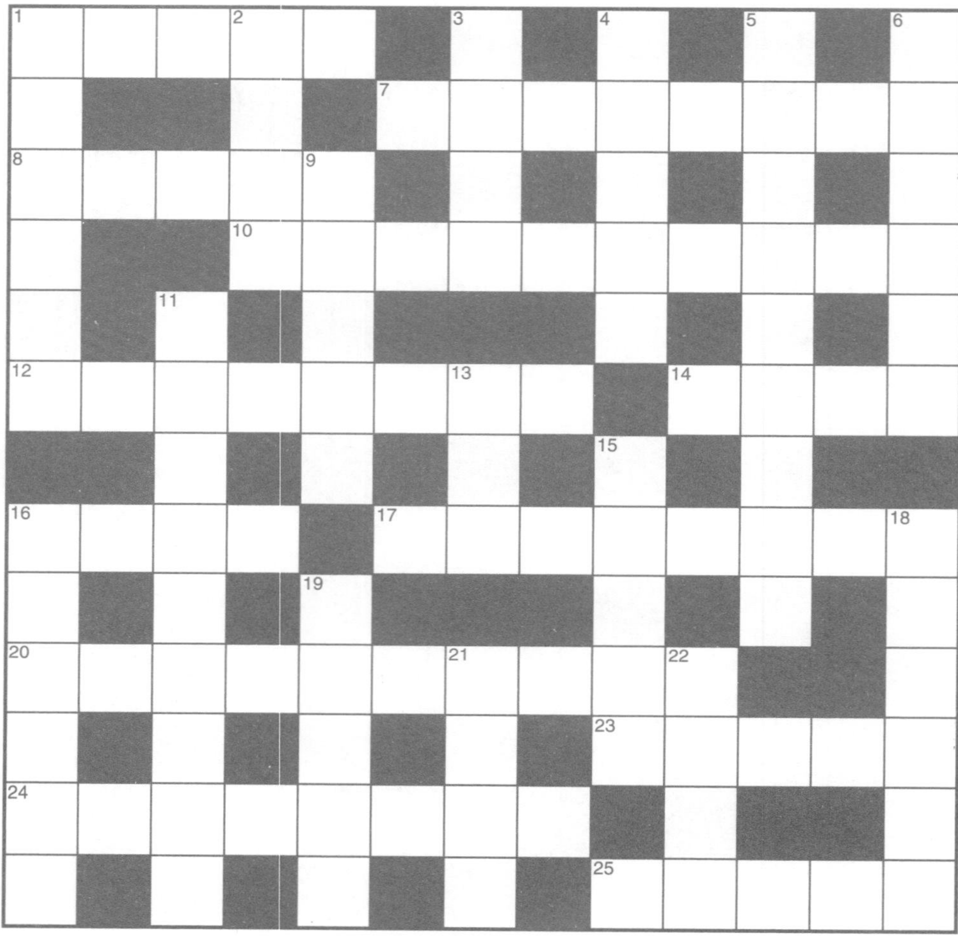

## ACROSS

1. Commenced
7. Rasping
8. Listened to
10. Hot season
12. Predict
14. Fitted with horseshoes
16. Competed
17. Germ-free
20. Rekindled
23. Totally demolished (of building)
24. Caper
25. Posed (question)

## DOWN

1. For, on ... of
2. Ventilates
3. Bathwater film
4. Milk (products)
5. Accomplishing
6. Consented
9. Wipes down (furniture)
11. Self-employed (journalist)
13. Install (carpet)
15. Restaurant patron
16. Edges
18. Rebuked
19. Cheerful
21. Curl (of smoke)
22. Low platform

# CROSSWORD 180

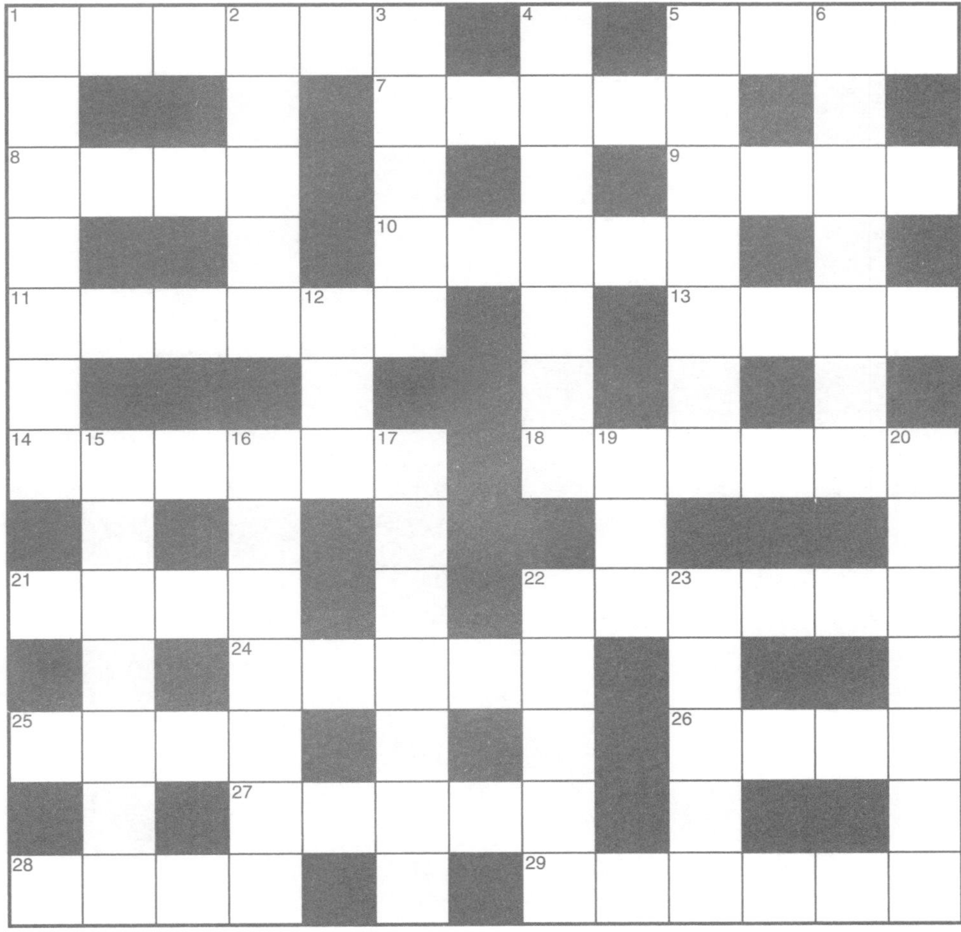

## ACROSS

1. Outward appearance
5. Actor, ... Nicholson
7. Tennis delivery
8. Work table
9. Put to the sword
10. Modify
11. Sprightly
13. Notion
14. Hare relative
18. Meat stew
21. Piebald
22. Ciphering
24. Tropical fruit
25. Breed (with)
26. Border upon
27. Sum up
28. Army dining hall
29. Ice dancer

## DOWN

1. Violinist
2. Leg joint
3. Long exam answer
4. Inventor
5. Making jokes
6. French castle
12. Hawaiian garland
15. Bring to life
16. Burrowing mammals
17. Nicotine plant
19. Bustle
20. Closer (of fit)
22. Sleeps in tent
23. Theatrical performance

# CROSSWORD 181

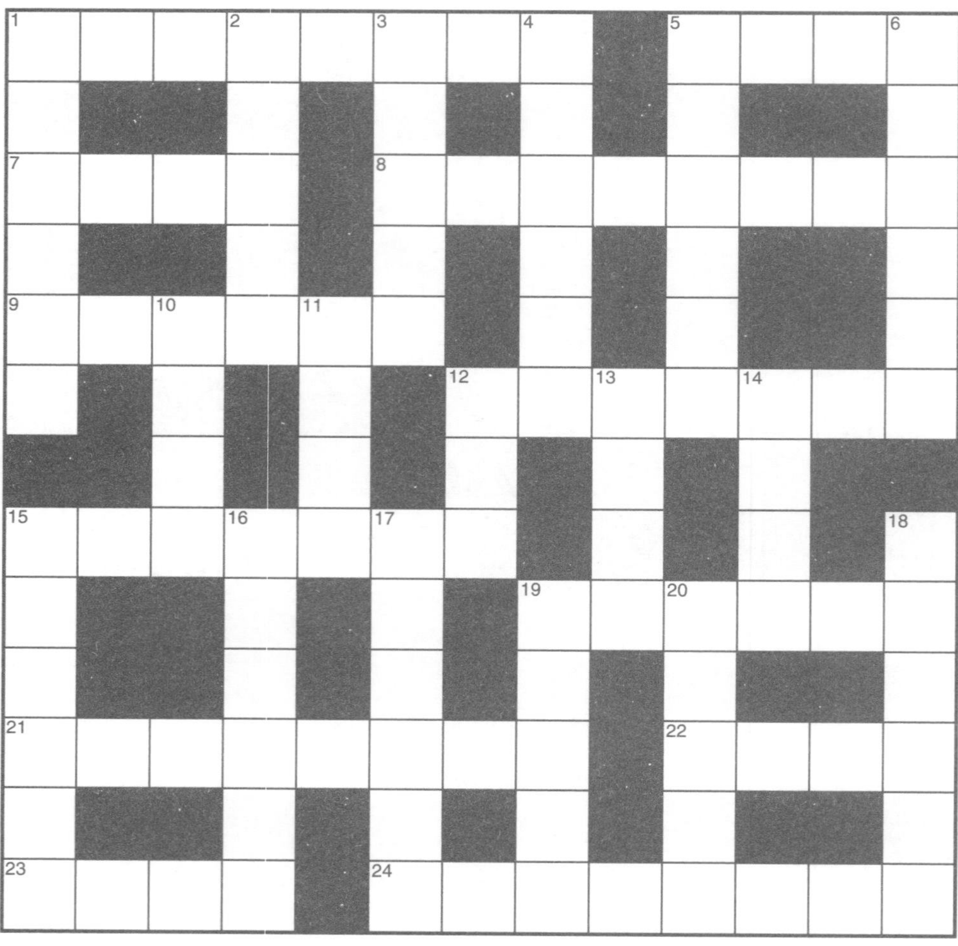

## ACROSS

1. Dig
5. New Orleans music
7. Soapy bubbles
8. Out of the ordinary
9. Soft
12. Revive
15. Told off
19. Moved from side to side
21. Regretted
22. Bluefin fish
23. Citrus peel
24. Insulin-secreting gland

## DOWN

1. Sculptured likeness
2. Confess
3. Maltreat
4. Absolve
5. Hurdler
6. Highest point
10. Insensible
11. Gated canal section
12. Purge
13. Went by air
14. Not hard
15. Steering device
16. Unclothed
17. Ensnare
18. Standards of perfection
19. Automobile body type
20. Daisy-like flower

# CROSSWORD 182

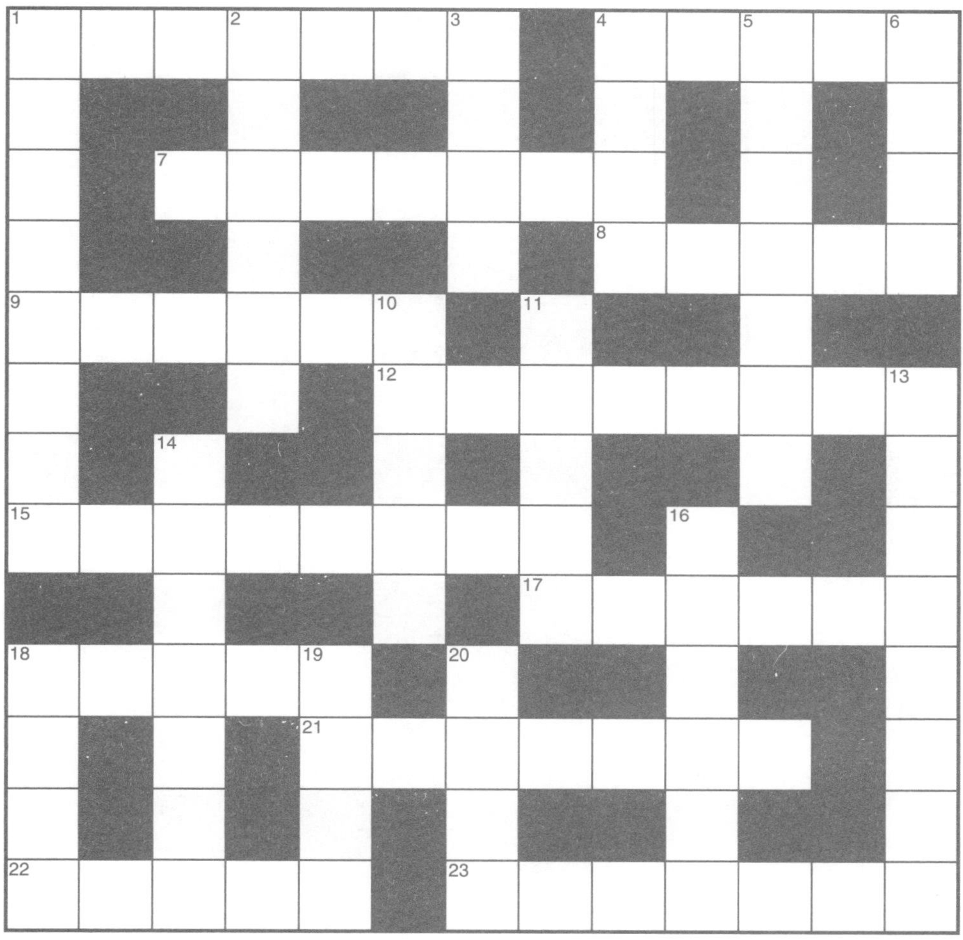

## ACROSS

1. Widened (pupils)
4. Comes towards
7. Noisy (hinge)
8. Company workers
9. Lampooning comedy
12. People of no consequence
15. Aristocrats
17. Barked in pain
18. Body lumps, lymph ...
21. Toy weapons
22. Day & ...
23. Slow flow from tap

## DOWN

1. Contempt
2. Clear (the accused)
3. Sketch
4. Negative votes
5. Stomach-settling powder
6. Individual identity
10. Hostile opponent
11. Dark wood
13. Set of symptoms
14. Tolerating
16. Medical rooms
18. Illuminating gas
19. Minor quarrel
20. Small stain

# CROSSWORD 183

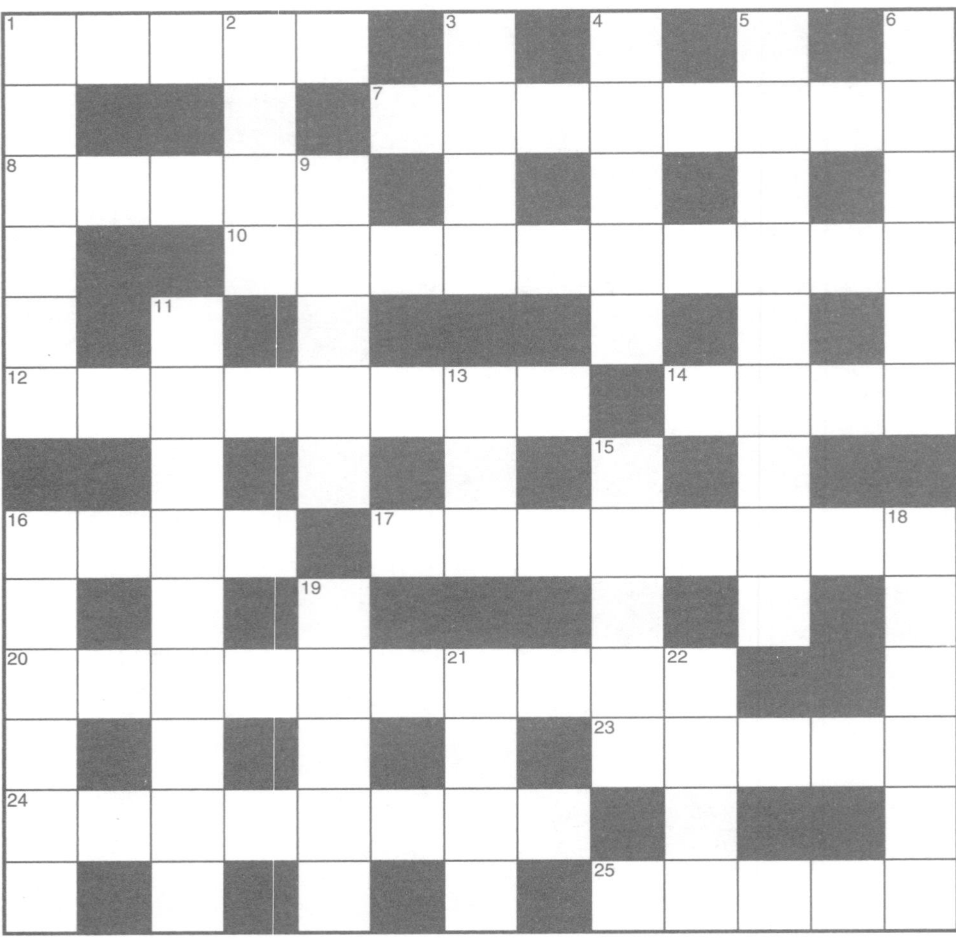

## ACROSS

1. Mauve flower
7. Positive thinking
8. Integral
10. Set apart
12. Letting fall
14. Make angry
16. Avenue
17. Wood sliver
20. Drawing (attention)
23. Solemn vows
24. Quivers
25. Reworked

## DOWN

1. Taxed
2. Unfortunately
3. Urge (on)
4. Circles
5. Regions
6. Smear
9. Jumps high
11. Author's income
13. Crab's pinch
15. Keyboard instrument
16. Responds
18. Woken
19. Doorposts
21. At that time
22. Opening in fence

# CROSSWORD 184

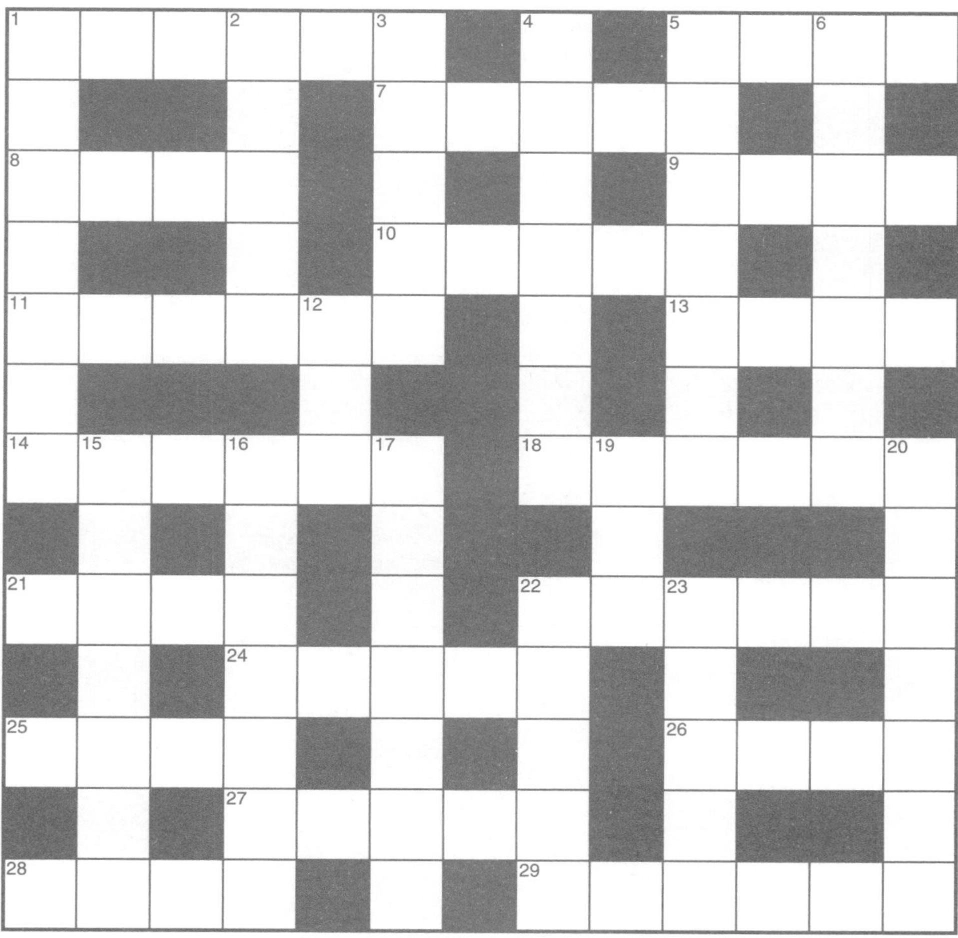

## ACROSS

1. Tobacco rolls
5. Metal-toothed fasteners
7. Priggish person
8. Prison
9. Off
10. Force out
11. Came to shore
13. Acceptable
14. Food toppings
18. Dwell
21. Horse farm
22. Womb
24. Slow speaking style
25. Small version
26. Capri or Wight
27. Enthusiastic
28. Maladies
29. Appoint

## DOWN

1. Coaxes
2. Troubled
3. Caught sight of
4. Rougher (ride)
5. Fanatical
6. Protest banner
12. Day before, ... of
15. Termite mound
16. Golfers' aides
17. Odd
19. Devour
20. Facing the rising sun
22. Extreme
23. Radiates

# CROSSWORD 185

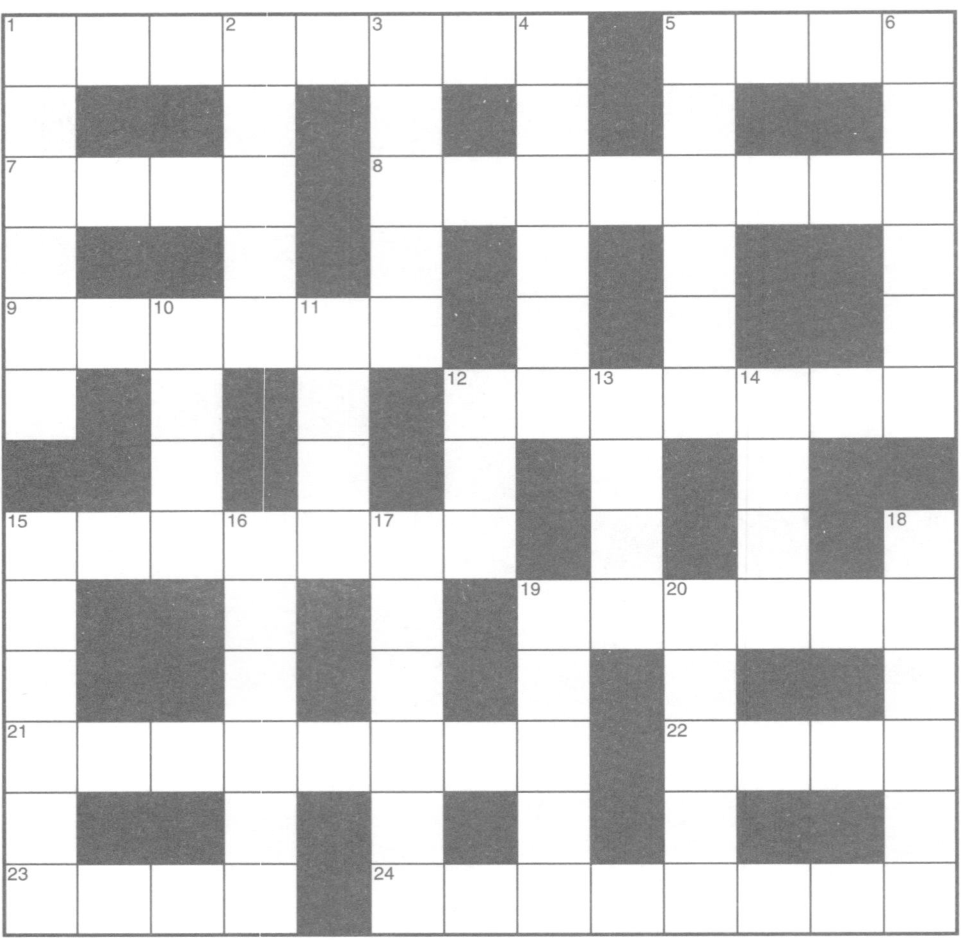

## ACROSS

1. Unit of electric power
5. Passport stamp
7. Sell
8. Wanders
9. Bobbed head
12. Medieval farm worker
15. Talked incessantly
19. Caused trouble, ... the boat
21. Tiered (garden)
22. Threat, do it or ...!
23. Metal track
24. Scams

## DOWN

1. Budging
2. Included
3. Directed
4. Hypnotic state
5. Visual recordings
6. Approval
10. Paint roughly
11. Fragrant type of tea, ... Grey
12. Wad
13. Jazz instrument, ... sax
14. Go berserk, run ...
15. Witty conversation
16. Keg
17. Executes (law)
18. Vipers
19. Diameter halves
20. Set of beliefs

# CROSSWORD 186

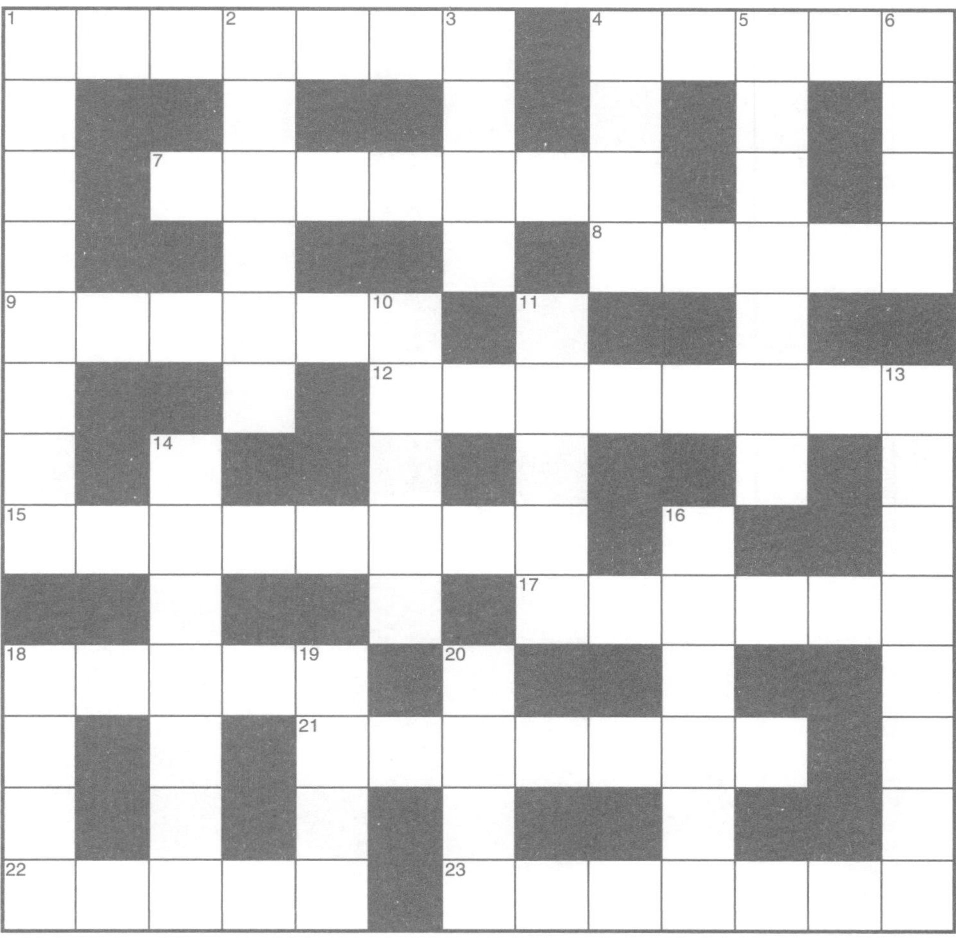

## ACROSS

1. Wild
4. Special skill
7. Aggravated
8. Burn with steam
9. Red salad fruit
12. Trainees
15. Magnificence
17. Gaped open
18. Skewered dish
21. Easily
22. Ships' spines
23. Male chicken

## DOWN

1. Making current
2. Yearly
3. 24-hour periods
4. Gently teases
5. Mortified
6. Variety
10. Of past times
11. Small magical being
13. Poorer quality
14. Sauerkraut vegetable
16. Bloats
18. Twist
19. Foundation garments
20. Twosome

# CROSSWORD 187

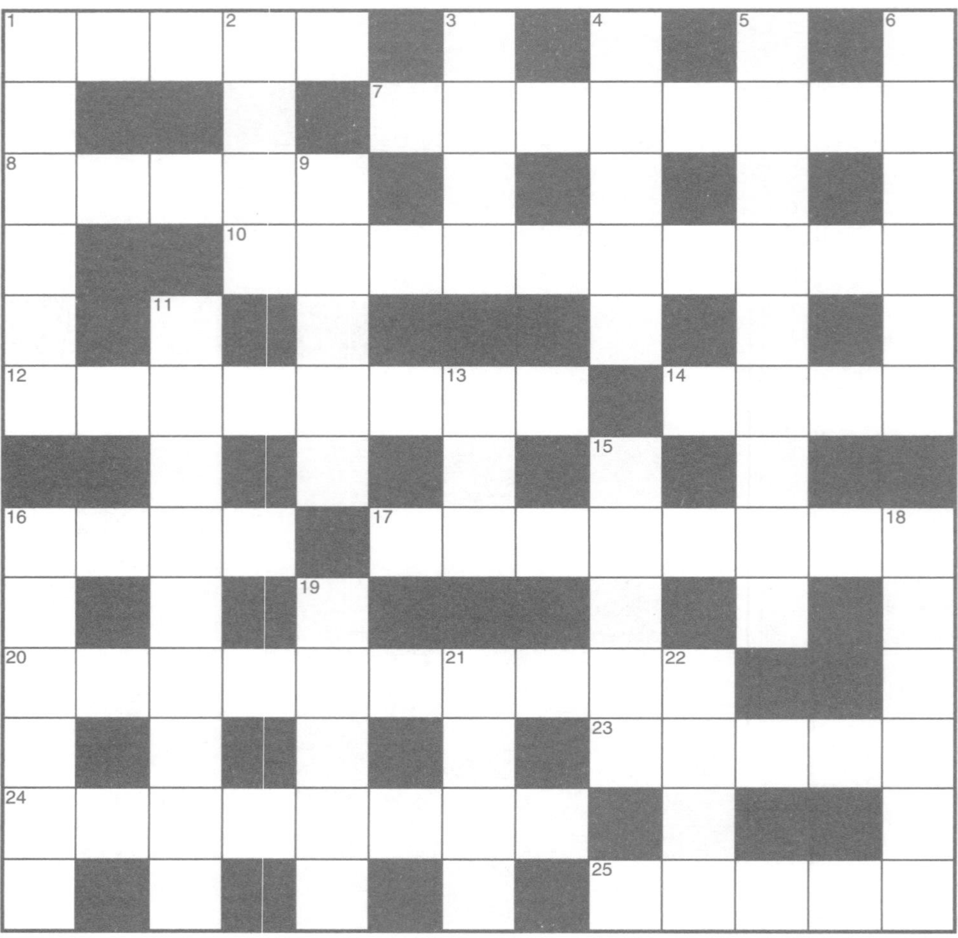

## ACROSS

1. Spread out
7. Science of flying
8. Boxing-ring surrounds
10. Ricocheting
12. Local languages
14. String tangle
16. Destiny
17. Weakened
20. Non-seafarer
23. Mixed (with poison)
24. Ludicrousness
25. Incidental comment

## DOWN

1. Astute
2. Overwhelmed
3. Sinful
4. Set of products
5. Idealist
6. Chess horse
9. Number of days in a week
11. Quickening
13. Male cat
15. Type of orange
16. Criminal act
18. Lag behind
19. Smooth & glossy
21. Low-pitched voice
22. Sunbeams

# CROSSWORD 188

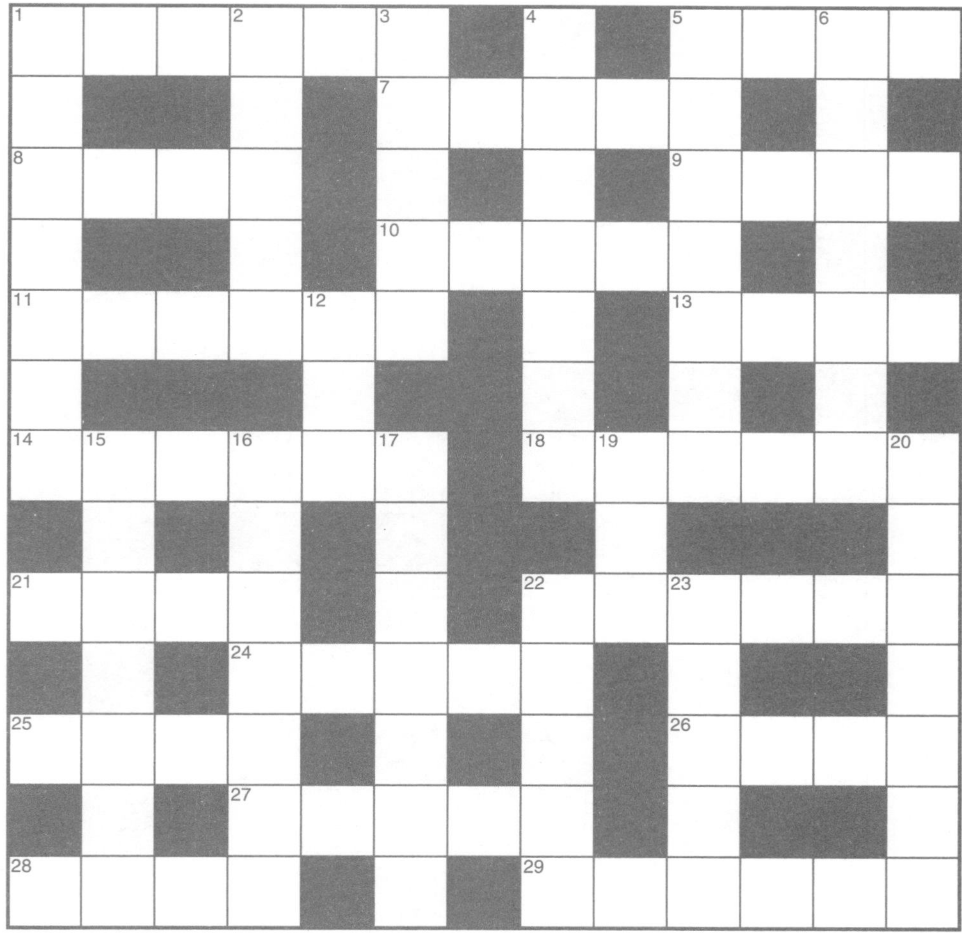

## ACROSS

1. Buccaneer
5. Vats
7. Sultana fruit
8. Rip
9. Rather this ... that
10. Vote in
11. Tended (patients)
13. Touch with tongue
14. Summer shoe
18. Oppose
21. Article
22. Partake of alcohol
24. Military first-aid attendant
25. Raise bid, up the ...
26. Lawn section
27. Plant secretion
28. Louts
29. Snow vehicle

## DOWN

1. Protects (invention)
2. Broad expanse
3. Urged, ... on
4. Food supplier
5. Water boilers
6. Peeks
12. Part of eon
15. Insect feeler
16. Light-intensity switches
17. Most obscene
19. Shady tree
20. Eleventh, ..., thirteenth
22. Computer symbols
23. Wash

# CROSSWORD 189

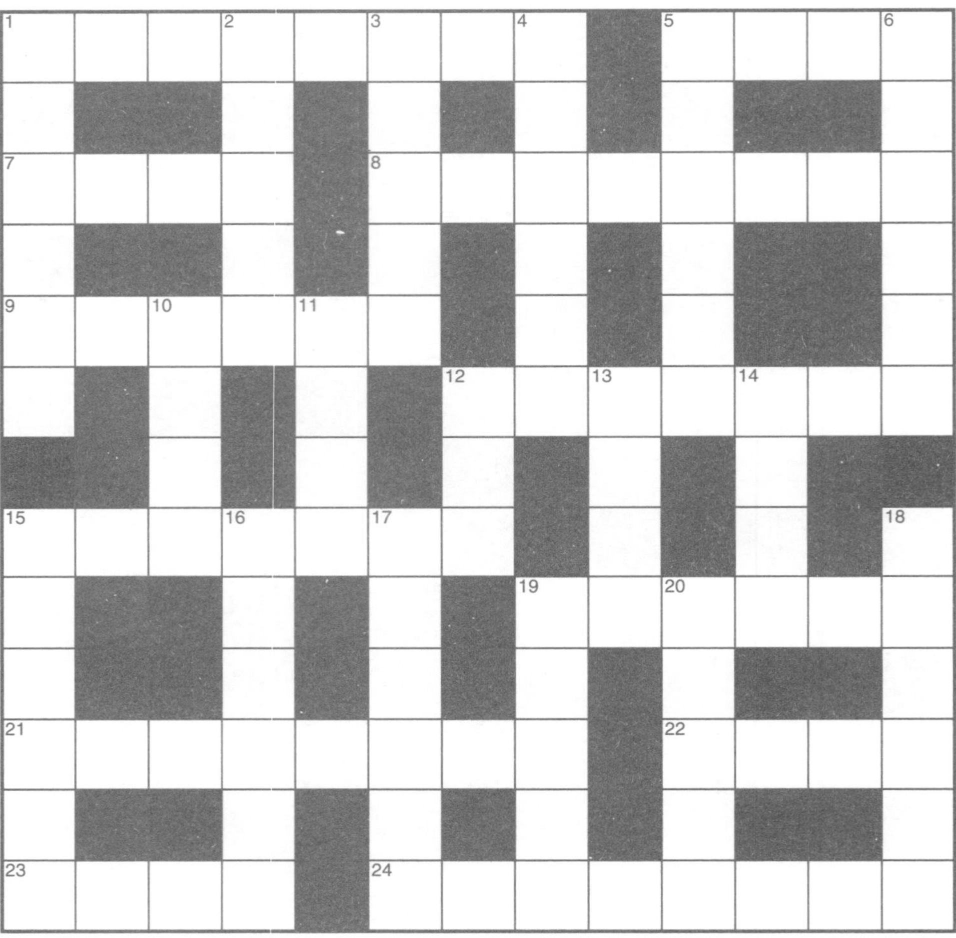

## ACROSS

1. Computer accessory
5. Rectangular courtyard
7. Heavy fencing sword
8. Retrieved (wreck)
9. Dull & overcast (sky)
12. House location
15. First Bible book
19. Cried in pain
21. Game bird
22. Impertinent
23. Tinted
24. Puts into bondage

## DOWN

1. Eagerly
2. Baker's loaf
3. Fire crime
4. Explored deeply
5. Tremble
6. Evades
10. Prayer ending
11. Very attentive, all ...
12. Donkey
13. Street protest
14. Receive as salary
15. Inhaled sharply
16. Increase
17. Of unsound mind
18. Work-shy people
19. Butterfly relatives
20. Major artery

# CROSSWORD 190

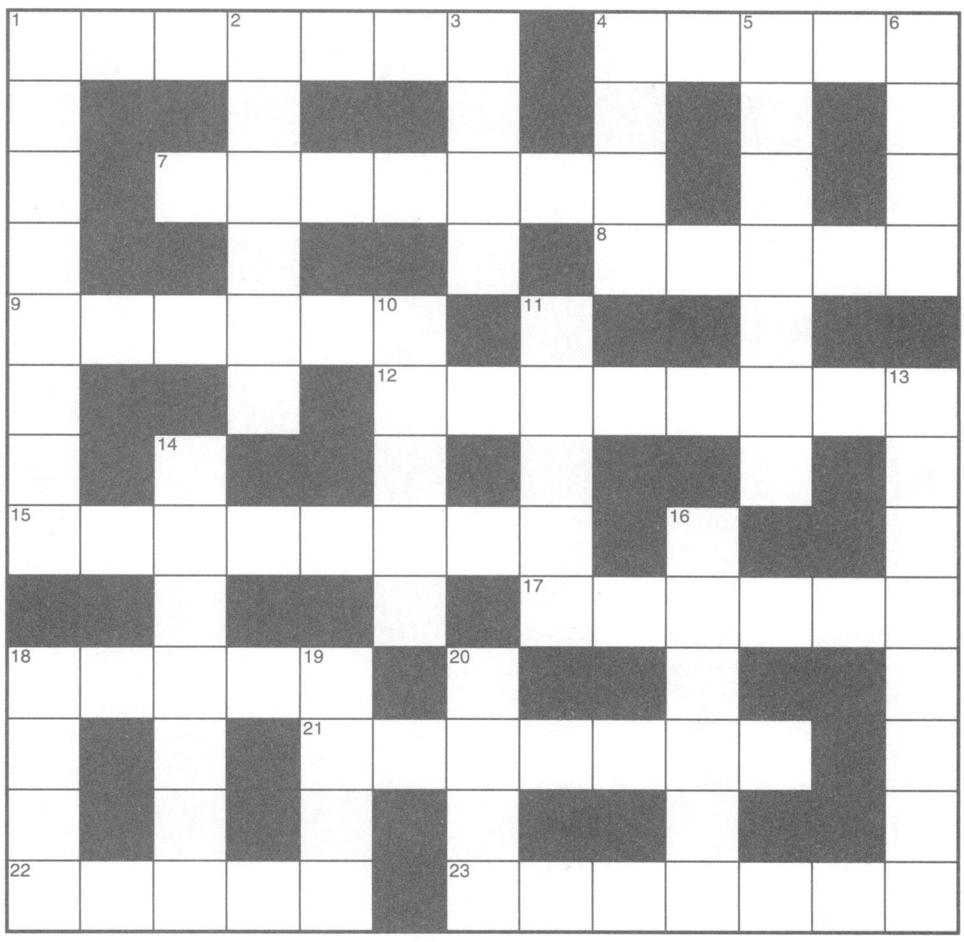

## ACROSS

1. Unknowing
4. Plait
7. Unconventional
8. Stockpile
9. Imaginary
12. Lack of response
15. Hearing impairment
17. Guttural
18. Smell
21. Sow's litter
22. Distributes cards
23. Legally kill

## DOWN

1. Evicted
2. Floated on the breeze
3. Female sheep
4. The pair
5. Water-related
6. Perished
10. Is fond of
11. Swamp
13. Headfirst descent (4,4)
14. Portable rocket-launcher
16. Ploy
18. Grew old
19. Gorillas or chimpanzees
20. Stare lustfully at

# CROSSWORD 191

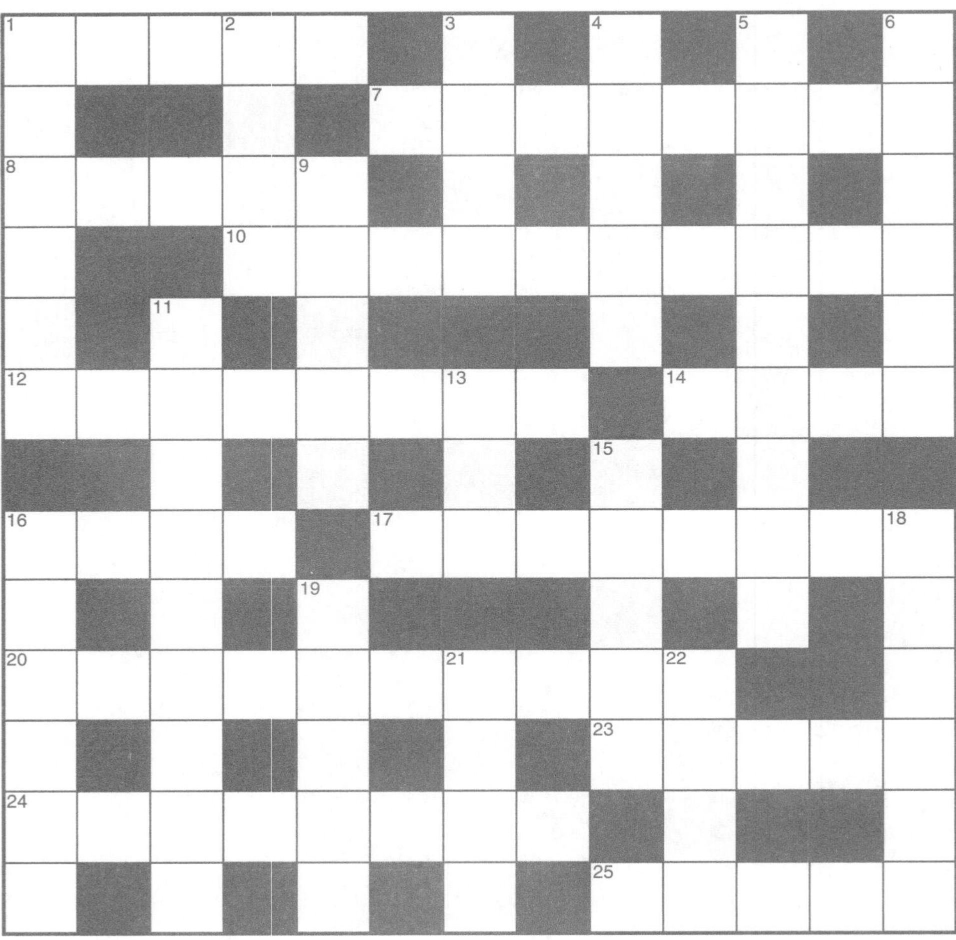

## ACROSS

1. Hand protector
7. Excessive eating
8. Was the proprietor of
10. Bitter feelings
12. Ocean voyager
14. Lion abode
16. Loading wharf
17. Wickedly enjoyable
20. Embellish
23. Lodge deeply
24. Foul (water)
25. Sacred song

## DOWN

1. Olive farms
2. Steer off course
3. Duct
4. Proclaim
5. Abates
6. Pearl-bearer
9. Blackball
11. Twin-hulled boat
13. Before (poetic)
15. Hindu social position
16. Squeamish
18. Bicycle for two
19. Severe pain
21. Ladder crossbar
22. Australian birds

# CROSSWORD 192

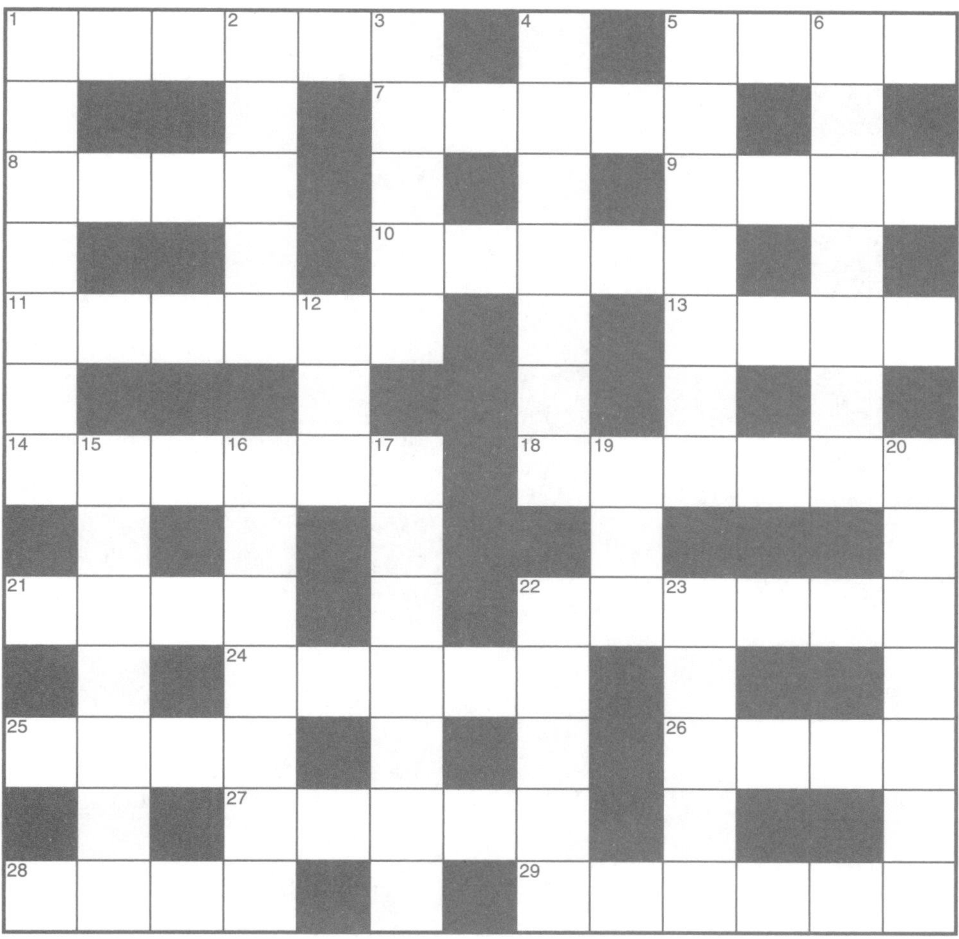

## ACROSS

1. Towards the middle
5. Over again
7. Circle (Earth)
8. Father
9. Focal points
10. Cutting utensil
11. Surprise victories
13. Chills
14. Injure
18. Failure (of enterprise)
21. Applications
22. Sitting down
24. Likeness
25. Responsibility
26. Asian sauce bean
27. Scottish fabric
28. Swiss mountains
29. Mists (up)

## DOWN

1. Confine (stray pet)
2. Lessen in severity
3. Arrives at wharf
4. Compelled
5. Religious non-belief
6. Symbols
12. Price label
15. Weapons cache
16. Helps
17. Compares
19. Sight organ
20. Makes beloved
22. Transmits
23. Gangway

# CROSSWORD 193

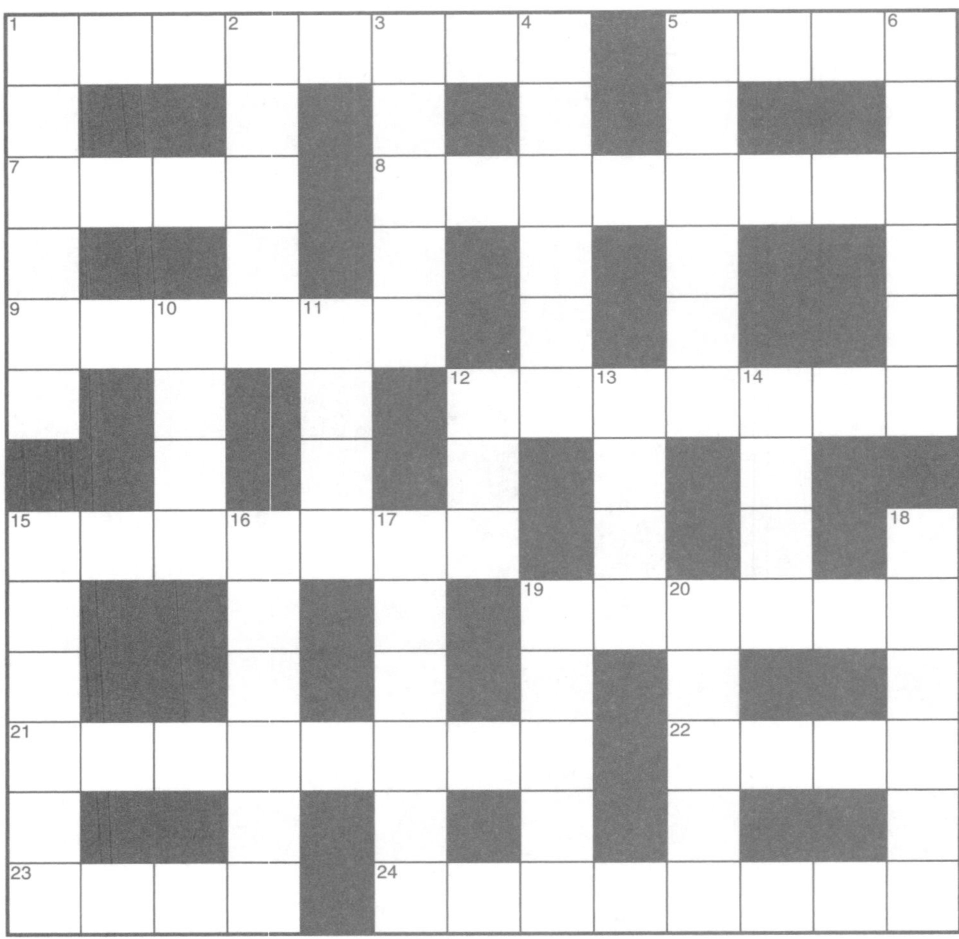

## ACROSS

1. Lengthens
5. Timber
7. Flight limb
8. Most ferocious
9. Via the mouth
12. Wearing away
15. Spanked
19. Shrouded
21. Representative (of)
22. Flying toy
23. Breeze
24. Bestride

## DOWN

1. Native American ceremony
2. Licit
3. Small & efficient
4. Meat spike
5. Sinful
6. Estimating age of
10. Sector
11. Watch
12. Finish
13. Seep out
14. Pagan statue
15. Teeter
16. Kept in check
17. Praises highly
18. Stick (to)
19. Clergyman
20. Riled

# CROSSWORD 194

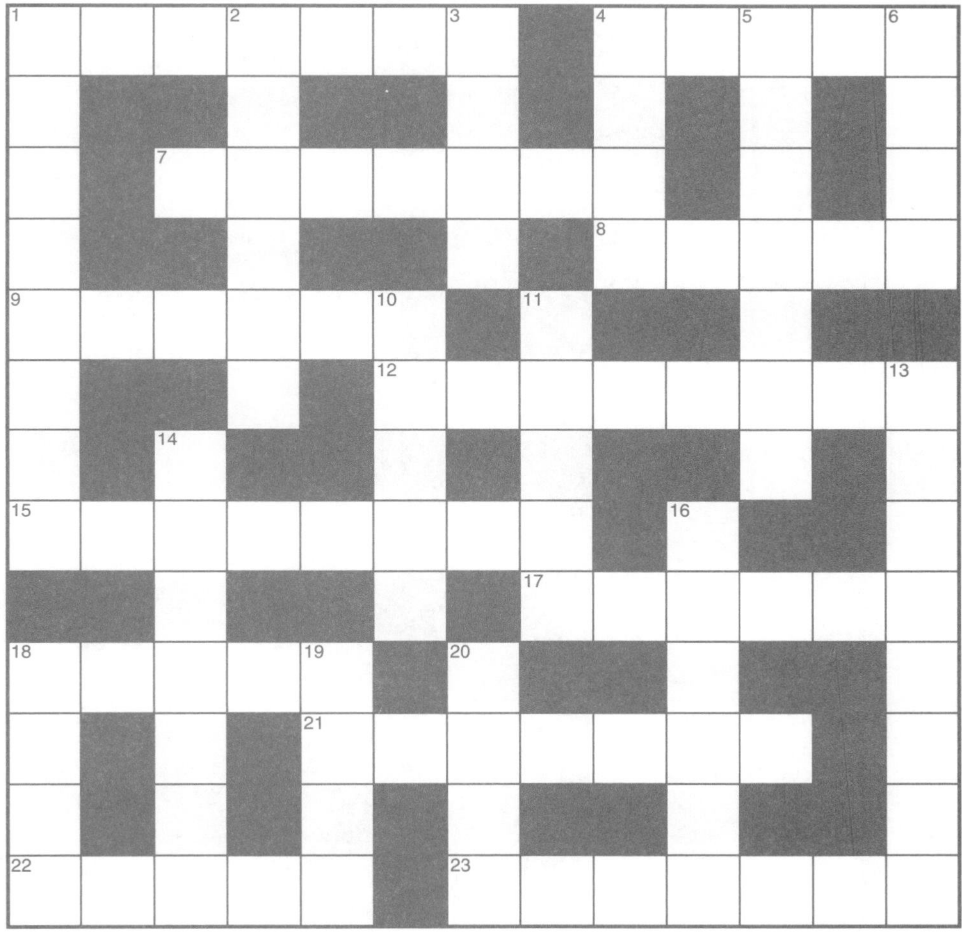

## ACROSS

1. Worn away
4. Public square
7. Mopped
8. Informal language
9. Agilely
12. Dreamt up
15. Venice canal boats
17. Degraded
18. Serenity
21. Technical sketch
22. Robbery
23. Listed (in book)

## DOWN

1. Pointing the finger at
2. Without exception
3. Outstanding loan
4. Pea casings
5. Gets
6. Excited
10. Succumb
11. Lightweight timber
13. Muffled
14. Beautify
16. Quit (premises)
18. Breathe rapidly
19. Revise (manuscript)
20. Indian robe

# CROSSWORD 195

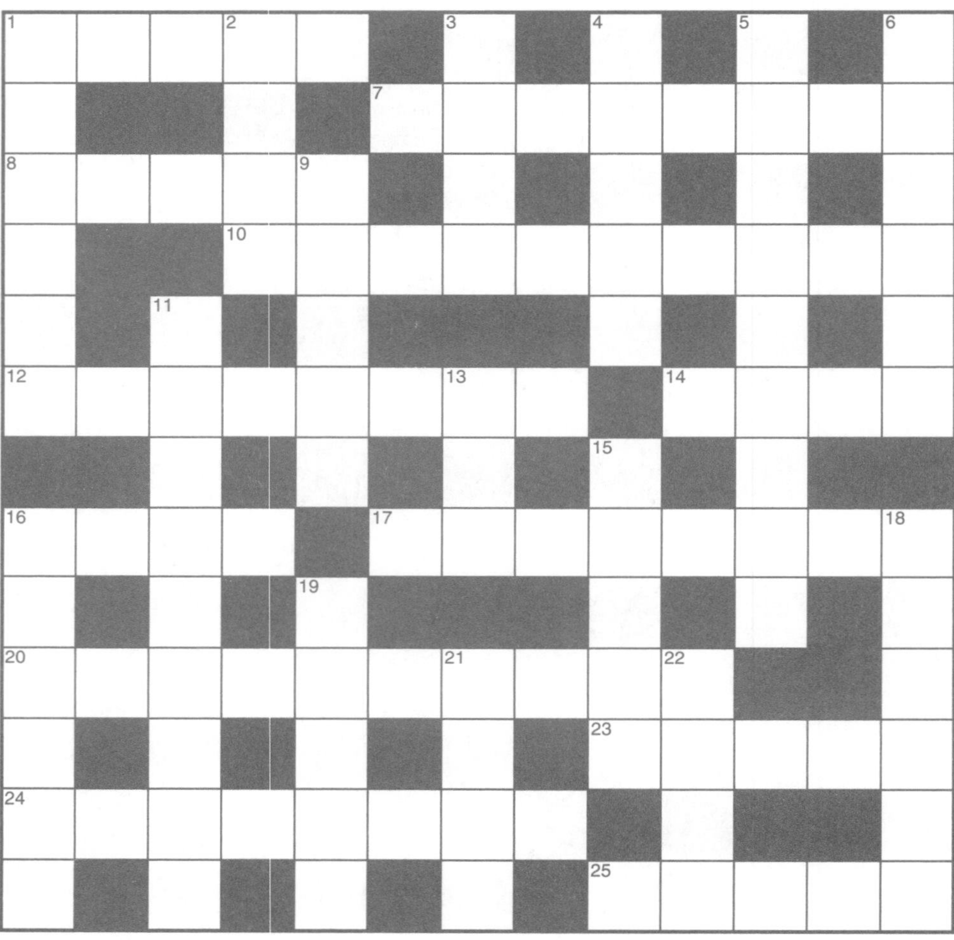

## ACROSS

1. Construct
7. Undo
8. Forms a puddle
10. Fabricating (report)
12. Arose (from)
14. Carnival
16. Most superior
17. Droplets of fat
20. Broken up
23. Foxtrot or rumba
24. Component parts
25. Glided on snow

## DOWN

1. Imperial realm
2. Young cow
3. Wildebeests
4. Blunder
5. According to principles
6. Puzzle
9. Cold meal
11. Sickened
13. Conger or moray
15. Flowed away
16. Shock absorber
18. Protective screen
19. Urge to action
21. Acorns or cashews
22. Unpleasantly damp

# CROSSWORD 196

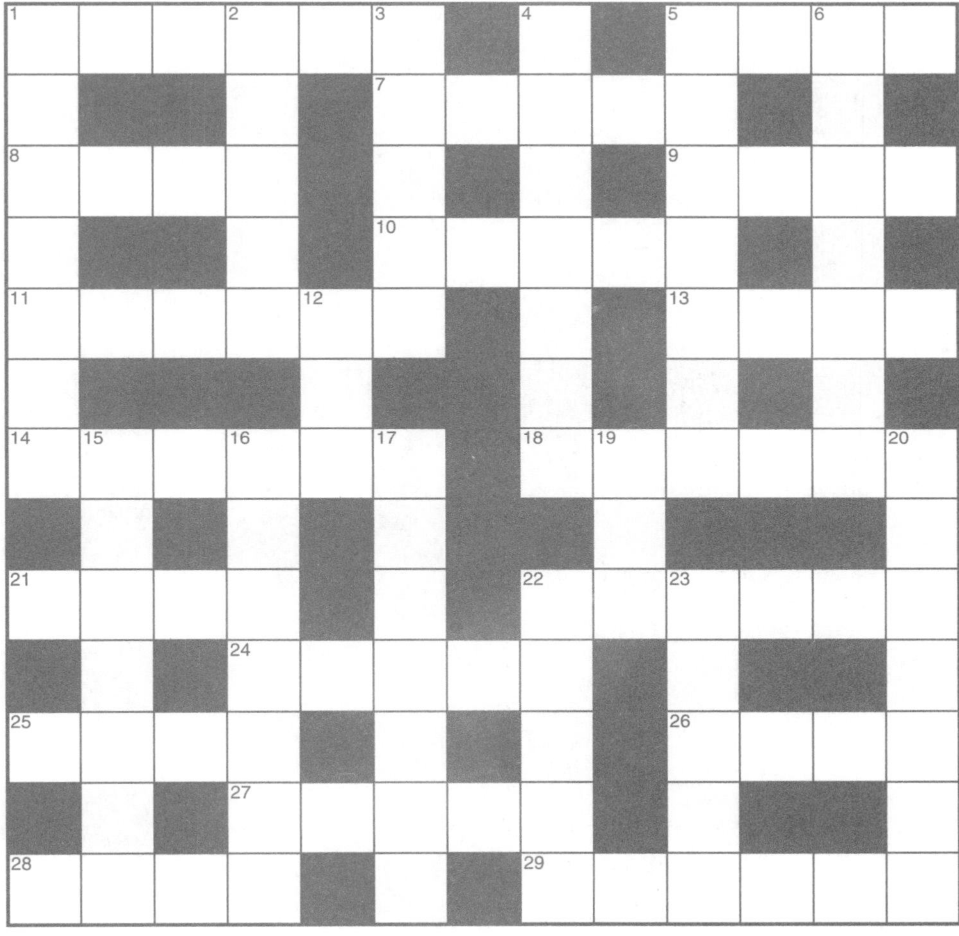

## ACROSS

1. Of the sea
5. Jobless benefit
7. Happen anew
8. Roman gown
9. Grecian pots
10. Making last, ... out
11. Cotton strand
13. Taunt
14. Swing loosely
18. Bestows
21. Long upholstered seat
22. Dazed state
24. Roofing stone
25. Orange-peel lining
26. Objective
27. Remove (DVD) from player
28. Lose (fur)
29. Ornamental ribbons

## DOWN

1. Underwent genetic change
2. Senseless (comment)
3. Slipped up
4. Overshadow
5. Medicated
6. Large archery weapon
12. The lot
15. Put an end to (law)
16. Ground (teeth)
17. Enclosed in shell
19. Louse egg
20. Extra
22. Cults
23. Impulses

# CROSSWORD 197

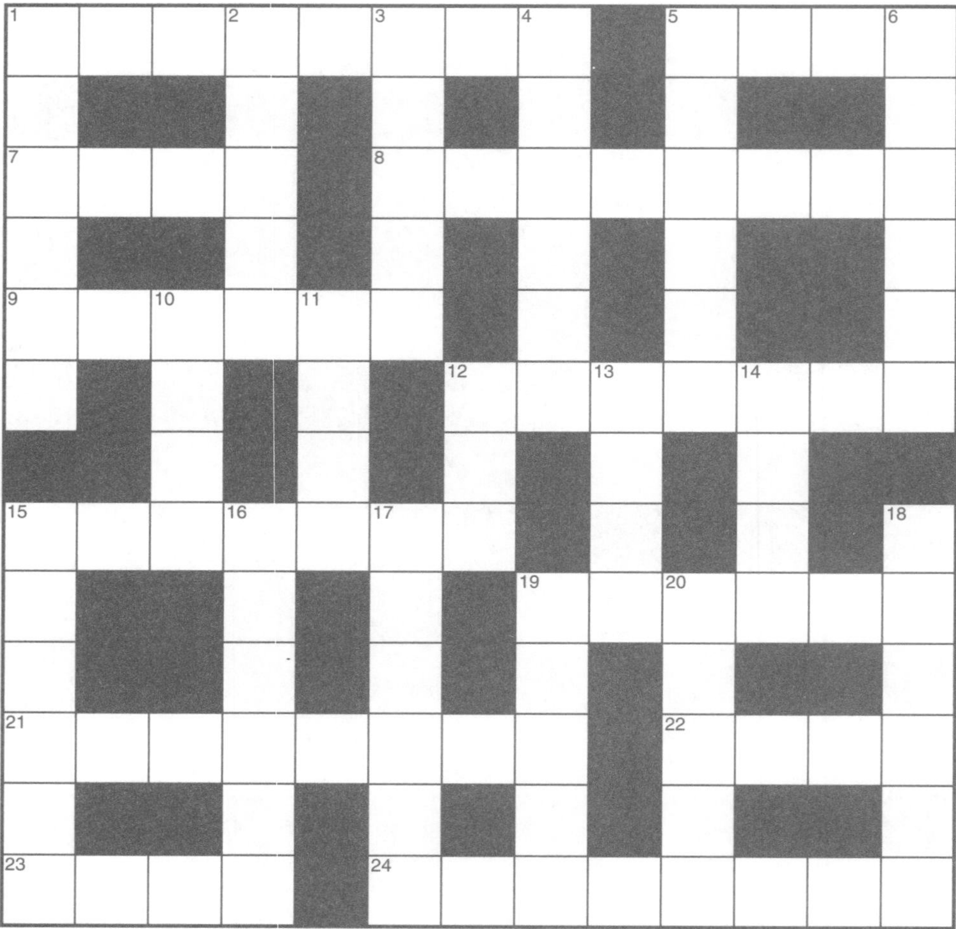

## ACROSS

1. Went back over
5. Be concerned
7. Secluded place
8. Increasing threefold
9. Classifies
12. Hand out again
15. Door lock aperture
19. Works (dough)
21. Tirade
22. Bicycle
23. Sudden invasion
24. Expanded

## DOWN

1. Break promise
2. Scraped (leaves)
3. Commends (for bravery)
4. Sprinkle with flour
5. Crowd brawls
6. Graduate's award
10. Force of troops
11. Resound
12. Regret
13. Steam press
14. Cleaning agent, caustic ...
15. Jewish food custom
16. Peril
17. Group of sports clubs
18. Take to the air
19. Rest on knees
20. Glowing coal

# CROSSWORD 198

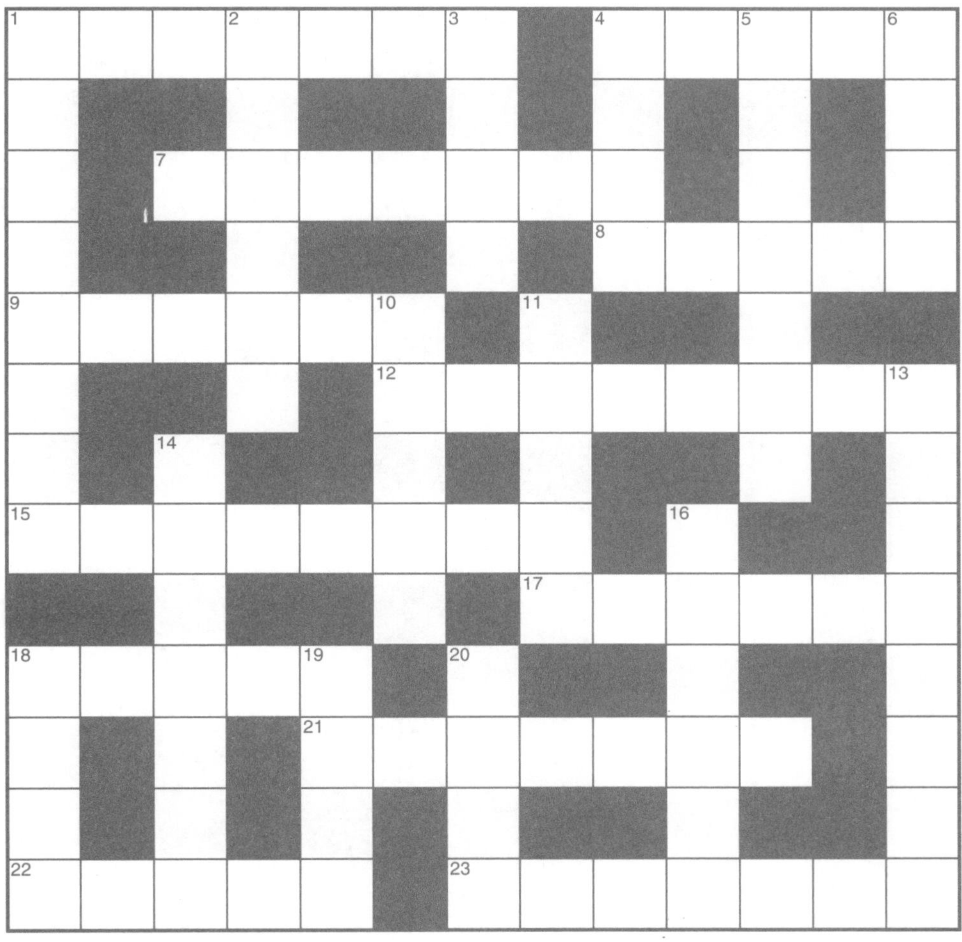

## ACROSS

1. Entangled
4. Army fabric
7. Salad pear
8. Is clad in
9. Doomed to fail
12. Unclasp (belt)
15. Confused rush
17. Wound (of river)
18. Strikes with foot
21. Dire calamity
22. Banjo sound
23. Perfume concentrate

## DOWN

1. Thievish small crows
2. Of cattle
3. Haul
4. Understand
5. Assaults
6. Printing fluids
10. ... & duchesses
11. Woodwind instruments
13. Witness box account
14. Eye cosmetic
16. Canoe oar
18. Retained
19. Male deer
20. Manufactured

# CROSSWORD 199

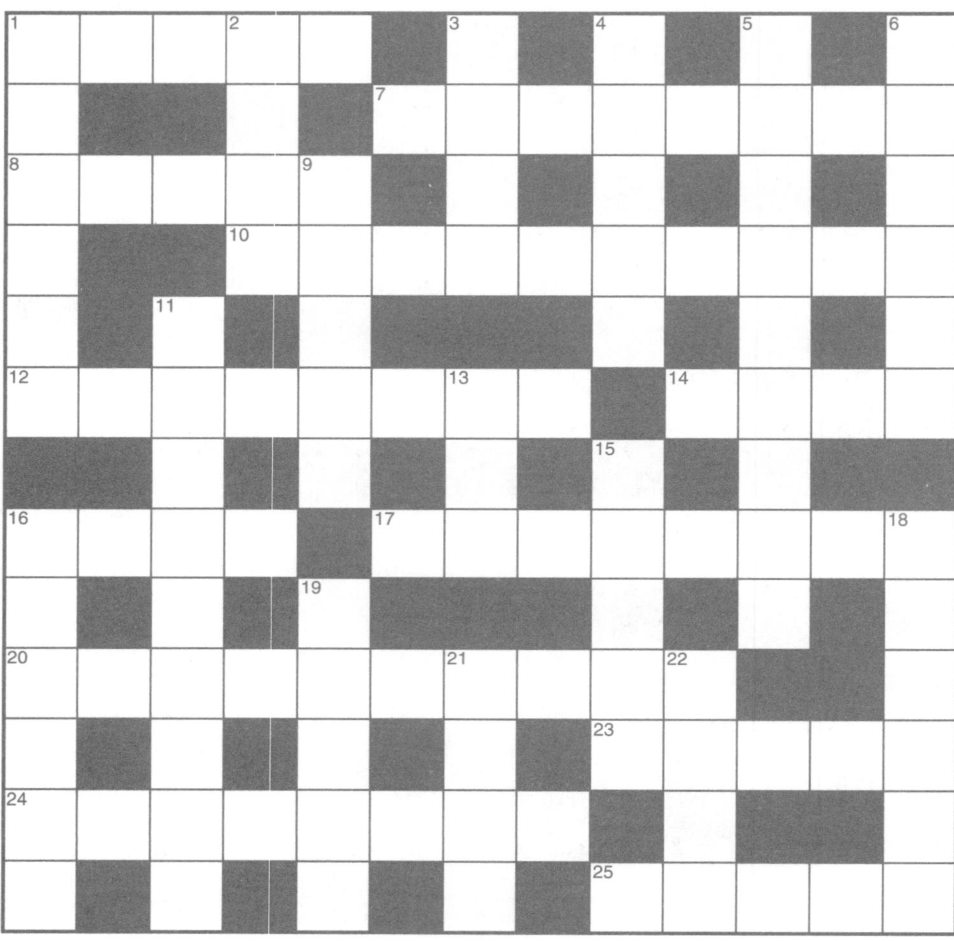

## ACROSS

1. Stratagems
7. Tropical swamp tree
8. Luggage shelves
10. Last golf hole
12. Restraining (dog)
14. Skidded
16. A great distance
17. Not required
20. Without superior
23. Length units
24. Fragile
25. Gave up (territory)

## DOWN

1. Package
2. Ox harness
3. Whip stroke
4. Giant monsters
5. Tarzan's scanty attire
6. Procedure
9. Vision
11. Pleasant tasting
13. Convent dweller
15. Fizzy
16. Refer subtly
18. Extinguished
19. Wooden barrier
21. Allows to
22. Overfill

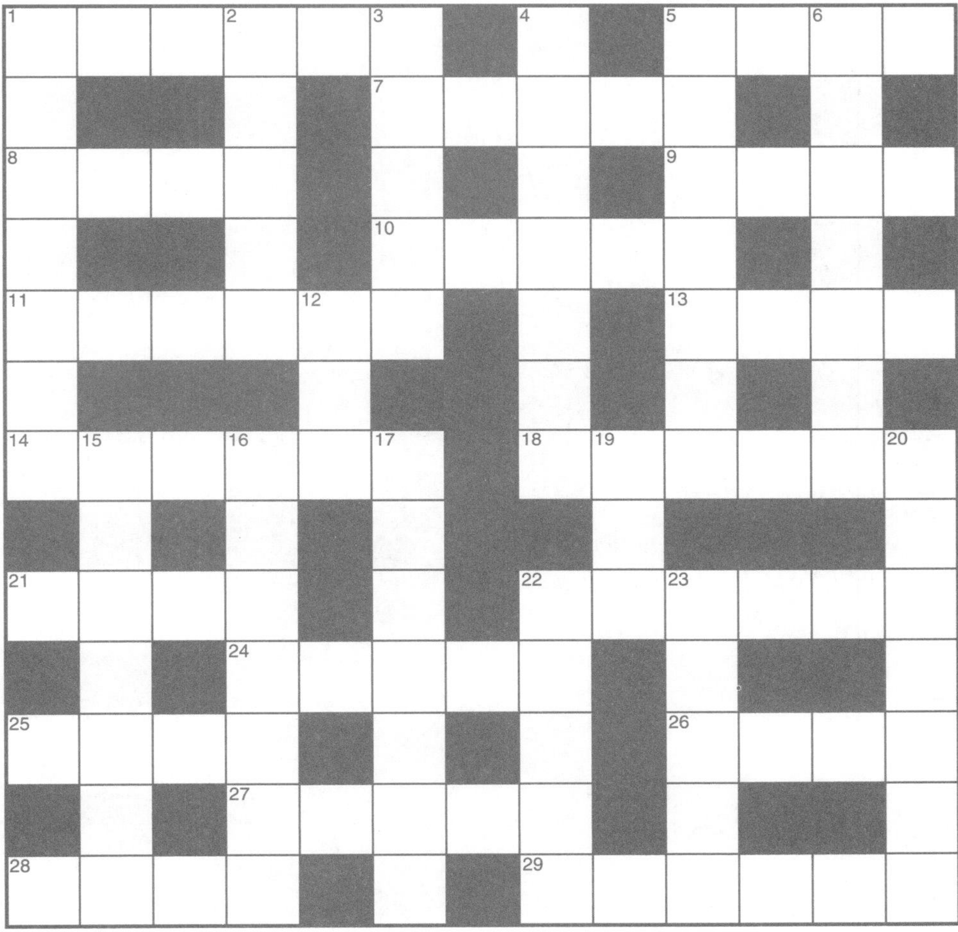

## ACROSS

1. Drumming insect
5. Honey makers
7. Quick wash
8. Discontinued (project)
9. Ethnic group
10. Happen
11. Silhouette
13. Mischievous sprites
14. Ran after
18. Croaked
21. Martial art
22. Wreckage
24. Goat mammary gland
25. Unbiased
26. Meditation routine
27. Elude (capture)
28. Contained
29. Mended with needle

## DOWN

1. Timeless
2. Helped
3. Archery missile
4. Door-tapper
5. Small fruits
6. Absconder
12. First number
15. Transport of goods
16. Scrubbed hard
17. Straight-faced
19. Beer
20. Throw out
22. Parched
23. Purchaser

# CROSSWORD 201

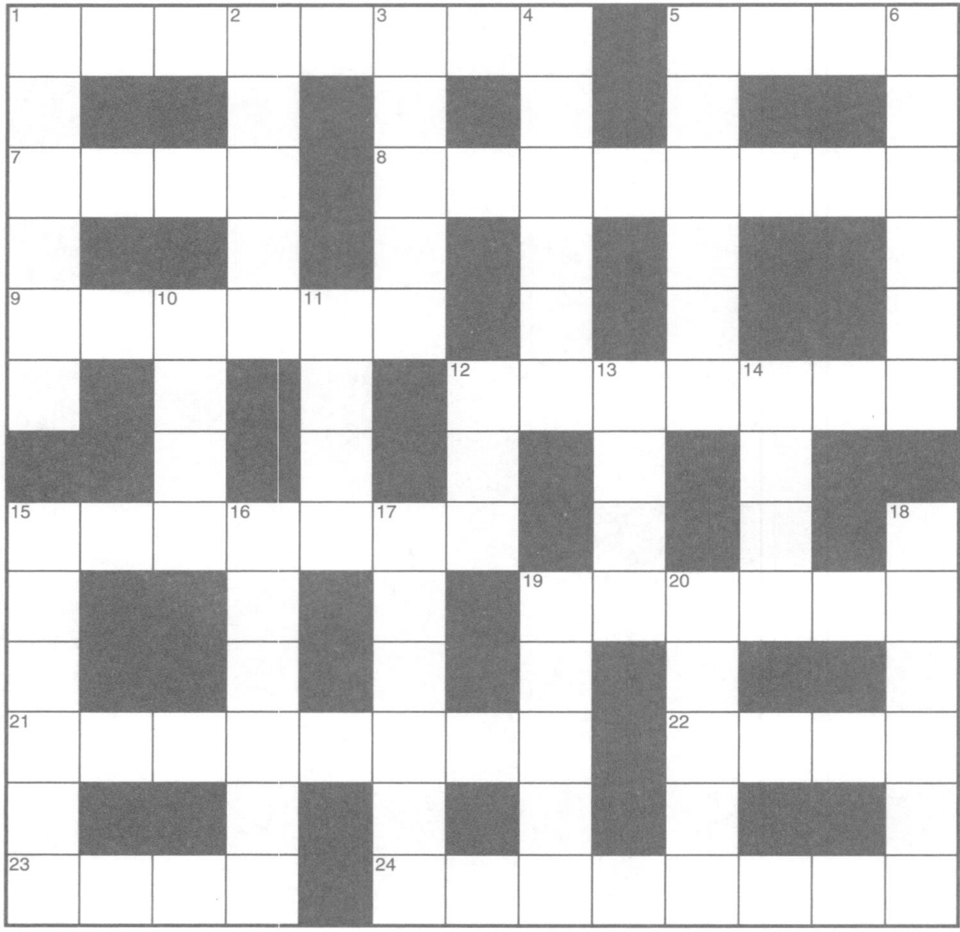

## ACROSS

1. Supplied
5. Witty remark
7. Sounded (of bell)
8. Spectators
9. Agreeably
12. More in want
15. Most orderly
19. Fussy & prim
21. Likely
22. Golly!
23. All square
24. Gift of money

## DOWN

1. Mother or father
2. Indistinct
3. Daily journal
4. Infer
5. Waited in line
6. Prior to WWI
10. Unnatural sleep
11. Vitality
12. Few, ... many
13. Always
14. Hotels
15. Teat
16. Sikh headwear
17. Wept
18. Punctuation mark
19. Groom feathers
20. Brick of silver

# CROSSWORD 202

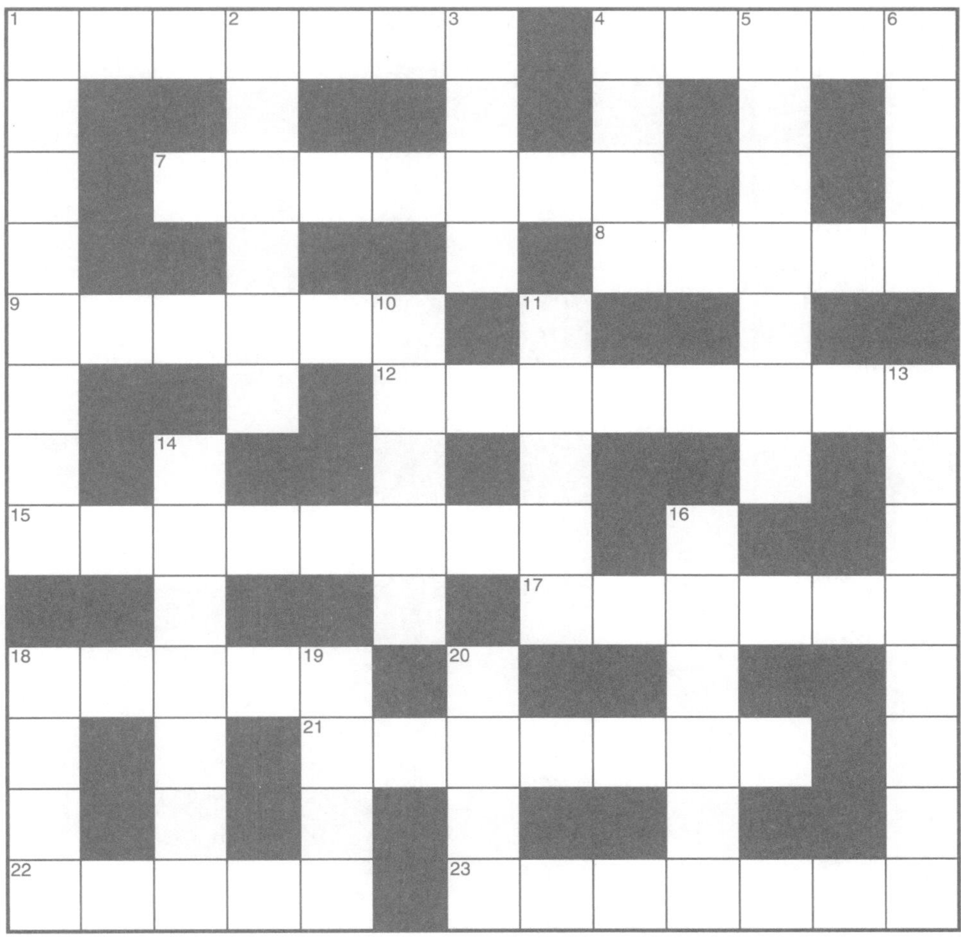

## ACROSS

1. Guest
4. Dips into drink
7. Trimmed with scissors
8. Sober
9. Fictitious
12. Modifying
15. Car seat part
17. Delighted
18. Less in number
21. Citrus crop
22. In which place?
23. Reptiles

## DOWN

1. Overcome in battle
2. Take no notice of
3. Tears
4. Failures
5. Wandering (tribe)
6. Pip
10. Slackened
11. Flour glue
13. Wholesomeness
14. Out of control
16. Filming machine
18. Fault
19. Went on horseback
20. Corridor

# CROSSWORD 203

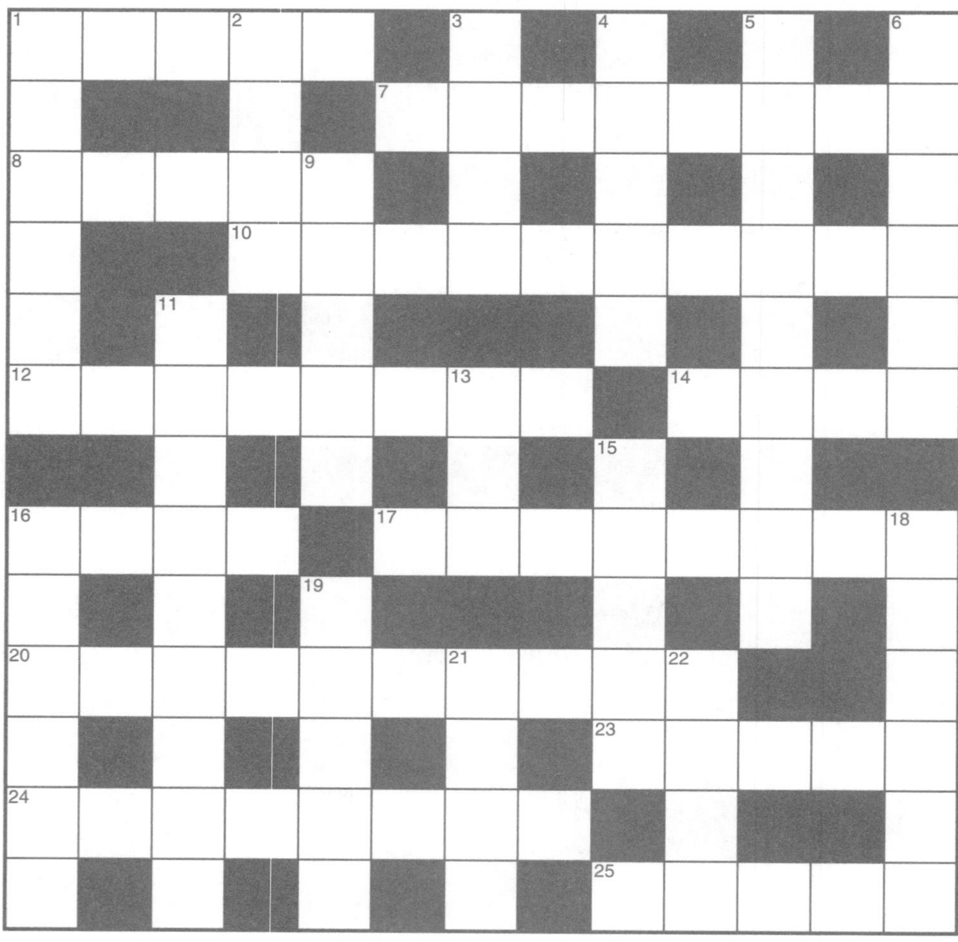

## ACROSS

1. Nonsense, mumbo ...
7. Remove jockey's seat
8. Clutch
10. Watering at the mouth
12. Stalemate
14. Requests, ... for
16. Throw in air
17. Counteractive medicine
20. Uncultivated region
23. Recorded
24. Washes (clothes)
25. Simmers

## DOWN

1. Sharply serrated
2. Employer
3. Against
4. Infidel
5. Confession
6. Rules as monarch
9. Buckets
11. Grand tomb
13. Tin container
15. Middle
16. Drying cloths
18. Secretes
19. Necklace balls
21. Average
22. Common seasoning

# CROSSWORD 204

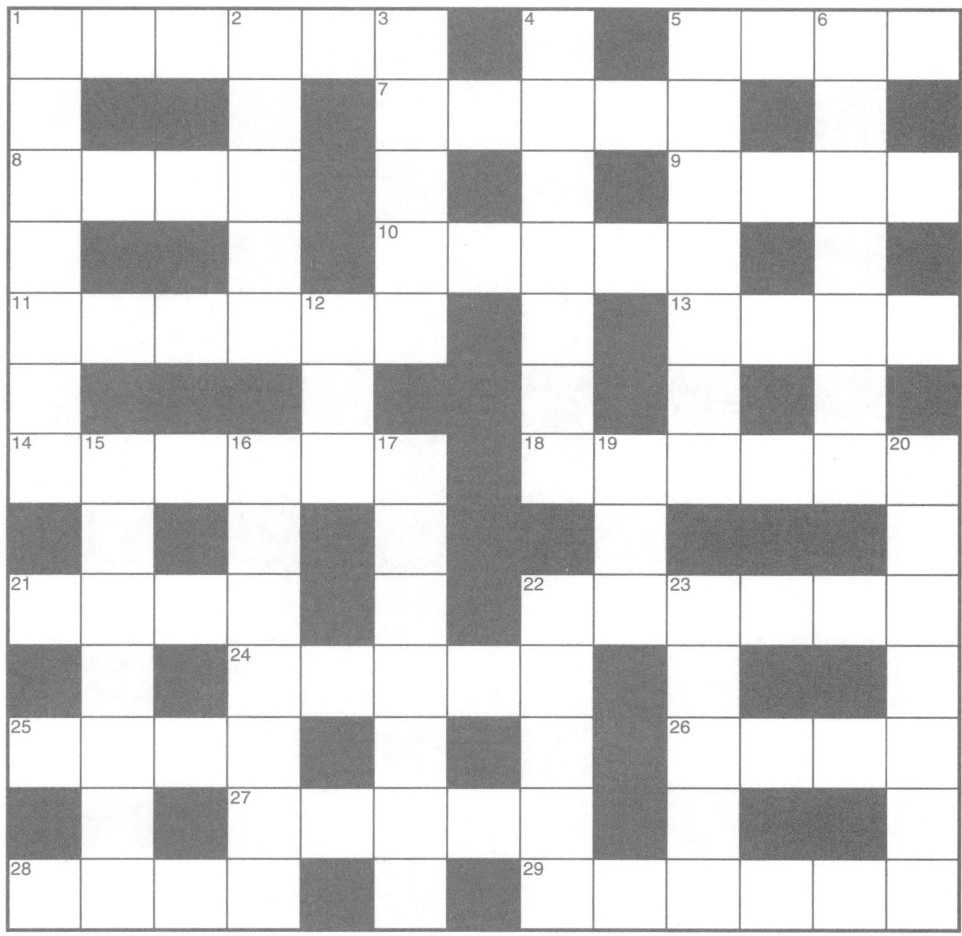

## ACROSS

1. Screens from sun
5. Radio knob
7. Coin-operated timer
8. Leave hurriedly
9. Component
10. Citrus fruit
11. Gradually develop
13. Male monarch
14. Earmarked
18. Strip bare
21. Competent
22. Displease
24. Hollywood prize, Academy ...
25. Scottish skirt
26. Raise (children)
27. Regional
28. Repulsive
29. Deeply desires

## DOWN

1. Quietest
2. Live
3. Grin
4. Staunched (flow)
5. Inebriated
6. Straightened
12. Compete
15. Strolling
16. Mightily
17. Make depraved
19. Pixie
20. Tolerates
22. Peculiarly
23. Land, terra ...

# CROSSWORD 205

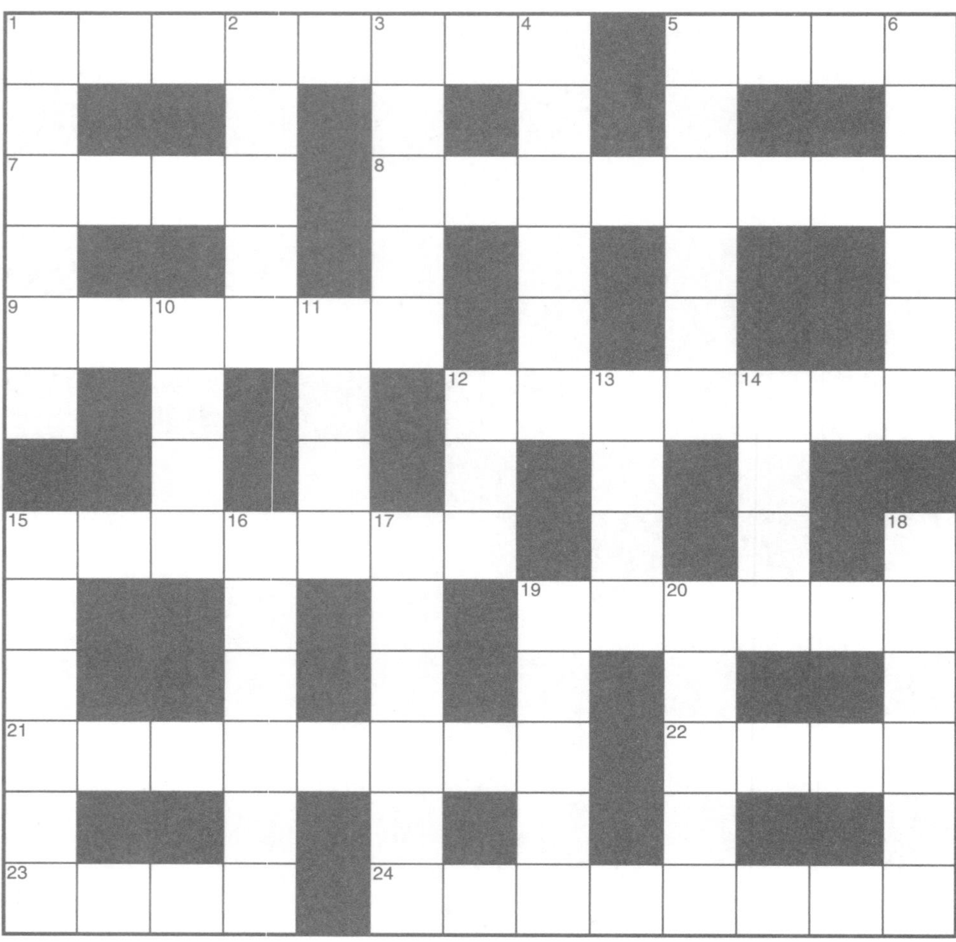

## ACROSS

1. Lavishly
5. Loose hood
7. Twinge
8. Visual deception
9. Receive
12. Epic journey
15. Remote
19. Hangs in folds
21. Mixes up (cards)
22. At one time
23. Reside
24. Beads of liquid

## DOWN

1. Parentless child
2. Cast a line
3. Official decree
4. Screamed
5. Universe
6. Companionless
10. Billiard sticks
11. US wild cat
12. Cereal grass
13. Count ... blessings
14. Large boat
15. Medieval maiden
16. Chewy confectionery
17. Secured by hammering
18. Estimate (damages)
19. Music genre
20. Ring-shaped coral reef

# CROSSWORD 206

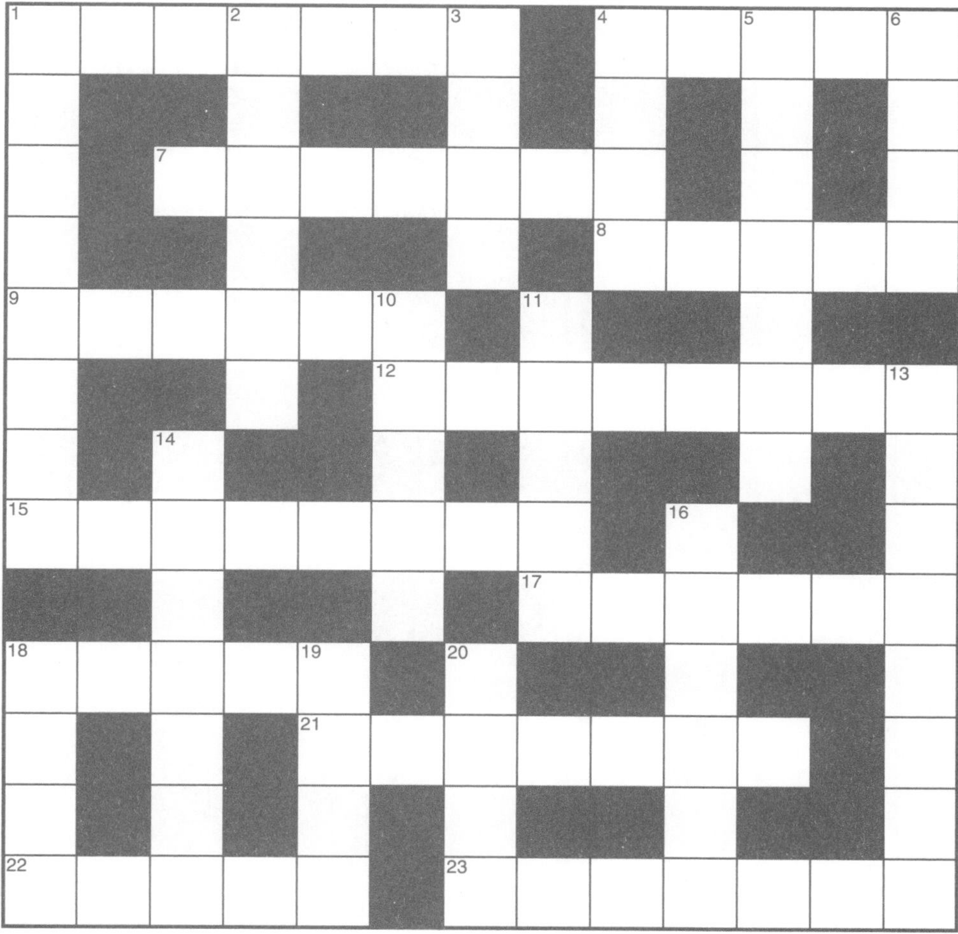

## ACROSS

1. Bored holes
4. Coronet
7. Shout
8. Stone fruit
9. Decimal (system)
12. Models
15. Assess
17. Go hungry
18. Synthetic fabric
21. Passed into law
22. Surgical light-ray instrument
23. Dashed

## DOWN

1. Devastate
2. Nonessential item
3. Faculty head
4. Short-term worker
5. Good-naturedly
6. Curved doorway
10. Red wood
11. Fence openings
13. Quietened
14. Deep gorges
16. Vocation
18. Spool
19. Soon, in the ... future
20. Speed of sound measure

# CROSSWORD 207

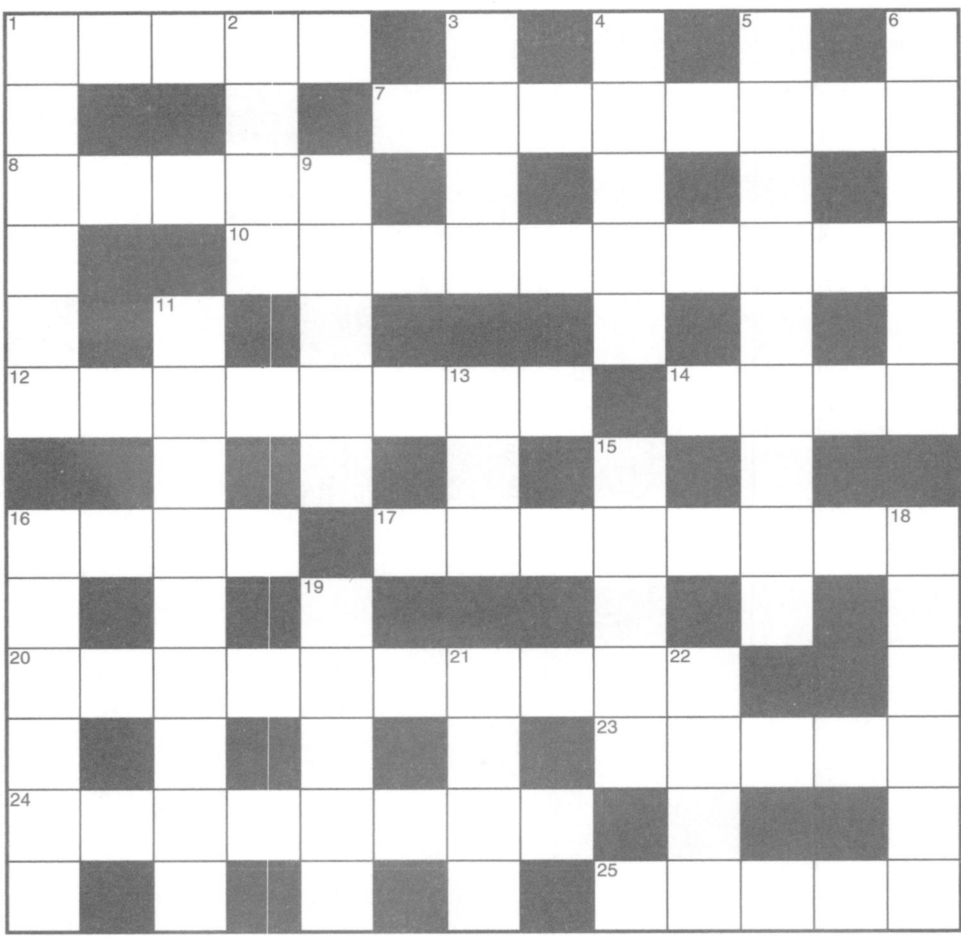

## ACROSS

1. Flower containers
7. Surpasses in cunning
8. Recoiled, ... away
10. Grow back (of vegetation)
12. Looked (for)
14. Many-stringed instrument
16. Perjurer
17. Red salad fruits
20. Meteorologist
23. Sat idly
24. Lopsidedly
25. Out of bed

## DOWN

1. Helmet face protectors
2. Jug
3. Adjust (piano)
4. Much of the time
5. Digging machine
6. Slumbering
9. Tennis 40/40
11. Information banks
13. Sense of self
15. Of birth
16. Legal
18. Web-spinner
19. Number in trio
21. Depend
22. Catches (thief)

# CROSSWORD 208

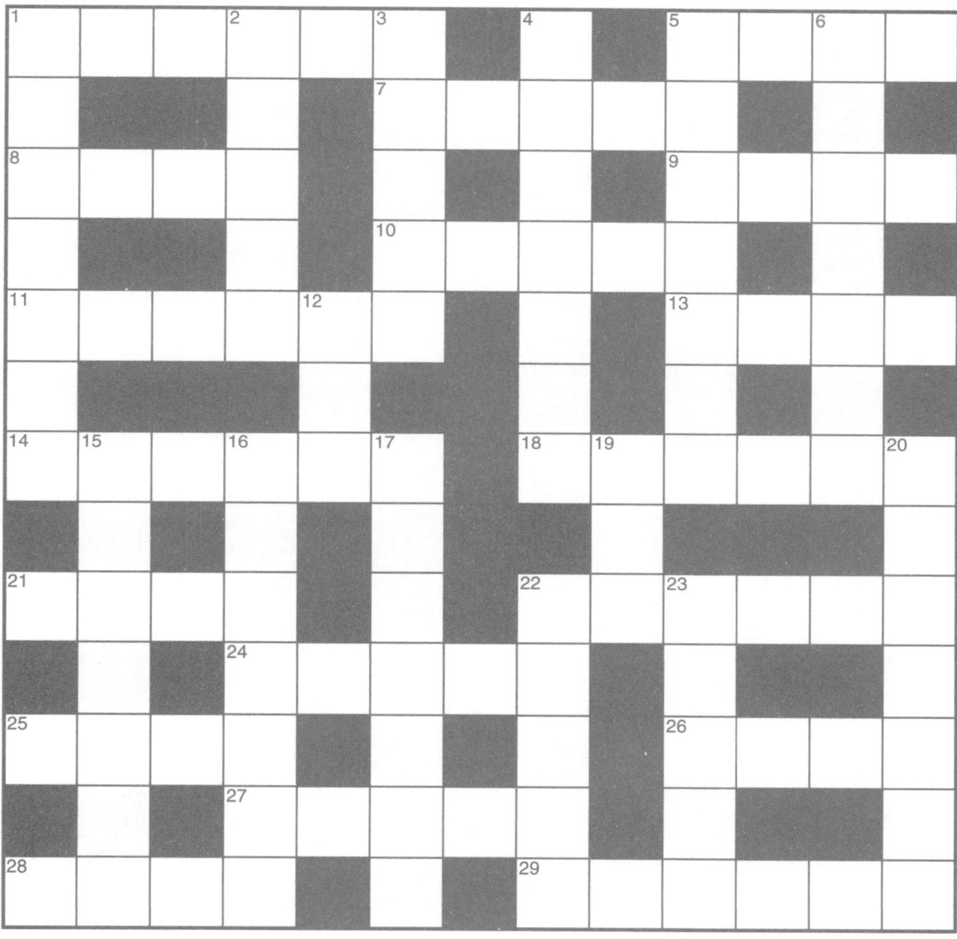

## ACROSS

1. Slender
5. Spiders' traps
7. Rabbit enclosure
8. Bass brass instrument
9. Farm produce
10. Astound
11. Protective headgear
13. Enthusiastic devotion
14. Traumas
18. Provoke to anger
21. Execute
22. Pranksters, practical ...
24. Bring together
25. Movie
26. Distinctive sound
27. Synthetic fabric
28. Military equipment
29. Least outgoing

## DOWN

1. Nicks
2. Domain
3. Bread cereal
4. Level
5. Breathed noisily
6. Suitcases
12. Deer
15. Shaggier
16. Pillars
17. Firmly
19. In the past
20. Most intrusive
22. Tough trousers
23. Perverted

# CROSSWORD 209

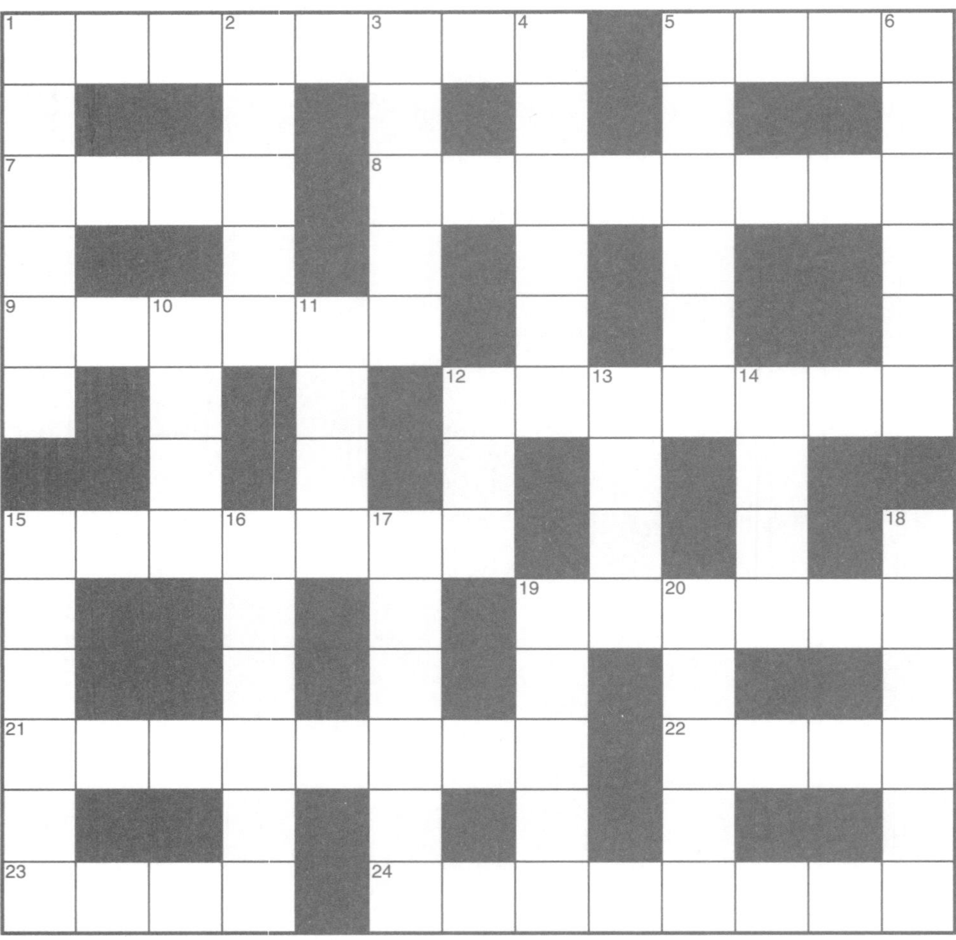

## ACROSS

1. Foremost
5. Violent (of movie)
7. Festive occasion
8. Confessed
9. Alpaca relatives
12. Sexes
15. Beer makers
19. Striped African animals
21. Undo
22. Clothing
23. Paved enclosure
24. Issue (medication)

## DOWN

1. Paid male escort
2. Danger alert
3. Knowledge tests
4. Place of worship
5. Removed innards
6. Sings Swiss alpine-style
10. Gifted
11. Assistant
12. Poison with fumes
13. Nominate
14. Not often, hardly ...
15. Attractiveness
16. Sorcerer
17. Severely defeated
18. Serviceable
19. Defined regions
20. Small trumpet

# CROSSWORD 210

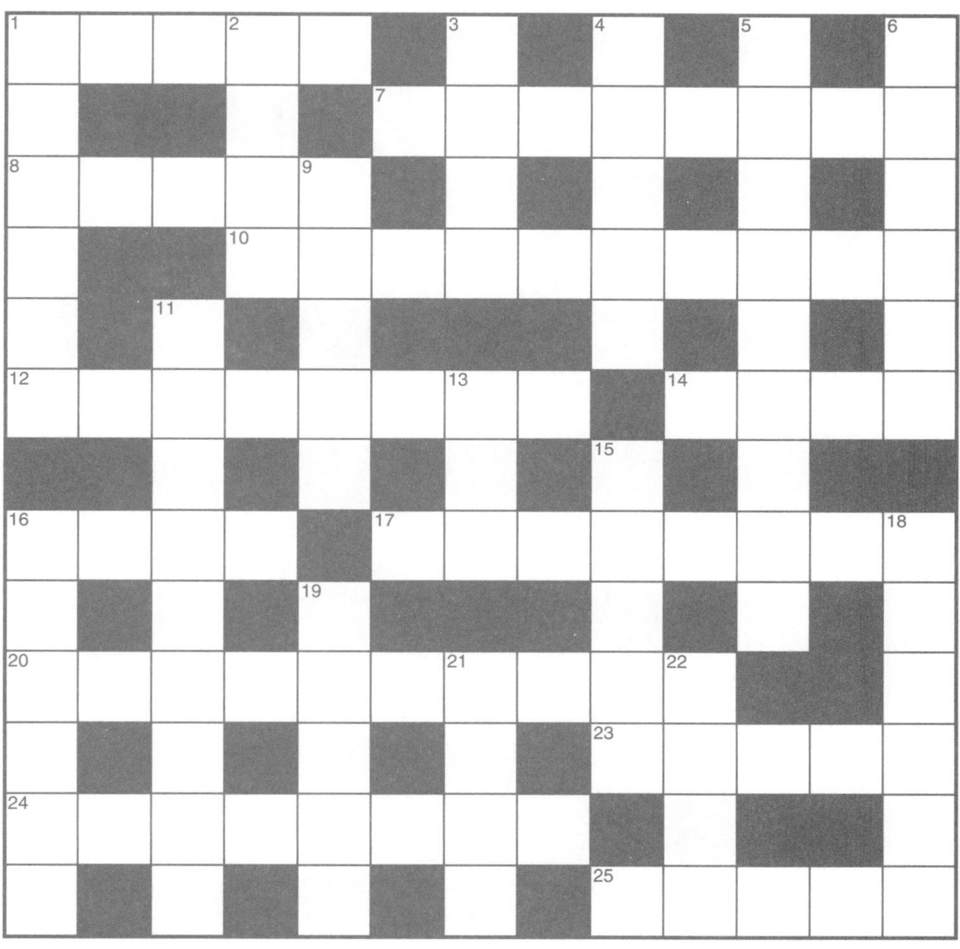

## ACROSS

1. Tycoon
7. Routinely
8. Wedding partner
10. Achievable
12. Poured (wine)
14. Low bark
16. Lion's cry
17. Vowed
20. Aristocratic female
23. Tore (along)
24. Hand bombs
25. Shut

## DOWN

1. Crowded in upon
2. Unfasten
3. Tiny amount
4. Alter (text)
5. Golf-course bar
6. Alone, by ...
9. Dark wood
11. Clambered
13. Make mistake
15. Besmirch
16. Go back on deal
18. Aimless scrawl
19. Automobile body type
21. Individuals
22. Large tack

# CROSSWORD 211

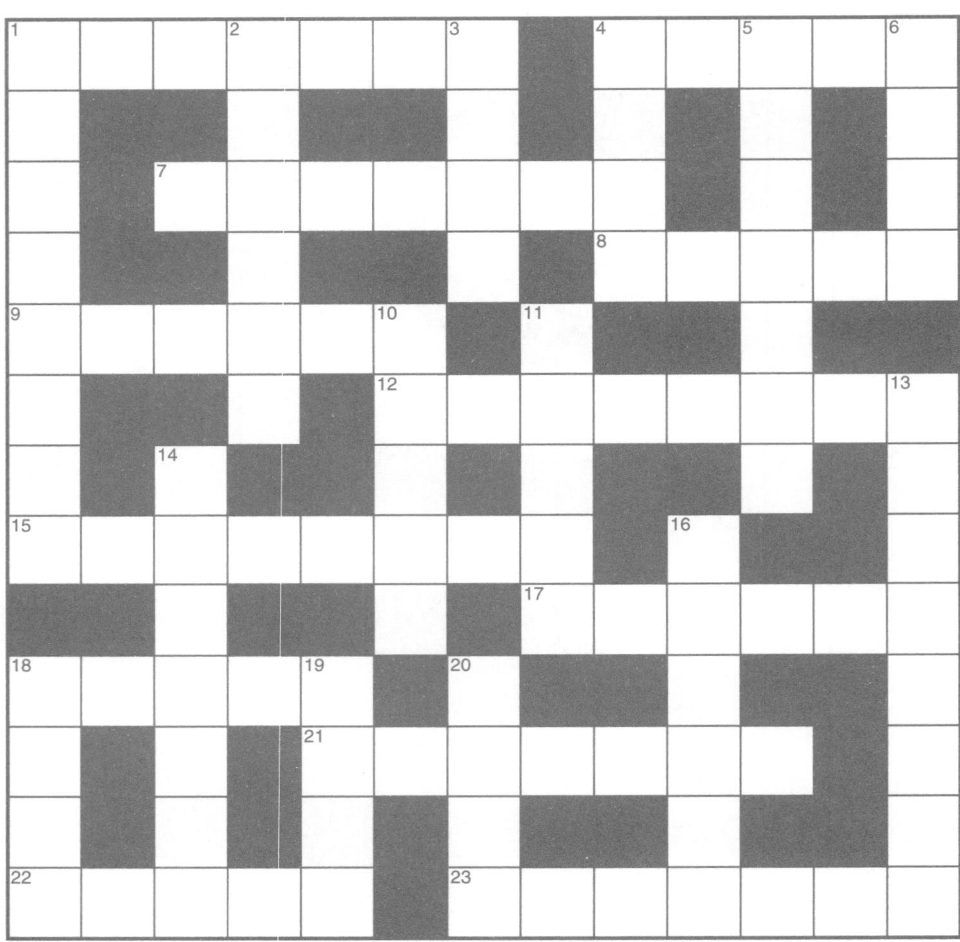

## ACROSS

1. Completely
4. Flood barrier
7. Lazed about
8. Decree
9. Fiction books
12. Gainfully (employed)
15. Pitfall
17. In short supply
18. Stage play
21. High plain
22. Small liquor measures
23. Become ill again

## DOWN

1. Not desired
2. Flees to wed
3. Hindu meditation
4. Vein of ore
5. Noticeably
6. Radiate
10. Sweetener
11. Birds' bills
13. Christmas
14. Card game
16. Yellow fruit
18. Expired
19. Gorillas or chimpanzees
20. Scalp growth

# CROSSWORD 212

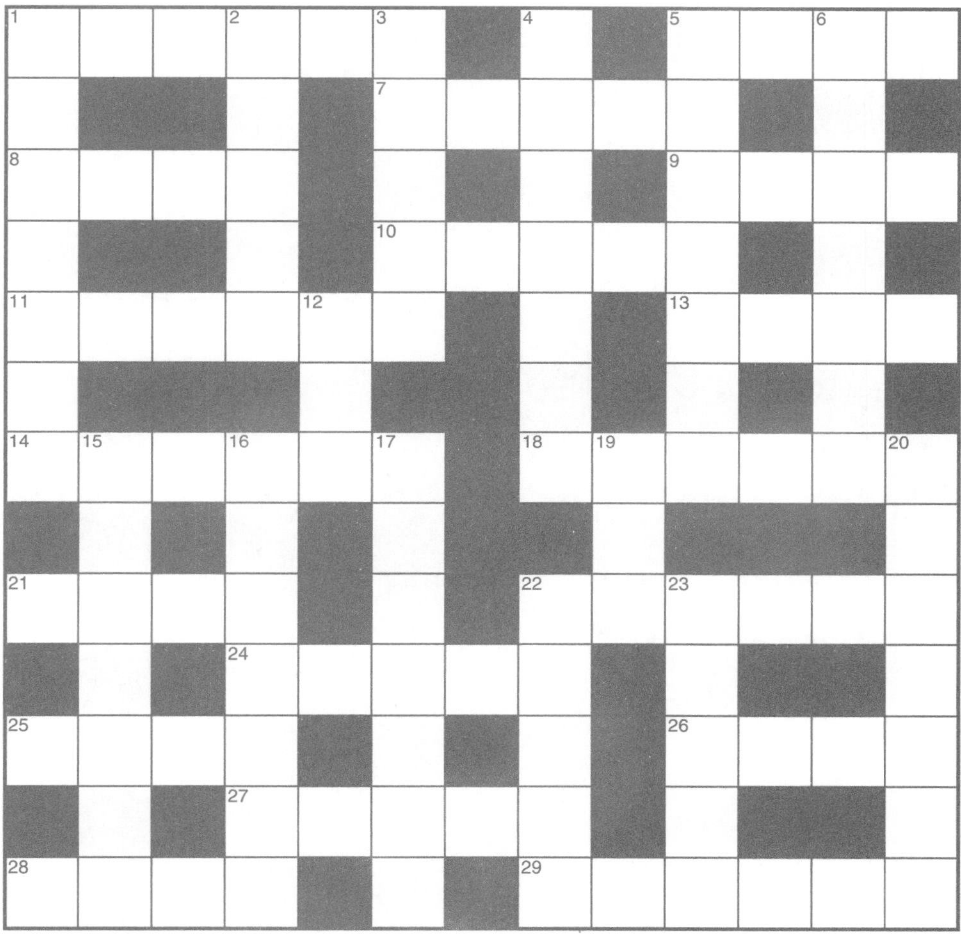

## ACROSS

1. Certainly
5. Beloved
7. Obliterate
8. At summit of
9. Did battle (with)
10. Pakistan currency
11. Give job to
13. Insert (bullet)
14. Sloops or ketches
18. Tapped
21. Power group
22. Sluggishness
24. Dull brownish-yellow
25. Megastar
26. Roman gown
27. Do well (at)
28. Betting chances
29. Absolve

## DOWN

1. Visual symbolism
2. Dismiss
3. Denounce
4. More cheerful
5. Progress by stages
6. Arithmetic mean
12. Cereal grass
15. Referred subtly
16. Interrupts (speaker)
17. Scrape
19. Egyptian cobra
20. Child-minding
22. Walkway between pews
23. Room within roof

# CROSSWORD 213

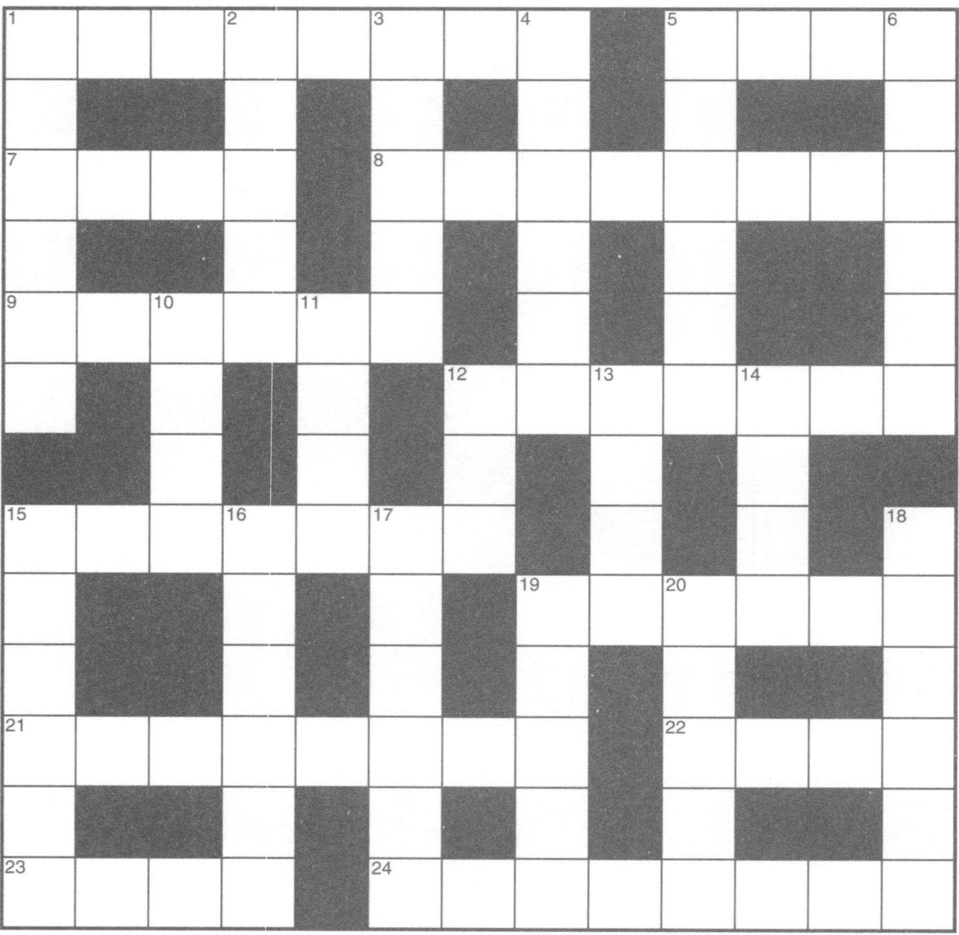

## ACROSS

1. Explosive in nature
5. Insensible
7. Have (to)
8. Fluid seepages
9. Lessened in severity
12. Burning surface of
15. Trained (team)
19. Luggage tags
21. Intimidate
22. Eyelid hair
23. Unable to speak
24. Reading disorder

## DOWN

1. Property wrecker
2. Financial records check
3. Lazed
4. Facilitate
5. Closer
6. Founding
10. Shade of blue
11. Per, for ...
12. Downcast
13. Opera song
14. Tiny landmass
15. Held back
16. Spider's network
17. Go too far
18. Respiratory ailment
19. Type of lily
20. Swell outwards

# CROSSWORD 214

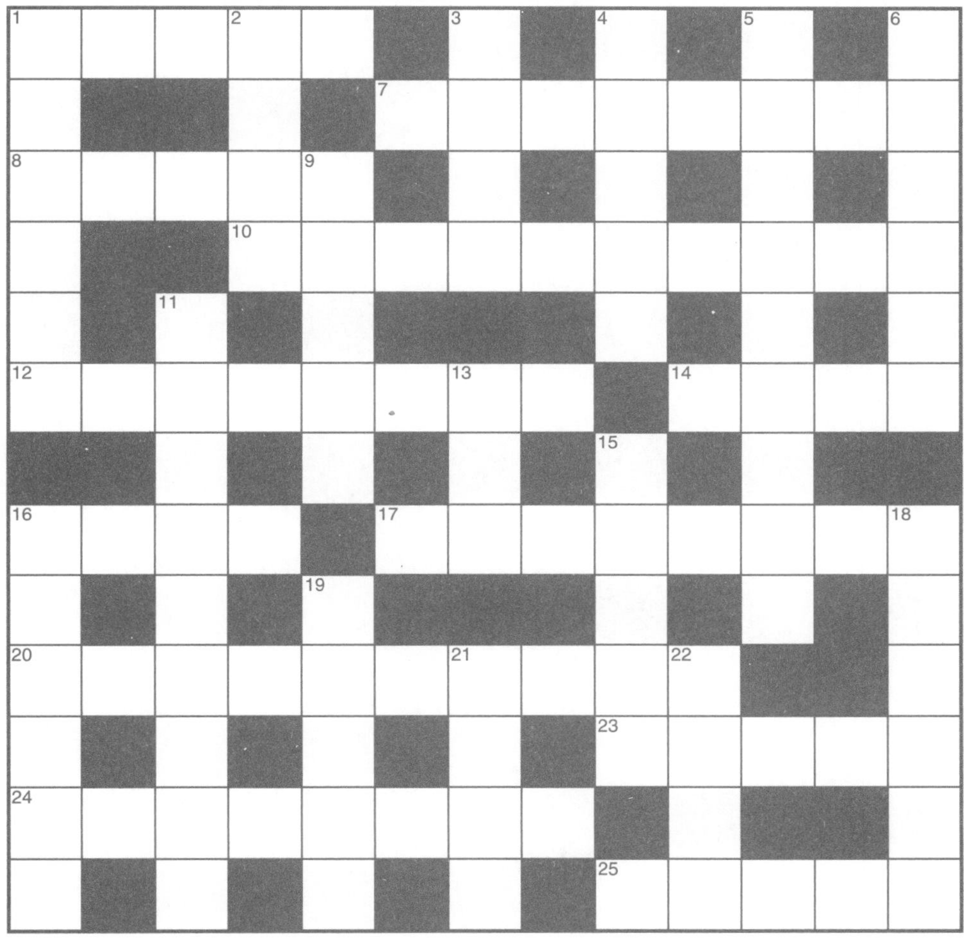

## ACROSS

1. Sense receptor
7. Surgical cut
8. Wide
10. Tearing jaggedly
12. Numbed
14. 100th of dollar
16. Pull
17. Announced
20. People in book
23. Crave, ... for
24. Children's vaulting game
25. Hidden stockpile

## DOWN

1. Arrested
2. Calf flesh
3. Respectfully, on bended ...
4. Concluding
5. Shareholders' payments
6. Horse-head chess piece
9. Valleys
11. Twin-hulled vessel
13. Use frugally, ... out
15. Milk-processing site
16. Placid
18. Saturate
19. Clumsy social error
21. Implement
22. Cult

# CROSSWORD 215

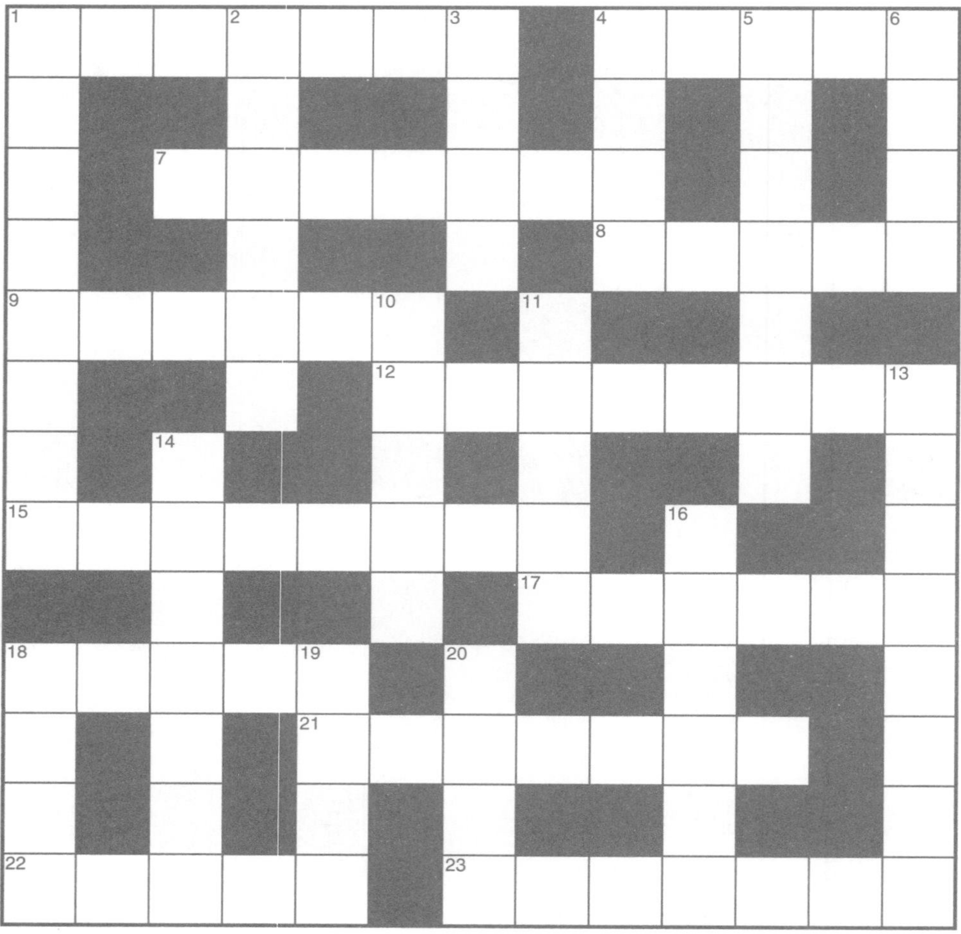

## ACROSS

1. Entangled
4. Shopping mall
7. Recognition
8. Serenity
9. Cotton strand
12. Not scared
15. Enthusiasm
17. Degraded
18. More mature
21. Sloped writing style
22. Army clergyman
23. Holding (grudge)

## DOWN

1. Aircraft lever
2. Tossed (rider off horse)
3. Bargain
4. Pageantry
5. Yearly book of events
6. Raise bid, up the ...
10. Deceives
11. Lightweight timber
13. Trawling (riverbed)
14. Enticed
16. Performs ballet
18. Cavort
19. Widespread
20. Fanciful story

# CROSSWORD 216

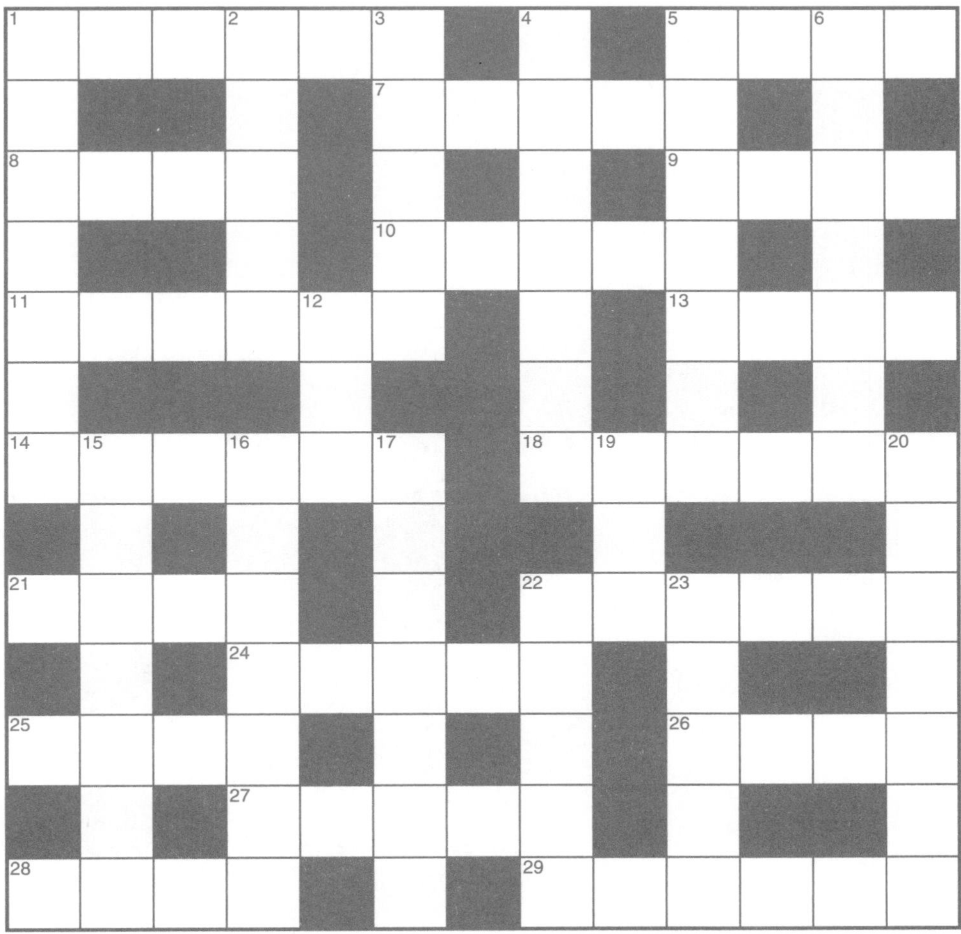

## ACROSS

1. Packing boxes
5. Provoke
7. Thin candle
8. Mutilate
9. Not here
10. Bring into force
11. Surpassed
13. Frozen, ... over
14. Painters' tripods
18. Respect, ... highly
21. Uncontrolled slide
22. Intimidates
24. Cinema attendant
25. Unbiased
26. Molten rock
27. Fencing blades
28. Poems
29. Artist's model

## DOWN

1. Write music
2. Domesticated
3. Knight's horse
4. Lecturer
5. Shredding (cheese)
6. Hobbyist
12. Out of sorts
15. Uncomfortable (situation)
16. Withstands
17. Caught view of
19. Geological age
20. Loss of hope
22. Rebuke, ... down
23. Dim

# CROSSWORD 217

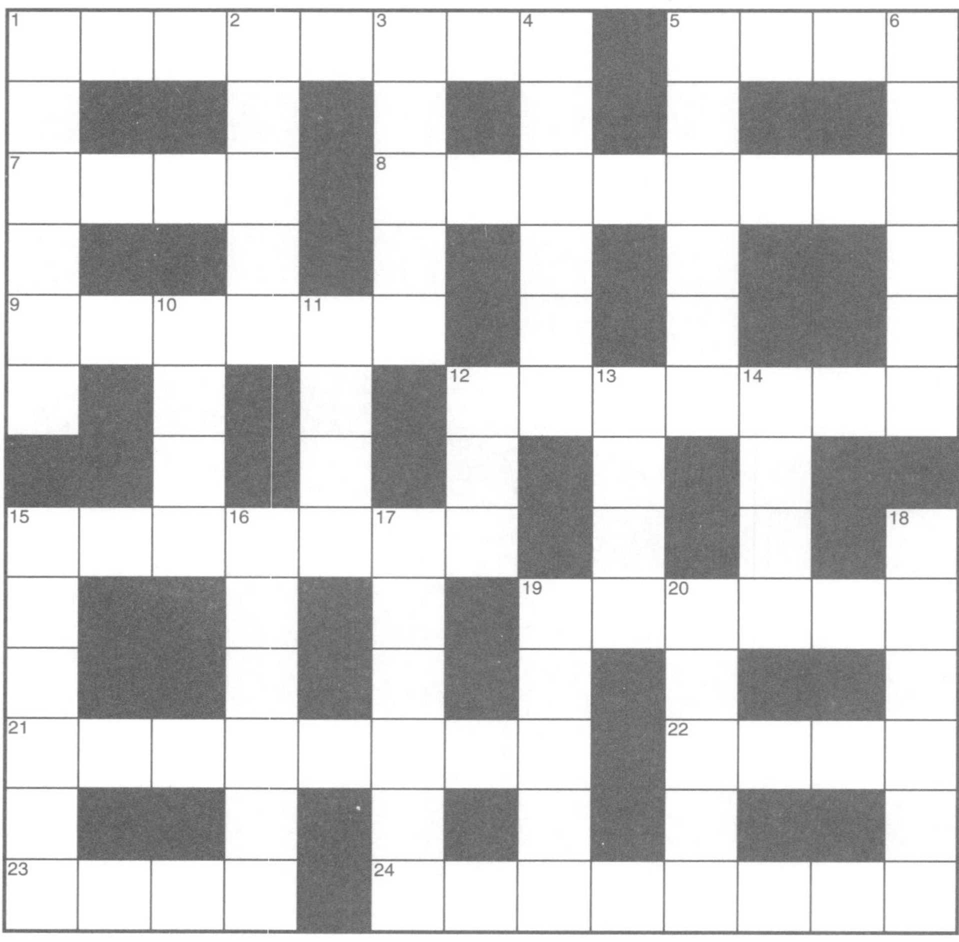

## ACROSS

1. Backed (venture)
5. Soapy bubbles
7. Arm bone
8. Nut-gathering rodent
9. Frisk (about)
12. Sellers
15. Feeblest
19. Dreaded
21. Single strand
22. ... & papa
23. Concludes
24. Sicknesses

## DOWN

1. Dowdy women
2. Anew
3. Social system
4. Tennis penalty, ... fault
5. Compelled
6. Grinding teeth
10. Region
11. Nucleus
12. Animal physician
13. Knob
14. In excess of
15. Belgian breakfast treat
16. Meat skewers, shish ...
17. Terrified cry
18. Principles
19. Deadly
20. Meant

# CROSSWORD 218

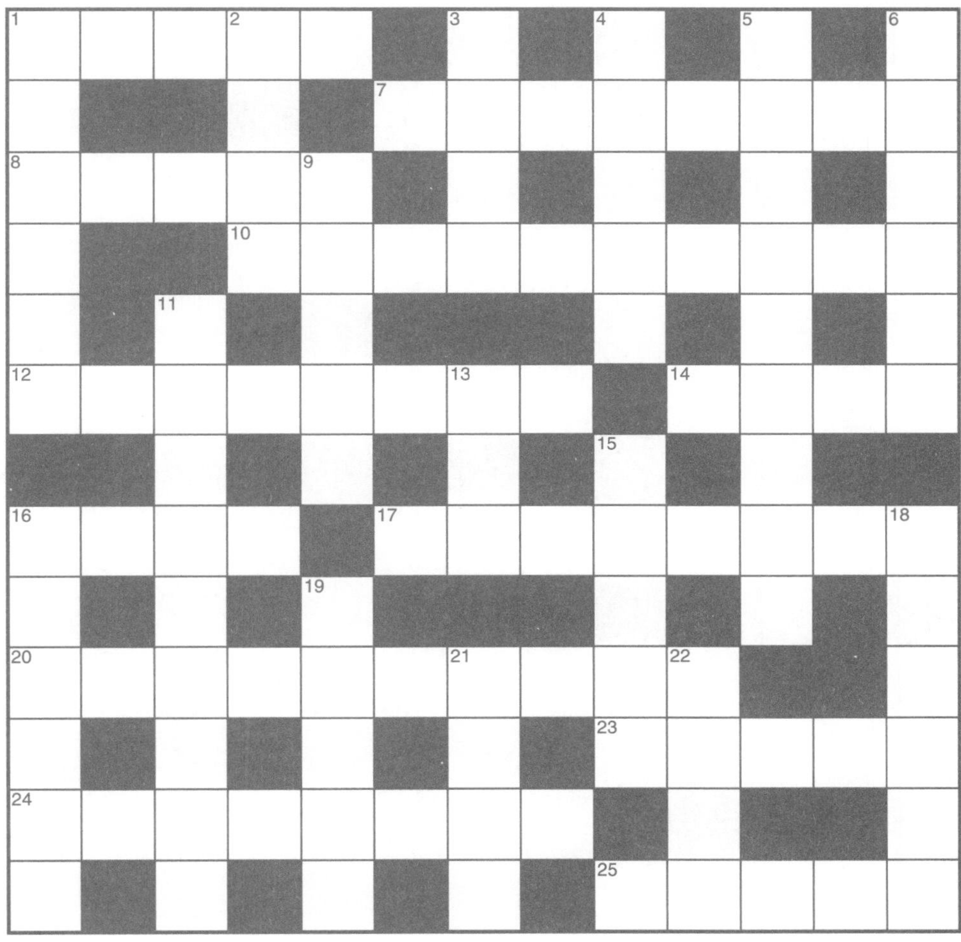

## ACROSS

1. Forward (message)
7. Rehearsal
8. Floorboard noise
10. Bread snacks
12. Youth
14. Henhouse produce
16. Repast
17. Private road
20. Senselessly
23. Shiny fabric
24. Leadership
25. Requested, ... for

## DOWN

1. Satellite launcher
2. Unfortunately
3. Poke
4. Bitter (taste)
5. Sleeping apparel
6. Army dining rooms
9. Covered-in canoe
11. Wildlife collection
13. Wheat tip
15. Wicked wrongs
16. Oversee
18. Gaped tiredly
19. Dismal
21. Like, ... as
22. Barks shrilly

# CROSSWORD 219

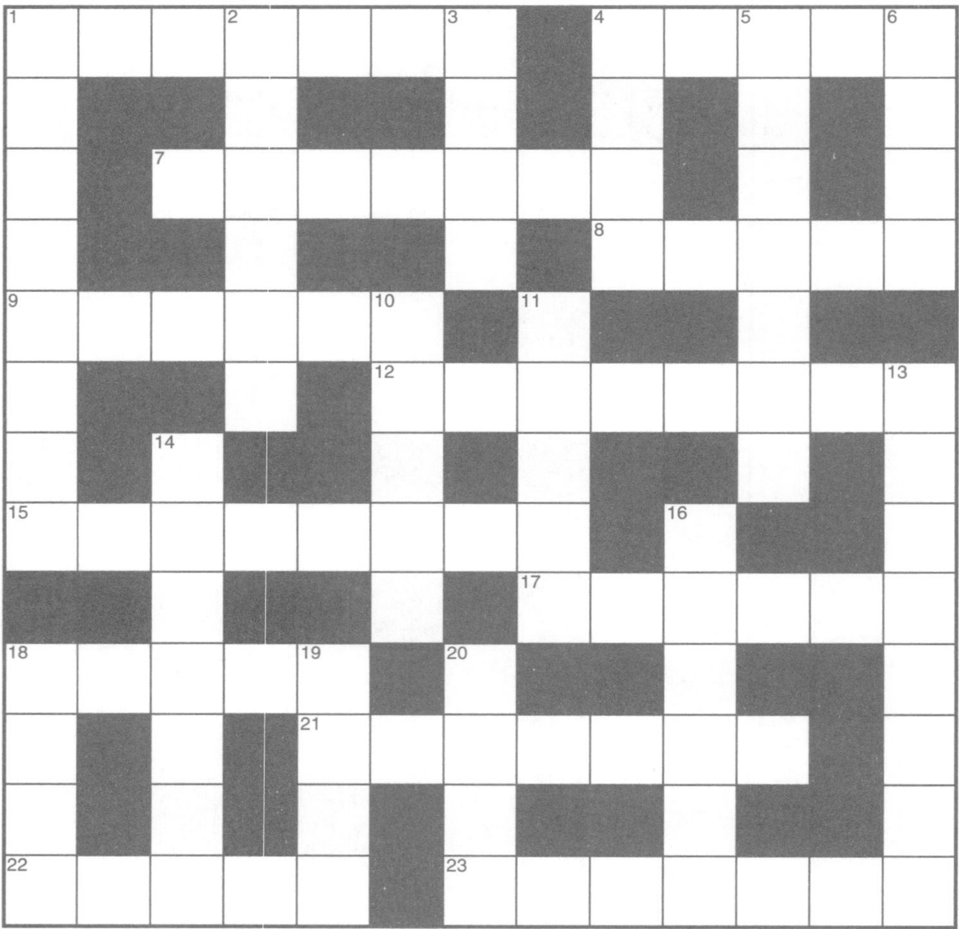

## ACROSS

1. Amazonian river fish
4. Trademark
7. Fistfuls (of flowers)
8. Small crown
9. Propose
12. Cellophane covers
15. Talked to sternly
17. Capitulates
18. Tasteless (food)
21. Responded
22. South American parrot
23. Sold on street

## DOWN

1. Of the body
2. Entertained
3. Dull pain
4. Head & shoulders sculpture
5. Shopping walkways
6. Scientific information
10. Old, cool star, red ...
11. Decorative tea tin
13. Fluctuated wildly
14. Of the Atlantic
16. Slay by guillotine
18. Deep resonant sound
19. Sketch
20. Sleep in tent

# CROSSWORD 220

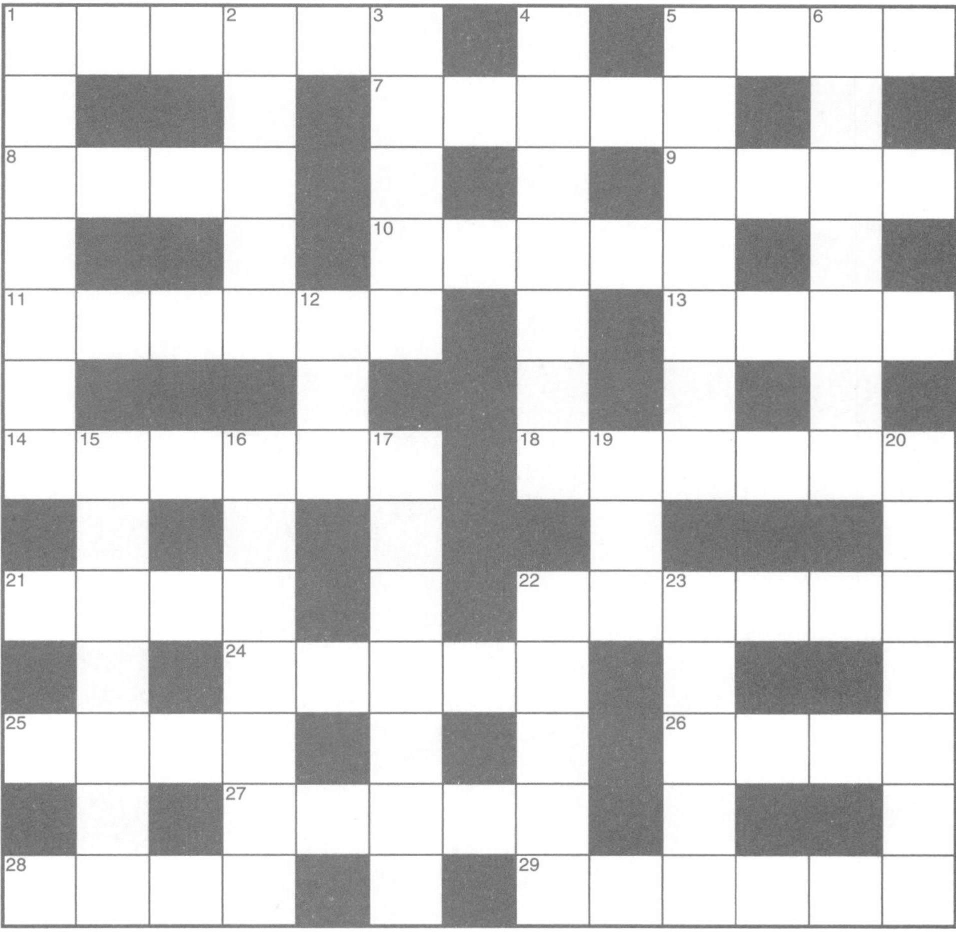

## ACROSS

1. Fasten
5. Objective
7. Dodge
8. Shark movie
9. Pen points
10. Fill with joy
11. Pitted (cherries)
13. Heavy weights
14. Mark of disgrace
18. Sheathe
21. Incite, ... up
22. Degrade
24. Exit
25. Tofu bean
26. Baseball glove
27. Wall recess
28. Not new
29. Croaked

## DOWN

1. Modifies
2. Incendiary crime
3. Carved into shape
4. Flair
5. Inherited (characteristic)
6. Pink-eyed rabbits
12. Disease-prone tree
15. Skin designs
16. Circlet of flowers
17. Progress
19. Named before marriage
20. Opted
22. Put off (from)
23. Jolts

# CROSSWORD 221

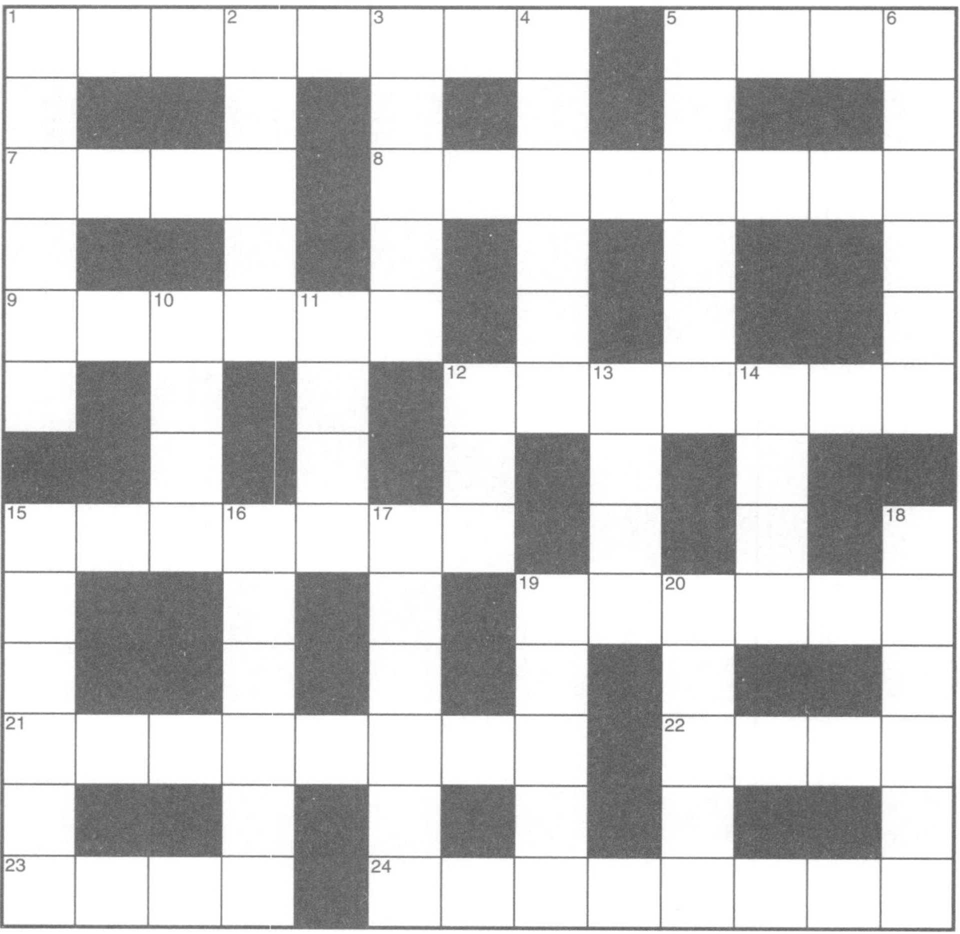

## ACROSS

1. Drifting on water
5. Ornate garden pots
7. Tennis court barriers
8. Pleasure-loving men
9. Tidily
12. Reaffirm
15. Let in again
19. Wild African canine
21. Small hollow pasta
22. Percussion instrument
23. Tinted
24. Suppositions

## DOWN

1. Imposing money penalty on
2. Advantage
3. Suggest
4. Type of beard
5. Unfasten (door)
6. Tahini paste seed
10. Spiritual glow
11. Tower (over)
12. Large rodent
13. Soft drink
14. Go berserk, run ...
15. Smashed into
16. Forceful request
17. Bring from overseas
18. Arranges in rows
19. Fruit liquid
20. Havana product

# CROSSWORD 222

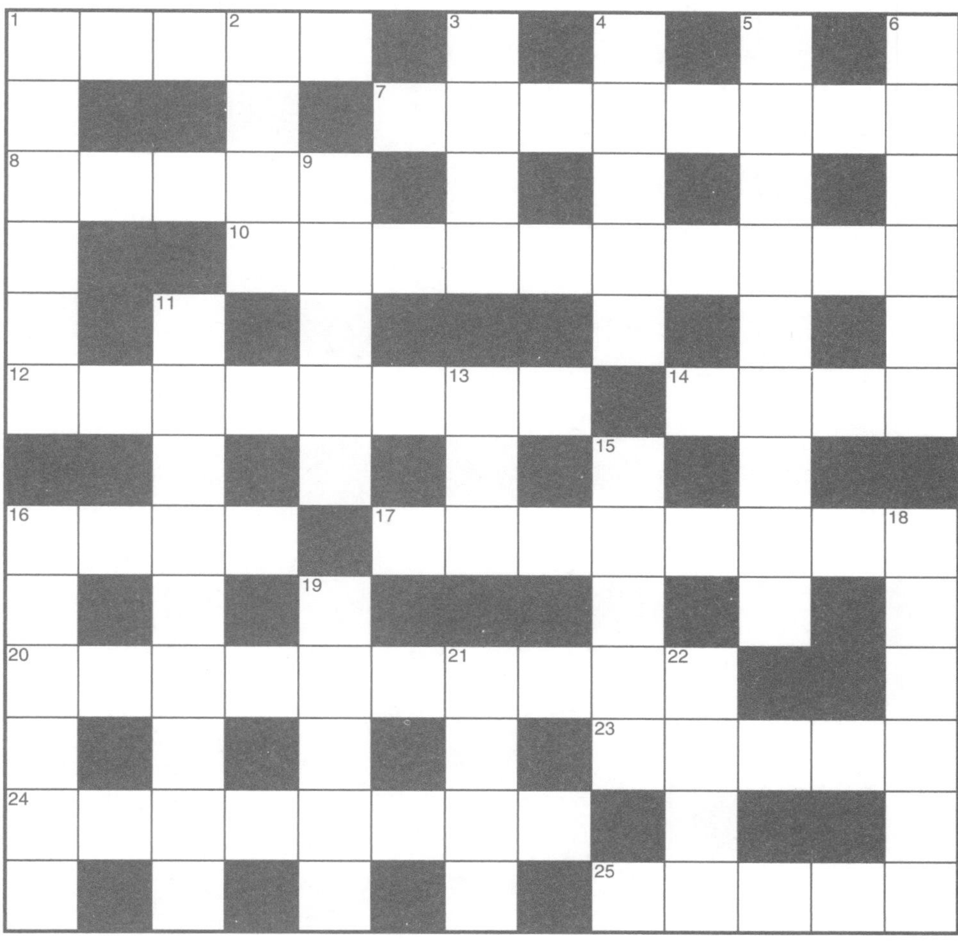

## ACROSS

1. Organic soil
7. Seized (aircraft)
8. Wise saying
10. Undergo
12. Going by (of years)
14. Lively dance
16. Heavy shoe
17. Beneath the waves
20. Car's lamps
23. Steam bath
24. Tough (skin)
25. Got up from chair

## DOWN

1. Funeral vehicle
2. Encourage
3. Drainage tube
4. Ocean liner bedroom
5. Most slender
6. Stick (to)
9. Have life
11. Wide views
13. Religious sister
15. Brave deeds
16. Witness
18. Embarkation call, all ...
19. ..., beta, gamma
21. Disease agent
22. Basic kitchen condiment

# CROSSWORD 223

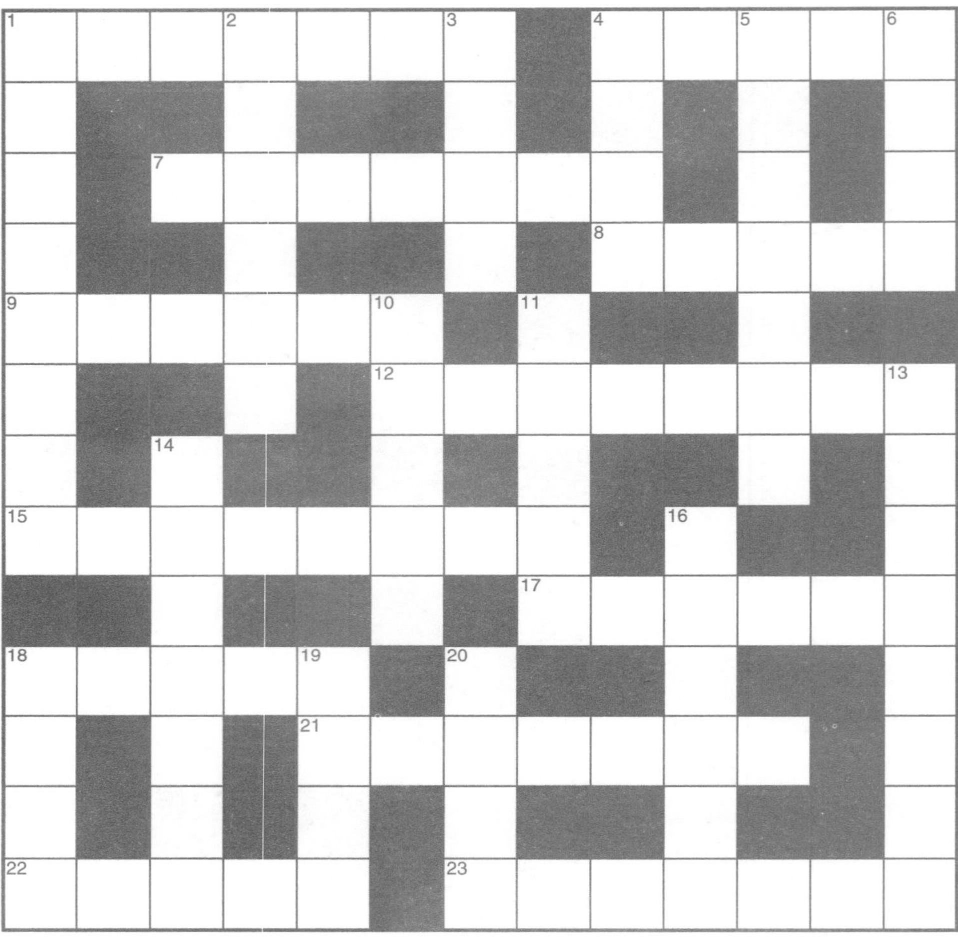

## ACROSS

1. Journeyed
4. Twist (nose)
7. Rejections
8. Playing-card jack
9. Annul
12. Models
15. Twelve-month-old horse
17. Radio interference
18. ... & females
21. Letter-jumble puzzle
22. Sidestep
23. Stored secretly

## DOWN

1. Nearby area
2. Stadiums
3. Dexterous
4. Chore
5. Involves
6. Wind-borne toy
10. Strange
11. Hooligan groups
13. Chained up
14. Returned to health
16. Oriental market
18. Temperament
19. In no peril
20. Deep cut

# CROSSWORD 224

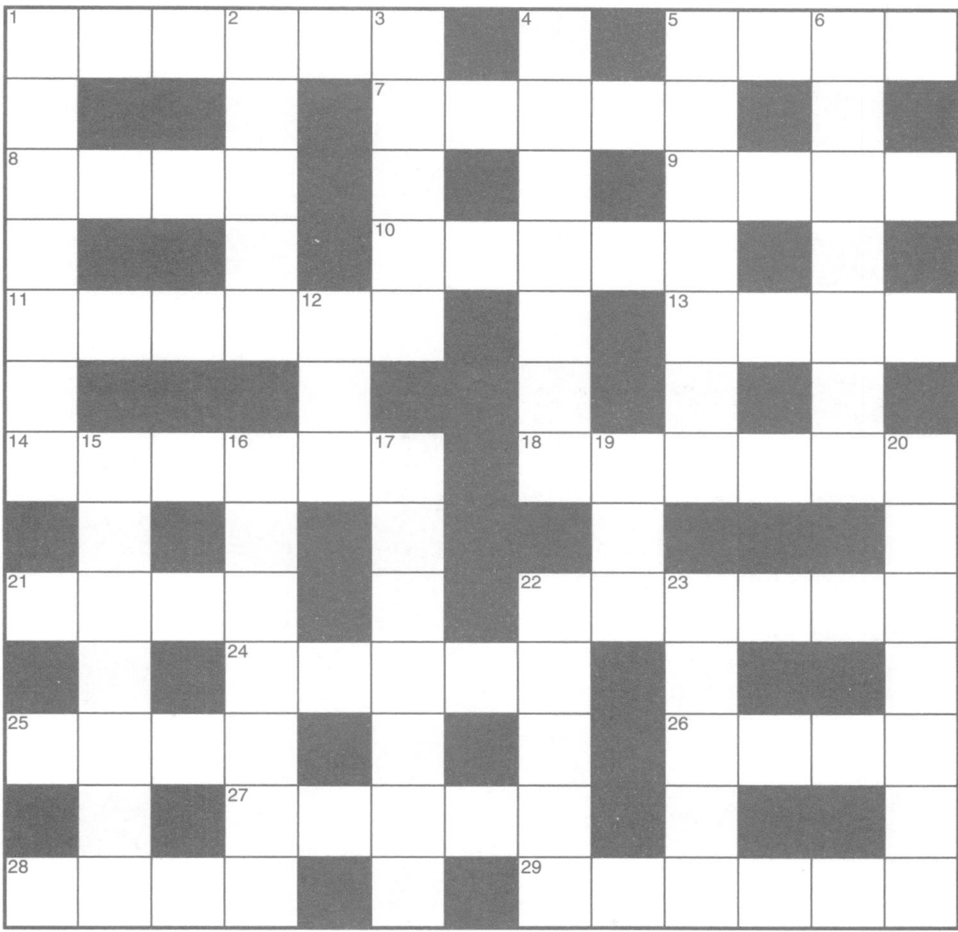

## ACROSS

1. Pulled sharply
5. Likable
7. Bird of prey
8. Tibetan monk
9. Big-scale movie
10. Leered at
11. Consecrate as priest
13. Committed perjury
14. Ambulance warnings
18. Brutality
21. Smartly-groomed
22. Book pages
24. Piece of glowing coal
25. Turn over
26. Thy
27. Pushes (shirt in)
28. Tallies
29. Religious dissent

## DOWN

1. Golden hues
2. Gumleaf-eating marsupial
3. Evil spirit
4. Eternally youthful
5. Aggravated
6. Sculptor's tools
12. Tavern
15. Took a breath
16. Excludes
17. Unwanted delay
19. In the past
20. Stingy
22. Not stale
23. Coating

# CROSSWORD 225

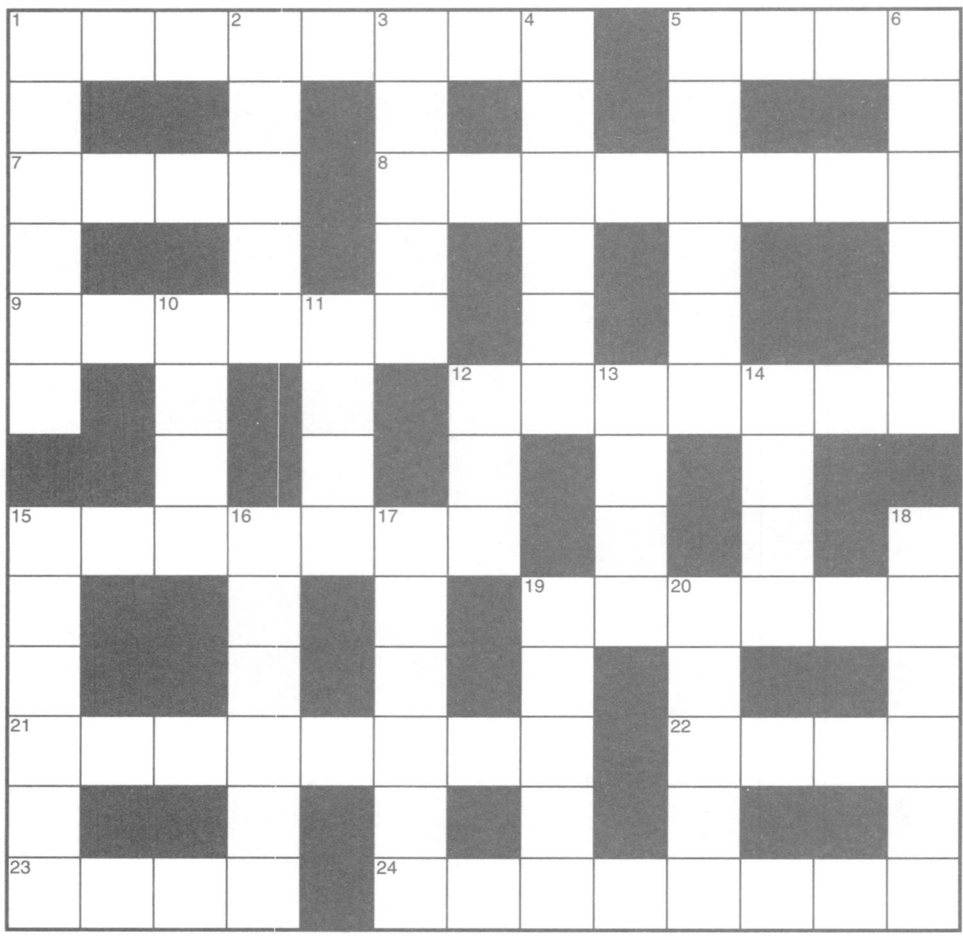

## ACROSS

1. Festive ribbon
5. Uterus
7. Was indebted to
8. By surprise
9. Accessories
12. Captivate
15. Disgraceful event
19. Fire-breathing monster
21. Signed protest document
22. Quantity of paper
23. Oxen harness
24. Raises

## DOWN

1. Preserved (meat)
2. Church senior
3. Handles roughly
4. Motive
5. Riches
6. Long-eared dog, ... hound
10. Bluefin creature
11. Filled with wonder
12. Conger fish
13. Singe
14. Very eager
15. Plainly
16. Beginner
17. For some time
18. Ugly elves
19. Tightly-packed
20. Main artery

# CROSSWORD 226

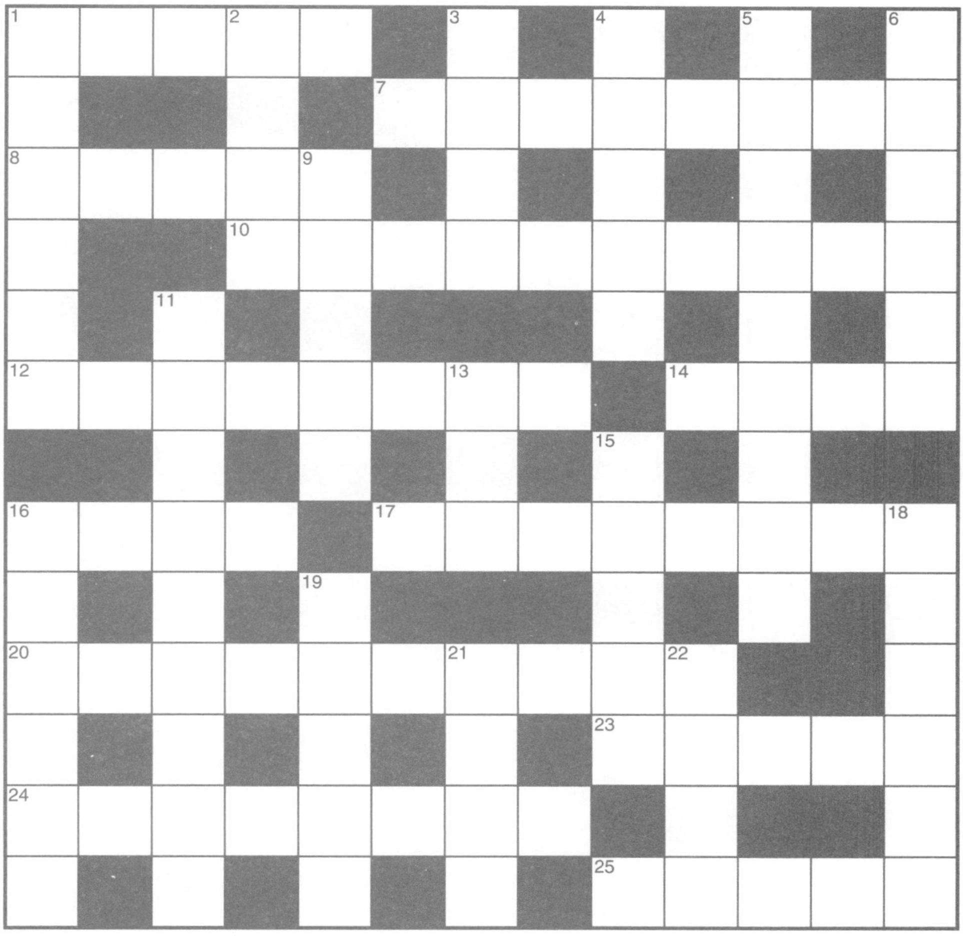

## ACROSS

1. Viral glandular disease
7. Movie caption
8. Camera image
10. Listens secretly
12. Insulin-related disorder
14. A single time
16. Spoken
17. Adopted battle formation
20. Sticking out
23. Light summer dish
24. Humorous account
25. Insinuating

## DOWN

1. Charted
2. Liver paste food
3. Reflect (on)
4. Learn for exam
5. Legal representatives
6. Leaseholder
9. Fertile desert spots
11. Self-contradictions
13. Female sheep
15. Blueprints
16. Parentless child
18. Lag behind
19. Small & shiny (eyes)
21. Adds (up)
22. Get

# CROSSWORD 227

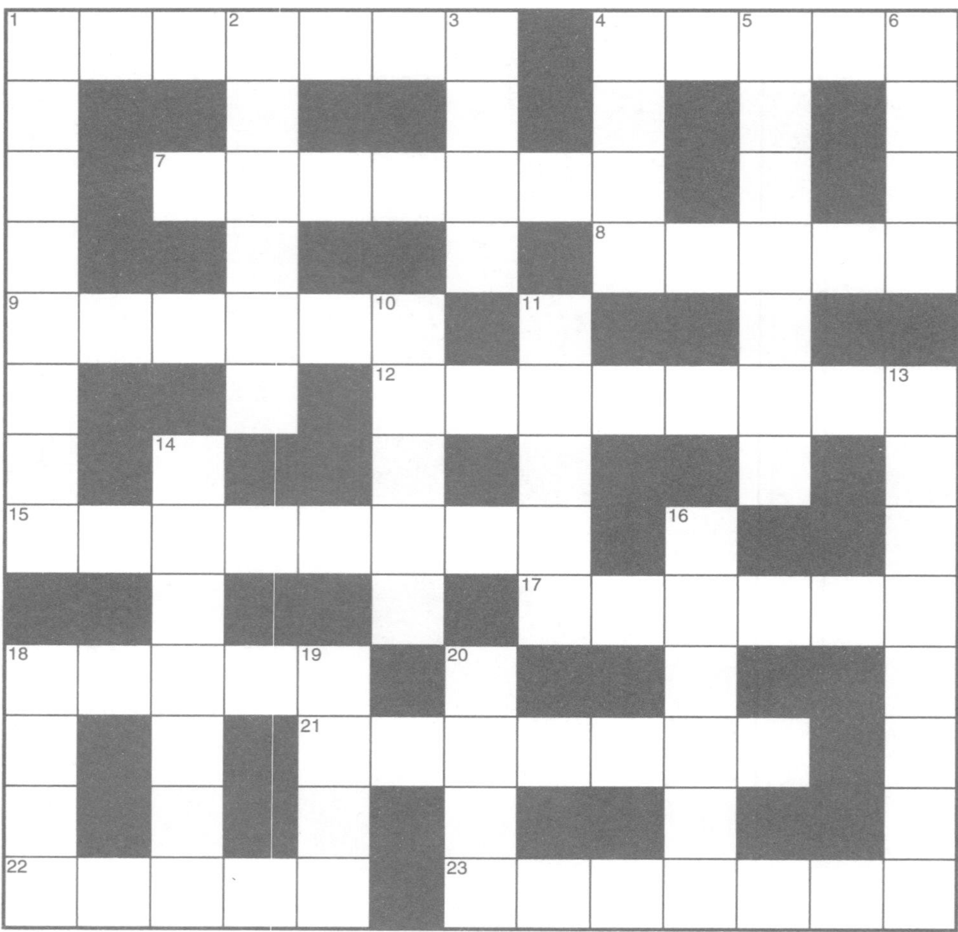

## ACROSS

1. Egyptian burial building
4. Shipment of goods
7. Wet slightly
8. Unpaid servant
9. Dribble
12. Made speechless
15. Lack of hearing
17. Snagged
18. Electrical units
21. Insulting (language)
22. Refashioned
23. Slow worker

## DOWN

1. Buffed to a sheen
2. Nuclear weapon, ... bomb
3. Obligation
4. Metal containers
5. Love affair
6. Exude
10. Fire remains
11. Sanctify
13. More poisonous
14. Blamed
16. Divided into two
18. Swerve
19. Dune material
20. Witty remark

# CROSSWORD 228

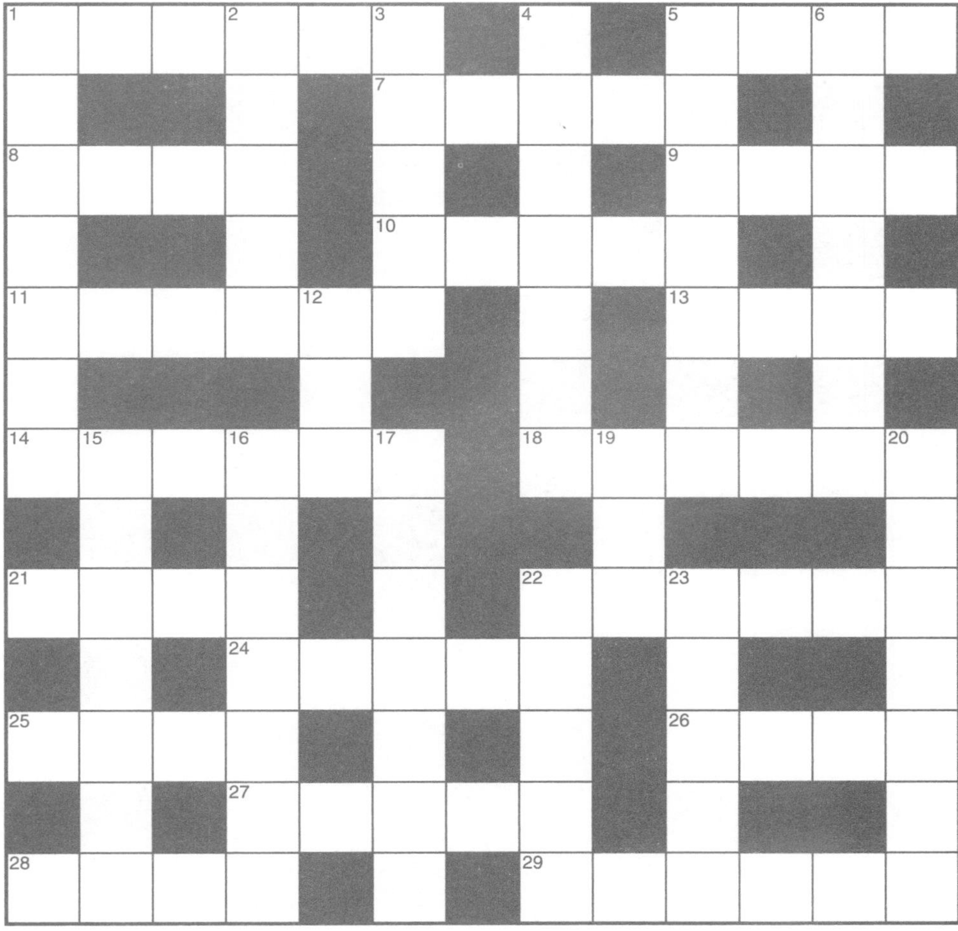

## ACROSS

1. Leave empty
5. Mats
7. Dog lead
8. Transmission setting, top ...
9. Unattractive
10. Ache
11. For each one
13. At a great distance
14. Bicycle for two
18. Monastery heads
21. Large bay
22. Complied with
24. Sloped
25. Dole (out)
26. Sleeveless garment
27. Scrounge
28. Body fluid lump
29. Corroded

## DOWN

1. Tramp
2. Say yes
3. Exclusive
4. Hungarian spice
5. Edible leafstalk
6. Courageous
12. Billiards stick
15. Intensely
16. Ricochet
17. Despoils
19. Girl's short haircut
20. Pacified by medication
22. Alternate
23. Folklore creatures

# CROSSWORD 229

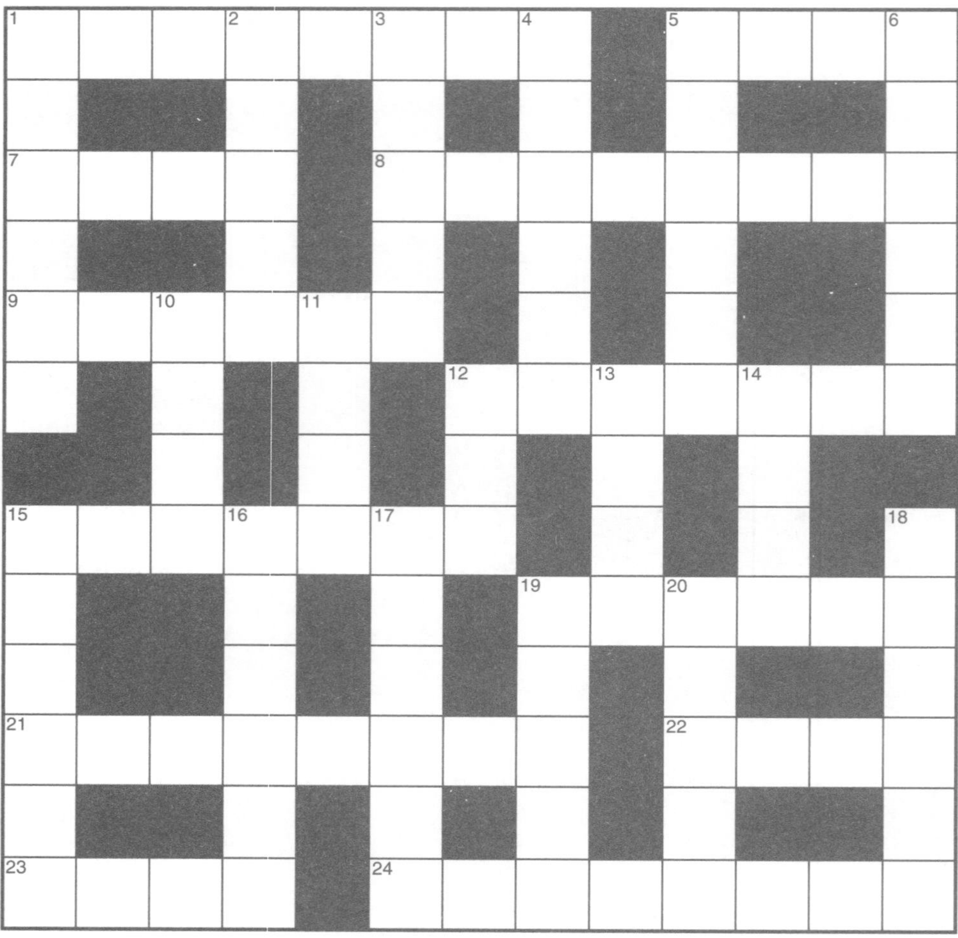

## ACROSS

1. Game bird
5. Noisy
7. Coral structure
8. Massaging
9. Declare illegal
12. Japanese hostesses
15. Drove
19. Moved at easy pace
21. Asylum seekers
22. Brief calm
23. Mental faculties
24. Admires

## DOWN

1. Prisoner's reprieve
2. Dreadful
3. Awry
4. Music sign, ... clef
5. Narrow shelves
6. Numerals
10. Baby-bottle top
11. A bit open
12. Deity
13. Single object
14. Salute
15. Bone core
16. Happens
17. Make beloved
18. Grown-ups
19. Donkeys
20. Prettiest girl, ... of the ball

# CROSSWORD 230

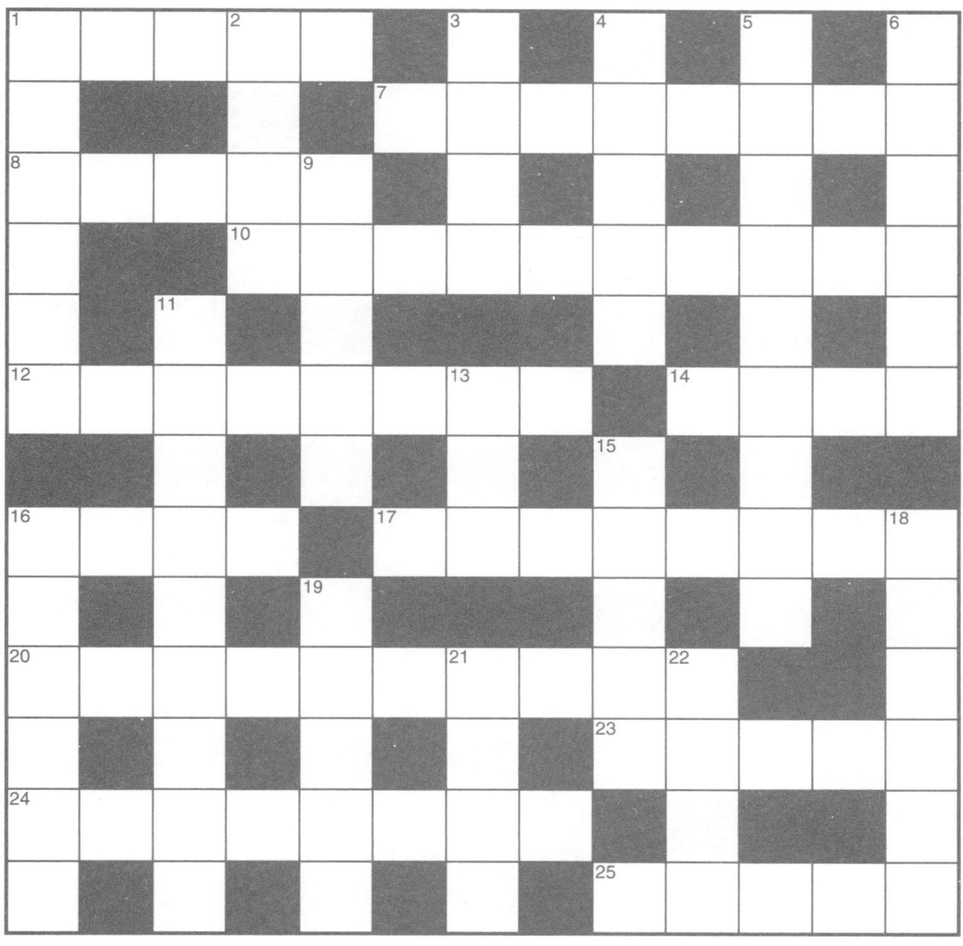

## ACROSS

1. Ships' spines
7. Warm outer garment
8. Evenly balanced
10. Comradeship
12. Rekindle
14. Raised (livestock)
16. Talk
17. Gained
20. Meteorologist
23. Undeveloped insect
24. Eager to please
25. Recurrent period

## DOWN

1. Zoo custodian
2. Frond
3. Egg-shaped
4. Disapproving look
5. Worrying
6. Foolish
9. Currency, ... tender
11. Pleasant tasting
13. Devour
15. Hackneyed
16. Rodeo rider
18. Widen (pupils)
19. Upper leg
21. Circle
22. Admiral's command

# CROSSWORD 231

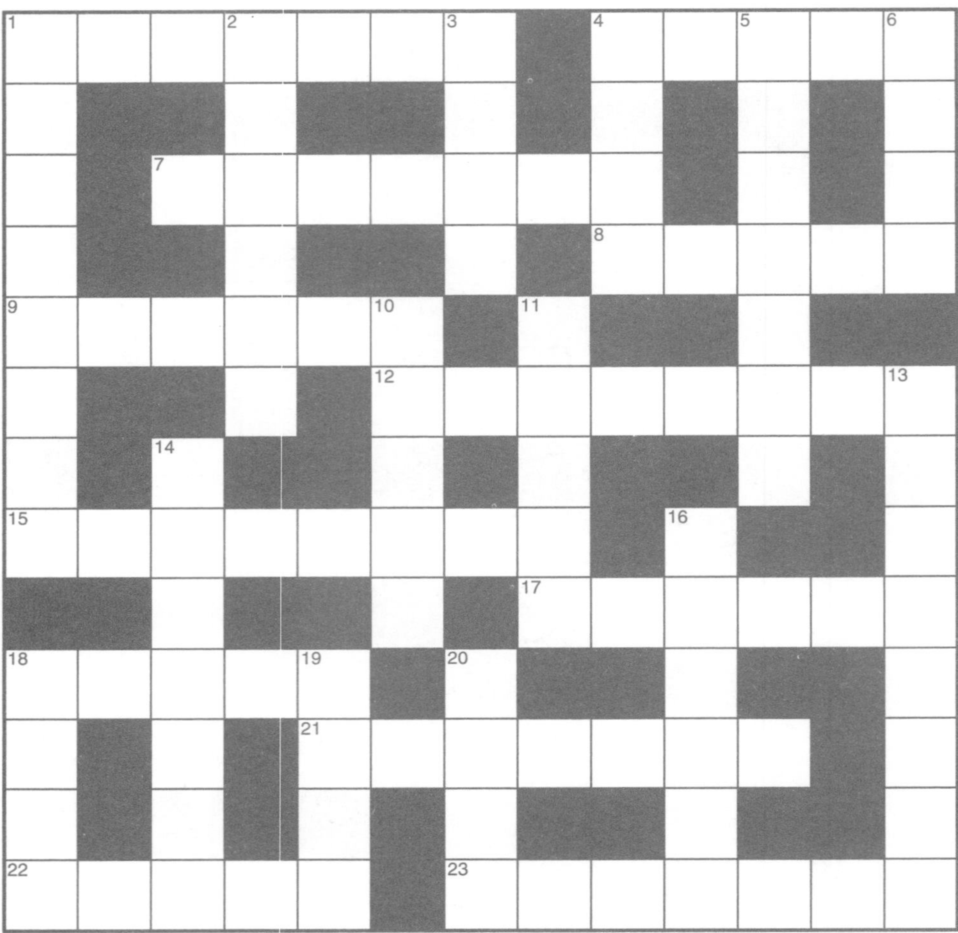

## ACROSS

1. Worn away
4. Dirt
7. Ballerina's garment
8. Burn with steam
9. Reinforced
12. Very worrying
15. Baby of the family
17. Went (towards)
18. Windshield blade
21. Without help
22. Assigned specific area
23. More raucous

## DOWN

1. Immune system protein
2. Business outlet
3. Dowdy
4. Trends
5. Maniac
6. Contained
10. Palm fruits
11. Confident belief
13. Horticulturist
14. Hick
16. Places bet
18. Exclamation, gee ...!
19. Regretted
20. Cut (timber)

# CROSSWORD 232

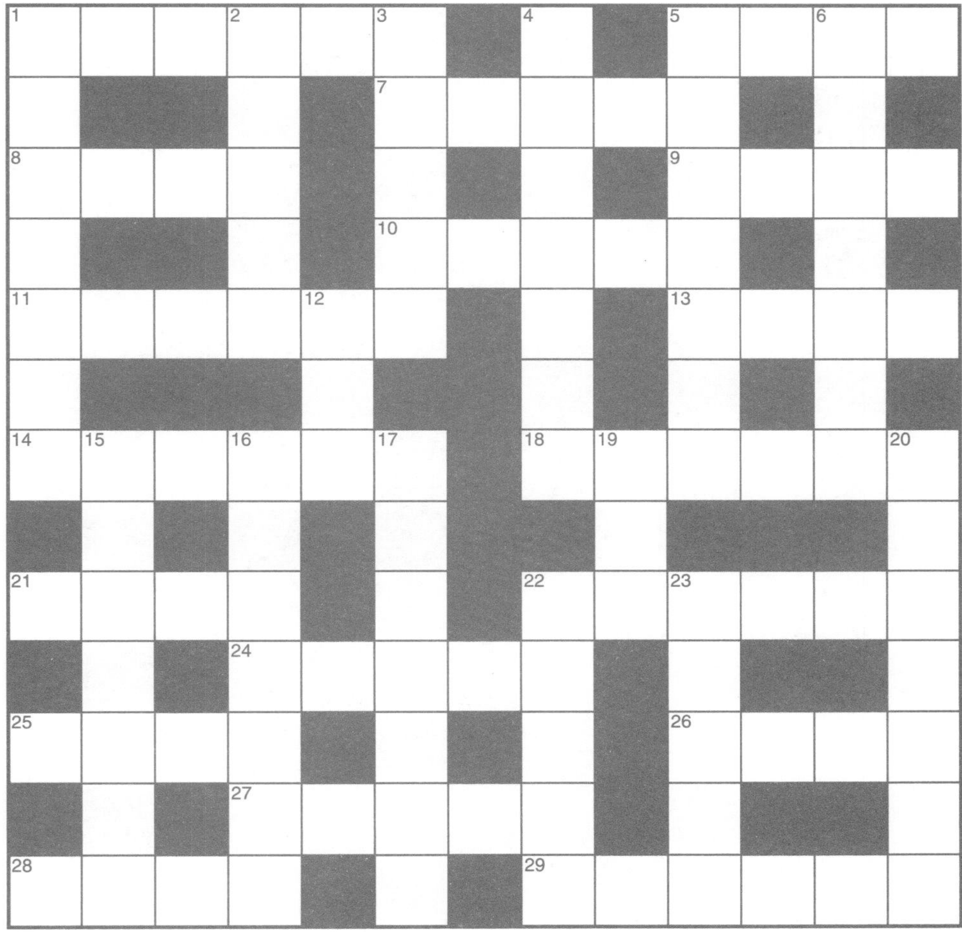

## ACROSS

1. Tile-chip design
5. Period of time
7. Haul strenuously
8. Smear
9. Respiratory organ
10. Fish commercially
11. Make an entrance
13. Charged atoms
14. Perfumed powder
18. Absorb (food)
21. Zodiac Cancer symbol
22. Utter bliss
24. Astonish
25. Cat's contented rumble
26. Arched roof
27. Miscalculated
28. Revise (manuscript)
29. Ruined

## DOWN

1. Craziest
2. Fossil resin
3. Grain slide
4. Mauled ferociously
5. Shouting
6. Window shelters
12. African antelope
15. Stranded (of boat)
16. Nightclub show
17. Gruesome
19. Anger
20. Smallest
22. Bears in mind
23. Of sound

# CROSSWORD 233

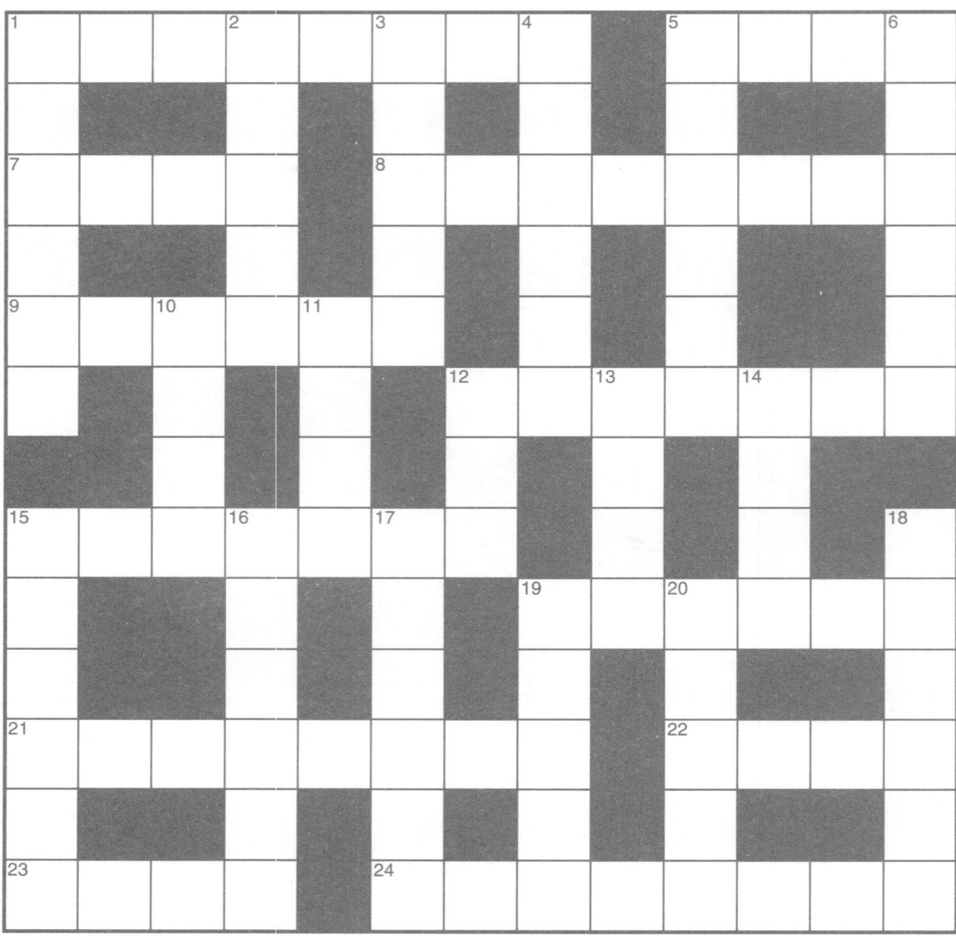

## ACROSS

1. Of the Middle Ages
5. Title document
7. Metric mass unit
8. Mimes
9. Rope loops
12. More in want
15. Speediest
19. Arm joints
21. Today
22. Challenge
23. Plate
24. Supported

## DOWN

1. Constructing
2. Cultural symbols
3. Evil habits
4. Confederacy
5. Covered with cloth
6. Expel from legal profession
10. Composer's work
11. Uncomfortable, ill at ...
12. In no way
13. Fragrant tea, ... Grey
14. Towards interior of
15. Stirred up (flames)
16. Wallop
17. Showers
18. Rise
19. Come next
20. Waited, ... one's time

# CROSSWORD 234

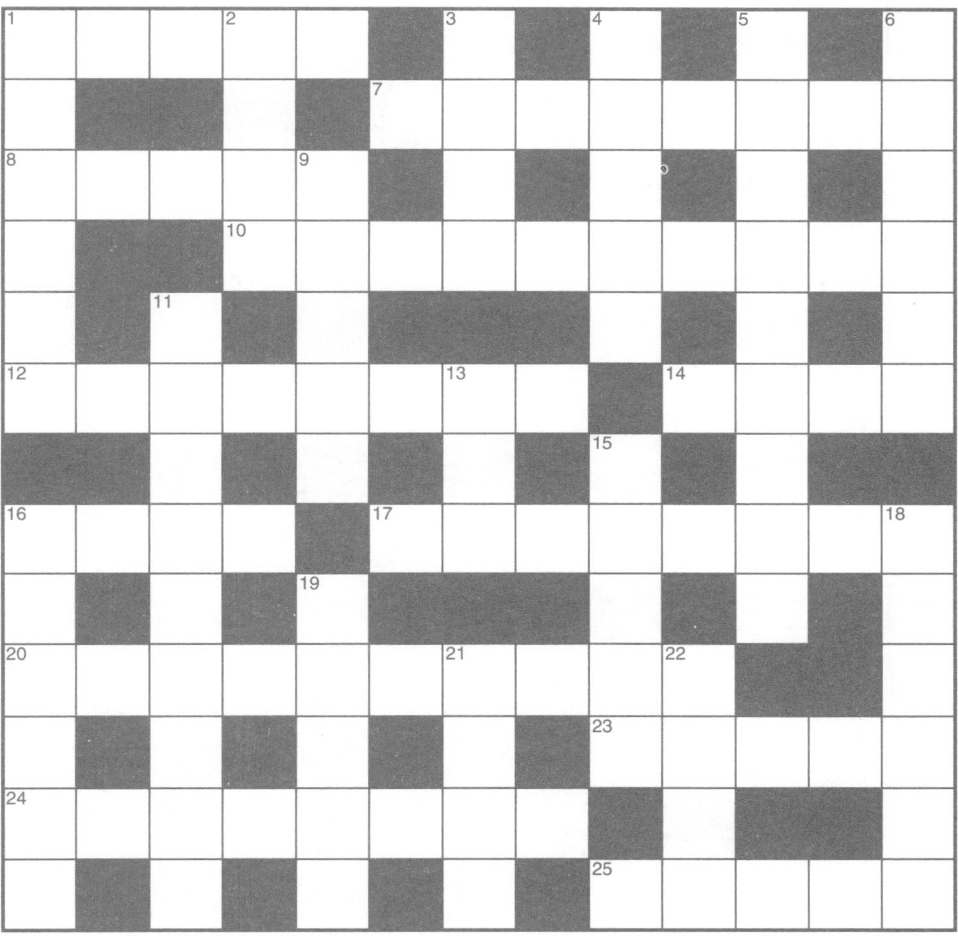

## ACROSS

1. Marine environment
7. Modestly
8. Publish
10. Media outlet
12. Driving-test official
14. Colony insects
16. Channel
17. Raised objections
20. Arrests
23. Keen
24. Most angular
25. Humiliation

## DOWN

1. Stand against
2. Kinswoman
3. He was, they ...
4. Hot & damp
5. Compassionately
6. Carrion-eating animals
9. Lukewarm
11. Cooking utensils
13. Large bird
15. Residence
16. Earnestly
18. Temperature unit
19. Send (cash)
21. Simple
22. Ornamental ribbon

# CROSSWORD 235

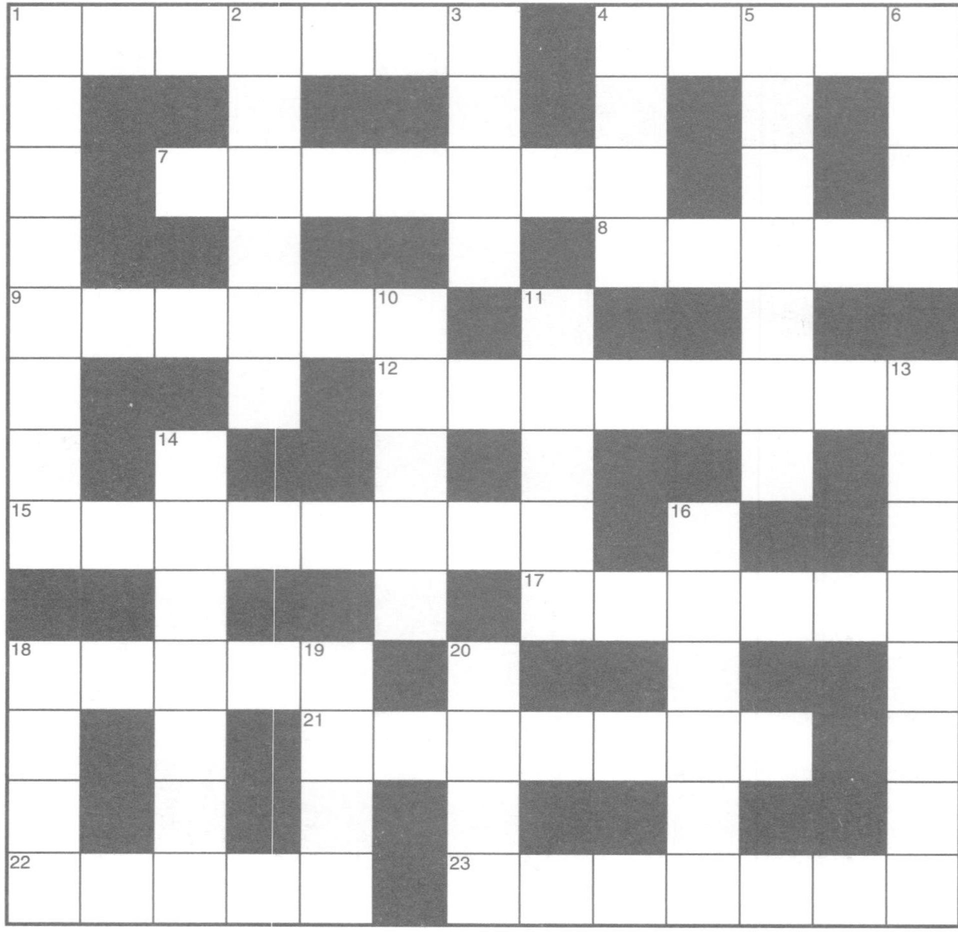

## ACROSS

1. Topic
4. Fatigued
7. Sign
8. Glides aloft
9. Surface wood layer
12. People taken from danger
15. Sword sheath
17. Spiritualist's meeting
18. Prestige
21. Twisted quickly
22. Greater (variety)
23. Competent

## DOWN

1. Withers
2. Abandoned (lover)
3. Compared to
4. Marries
5. Relieved
6. Tropical root vegetables
10. Ease up
11. Incursions
13. Agenda
14. Walked like duck
16. Cinematographer's apparatus
18. Was conversant with
19. Night sky object
20. Metal with the symbol Zn

# CROSSWORD 236

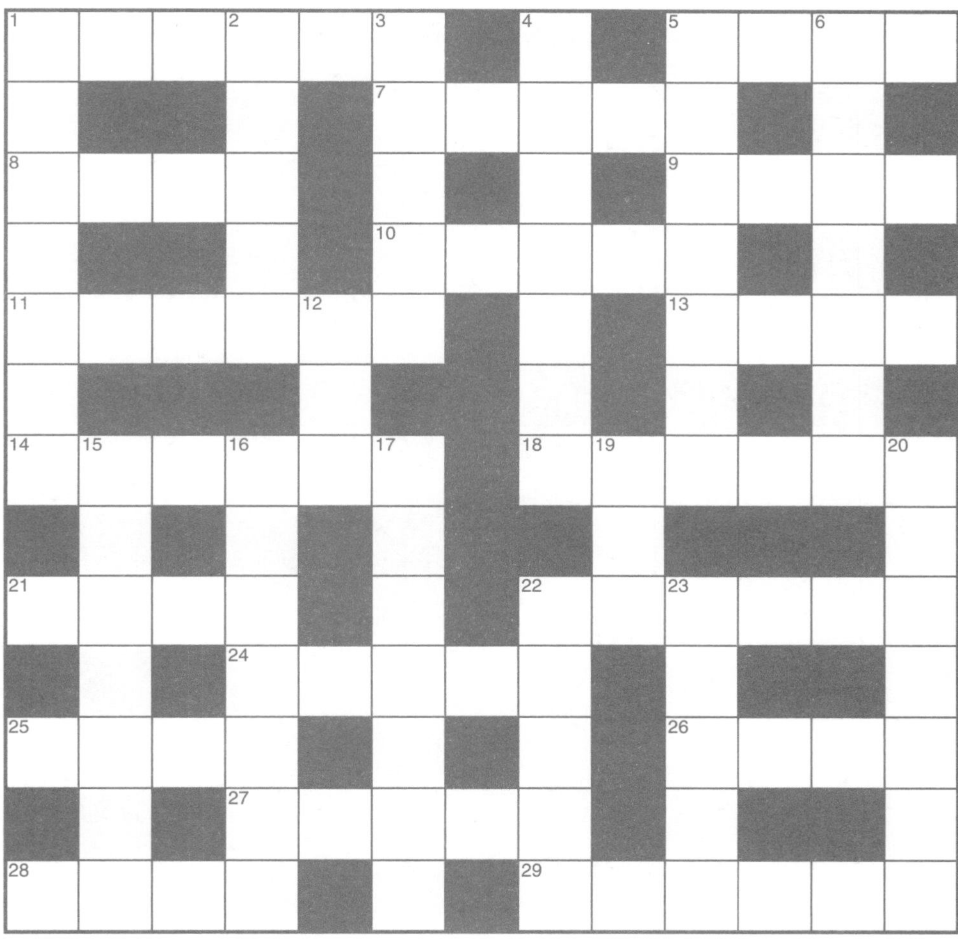

## ACROSS

1. Risk
5. Pounce
7. Reflection
8. Was dressed in
9. Complain
10. Kingdom
11. Immensely
13. Pigmented eye membrane
14. Scoundrel
18. Short pointed knife
21. Couch
22. Detour round
24. Become liable for
25. Rural property
26. Antlered deer
27. Levels
28. Crease
29. Rests on knees

## DOWN

1. Despite this
2. Forestall
3. Daily journal
4. Pillaged
5. Arctic rodent
6. Greed
12. Poetic term for field
15. Pear-shaped fruit
16. Asserted
17. Blood-sucking worms
19. Some
20. Quits job
22. Quick (walk)
23. Sheriff's pursuit team

# CROSSWORD 237

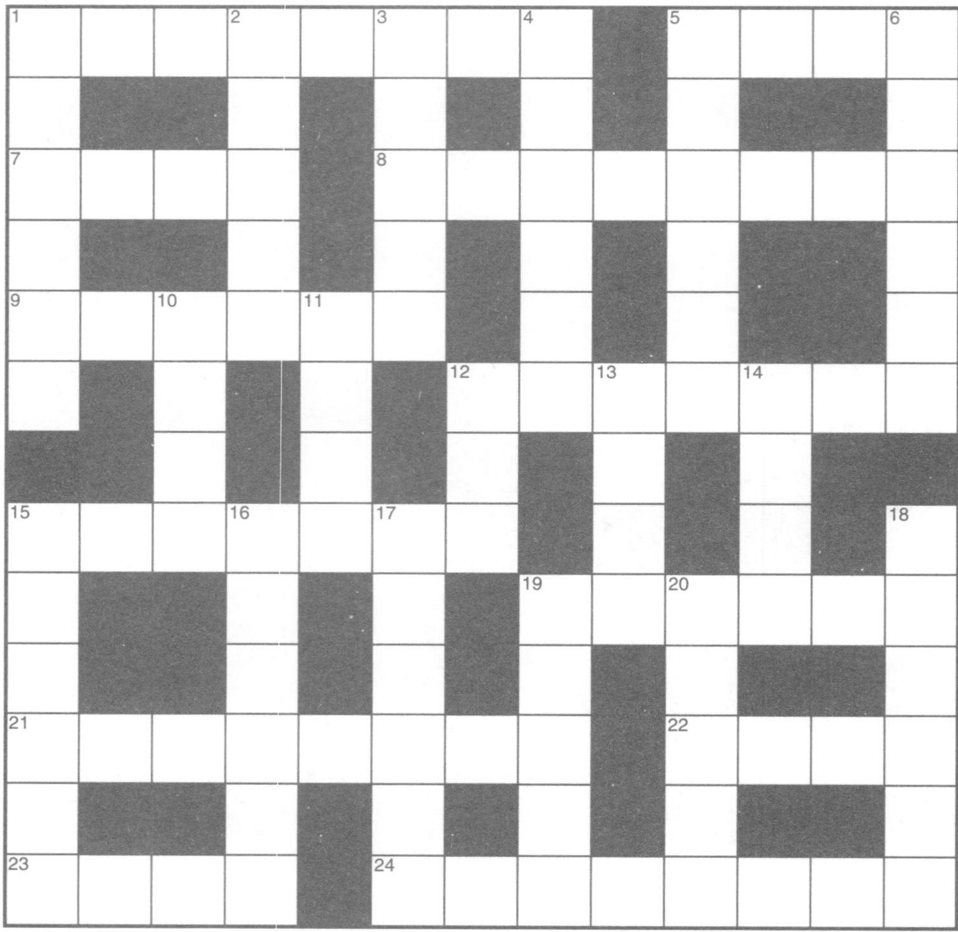

## ACROSS

1. Marine creature's home
5. Grass skirt dance
7. Parsley or sage
8. Railway bridges
9. Barely
12. Ground (teeth)
15. Crept stealthily
19. Trader
21. Spanish treasure ships
22. Unknown writer
23. Nurture
24. In an instant

## DOWN

1. Diagram
2. Paintbrush hair
3. Diplomatic messenger
4. Dull & overcast (sky)
5. Abodes
6. Ridiculous
10. Risotto ingredient
11. Seepage
12. Gallivant (about)
13. Wheel shaft
14. Cure
15. Tried to find
16. Sharply bent
17. Repeats
18. Wild excitement
19. Gave medicine to
20. Lessen in severity

# CROSSWORD 238

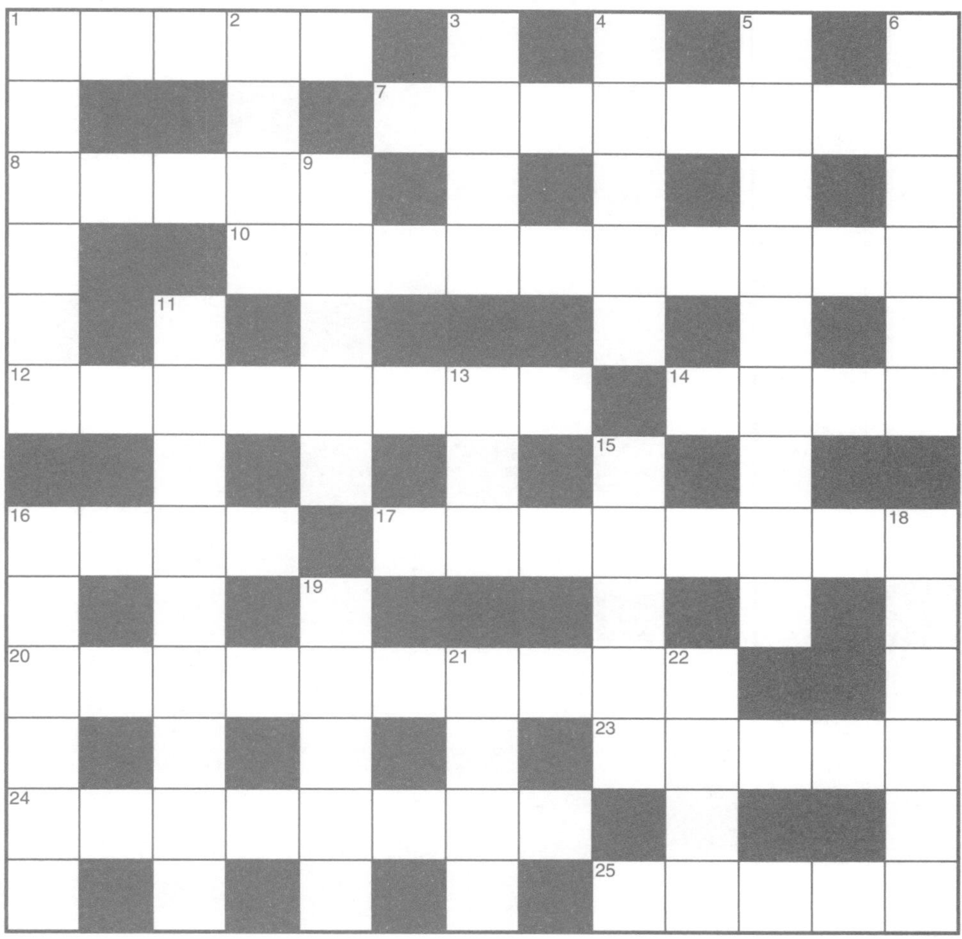

## ACROSS

1. Blusters, ... & puffs
7. Marooned
8. Tropical fruit
10. Exhilaration
12. Lately
14. Branch
16. Advance
17. Fort
20. Juvenile
23. Levied
24. Inclinations
25. Wolf calls

## DOWN

1. Taller
2. Number in quintet
3. Puncture with knife
4. Carnivals
5. The very same
6. Verb modifier
9. Dropping (TV show)
11. Eight-sided
13. Auction item
15. Minimal
16. Accountable
18. Wears away
19. Brown photo shade
21. Aviary
22. Filled tortilla

# CROSSWORD 239

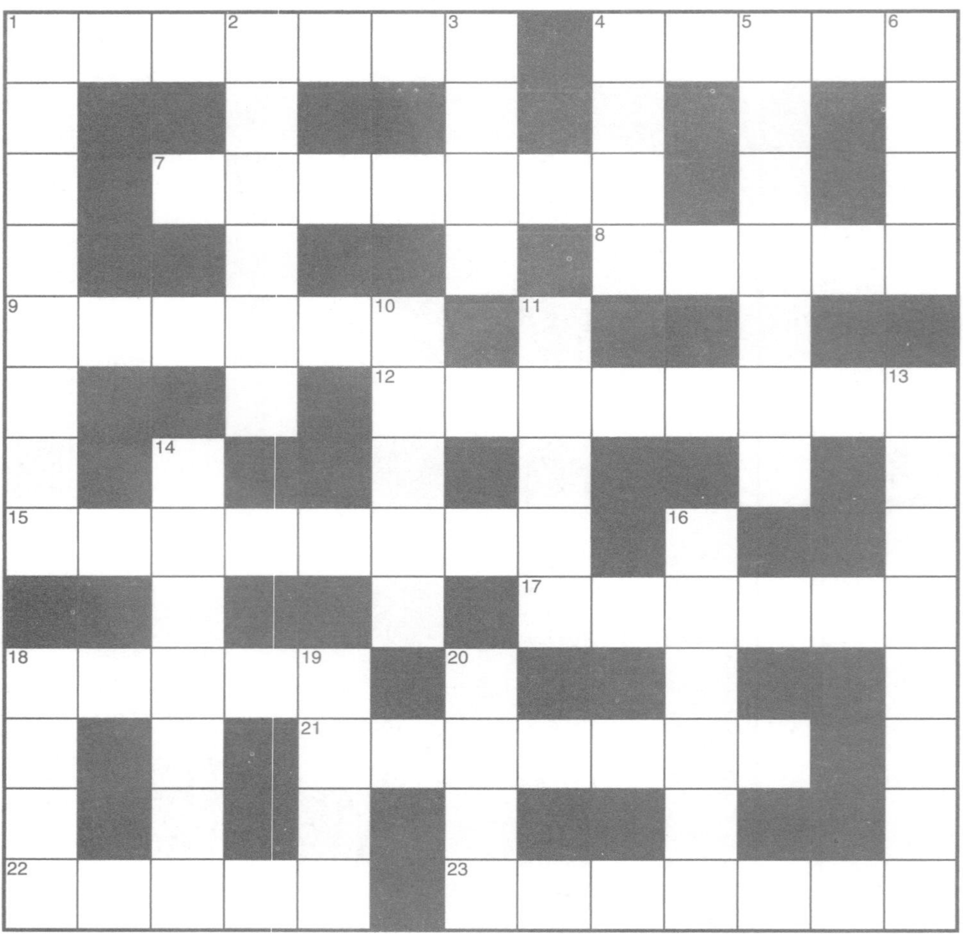

## ACROSS

1. Financial aid
4. Dough-raising agent
7. Repeat subscription
8. Situate
9. Act properly
12. Inquisitiveness
15. Shut out
17. Expunged
18. Bygone (days)
21. Citrus crop
22. Roman robes
23. Ore smelter

## DOWN

1. Walked unsteadily
2. Teeter
3. Tired sigh
4. Pained bark
5. Displayed
6. Ticking explosive, ... bomb
10. Ledger item
11. Reserve, set ...
13. Combination of symptoms
14. Tolerating
16. Cave chamber
18. Unseat from power
19. Indicates consent
20. Baby whale

# CROSSWORD 240

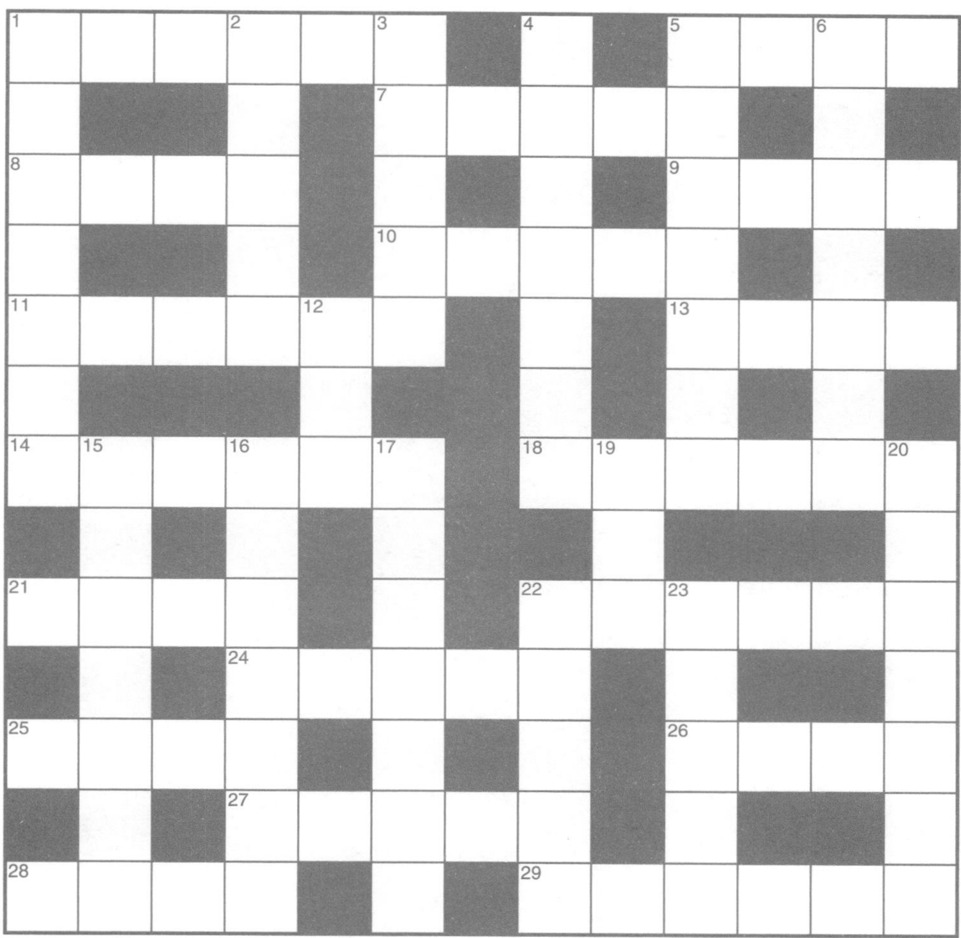

## ACROSS

1. Floral memorial ring
5. Sinful
7. Adulate
8. Fluent & insincere
9. Large family
10. Midday meal
11. Smells
13. Curved-bill wading bird
14. Spiced sausage
18. Earmarked
21. Fuse (metal)
22. Curiously coincidental
24. Frosting
25. Equitable
26. Whirled
27. Surpass
28. Consumer
29. Expenditure

## DOWN

1. Native American tents
2. Snapshots book
3. Shoe parts
4. Sincere
5. Inscribing
6. Dream
12. Give weapons to
15. Boulevards
16. Accounts examiner
17. Demands
19. Atmosphere
20. Wholesomeness
22. Arctic Circle snow house
23. Beginning

# CROSSWORD 241

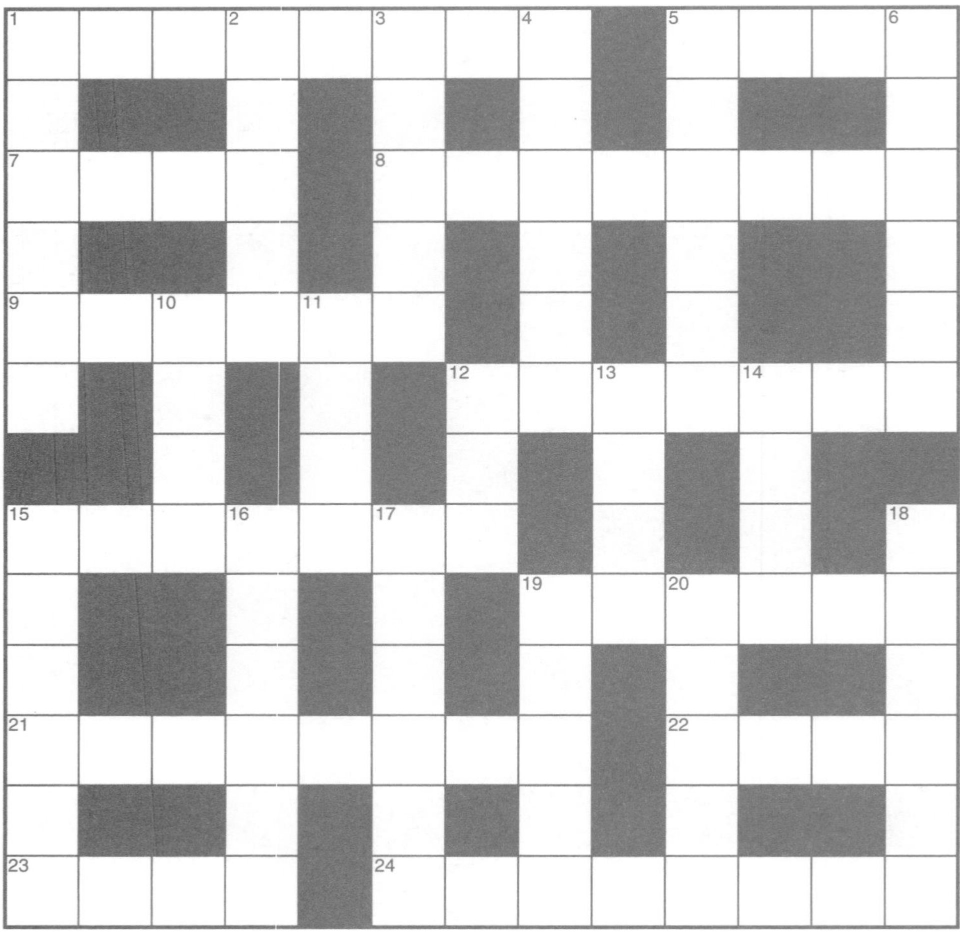

## ACROSS

1. Languidness
5. Adorable
7. Hopping insect
8. Gripping (tale)
9. Sidesteps
12. Concentrated scent
15. Saturday & Sunday
19. Moral goodness
21. 3-sided object
22. Excess weight
23. Symbol of peace
24. Wishing for

## DOWN

1. Hoisted
2. Detected sound
3. Goes by horse
4. Hankers
5. Rough in texture
6. Agitate
10. Land unit
11. Rim
12. Outcome
13. Indian dress
14. Subsequent
15. Needed
16. Japanese martial art
17. Scolded repeatedly
18. Mattress pest
19. Eyes (carefully)
20. Mention, ... to

# CROSSWORD 242

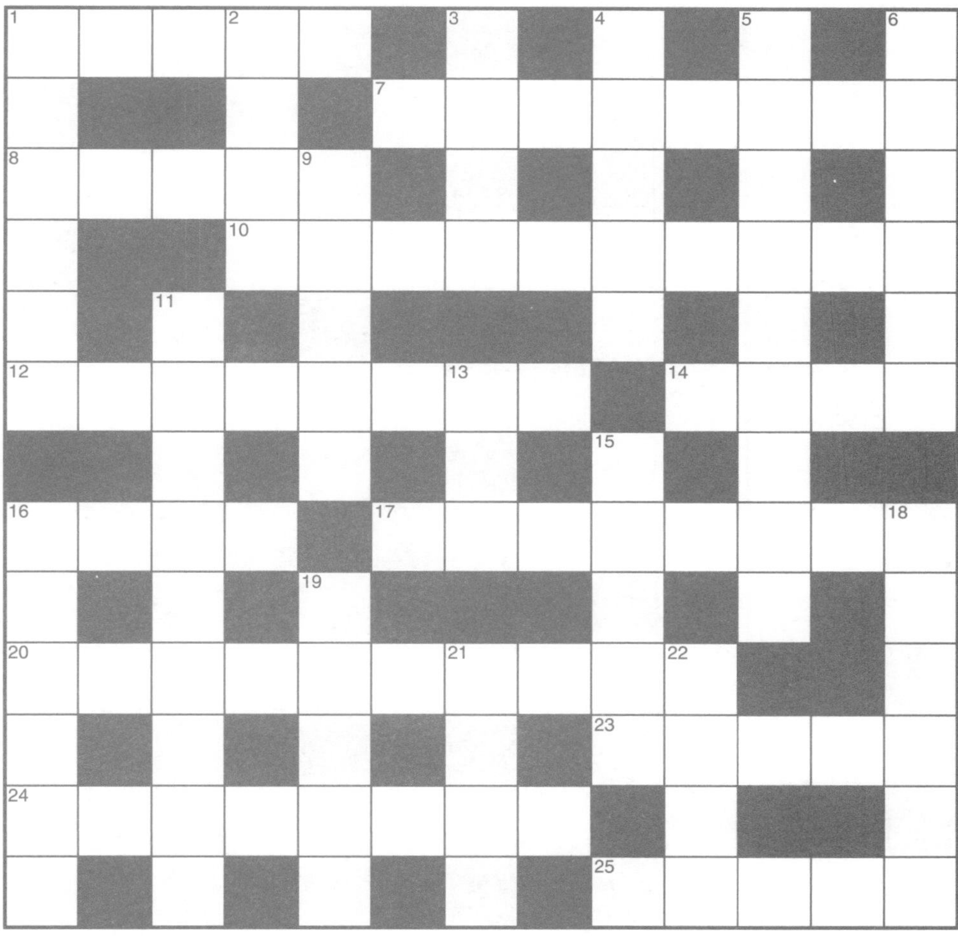

## ACROSS

1. Kiosk
7. Sliding out of control
8. Skewered dish
10. Enticement
12. Leading astray
14. Orchestral brass
16. Warm up
17. Disclosed
20. Far-fetched
23. Sailing boat
24. Occupying
25. Traditional

## DOWN

1. Bread makers
2. The one there
3. Jump rope
4. Standard of perfection
5. Savagely
6. Meeting schedule
9. Backless seat
11. Head start
13. Formerly named
15. Of topical interest
16. Cried (of owl)
18. Of teeth
19. Shuts noisily
21. Metal depression
22. Old witches

# CROSSWORD 243

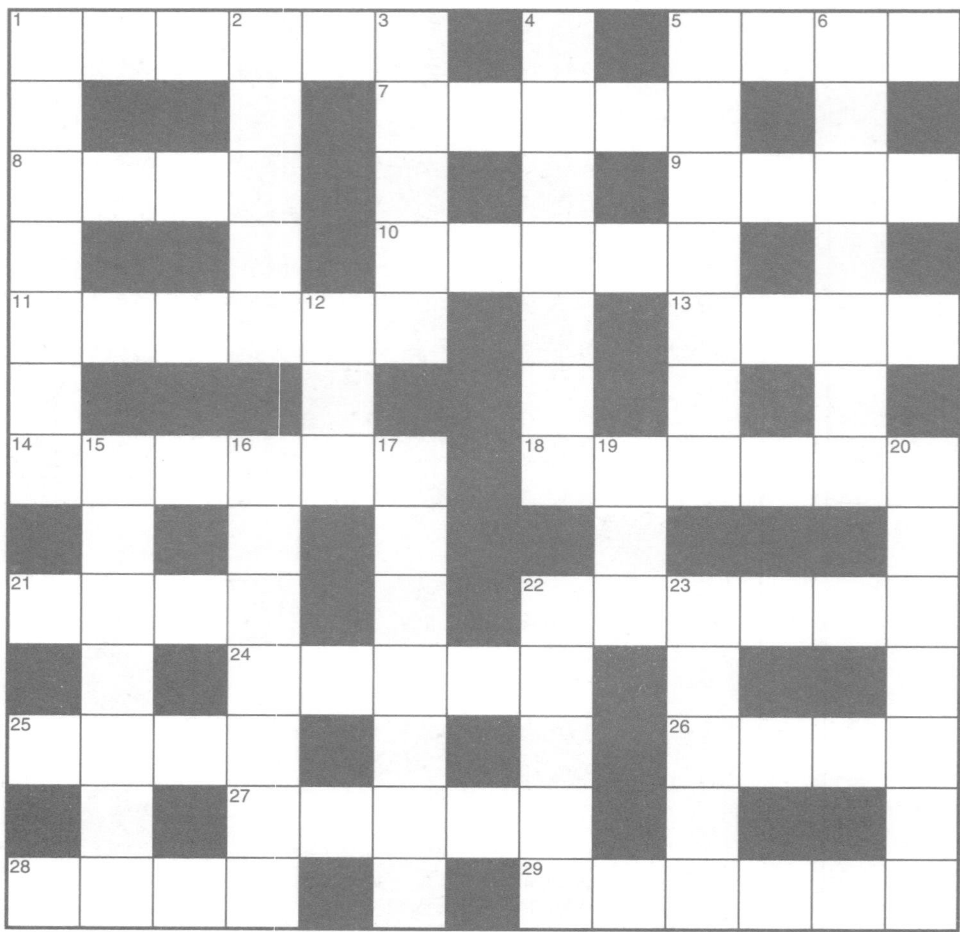

## ACROSS

1. Cavort
5. Short-term worker
7. Hotel foyer
8. Curve
9. Actual
10. Craze
11. Form of dermatitis
13. Naming word
14. Game park tour
18. Made home in tree
21. Rear (legs)
22. Radiated
24. Musical drama
25. Injury
26. Stare lustfully at
27. Incident
28. Coffee seed
29. Stinking

## DOWN

1. Wine cups
2. Emblem
3. Peruvian mammal
4. Forsake
5. Oppressive rulers
6. Take dimensions of
12. Disfigure
15. Stir up
16. Stomach
17. Alphabetical listings
19. December 31, New Year's ...
20. Feeble with age
22. Enticements
23. Emerged

# CROSSWORD 244

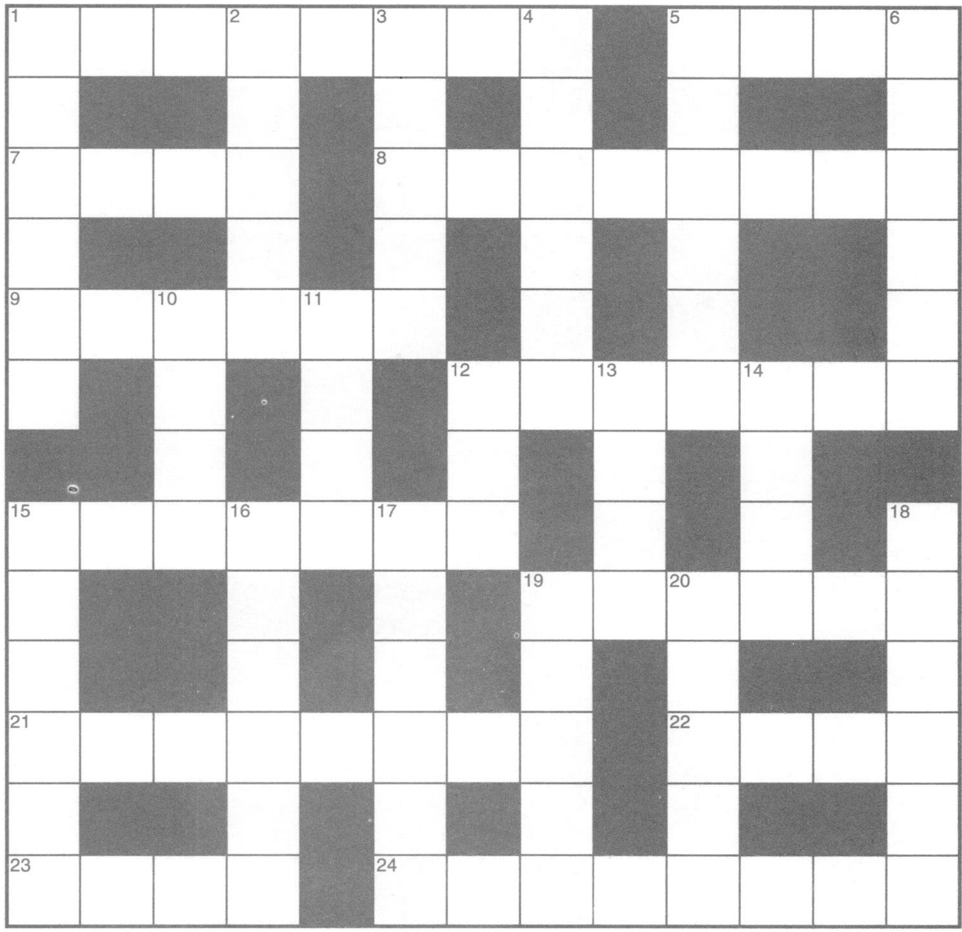

## ACROSS

1. Moved forward
5. College supervisor
7. Mimicked
8. Frolicking
9. Banishes from school
12. Holds tenderly
15. Blood relationship
19. Banquets
21. Adjoining
22. Control knob
23. Lengthy story
24. Recommends

## DOWN

1. Wise sayings
2. Muddle
3. Manages
4. Sliding shelf
5. Quickly lowered head
6. Hours of darkness
10. Physical hurt
11. Luxuriant
12. Baseball headgear
13. Pimples
14. Chops (branches)
15. Covered-in canoes
16. Musical composition
17. Obstruct
18. Biblical prayers
19. Entertained lavishly
20. Viper, puff ...

# CROSSWORD 245

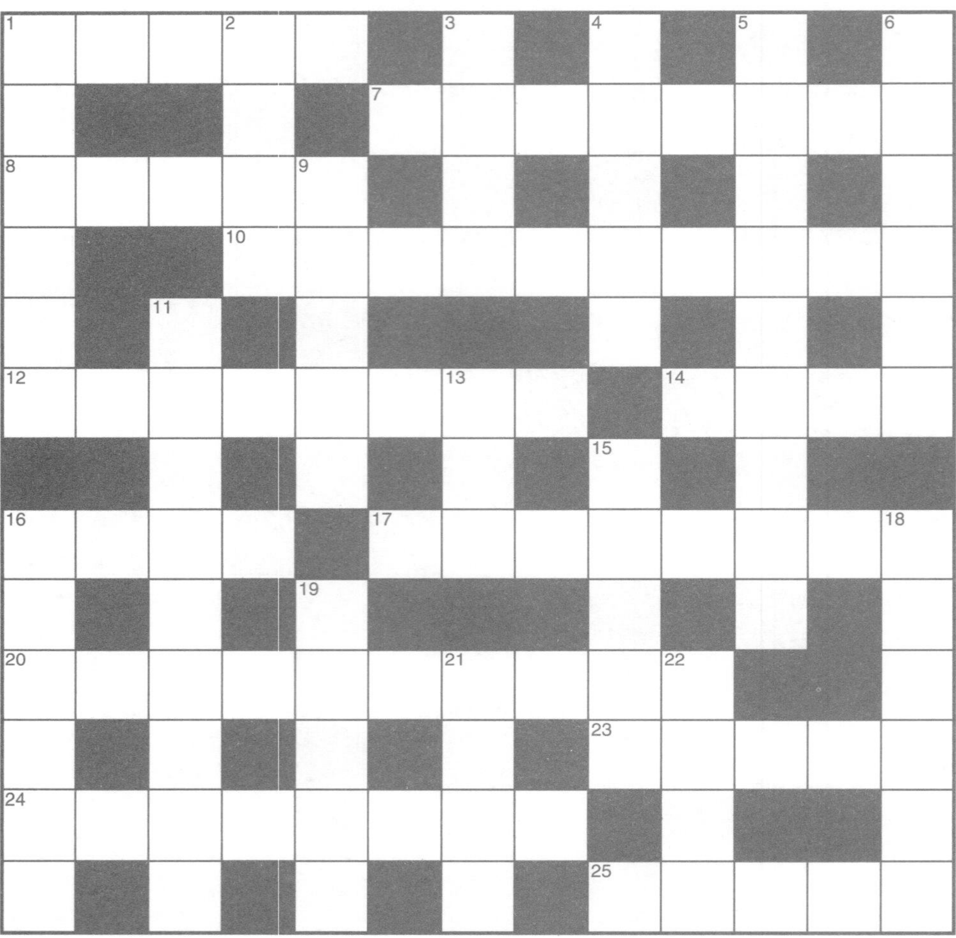

## ACROSS

1. Scanning device
7. Explosive stick
8. Wooden barrier
10. German cabbage dish
12. Astronauts
14. Invasive plant
16. Male bird
17. Took exception
20. Wicked
23. Recorded
24. Outlaw
25. Spry

## DOWN

1. Long firearms
2. Crescents
3. Heavily promote
4. Revels (in)
5. Connective tissues
6. Thawed
9. Painter's tripod
11. Manlike
13. Fade away
15. Premiere
16. Undercover
18. Sprinkle with flour
19. Giggle
21. Wearing nothing
22. Chanted

# CROSSWORD 246

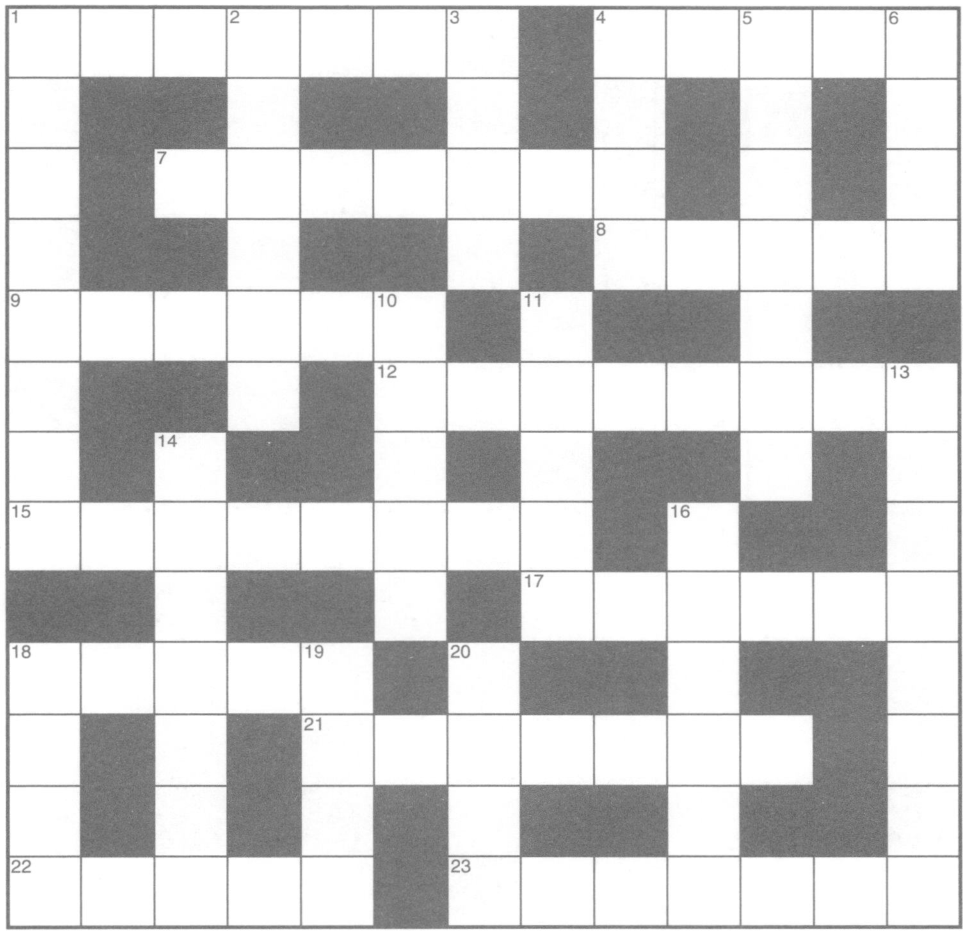

## ACROSS

1. Applause
4. Facial hair
7. Meet (requirements)
8. Retail outlets
9. Deliver sermon
12. Unlatched
15. Reconstructs
17. Afraid
18. Flight recorder, ... box
21. Stupidly
22. Founded
23. Supply funds for

## DOWN

1. Resident
2. Little crowns
3. Plane tip
4. Howls
5. Assails
6. Wolf lairs
10. Throws
11. Chasm
13. Task-completion date
14. Gets
16. Mexican flower
18. Tulip or daffodil
19. Thoughtful
20. Hooked fishing-stick

# CROSSWORD 247

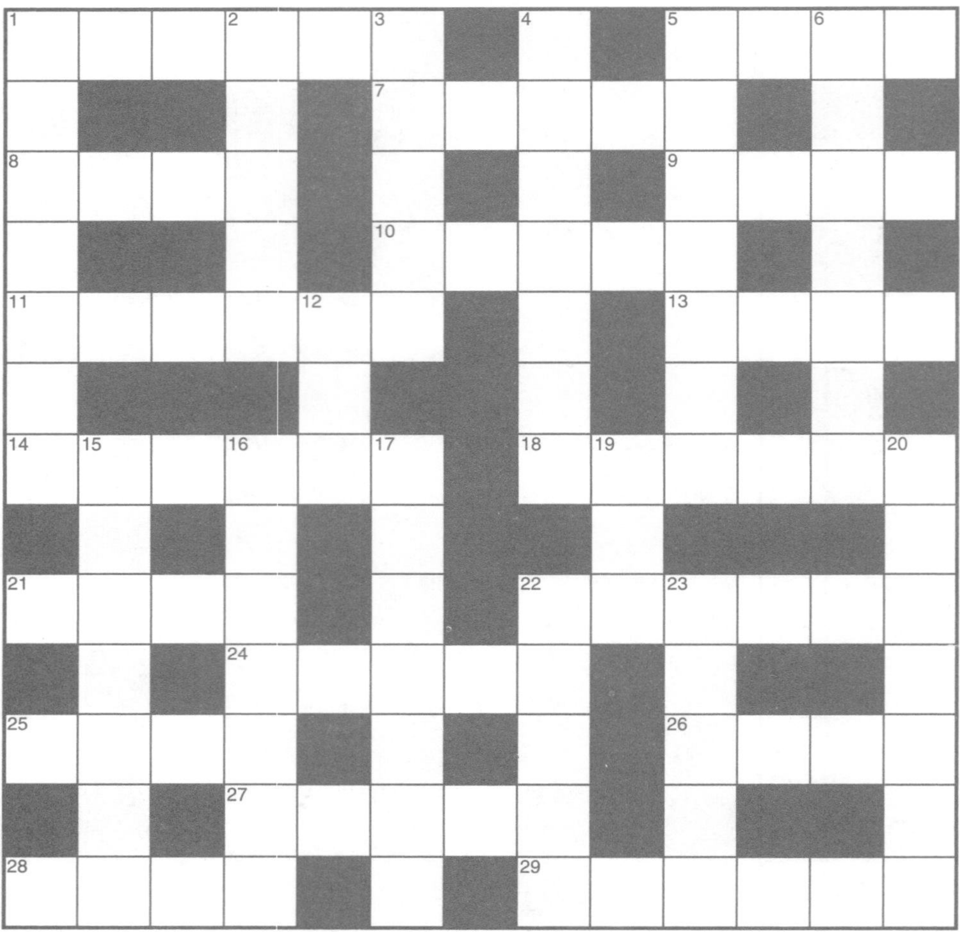

## ACROSS

1. Dog's house
5. Curved doorway
7. Speak in public
8. Reed instrument
9. Steals from
10. Off-limits
11. Smooches
13. Defeat
14. Destruction
18. Fraudulent scheme
21. Skin irritation
22. Tattooist's work tool
24. Charter
25. Nibble
26. Prison
27. On two occasions
28. Present
29. Sounds alike

## DOWN

1. Bumped
2. Requires
3. Oafs
4. Rover
5. Of heart/lung exercises
6. Sauerkraut vegetable
12. Poultry product
15. Straddling
16. Sports competitor
17. Unpredictable
19. Unreachable serve
20. Garden lattice
22. More recent
23. Relish

# CROSSWORD 248

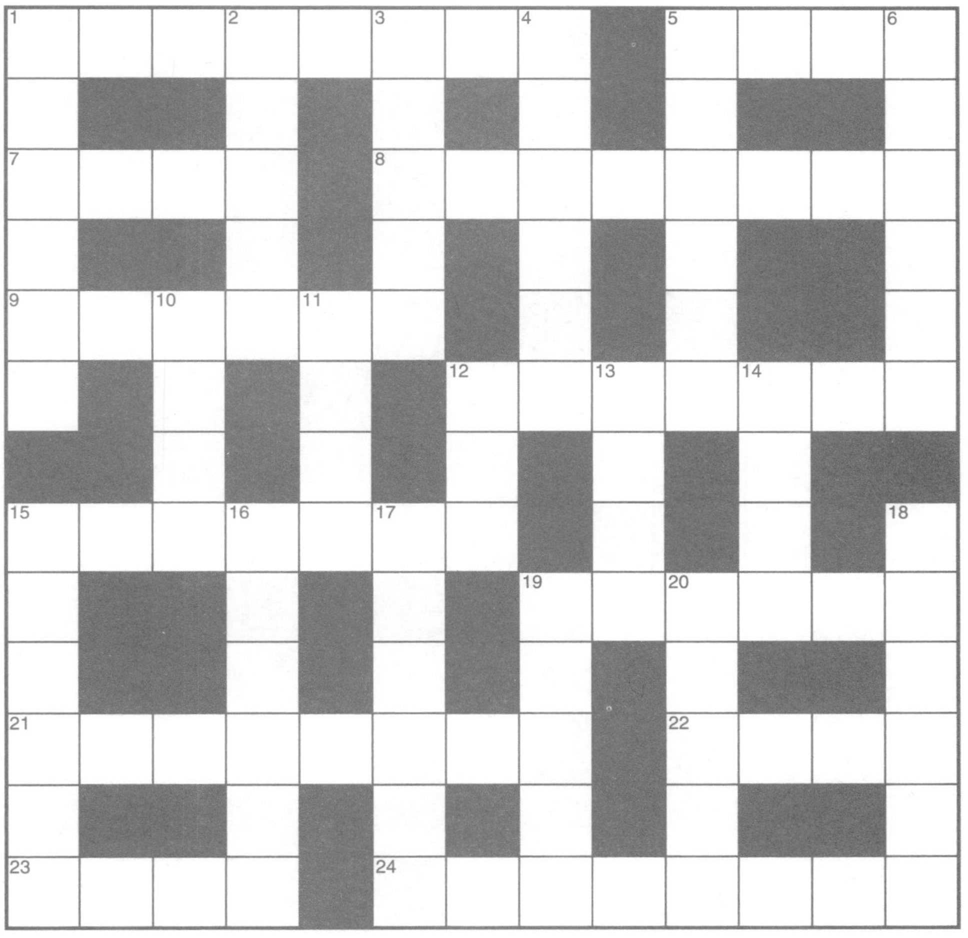

## ACROSS

1. Window above door
5. Snatch
7. Violently tear
8. Became blacker
9. Agreeably
12. Mislead
15. Bumped in crowd
19. Bravery decorations
21. Restore
22. Shapeless mass
23. Performed
24. Catastrophe

## DOWN

1. Managing (well)
2. Soup-serving spoon
3. Dizzy
4. Marine reptile
5. Lubrication
6. Dress top
10. Milking animals
11. Lounge about
12. Carried out
13. Coffee bar
14. Novel thought
15. Laughed sneeringly
16. Monarch's seat
17. Fetching task
18. Pressure line on map
19. Encounters
20. Financial obligations

# CROSSWORD 249

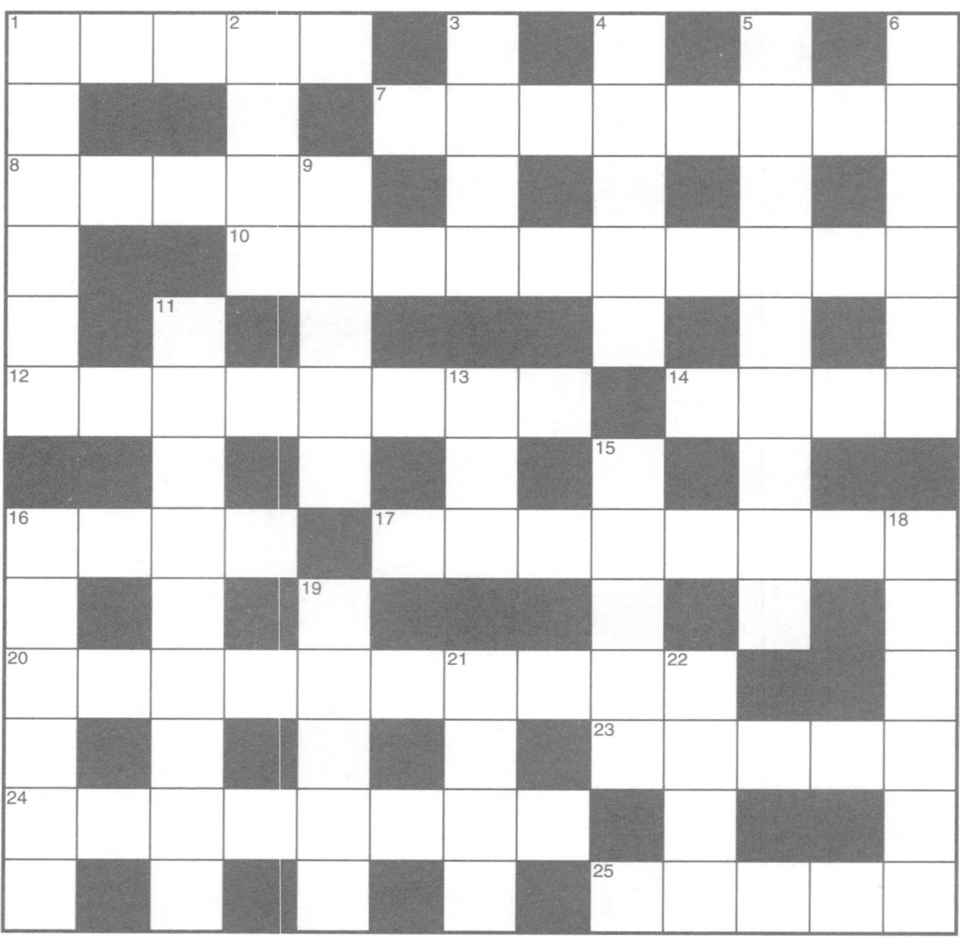

## ACROSS

1. Elliptic shapes
7. Imparted knowledge
8. Drifter
10. Reusable
12. Sailor
14. Congealed blood
16. Duck or chicken
17. Overly precise
20. Willingly
23. Gobbled up
24. Tenth, ..., twelfth
25. Glided on snow

## DOWN

1. Liquid units, fluid ...
2. Fibber
3. Ill at ease
4. Chide
5. Steadiness
6. Strangest
9. Rot
11. Careless pedestrian
13. Detective, private ...
15. Canadian leaf symbol
16. Deceived
18. Tinned
19. Storybook monsters
21. Pecans or almonds
22. Pull sharply

# CROSSWORD 250

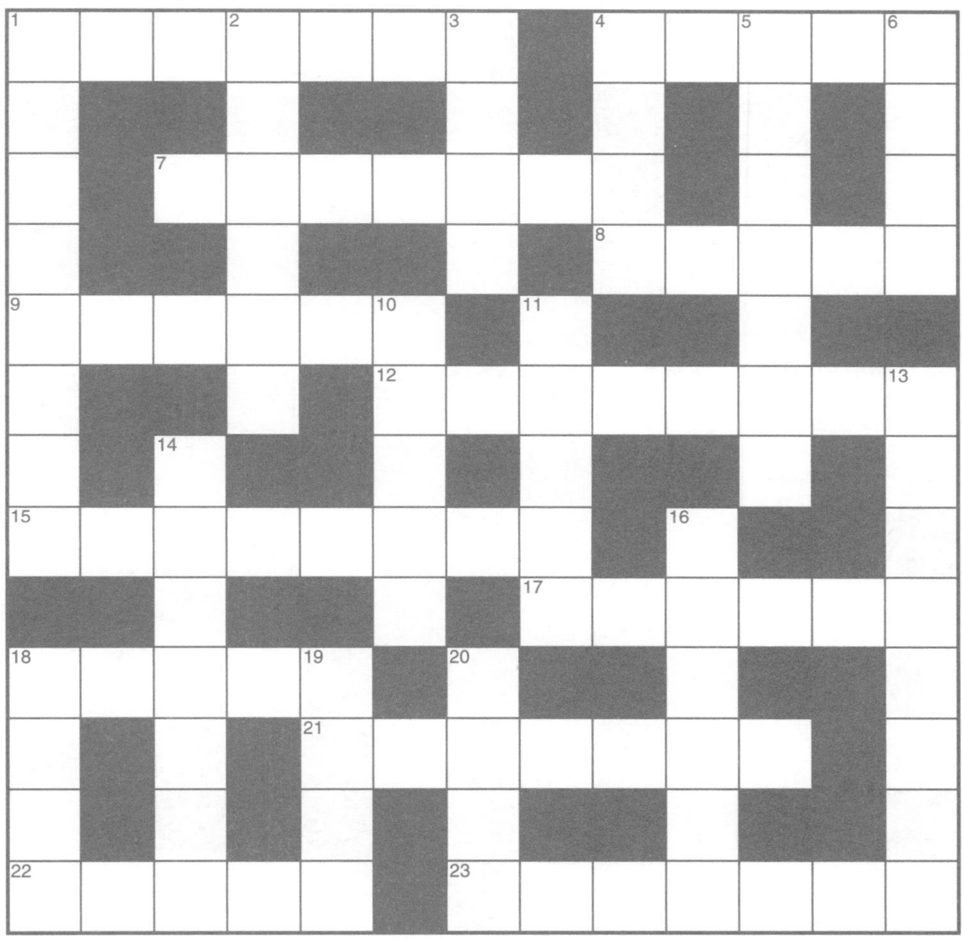

## ACROSS

1. Game park tours
4. Wished
7. Clap
8. Implant
9. Body of warships
12. On the lookout
15. Top tennis player
17. Adolescents
18. Australian gems
21. Subtleties of meaning
22. Informal language
23. Weeping

## DOWN

1. Now & again
2. Show up
3. Remain
4. Take cover
5. Irrational fears
6. Mideast lake, ... Sea
10. Sidestep
11. Acute pain
13. Saluting with drink
14. Tropical disease
16. Excellent
18. Chooses
19. Warm & protected
20. Marsupial pouches

# CROSSWORD 251

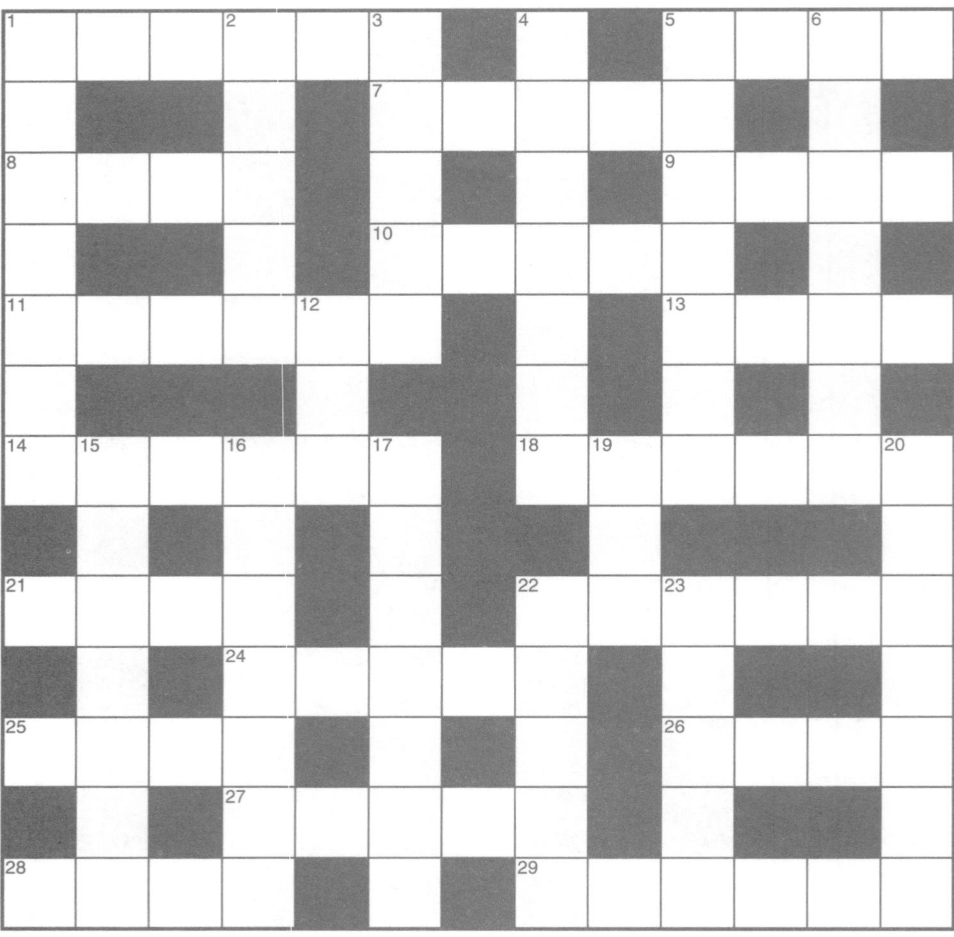

## ACROSS

1. Swell
5. Computer part, silicon ...
7. Marine mammal
8. Creep (towards)
9. Hawaiian garlands
10. Identifying sticker
11. Metal attracting bar
13. Very dry
14. Cup & ...
18. Heedlessly
21. Fervent request
22. Distant
24. V-shaped block
25. Bottom of boat
26. Recited
27. Large pitchers
28. Horse-breeding farm
29. Deserved

## DOWN

1. Puzzles
2. Pale with shock
3. Lived
4. Betting man
5. Basements
6. First letter
12. Before (poetic)
15. Affliction
16. Moved on hands & knees
17. Peppered (with holes)
19. Mature
20. Bowed to the inevitable
22. Recycle
23. Mean person

# CROSSWORD 252

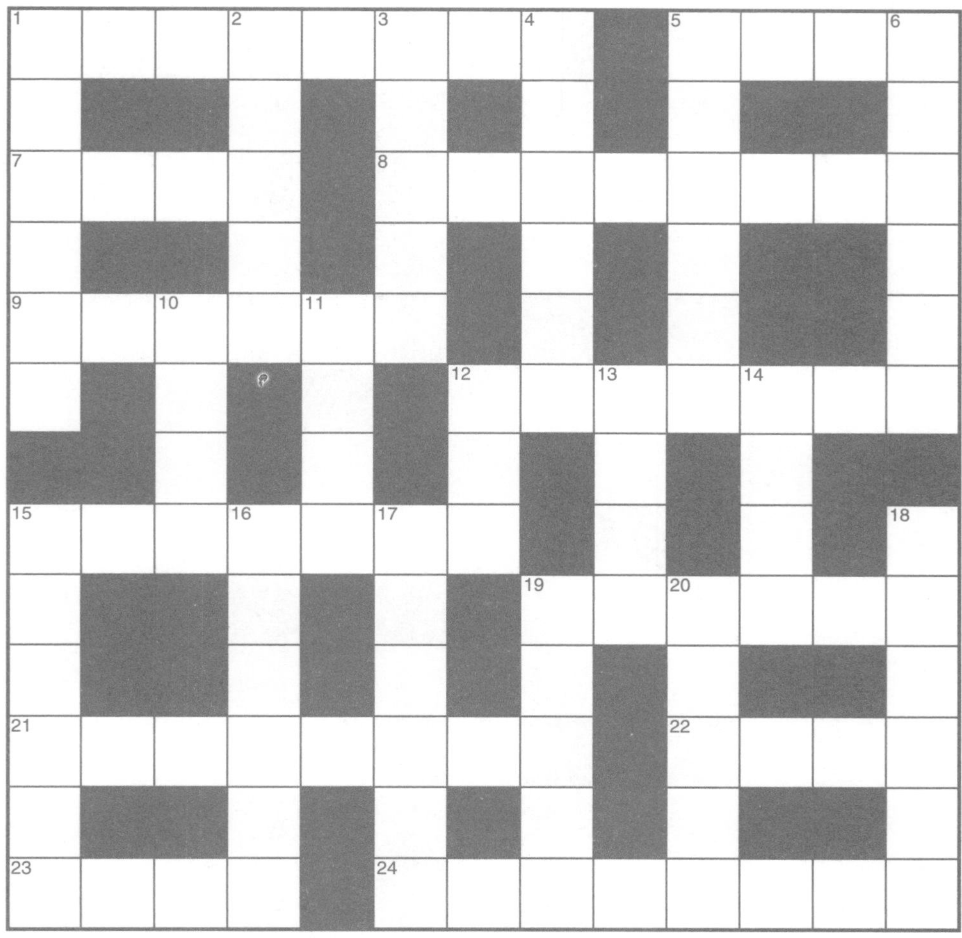

## ACROSS

1. Suspended beds
5. Sheep meat
7. Vulgar
8. Circling
9. Executes (law)
12. Rupturing (muscle)
15. Noisier
19. Small ribbon-tied hat
21. Searching for food
22. Admire
23. Fencing sword
24. Relaxed severity

## DOWN

1. Receptacle
2. Field hospital worker
3. Chefs
4. Delicate (perfume)
5. Opposite of former
6. Important person
10. Affirm
11. Travel along runway
12. Sticky coal by-product
13. Female chorister
14. Sacred effigy
15. Fluff up (feathers)
16. Give (to charity)
17. Weirder
18. Be present
19. Ring-shaped bun
20. Synthetic fabric

# CROSSWORD 253

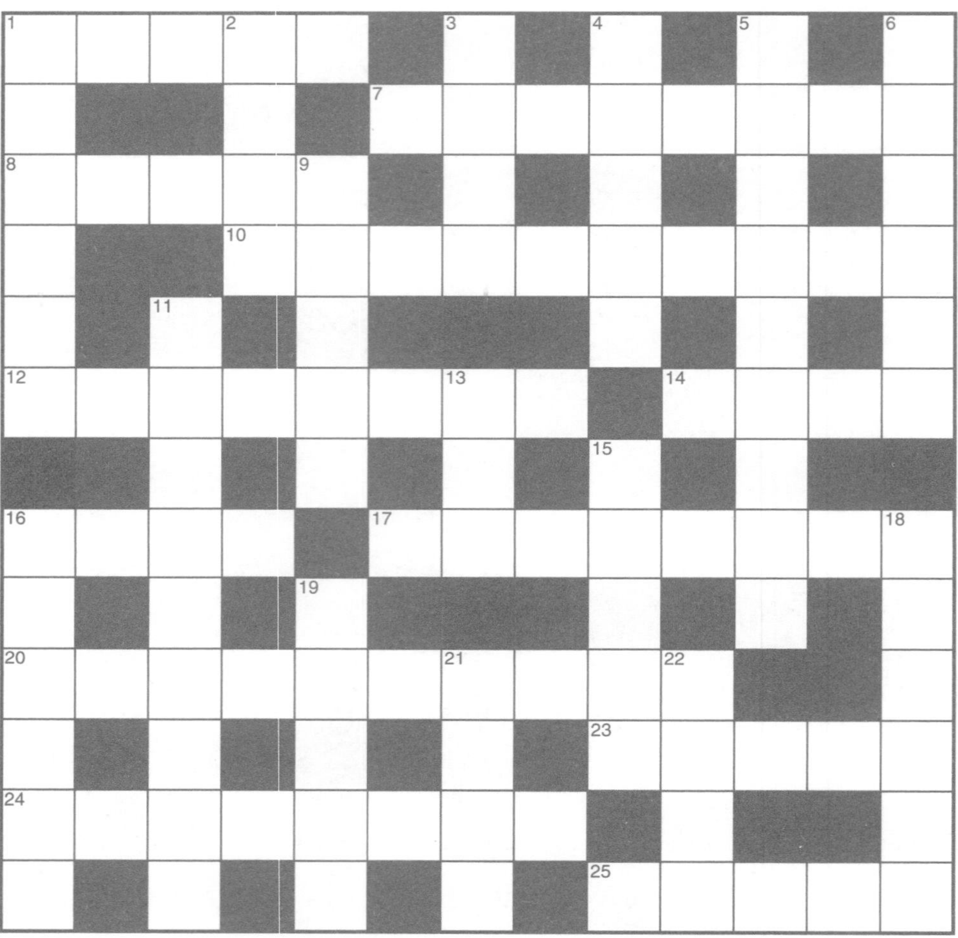

## ACROSS

1. Cautions
7. Sporting parachutist
8. Screams
10. Washing (clothes)
12. Aged (of paper)
14. Perfumed powder
16. Dock
17. Communally
20. Mix together
23. More rational
24. Opulence
25. Get off the point

## DOWN

1. Ambush
2. Not binding
3. Body's outer layer
4. Contributed
5. Ready for use
6. Terribly sad
9. Beauty establishment
11. Official permission
13. Self-image
15. Sorts (through)
16. Stone excavation pit
18. Annual
19. Spy, secret ...
21. Bulk
22. Opposite of west

# CROSSWORD 254

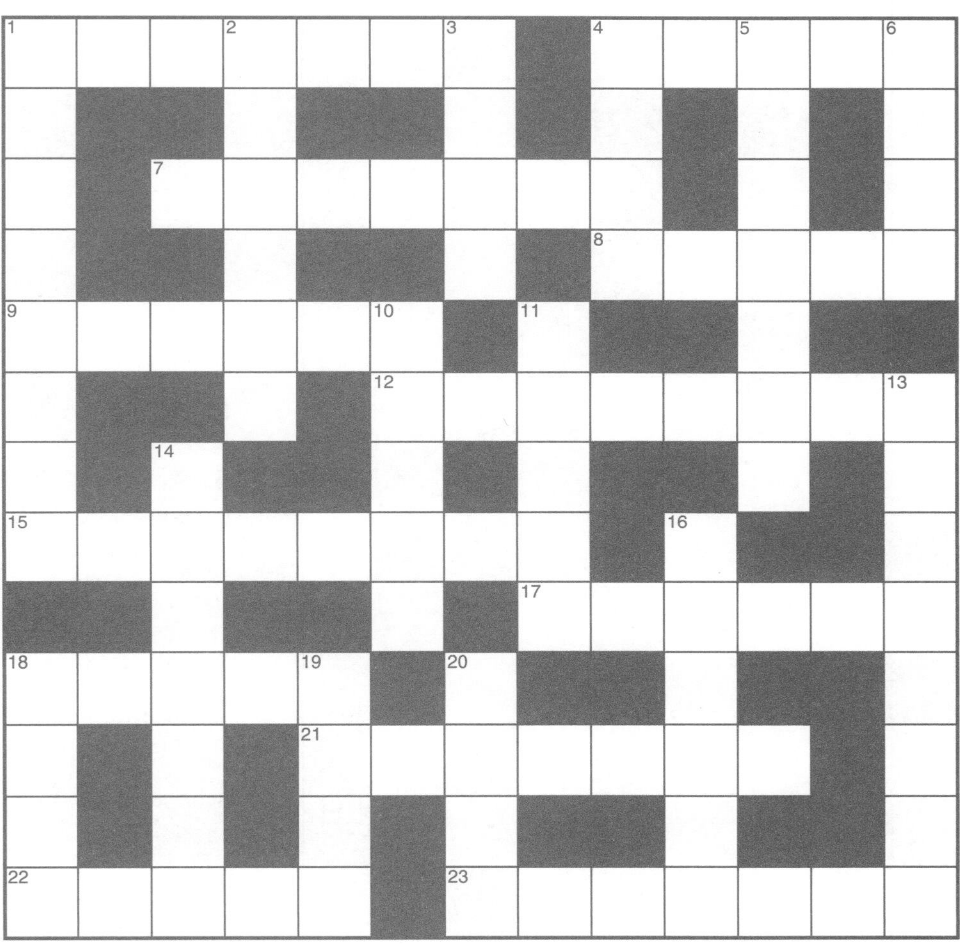

## ACROSS

1. Blinded by light
4. Store away greedily
7. Has effect (on)
8. Cardiac organ
9. Growing dim
12. Making suitable
15. Technical sketches
17. Husky
18. Fairy-tale hag
21. Passed (of years)
22. Slashes
23. Female goats

## DOWN

1. Denied ownership of
2. Walking corpse
3. Wharf
4. Sudden silence
5. Stomach-settling medicine
6. Grime
10. Festive occasions
11. Low wetland
13. Study of heredity
14. Digestive fluids, ... juices
16. Pub
18. Accompanied by
19. Cuts into shape
20. Young deer

# CROSSWORD 255

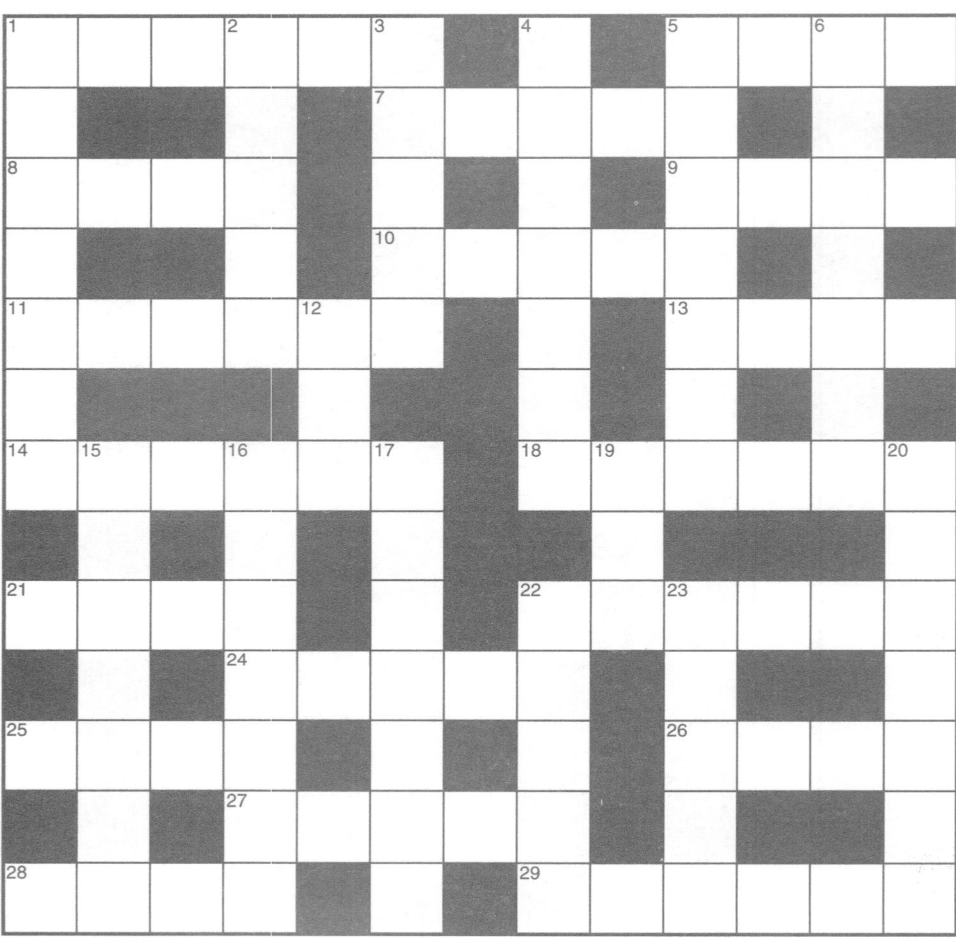

## ACROSS

1. Necessitate
5. Scatters (seeds)
7. Degrade
8. Against
9. Support devices
10. Brings up (child)
11. Drying cloths
13. Smooth out (shirt creases)
14. Military students
18. T-bones or sirloins
21. Sore crust
22. Disorderly crowd
24. Mountain chain top
25. Sailor's greeting
26. Enthusiastic
27. Pacific or Indian
28. Moose
29. More sorrowful

## DOWN

1. Stretchy tape
2. Not dissimilar
3. Wolves' homes
4. Party titbits
5. Coastal
6. Matrimony
12. Allow to
15. Liquor
16. Newly conceived babies
17. Pacifies
19. Leaf beverage
20. Narrow
22. Horse control straps
23. Get on (ship)

# CROSSWORD 256

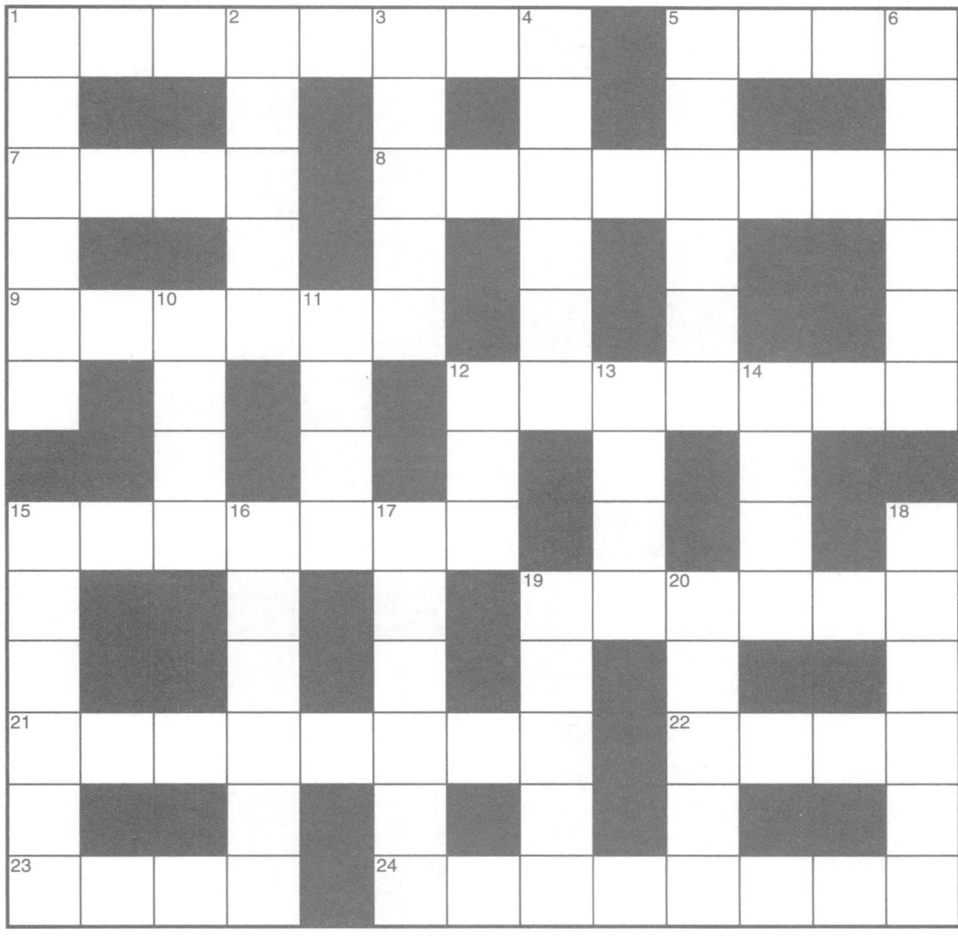

## ACROSS

1. Squid
5. Poses (for portrait)
7. Molecule part
8. Arose (from)
9. Settled in armchair
12. Receives (award)
15. Unhappy
19. Takes in (child)
21. Cloudy eye condition
22. Reverberate
23. Dashed
24. Birthright

## DOWN

1. Provision in will
2. Allow inside
3. Rectify
4. Sloping (typeface)
5. Sculpture
6. Moves furtively
10. Wartime friend
11. If not, or ...
12. Donkey
13. Clothed
14. Inflate, ... up
15. Fruit extracts
16. Gecko or iguana
17. Crush
18. On dry land
19. Out of bed
20. Open to view

# CROSSWORD 257

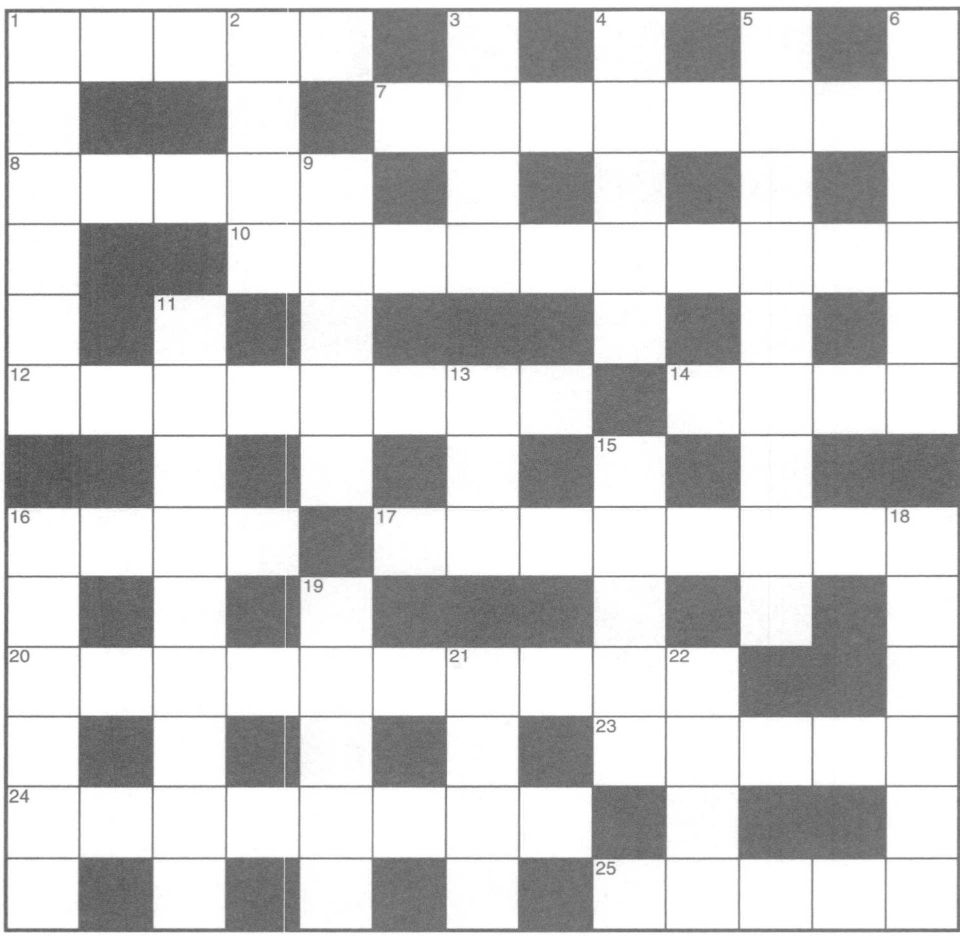

## ACROSS

1. Large pieces
7. Kitchen strainer
8. Spiral shell
10. Abductors
12. Sketching carbon
14. Glimpse
16. Other way, ... versa
17. Romcom, ... comedy
20. Vehicle franchise
23. Dining surface
24. First
25. Actor's platform

## DOWN

1. Very busy
2. Cheap thrill
3. Maize
4. Lanterns
5. Hardship
6. Brash
9. Tether
11. Artificial sweetener
13. Commotion
15. Routine
16. Visual recordings
18. Edam or Brie
19. Keepsake
21. Fabric join
22. Days of yore

# CROSSWORD 258

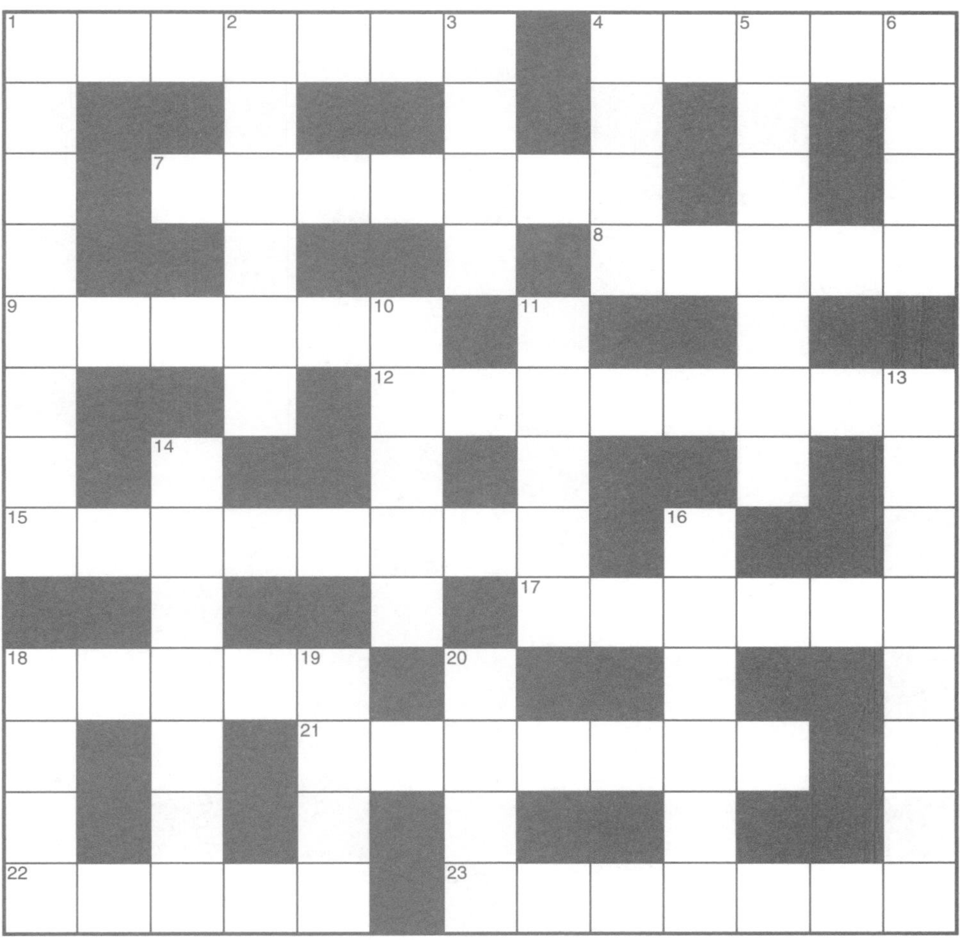

## ACROSS

1. Traversed
4. Theme
7. Pope
8. Criminal deception
9. Rouses (from sleep)
12. Occasion
15. Restate (position)
17. Complete
18. Short-lived
21. Long-standing feud
22. Flat dish
23. Scanning book

## DOWN

1. Morals campaigner
2. Frightens (cattle)
3. Platform
4. Petty quarrel
5. Royal homes
6. Clay lump
10. Was loyal to, ... with
11. Sharp (pain)
13. Thinning out, ... off
14. Chocolate, strawberry or ...
16. Gazed fixedly
18. Radar screen spot
19. Independent
20. Not often, hardly ...

# CROSSWORD 259

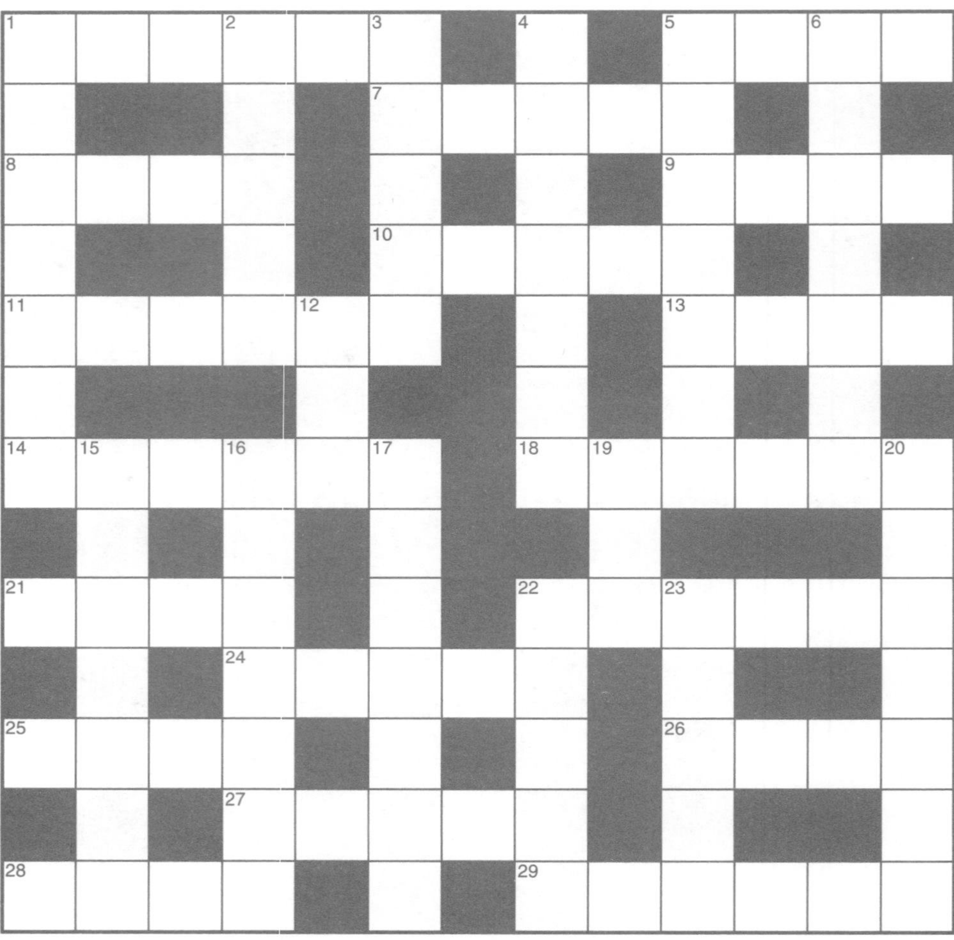

## ACROSS

1. Dramatic conclusion
5. Appliance cord
7. Cutting utensil
8. Back of neck
9. Chills
10. Comes closer to
11. Leapt
13. On top of
14. Effortlessly
18. Flattened
21. Head-injury unconsciousness
22. Predatory birds
24. Piano adjuster
25. Nickel & ...
26. Reverse the effects of
27. Ruled (paper)
28. It is, ... are
29. Withstand

## DOWN

1. Refined style
2. Sports stadium
3. Using frugally, ... out
4. Impair
5. Recreation
6. Amazing
12. No score
15. Eliminate
16. Angrily
17. Gaping
19. By that route
20. Remove garments
22. Wear away
23. Pasted

# CROSSWORD 260

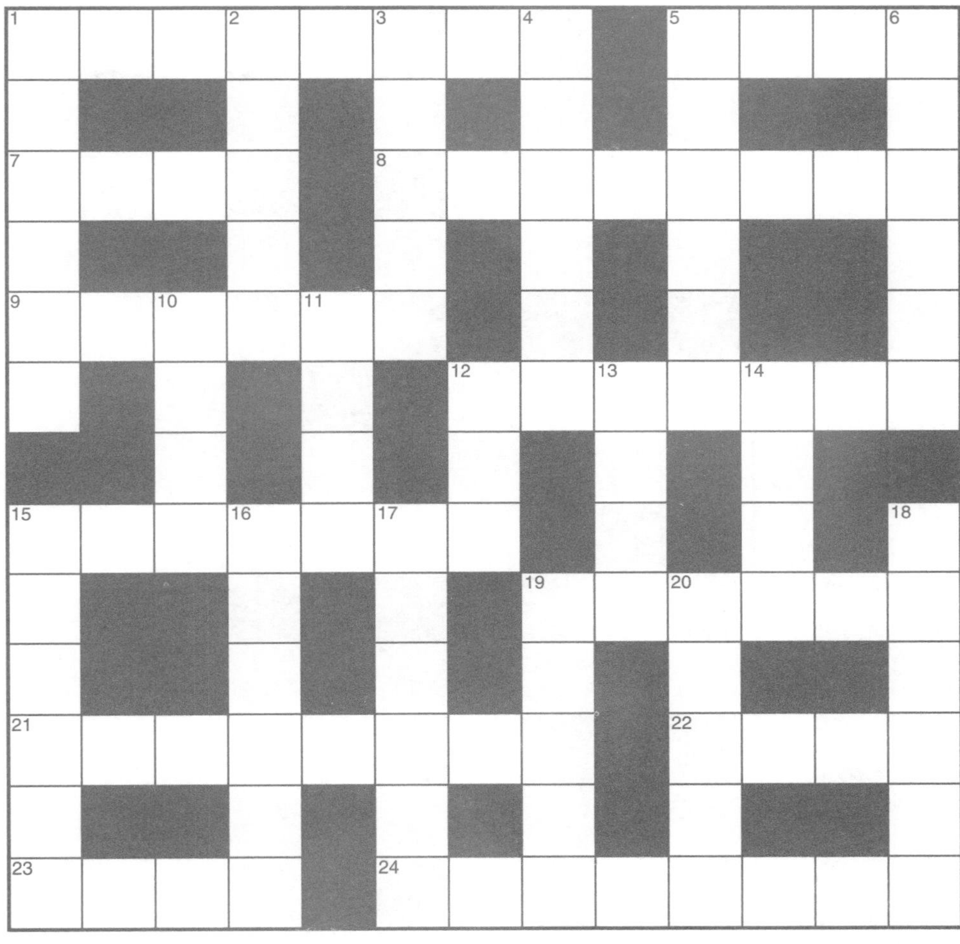

## ACROSS

1. Overjoyed
5. Hair dye
7. Male monarch
8. Said again
9. Trapped (fish)
12. Pastures
15. Degraded
19. Moved from side to side
21. Information bank
22. Greek liquor
23. Utter (cry)
24. Gets ready

## DOWN

1. Jesting
2. Brick of precious metal
3. Ventilated
4. Wrestle
5. Tracked down
6. Neatens
10. Pharaoh's resting place
11. Periods of time
12. Angry
13. Afresh
14. Indulgent spree
15. Absent-minded scribble
16. Shocked
17. Pitch tent
18. Repugnant
19. Military blockade
20. Scent

# CROSSWORD 261

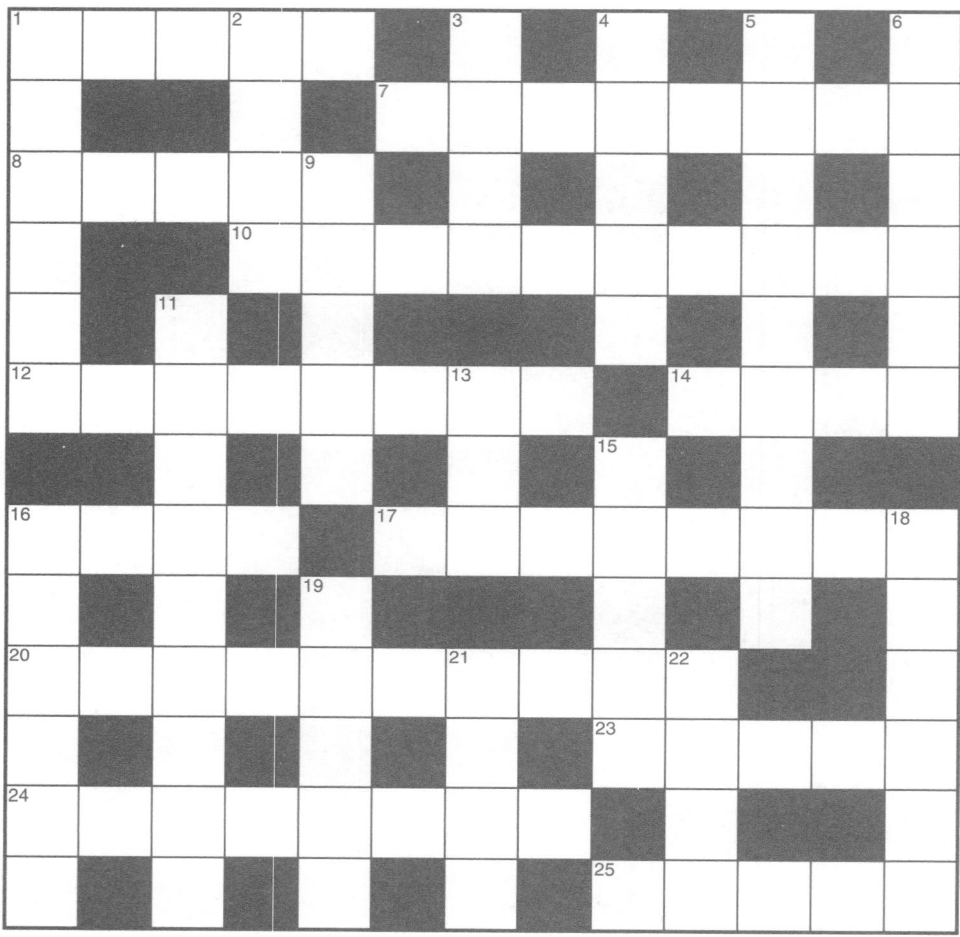

## ACROSS

1. Jumping parasites
7. Remove jockey's seat
8. False gods
10. Heading for the ground
12. Complete disorder
14. Plant stalk
16. Prank
17. Decreed
20. Open-air eaters
23. Hillbilly
24. Precious stones
25. Encrypts

## DOWN

1. Monastery dwellers
2. Competent
3. Mend (of bones)
4. Smears
5. Fine-tuning
6. Hardly ever
9. South American dance
11. Empty hotel rooms
13. Make slip-up
15. Loiter
16. Occur
18. Rigorously trains
19. Temporary visitor documents
21. Young goats
22. Alone

# CROSSWORD 262

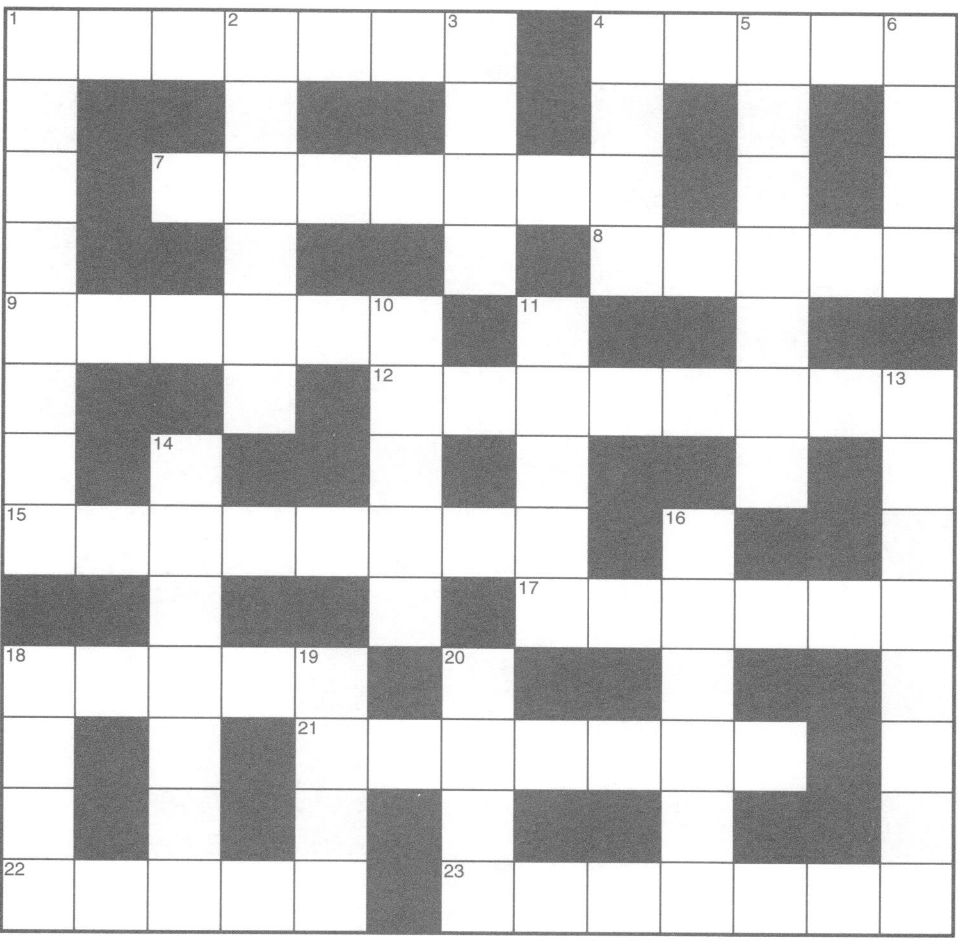

## ACROSS

1. Fairway sport
4. Gain knowledge
7. Upper-case letter
8. Small fenced-in areas
9. Regard as equivalent
12. Re-evaluate
15. Granted permit to
17. Desexed
18. Hair parasite
21. Detests
22. Lessens
23. Detecting

## DOWN

1. Thankful
2. Noisy quarrel
3. Field entrance
4. Pond flower
5. Prevented (disaster)
6. Front page stories
10. Efface
11. Delivers, ... over
13. Clarifying, ... light on
14. Clears of charge
16. Hotel employees
18. Shoe cord
19. Shady trees
20. Moves (tail)

# CROSSWORD 263

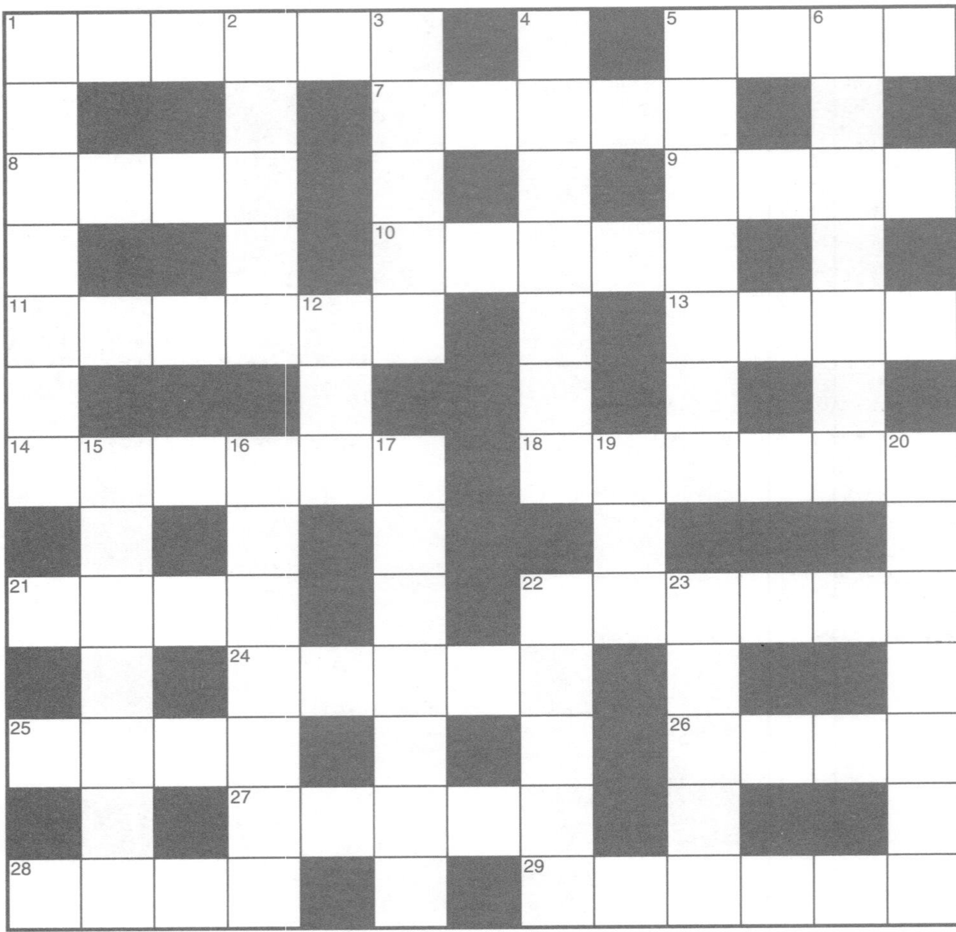

## ACROSS

1. Delved
5. Swell, ... up
7. Says yes to
8. School test
9. Hindu exercise routine
10. Fast jet effect, ... boom
11. Ruffle (hair)
13. Weeded
14. Delicate
18. Regatta entrants
21. Bung
22. Criminals
24. Canyon
25. Tick over (of engine)
26. Motorist's fury, road ...
27. Tendency
28. Functions
29. Family vehicles

## DOWN

1. Sewn in folds
2. Explosive weapons
3. Extinguish
4. Indistinctly
5. Clairvoyant
6. Illusion, ... of the imagination
12. Ignited
15. Refers indirectly
16. Lumps of gold
17. Deeply desired
19. He is, they ...
20. Siblings
22. Nourishes
23. Garish

# CROSSWORD 264

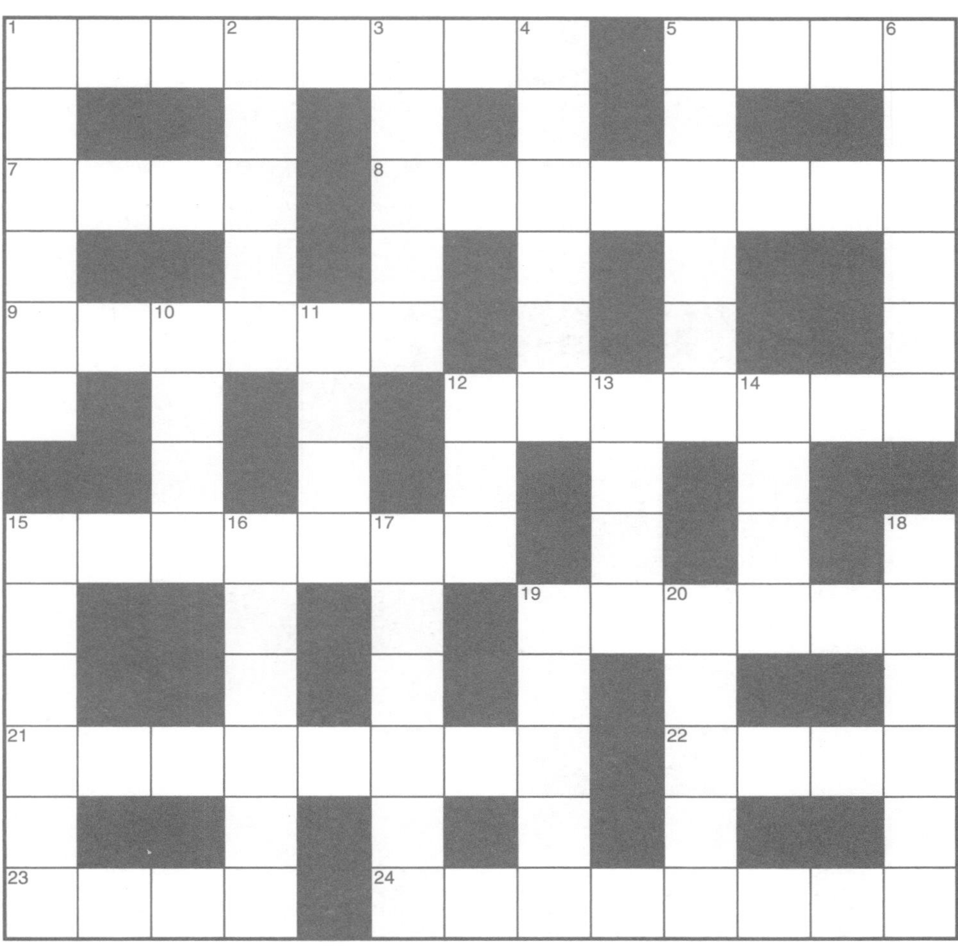

## ACROSS

1. Chewing daintily
5. New Orleans music
7. Sinister sign
8. Stepping (on)
9. Lewd man
12. Inserting (bullets)
15. Corrected (wrong)
19. Horse-bucking shows
21. Christmas season
22. Threesome
23. Resentful longing
24. Land use entitlement

## DOWN

1. Asian food item
2. Bouquet, ... of flowers
3. Bury (corpse)
4. Racial enclave
5. Adjudicated
6. Move in jagged course
10. Rugged peak
11. Leave room
12. ... & lass
13. Too
14. The ... of Capri
15. Rewrite on keyboard
16. Immensely
17. Donkey or zebra
18. Usher (to seat)
19. Fishing spools
20. Fact

# CROSSWORD 265

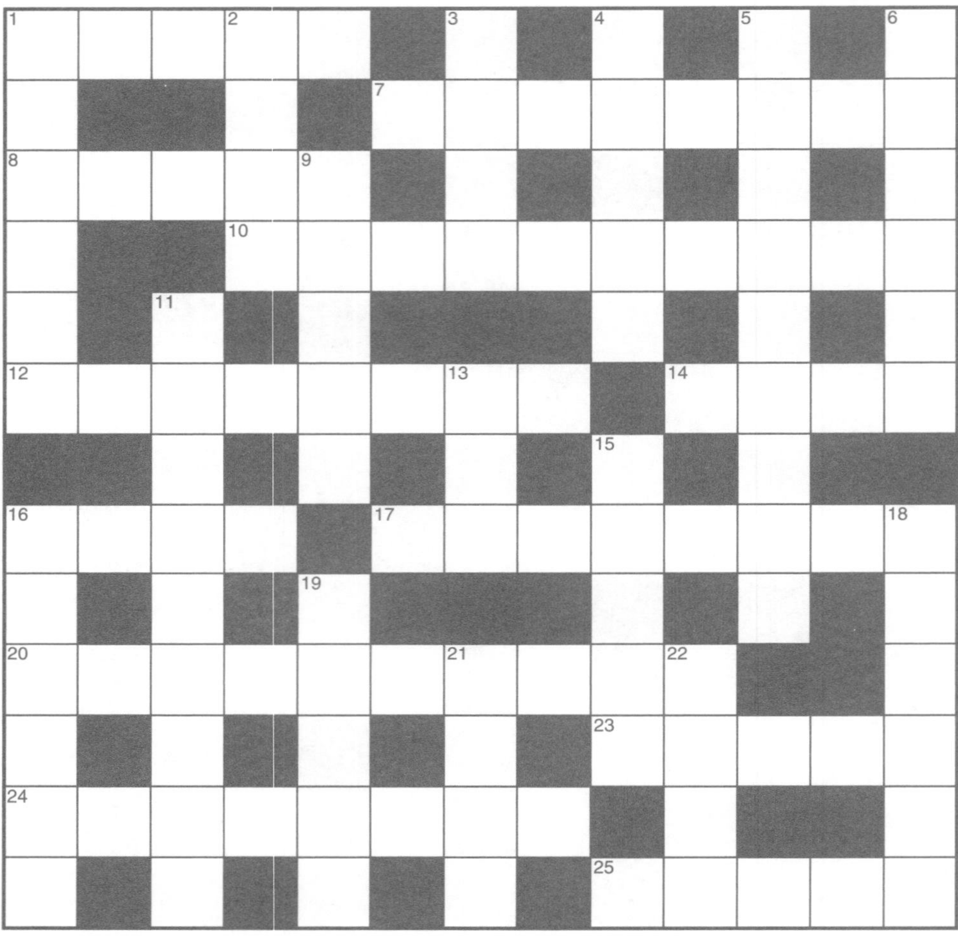

## ACROSS

1. Of the city
7. Carved
8. Filleted
10. Insolence
12. Insulin-deficient person
14. Amongst
16. Vain display
17. Injured (joint)
20. Unwillingness
23. Shrill barks
24. Moved restlessly
25. Court attendant

## DOWN

1. Straighten
2. Discontinued
3. Disfiguring mark
4. Water bottle
5. Flowing
6. Prepared for publication
9. Risky
11. Orange-rind spread
13. Scamp
15. Elaborate
16. Decontaminate
18. More tightly-packed
19. Broad expanse
21. Tip of triangle
22. Congers or morays

# CROSSWORD 266

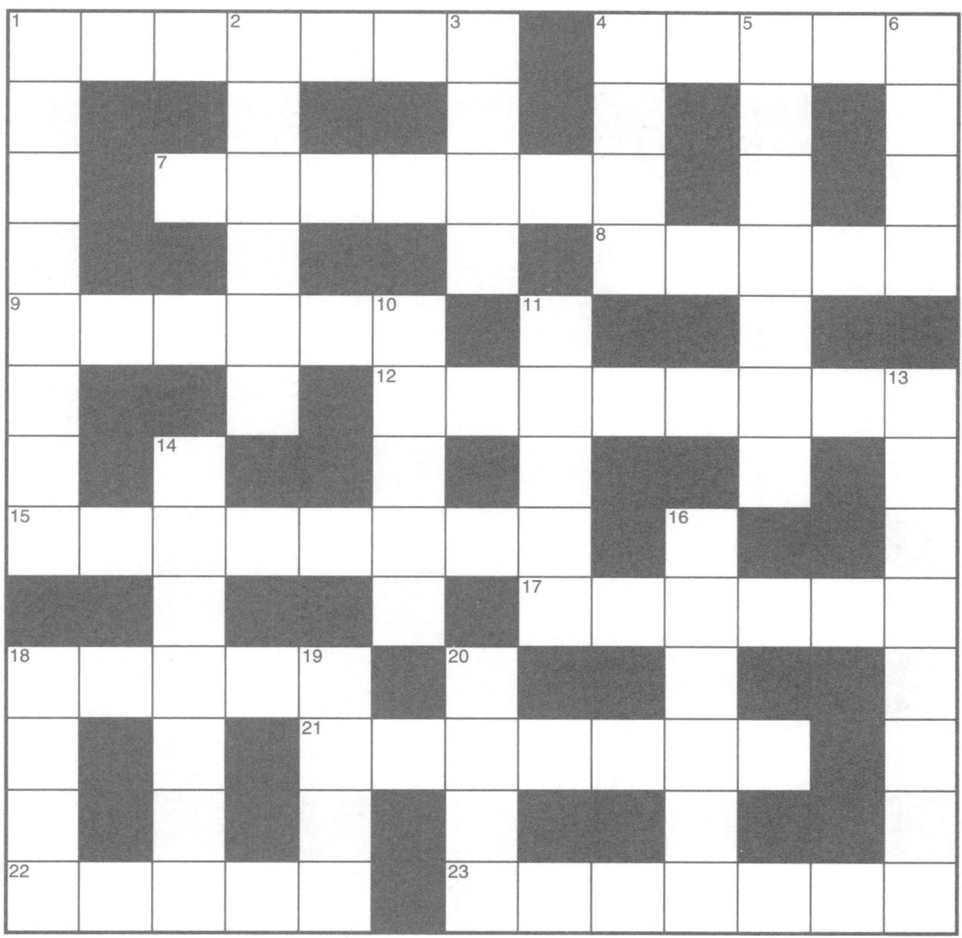

## ACROSS

1. Carpentry tool
4. Confederation
7. Pouch-beaked bird
8. Trophy
9. Part of eye
12. Slenderness
15. Average
17. Lessens
18. Written defamation
21. Eastern veil
22. Prod
23. Showered

## DOWN

1. Barbers' trims
2. Tinting
3. Candle string
4. Forearm bone
5. Occupies by force
6. Must-have
10. Also known as
11. Black & white Chinese animal
13. Sunk
14. Prattled
16. Curved fruit
18. Pork cut
19. Ancient harp
20. Vipers

# CROSSWORD 267

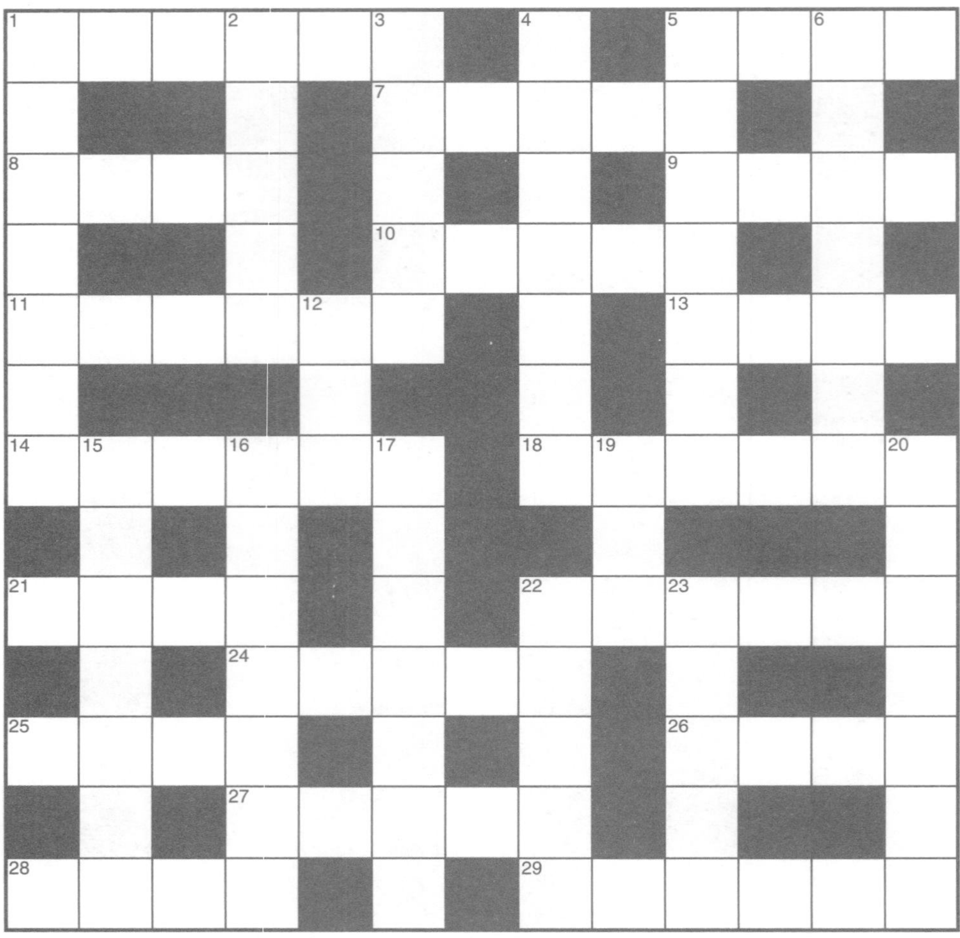

## ACROSS

1. Politely stooping
5. Durable timber
7. In need of scratching
8. Eating utensil
9. Drama
10. Horse's cry
11. Between
13. Unfasten
14. Four-sided shape
18. Spanish Mrs
21. Papier-mache material
22. Worn thin
24. Shrub fence
25. Sector
26. Boorish
27. Sister's girl
28. Dedicatory verses
29. Public drains

## DOWN

1. Prairie animal
2. Irritated
3. Colossal
4. Is frugal
5. Violent tropical storm
6. Unpaid sportsman
12. Solar body
15. Smudged (image)
16. Deprives of parents
17. Resented
19. Hearing organ
20. House location
22. Festivals
23. Archery missile

# CROSSWORD 268

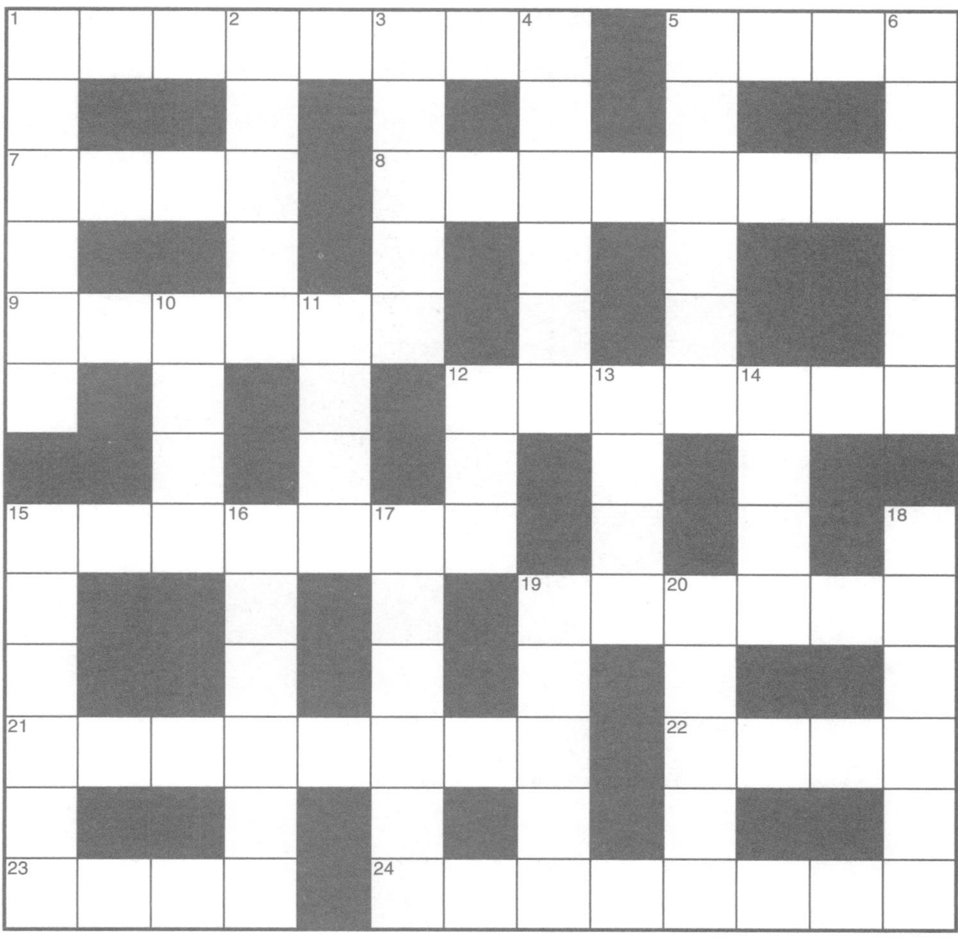

## ACROSS

1. Risked
5. Presidential duration
7. Minuscule amount
8. Foot-operated levers
9. Engraver
12. Inflexible
15. Turned down (offer)
19. Skewers of meat
21. Lung inflammation
22. Indian teacher
23. Sandal or boot
24. Ignite

## DOWN

1. Flagged down (cab)
2. Flooded by waves
3. Discourage
4. Followed healthy eating plan
5. Monotonous routine
6. Lucky emblem
10. Sleeve part
11. Flows away
12. As well
13. The A of AM
14. Greenish-blue
15. Play area, ... room
16. Uncertain
17. Tax on goods
18. Guarantee
19. Paddling craft
20. Commenced

# CROSSWORD 269

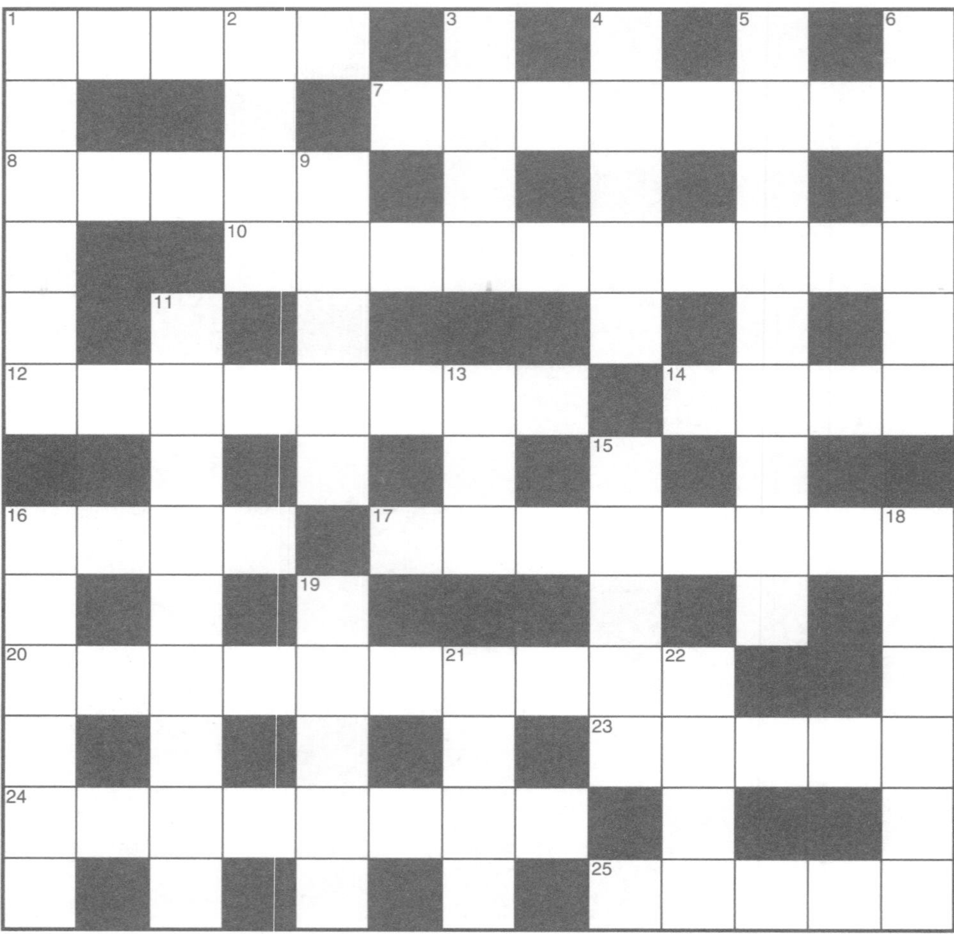

## ACROSS

1. Yellow parts of eggs
7. Taking on (task)
8. Drugged (horse)
10. Commit (crime)
12. Seeks, ... for
14. Historical ages
16. Incapacitate
17. Policemen
20. Depravity
23. Gestured with hand
24. Access point
25. Quizzed

## DOWN

1. Sings alpine-style
2. Retain
3. Hornet relative
4. Satirical sketches
5. Fails to concur
6. Heron-like birds
9. Tennis 40/40
11. Graduate (gauge)
13. Pixie
15. Bereaved woman
16. Cleaned (floor)
18. Ranked (players)
19. Of the kidneys
21. Cloth bag
22. Catches (thief)

# CROSSWORD 270

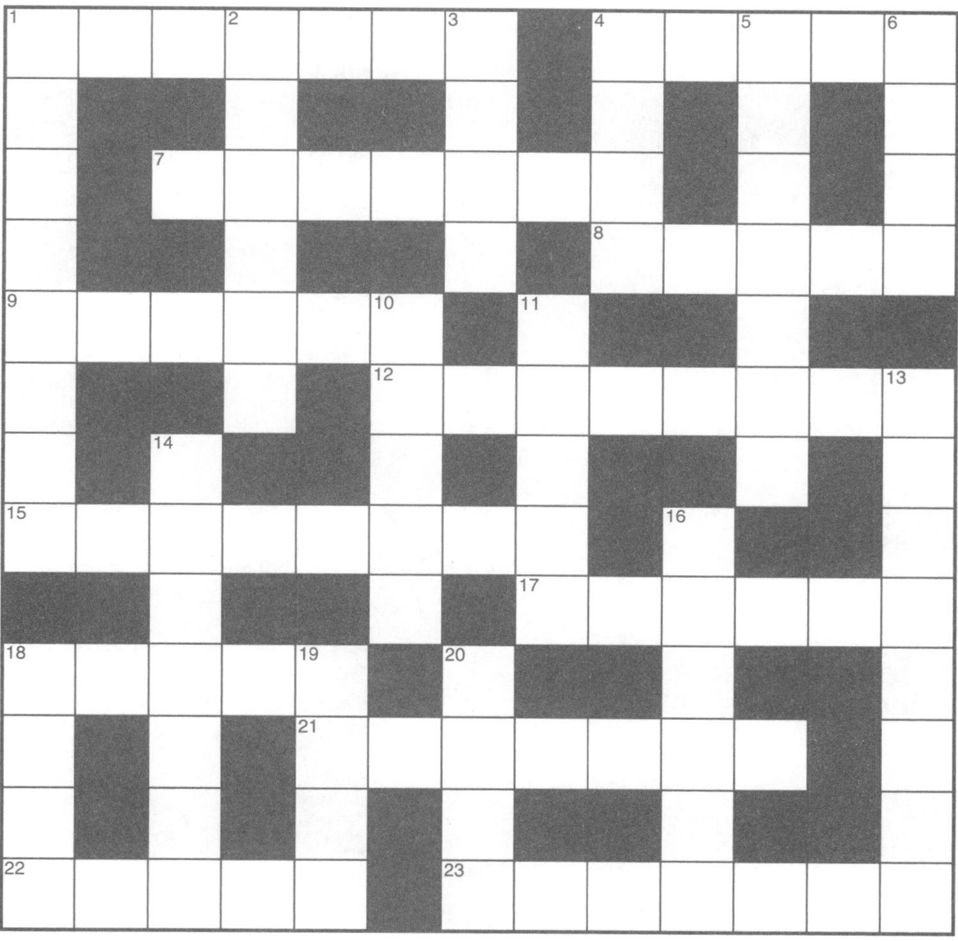

## ACROSS

1. Saliva
4. Hang limply
7. Praise
8. Unadventurous
9. Looked upon
12. Refereeing
15. Went aboard ship
17. Escaped
18. Special skill
21. Power plant, ... reactor
22. Moisten while roasting
23. Cost

## DOWN

1. Minor dispute
2. Small garden digger
3. Viewed suspiciously
4. Fathers
5. Naturally grown
6. Walk with heavy steps
10. Dips (food) in liquid
11. Playing card symbol
13. Instruction
14. Chafes
16. Automobile repair shop
18. Door handle
19. Leg joint
20. Feel pain

# CROSSWORD 271

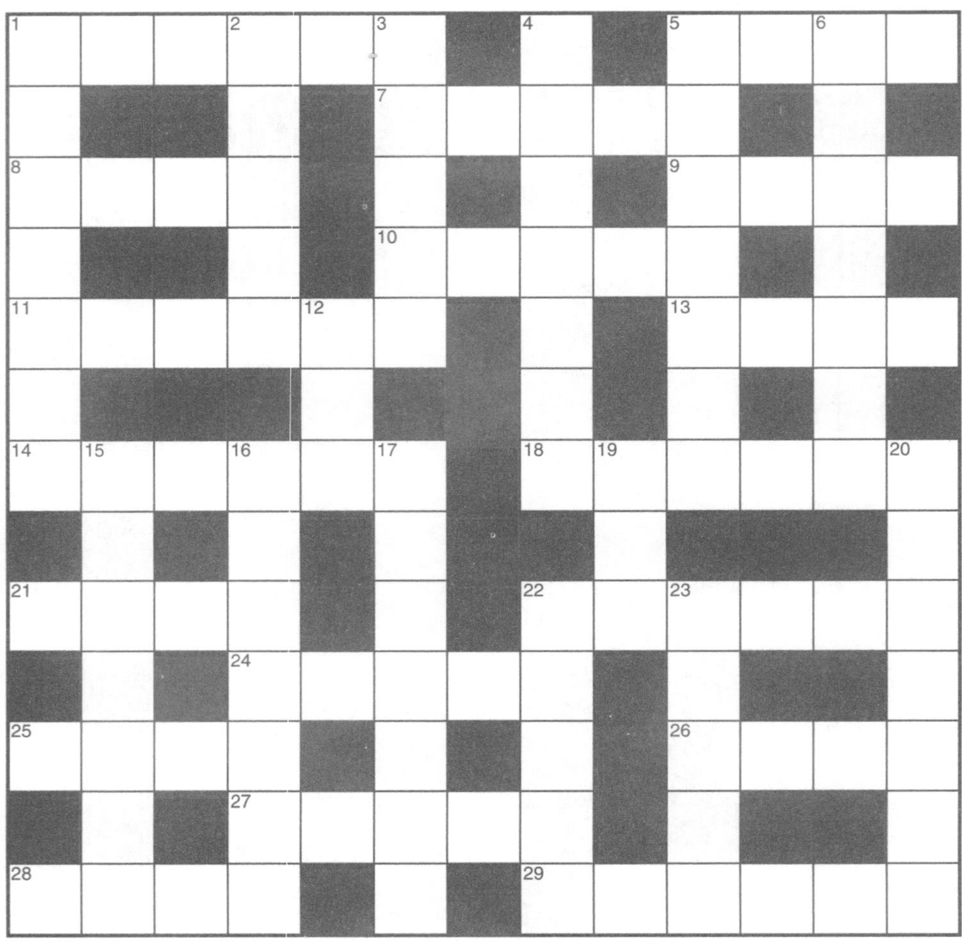

## ACROSS

1. Vegetable tuber
5. Move (wings)
7. River mammal
8. Printing fluids
9. Iridescent gem
10. Jostle
11. Decapitate
13. Twig shelter
14. Painters' stands
18. First-born
21. Wild pack canine
22. Was scared of
24. Transpire
25. Fossil fuel
26. Body of ship
27. Hang in folds
28. Fitness clubs
29. Less bright

## DOWN

1. Flexible
2. Gangway
3. Leaked slowly
4. Bristly chin growth
5. Scowled
6. Accumulates
12. Afflict
15. Expression of regret
16. Wraps around
17. Out of the ordinary
19. Rest on bed
20. Small child
22. Liberated
23. Hate

# CROSSWORD 272

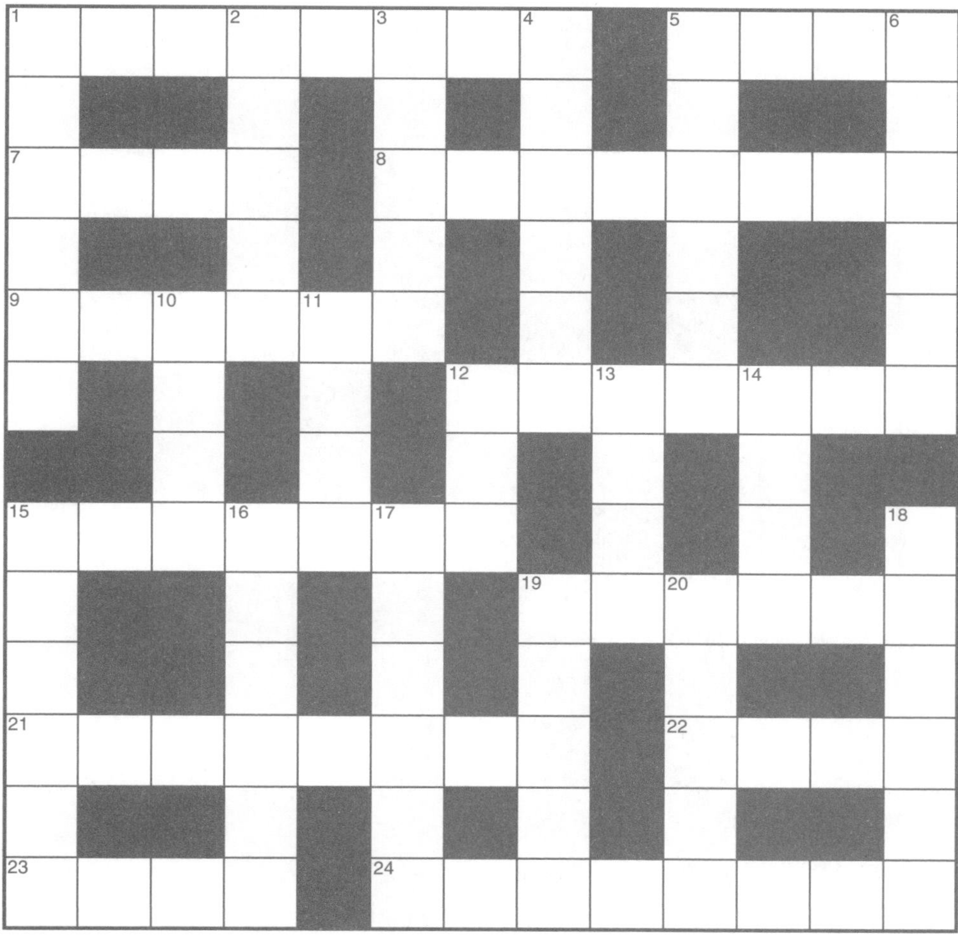

## ACROSS

1. Exhaust gas, carbon ...
5. Grasp
7. Cavity
8. Surgical inserts
9. Give disease to
12. Nationwide
15. Bargained
19. Restored to health
21. Excessively proud
22. Trifling
23. Stops
24. Meeting plan

## DOWN

1. Hair of angora goat
2. Overweight
3. Simpleton
4. Uncover
5. Funeral vehicle
6. Scatter
10. Cloth emblem
11. Loop
12. Short-lived trend
13. Open valley
14. Electoral list
15. Compassionate
16. Brides & ...
17. School compositions
18. Cling (to)
19. Trapdoor
20. Furnished with guns

# CROSSWORD 273

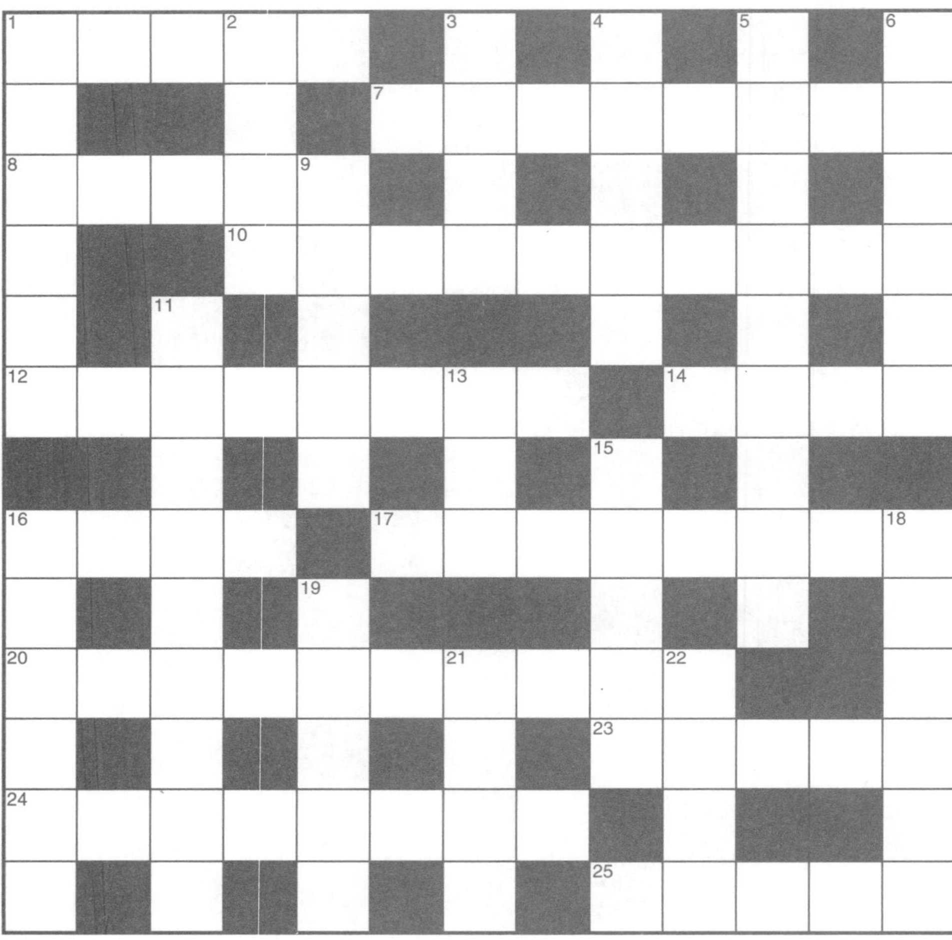

## ACROSS

1. Massage
7. Adventurous
8. Samurai weapon
10. Theory of numbers
12. Regional speech types
14. Vats
16. Run of bell-chimes
17. Misting (up)
20. Embellish
23. Pulls with a jerk
24. Mockery
25. Investigate furtively

## DOWN

1. Touched lips
2. Surrounding atmosphere
3. Single entity
4. Most important
5. Unenthusiastic
6. Decrees
9. Parched
11. Twin-hulled boat
13. Little child
15. Impetuous
16. Abundance
18. Idle talk
19. Leers at
21. Decays
22. Make (profit)

# CROSSWORD 274

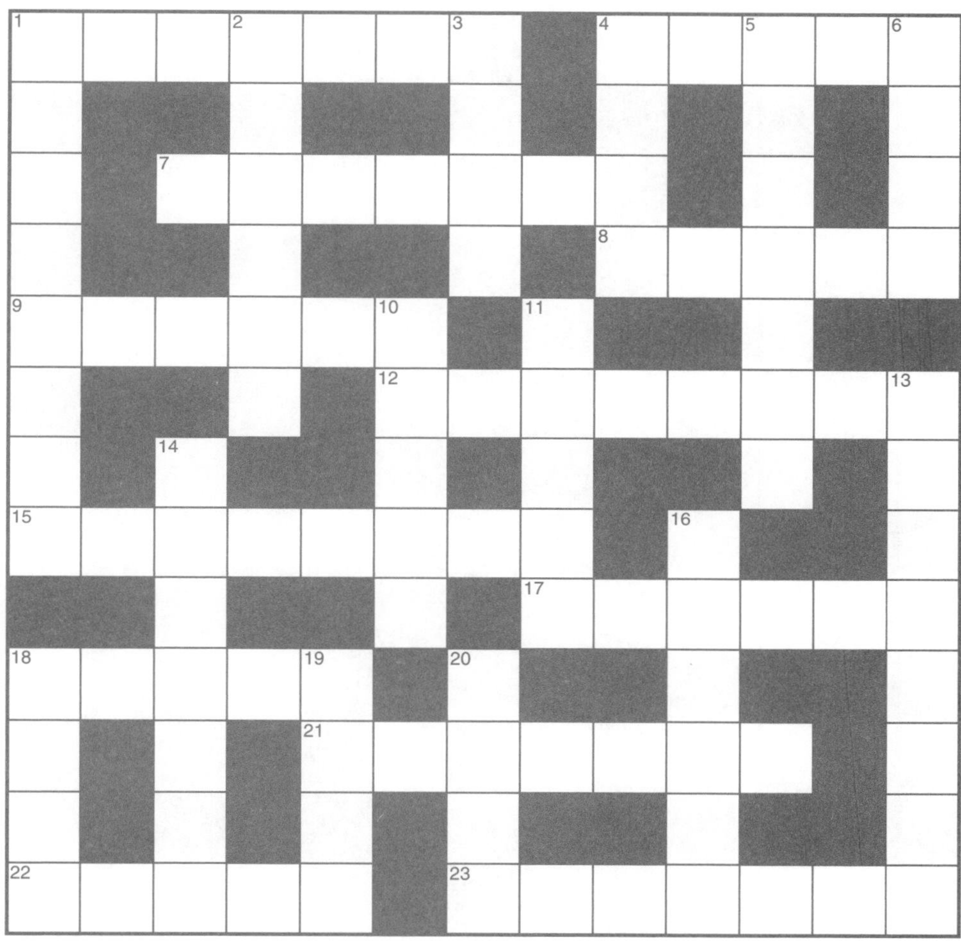

## ACROSS

1. Wide area
4. Forward
7. Nervously restless
8. Slide on ice
9. Solicitor
12. Aloft
15. Hand motions
17. Desires greatly
18. Small pheasant relative
21. Visual symbolism
22. Topic
23. Lack of success

## DOWN

1. Making possible for
2. Forever
3. To ... her own
4. Sunbeams
5. Detected
6. Ox harness
10. Lion calls
11. Untidy
13. Melt away
14. Absconder
16. Security round
18. Resign
19. Reside
20. Fifty per cent

# CROSSWORD 275

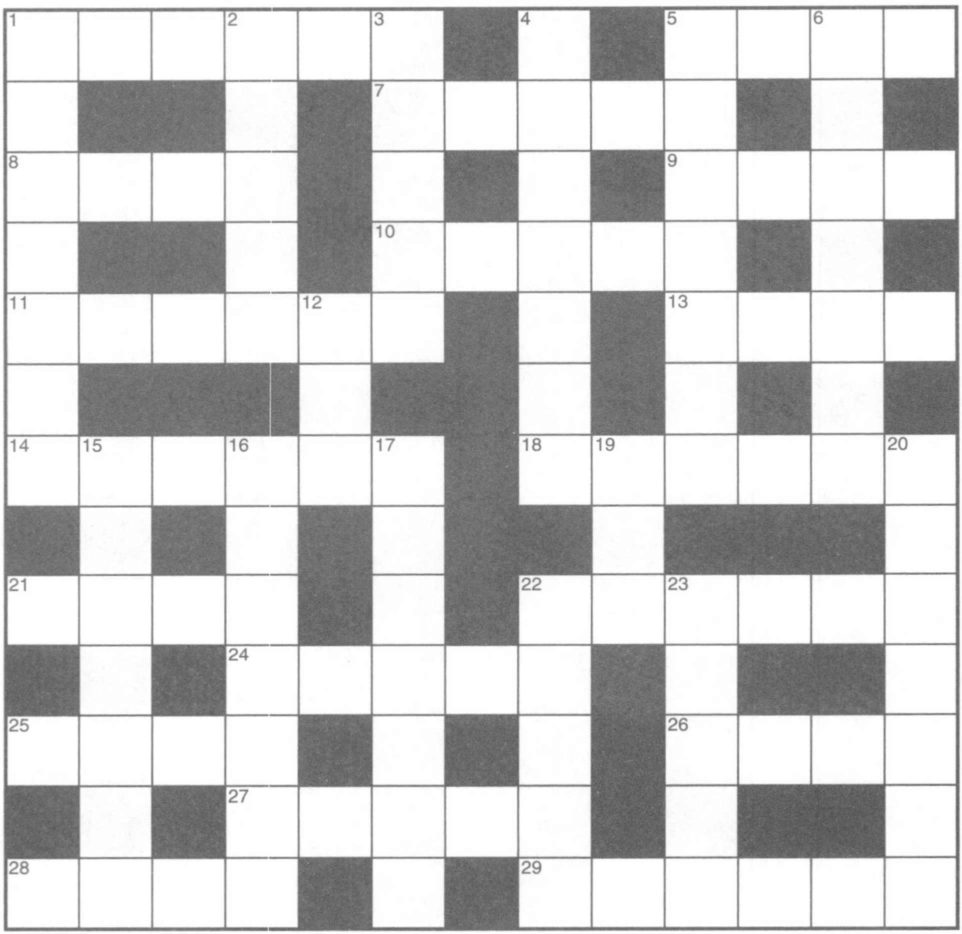

## ACROSS

1. Blunt refusal
5. Vicious dogs
7. Live coal
8. Bread quantity
9. Hotels
10. Provide with gear
11. Sales talk
13. Beseech
14. Swirled
18. Creeps stealthily
21. Win easily, ... home
22. Spasm
24. Banishment
25. Sleigh
26. Tower (over)
27. Wield (influence)
28. States further
29. Loathing

## DOWN

1. Fall ill again
2. Physically out of condition
3. Less in number
4. Kidnaps
5. Disable
6. Pillage
12. Ram's mate
15. Slobbered
16. Obstructs
17. Specifies
19. Currently
20. Conspired
22. Molars or canines
23. Estuary

# CROSSWORD 276

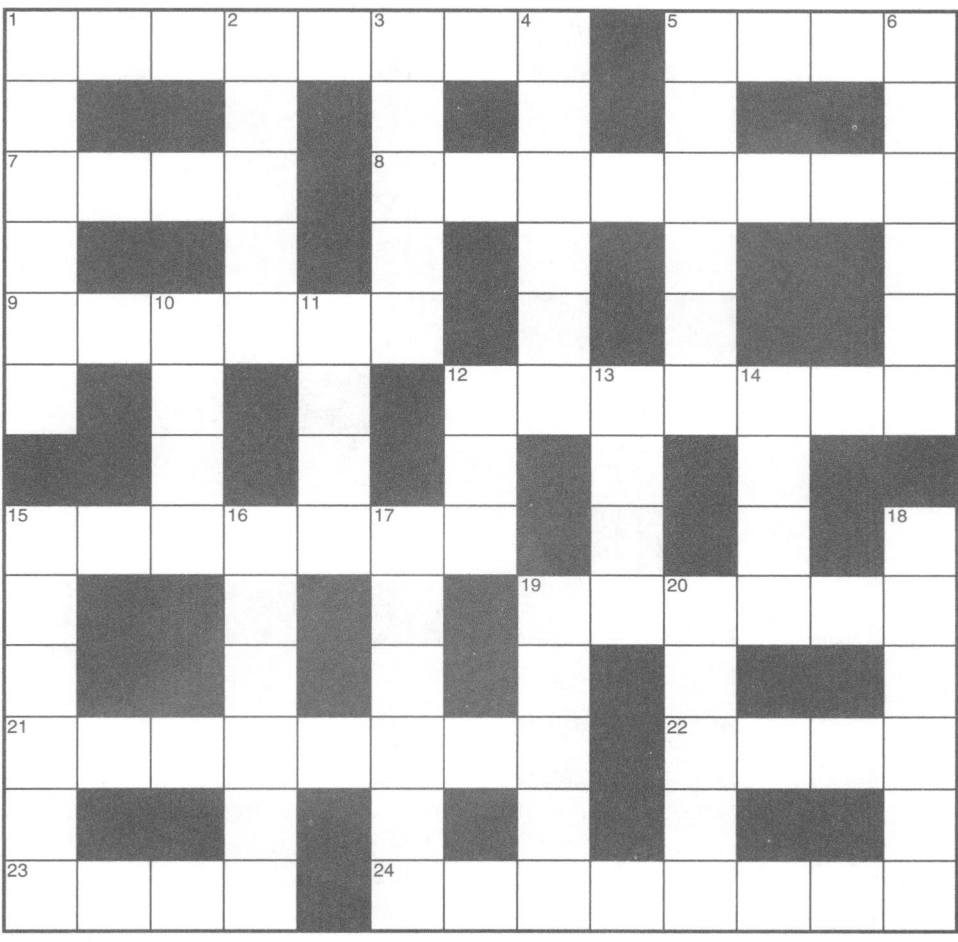

## ACROSS

1. Makes headway
5. Despicable
7. Unable to speak
8. Tidiness
9. That is to say
12. Female beneficiary
15. Solemn promises
19. Seizes (power)
21. Biblical letters
22. Breeze
23. Fixing pin
24. Bullfighters

## DOWN

1. Helping
2. Leisurely walk
3. Shrewd
4. Rarely encountered
5. Retailer
6. Follows on
10. Nutmeg spice
11. Lengthy
12. Is compelled (to)
13. Troubles
14. Jug
15. Homing bird
16. Killer whale's back fin
17. Pictorial symbol
18. Stage whispers
19. Overturn
20. Unmarried

# CROSSWORD 277

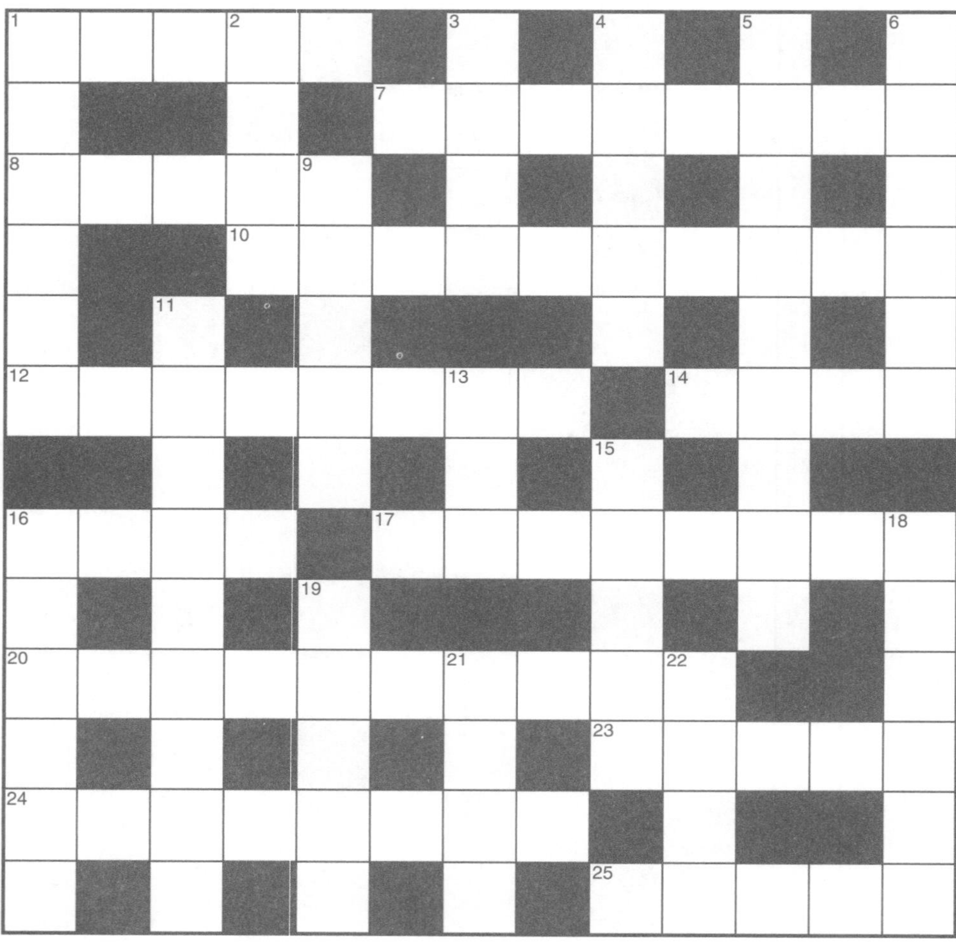

## ACROSS

1. Imaginative thoughts
7. Passages from book
8. Appeal earnestly
10. Fair
12. Boldly decorate
14. Principal
16. Serving platter
17. Ridiculously
20. Field glasses
23. Oyster casing
24. Curled hair locks
25. Scottish fabric

## DOWN

1. Pierce with spike
2. A great way off
3. Graph line
4. Smooths out (shirt creases)
5. Sword sheaths
6. Aft
9. Postpone
11. Acquiring
13. Ball
15. Cat's contented rumbles
16. Underground stems
18. Screamed
19. Clean (fish)
21. Medieval guitar
22. Reveal

# CROSSWORD 278

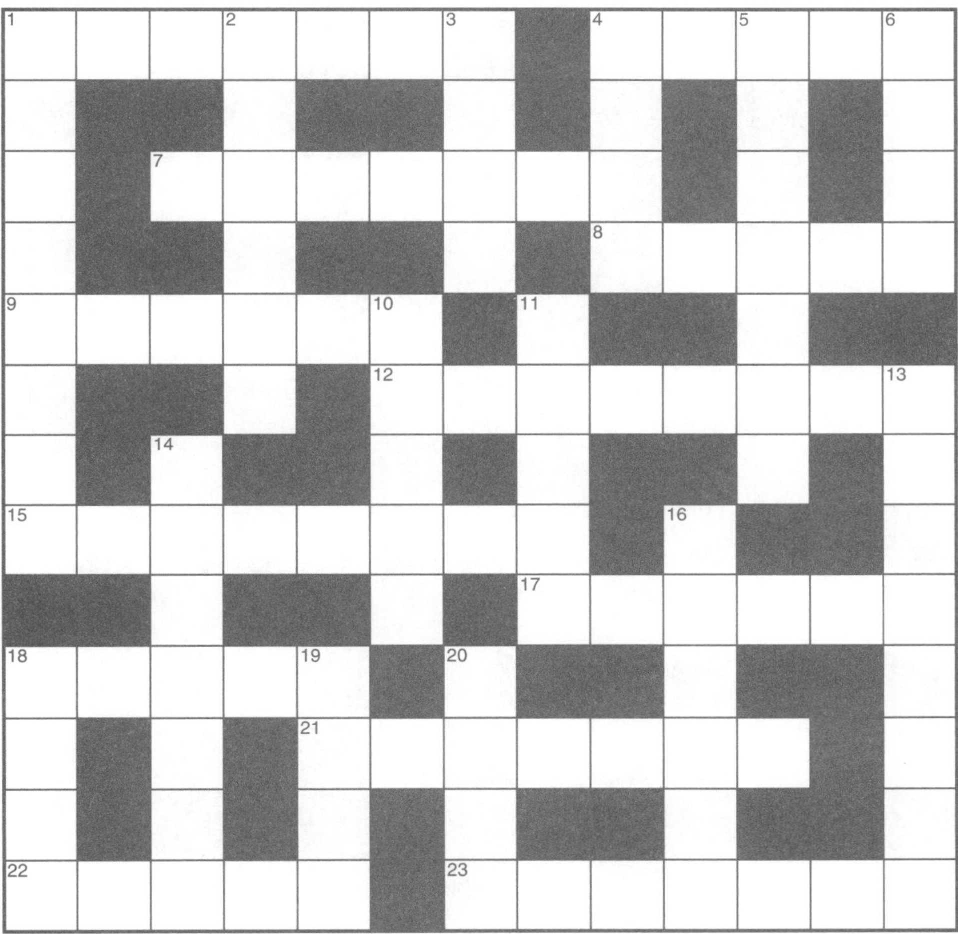

## ACROSS

1. Resistant to wear
4. Tennis or golf
7. Put on (make-up)
8. Remain on feet
9. Group confidence
12. Discarding
15. Waste discharge
17. Delighted
18. Interweave
21. Goes by (of time)
22. Snap
23. Small plums

## DOWN

1. Severely damage (crop)
2. Request for aid
3. Long movie
4. Soap foam
5. Of the Pacific or Atlantic
6. Stomped (on)
10. Fringed
11. Voice
13. Farewells
14. Friendly
16. Peaceful resorts
18. Fish-hook point
19. Office table
20. Repel, ... off

# CROSSWORD 279

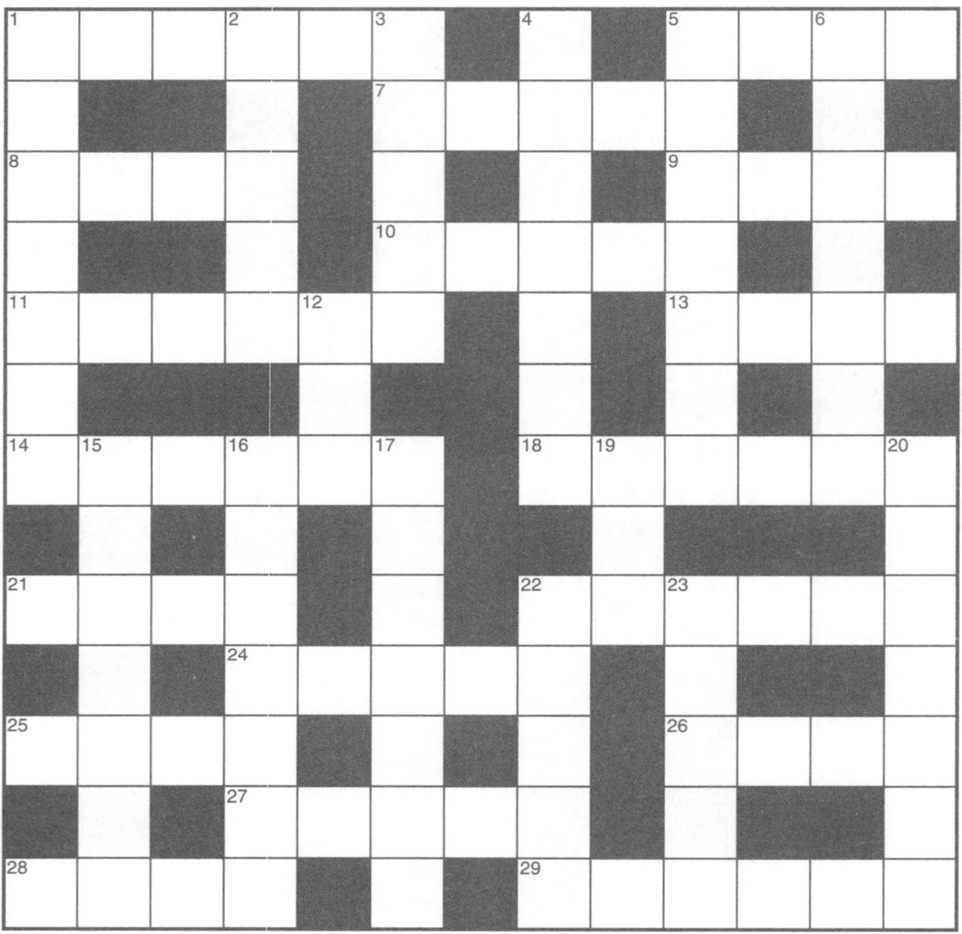

## ACROSS

1. Not casual (attire)
5. Forgery
7. Abysmal
8. Unfeeling
9. Current units
10. Alcoves
11. Loves deeply
13. Shades
14. Gravies
18. Cruelty
21. Similar
22. Zigzagged (through traffic)
24. Aristocratic
25. Tropical starchy cereal
26. Sea bird
27. More agreeable
28. ... & evens
29. Considered

## DOWN

1. Refusals
2. Unintoxicated
3. Tired sighs
4. Attempts
5. Sparked
6. Smoked herrings
12. Supplement, ... out
15. Ungainly
16. Heavy weapons
17. Relapse in recovery
19. Imitate
20. Bewildered
22. Bizarre
23. Debate

# CROSSWORD 280

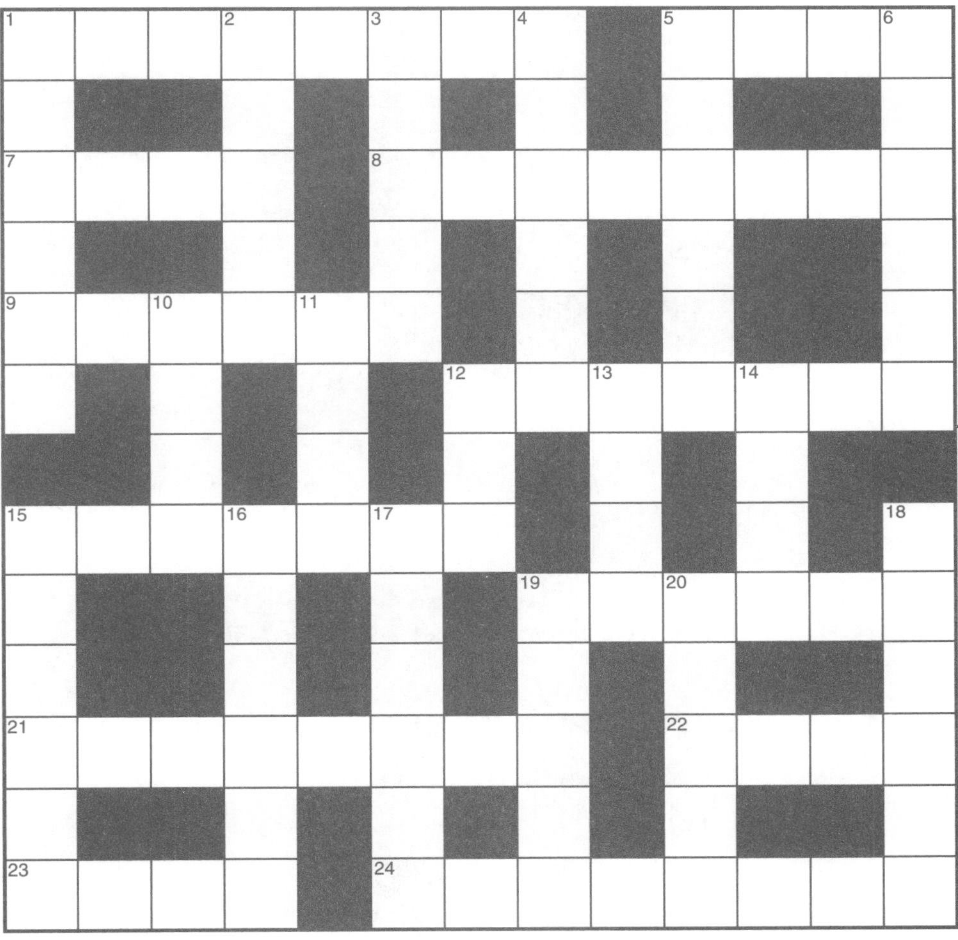

## ACROSS

1. Remodels
5. Rouse from sleep
7. Drinks slowly
8. Scrambles up
9. Exchanged
12. More sugary
15. Occupancy
19. Not genuine
21. Untangles
22. Festival
23. Go berserk, run ...
24. Wavered

## DOWN

1. Readjusts (clock)
2. Watered with tube
3. Walked back & forth
4. Follow closely
5. Shaky movement
6. Simpler
10. Prayer ending
11. Equal
12. Heavens
13. Universal ages
14. Ballet dress
15. Emotional shock
16. Assault
17. Concrete ingredient
18. Craven person
19. Flour glue
20. Golfer's two under par

# CROSSWORD 281

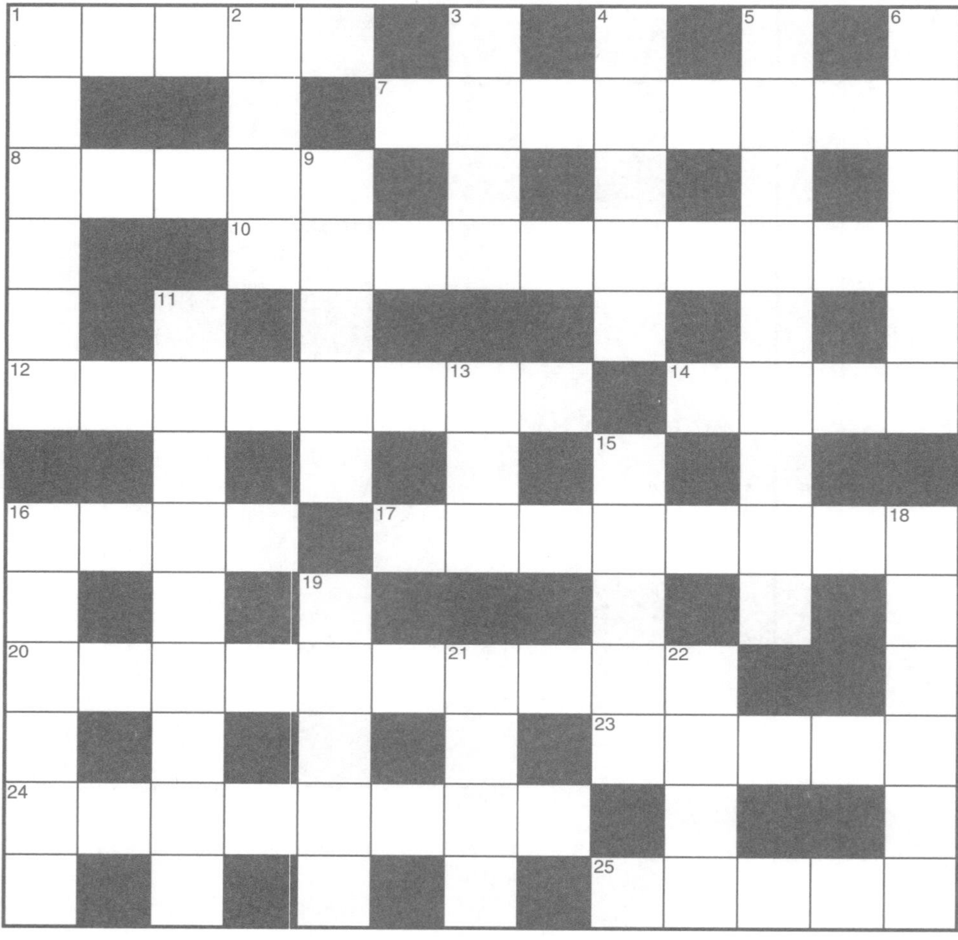

## ACROSS

1. Rap
7. Divide
8. Competitor
10. Jingling instrument
12. Seepages
14. Surrender (territory)
16. Nip with beak
17. Harsher
20. Dining-room cupboards
23. Finnish steam bath
24. Richly
25. Liquid

## DOWN

1. Nut
2. Winter garment
3. Doing word
4. Ruined
5. Policy statement
6. Go back on deal
9. Tibetan monks
11. Tumbling (water)
13. Have a meal
15. Flying creatures
16. Moving engine part
18. Amusingly coarse
19. Aids in crime
21. Competently
22. Travel by yacht

# CROSSWORD 282

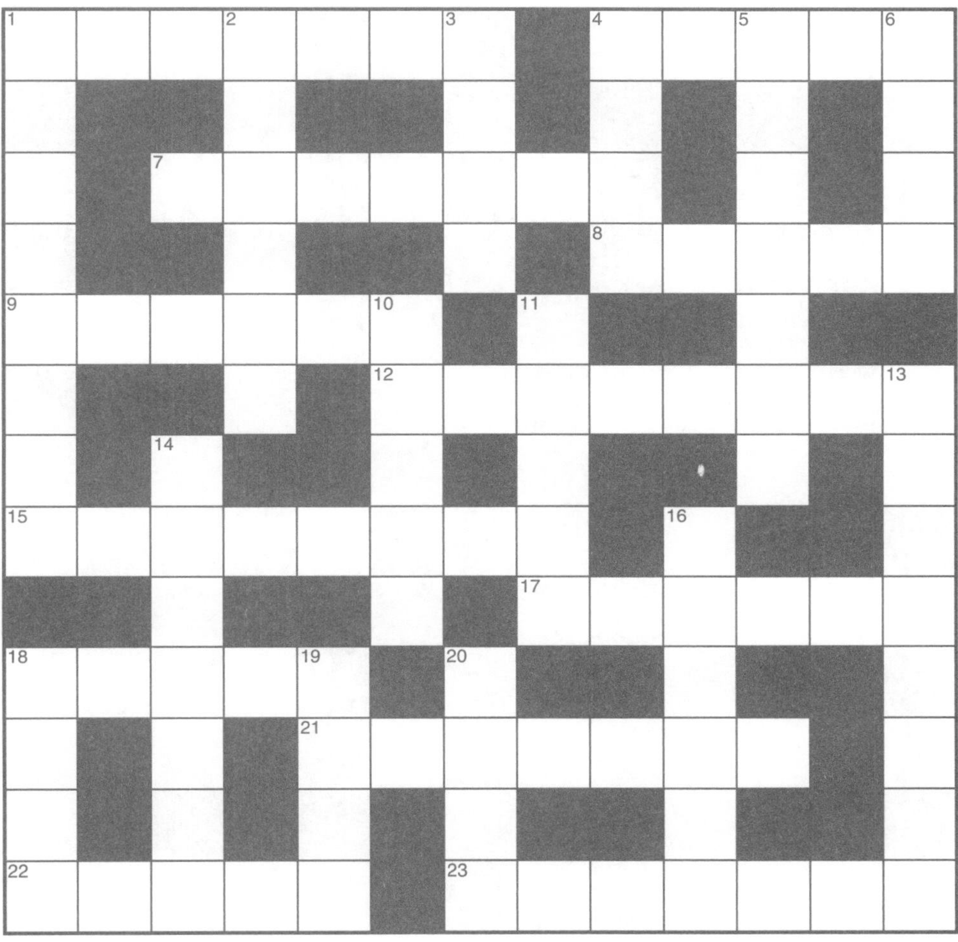

## ACROSS

1. Disapproving whistle
4. Swindled
7. Feathers
8. Cunningly
9. Rock levels
12. Carpentry
15. Predicting
17. Warning bells
18. Reproductive organ
21. Speaking publicly
22. Renter
23. Layer under topsoil

## DOWN

1. Stroked lovingly
2. Wine store
3. Foliage part
4. Perishes
5. Hugh Hefner publication
6. Drowsy
10. Look forward to
11. Latin American line dance
13. Relatives
14. Pilot
16. Mode
18. Yell of pain
19. Belonging to you
20. Paint roughly

# CROSSWORD 283

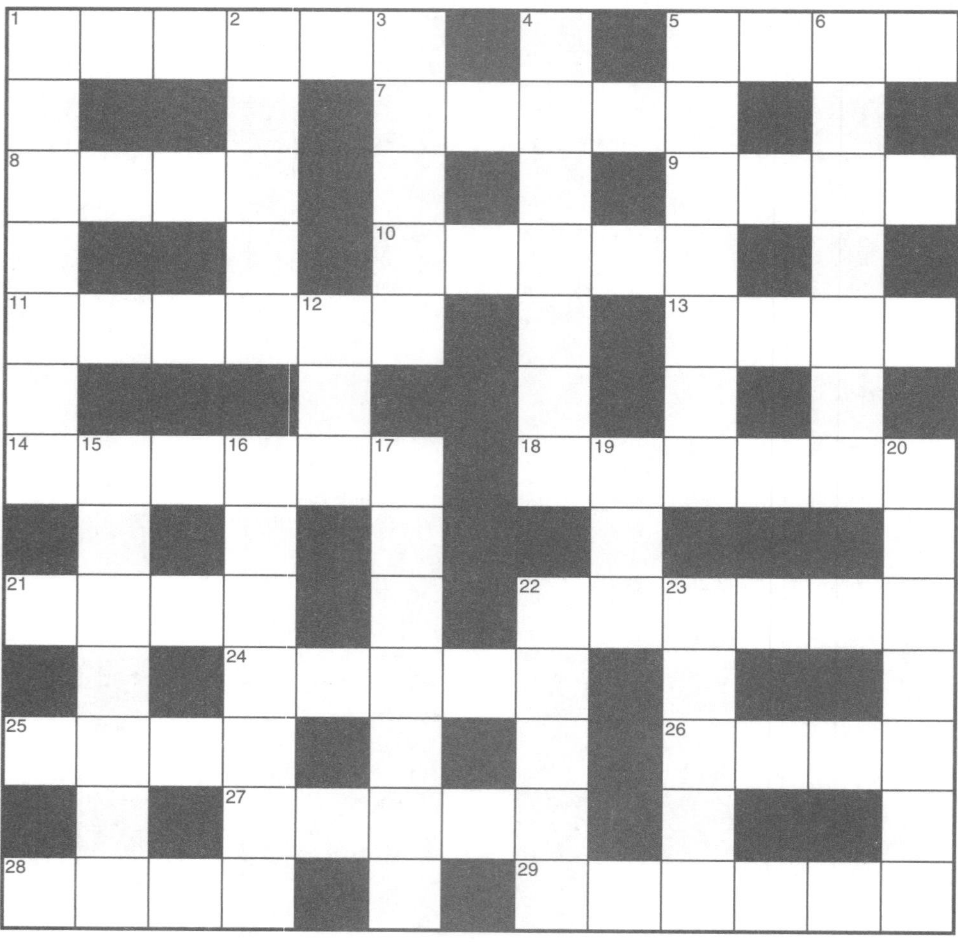

## ACROSS

1. Didn't remember
5. High tennis deliveries
7. Greeting word
8. Beseech
9. Scarcity
10. Drive forward
11. Livestock feed
13. Lazily
14. Libel
18. Absorb (nourishment)
21. Singer's solo
22. Mariner
24. Striped African animal
25. Tiny (version)
26. Travel permit
27. Lasso loop
28. Boast
29. Seasoned (food)

## DOWN

1. Puffed out (pillow)
2. Avarice
3. Belonging to them
4. Pruned
5. Slouching (on sofa)
6. Belt fasteners
12. Deciduous tree
15. Prior
16. Astounding
17. Arch over eye
19. Wrath
20. Large beer mug
22. Bank vaults
23. Metal-working block

# CROSSWORD 284

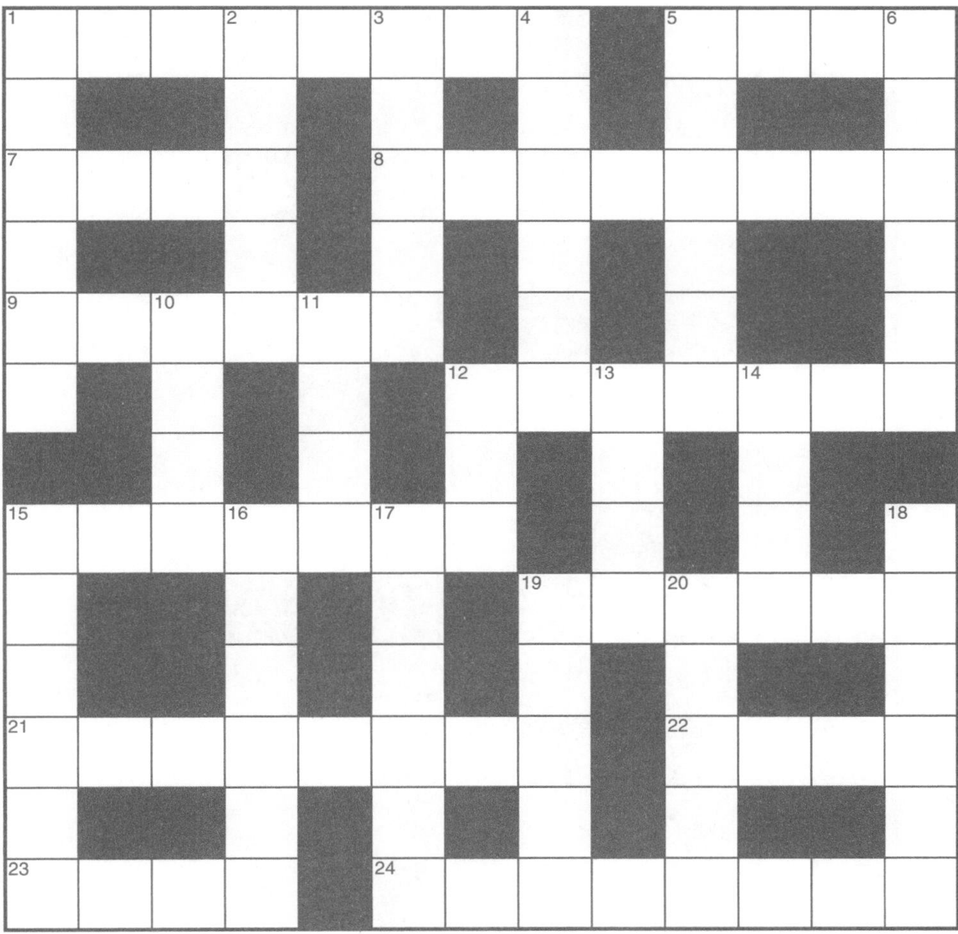

## ACROSS

1. High point
5. Wander
7. Fix
8. Pleads with
9. Hired
12. Adventurous journey
15. Clear of blame
19. Walks heavily
21. Clamber
22. Wild cat
23. Equivalent
24. Lifted

## DOWN

1. Face blemish
2. Naked models
3. Boy or girl
4. Caught sight of
5. Perches
6. Primarily
10. Plans
11. Noble rank
12. Mineral rock
13. Twelve months
14. Move through water
15. Degrades
16. Narcotic drug
17. Practicable
18. Sicily or Corsica
19. Neither ... nor those
20. First Greek letter

# CROSSWORD 285

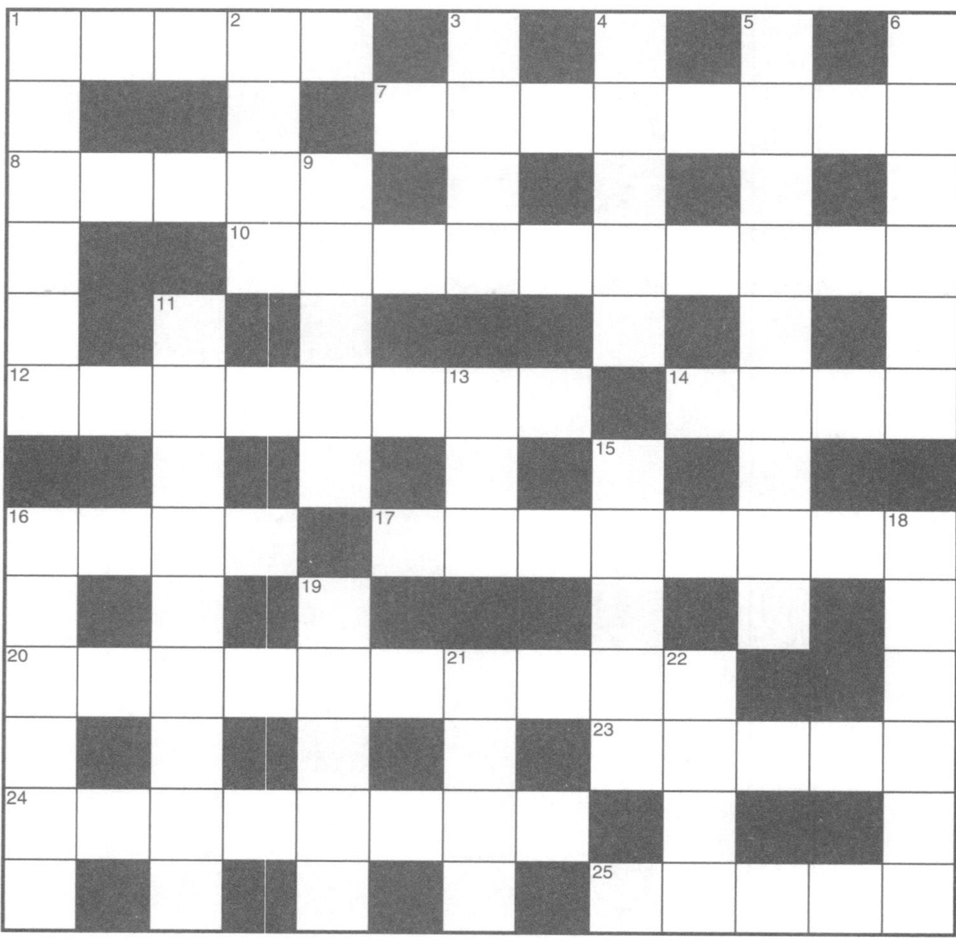

## ACROSS

1. Shut out
7. One million watts
8. Vindictiveness
10. Secretly ruining
12. Stimulating
14. Skidded
16. Upon
17. Throttle
20. Called
23. Soft leather
24. Still sealed
25. Used keyboard

## DOWN

1. Wish for
2. Picnic pests
3. Refuse consent to
4. Death-causing
5. Science of medical scans
6. Put on (event)
9. Our planet
11. Young male student
13. Louse egg
15. Fierce winds
16. Wily
18. Lengthen
19. Retail therapy splurge
21. Is obliged to pay
22. Task

# CROSSWORD 286

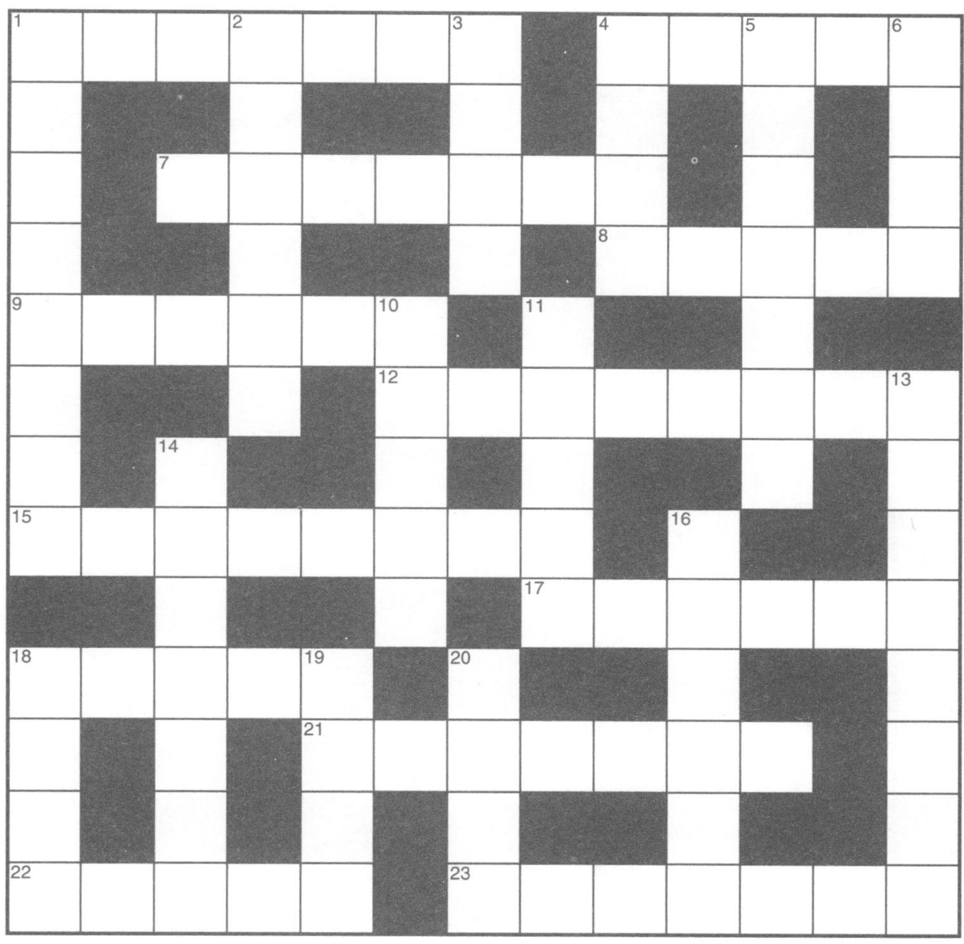

## ACROSS

1. Chronicle
4. Extendibility
7. Property size
8. Earnest
9. Sharp-tasting
12. Slanted
15. More poisonous
17. Approached
18. Domain
21. Endorsing
22. Dashed
23. Bow and arrow sport

## DOWN

1. Scored (on par)
2. Shopping corridor
3. Stuff
4. Shipping hazard
5. Achieves
6. Hind leg joint
10. Municipal
11. Open contempt
13. Hard menial work
14. Overzealous supporter
16. Fire (rocket)
18. Raise (children)
19. Temper
20. Statistics

# CROSSWORD 287

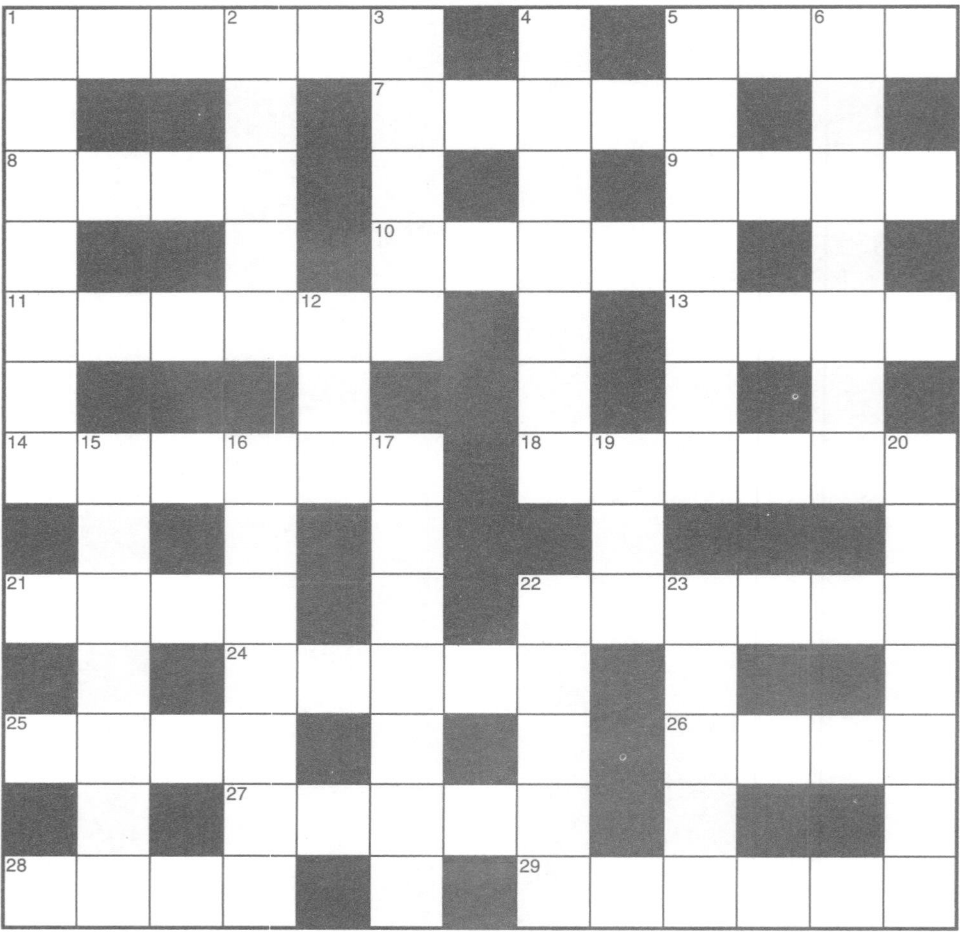

## ACROSS

1. Nauseated
5. Twist
7. Privileged class
8. Ancient
9. Miscalculates
10. Superheroes, Batman and ...
11. Widespread fame
13. Ostrich relatives
14. Pricked (boil)
18. Any one of two
21. ... & puff
22. Put into cipher
24. Physically weak
25. Sugar source
26. New Zealand bird
27. Sum up
28. Bodies of water
29. Relieving

## DOWN

1. Feud
2. Of hearing
3. Long (for)
4. Part of pelvis
5. Most eager
6. Carefully tend
12. Misfortune
15. Exalt
16. Money stores
17. Make depraved
19. Charged particle
20. Swaying on heels
22. Flee with lover
23. Soap bars

# CROSSWORD 288

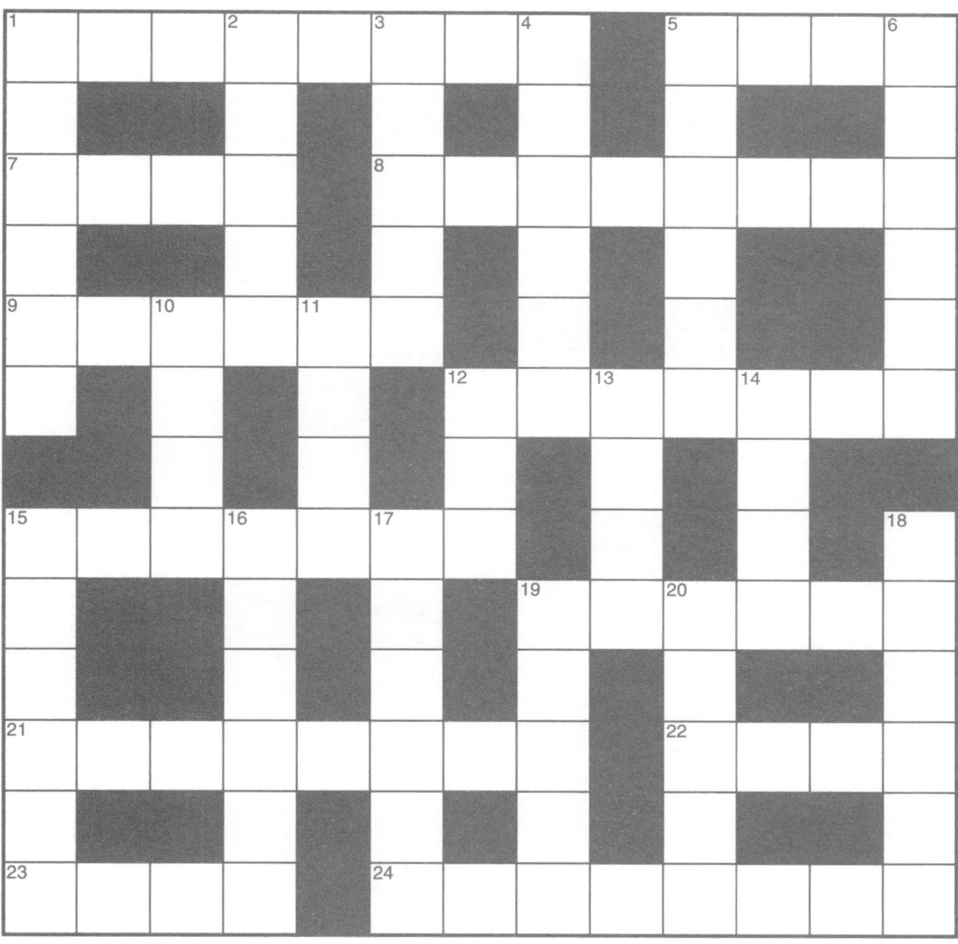

## ACROSS

1. Funded (events)
5. Uterus
7. Magician's rod
8. Protest signs
9. Left room
12. Mooring weights
15. Return game
19. Dairy cattle breed
21. Obsession
22. Gaffe, ... pas
23. Inscribe
24. Esteems

## DOWN

1. Bowed & scraped
2. Check (accounts)
3. Managed
4. Clergyman
5. Riches
6. Washbowls
10. Single article
11. Revise (text)
12. Hearth dust
13. Aviary
14. Individuals
15. Fundraising lottery
16. Fasten
17. Fish roe
18. Sharp-eyed felines
19. Chinese sail boats
20. Firearm

# CROSSWORD 289

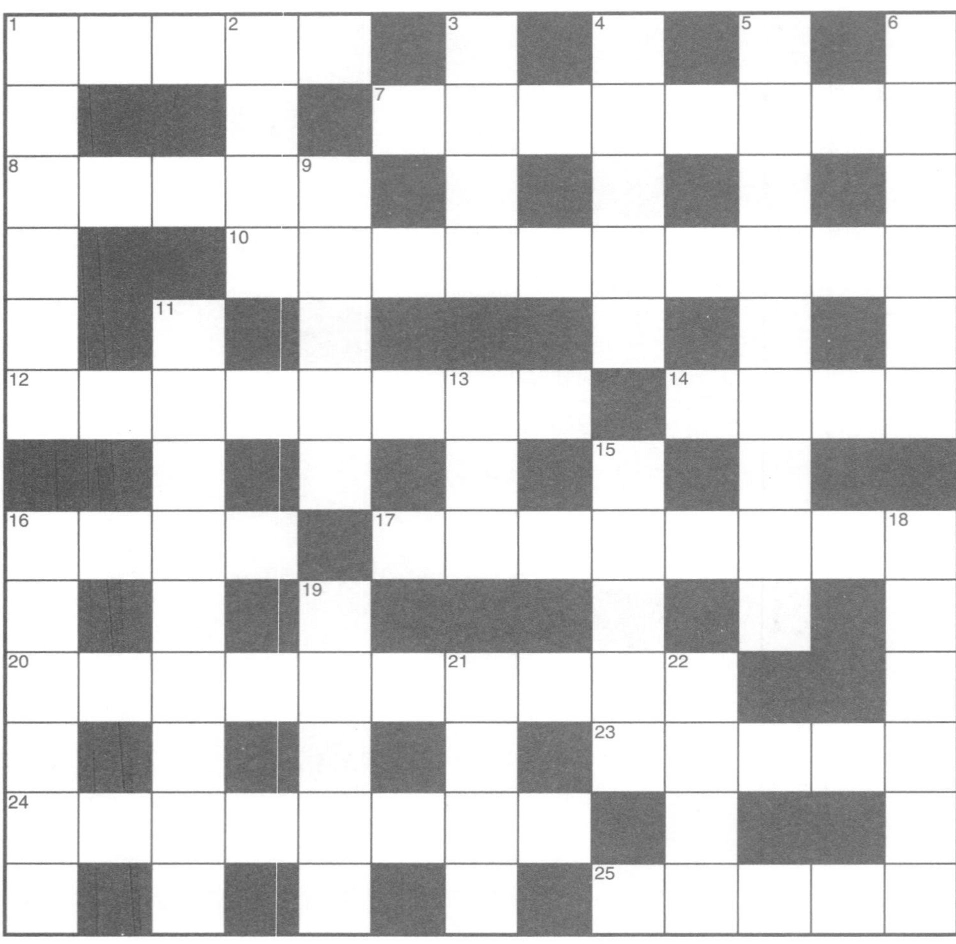

## ACROSS

1. Sorts
7. Announced
8. To the fore
10. Grow back (of vegetation)
12. Burning with hot water
14. Oil-drilling platforms
16. Commend (for bravery)
17. Poured (wine) into jug
20. Playful interest
23. Spooky
24. Style
25. Cuts with scissors

## DOWN

1. Playing-card jacks
2. Expensive
3. Festival
4. Peels (fruit)
5. Perfectionists
6. Vipers
9. Feats
11. Skippered
13. Maiden name indicator
15. Slender boat
16. Manacled
18. Forcible restraint
19. T-bone or chuck
21. Diplomacy
22. Shop light, ... sign

# CROSSWORD 290

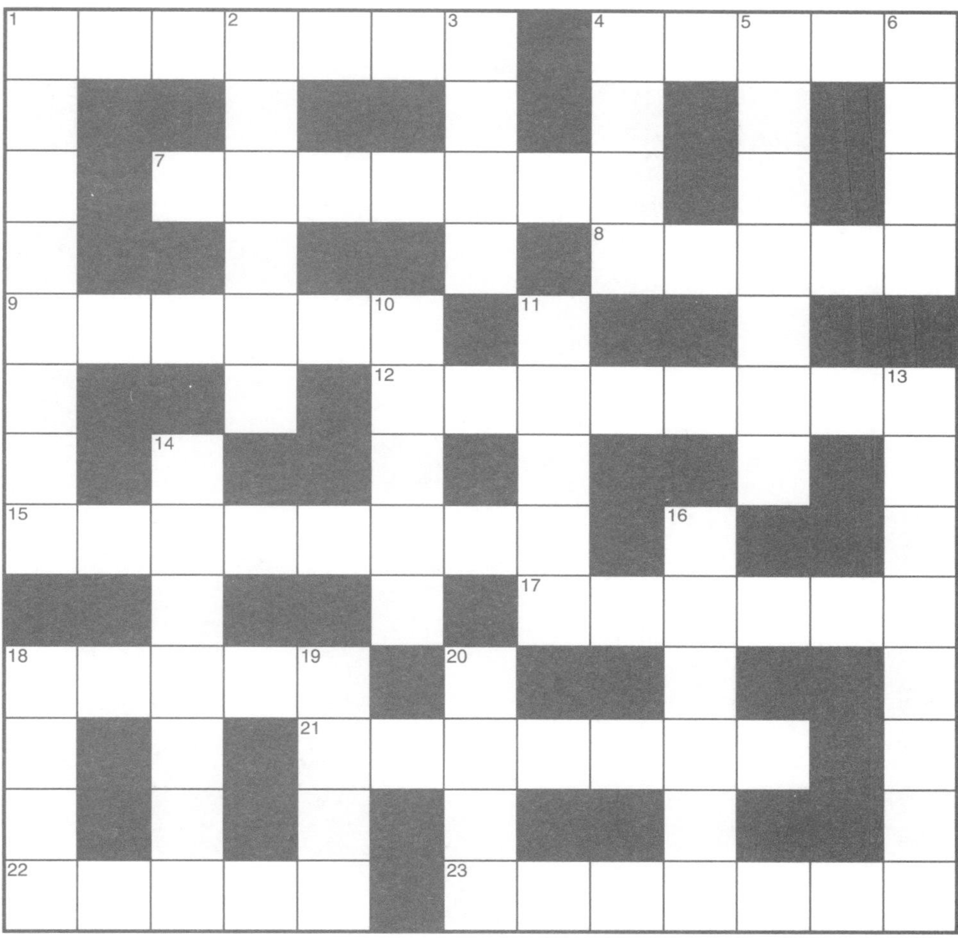

## ACROSS

1. Fine clothes
4. Bread-raising agent
7. Petty
8. Australian marsupial
9. Had (to)
12. Inflexibility
15. Street art
17. Honey drink
18. Juvenile
21. National finances
22. Ventured
23. Worrying needlessly

## DOWN

1. Processing (oil)
2. Scrape away
3. Amongst
4. Nucleus of egg
5. Of water
6. Garment worn in ancient Rome
10. Empty (glass)
11. Encore!
13. Year-old animal
14. More fully developed
16. Rascals
18. Paved enclosure
19. Castrate (horse)
20. Reindeer foot

# CROSSWORD 291

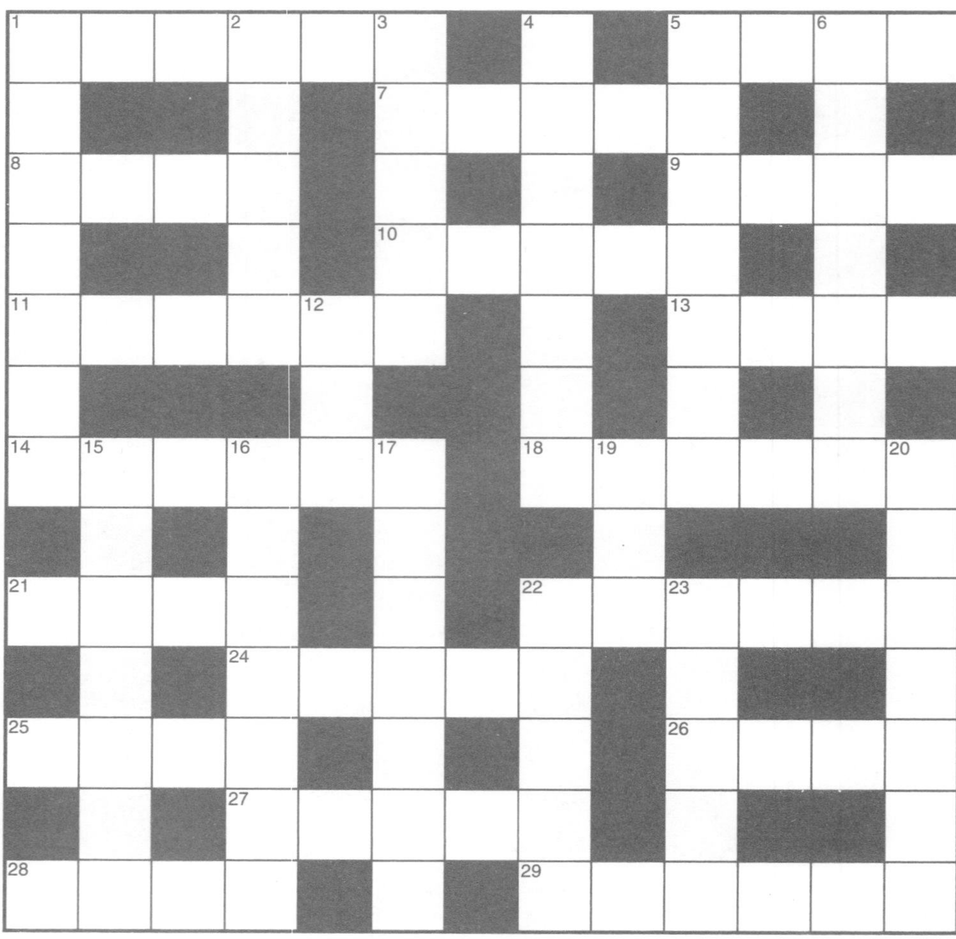

## ACROSS

1. Fooled
5. Squash (insect)
7. Ordain by law
8. Dreary
9. Not at home
10. Throat part, ... cords
11. Container for boiling
13. Songbird
14. Table linen item
18. Computer/phone links
21. Student sleeping hall
22. Wellbeing
24. Greek oil fruit
25. Profit
26. Finished
27. Was the proprietor of
28. Sacred commitments
29. Aromas

## DOWN

1. Glove material
2. Ledger entry
3. Probe
4. Bone mineral
5. Killed (engine)
6. Word conundrum
12. Hawaiian garland
15. Guacamole ingredient
16. Japanese robes
17. Countries
19. Poem
20. Globes
22. Groups of cattle
23. With no one

# CROSSWORD 292

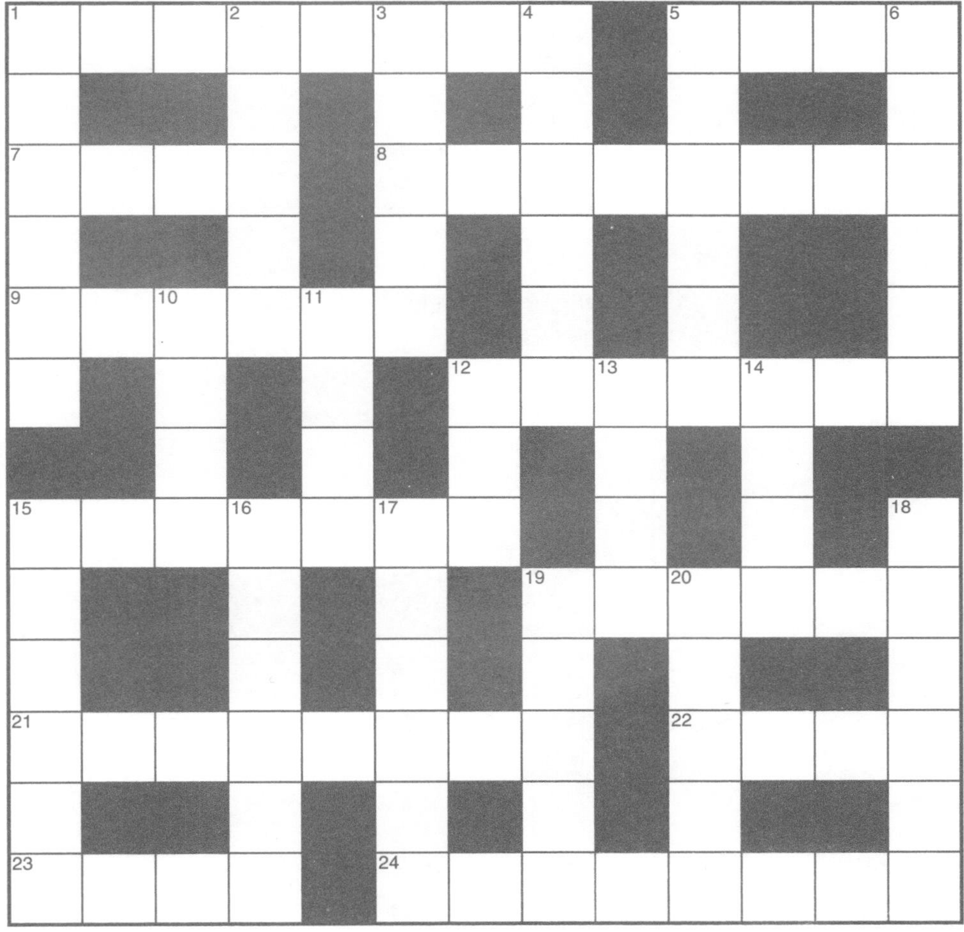

## ACROSS

1. Cuts for examination
5. Incendiary device
7. Talk indiscreetly
8. Medieval farm workers
9. Twitter comments
12. Charlie Brown cartoon
15. Steal limelight from
19. Walk wearily
21. Dig
22. Father
23. Annoys constantly
24. Douse

## DOWN

1. Formal argument
2. Marten pelt
3. Sleeveless coats
4. Go hungry
5. Navigational warning light
6. Besieges
10. Very attentive, all ...
11. Salad fish
12. Pastry dish
13. Not fully shut
14. Expended, ... up
15. Invisible
16. Sums
17. Glows
18. Pertain (to)
19. Special pleasure
20. Higher (part)

# CROSSWORD 293

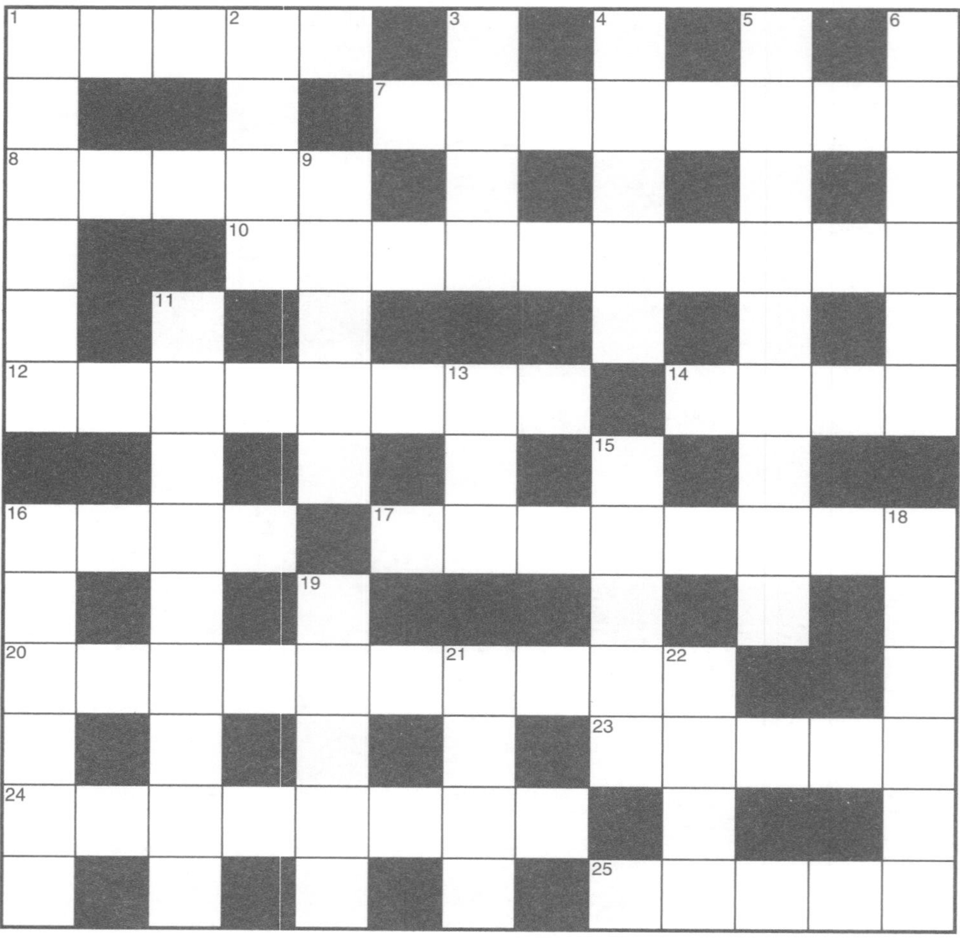

## ACROSS

1. Healing abrasions
7. Tooth-care specialists
8. Reject
10. Shielded from noise
12. Edge of highway
14. Young woman
16. Snare
17. Spiritually raised
20. Uncut
23. Determined age of (fossil)
24. Throbs
25. Steeple needle

## DOWN

1. Sibling
2. Metal rods
3. Climbing vegetable
4. Ladder rungs
5. Colleague
6. Handy
9. Gallows rope
11. Pleasant tasting
13. Short swim
15. Performed charade
16. Thuds
18. Dally
19. Super
21. Roe or buck
22. Moist

# CROSSWORD 294

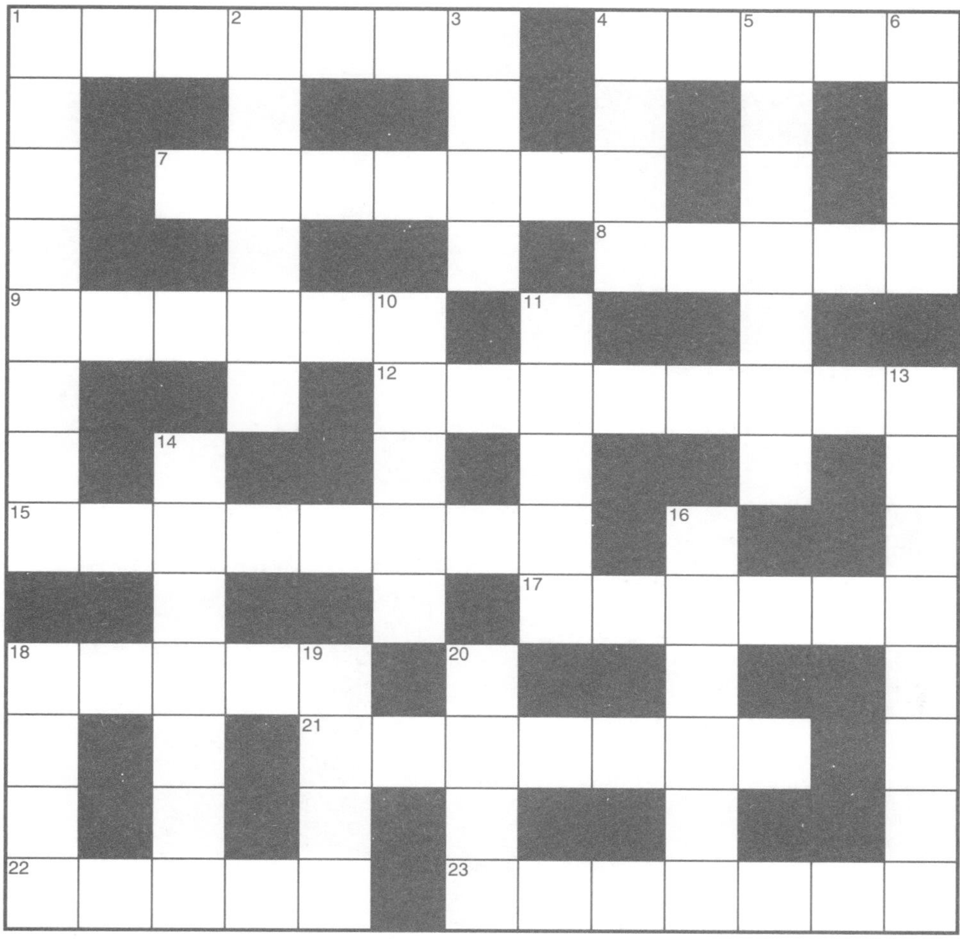

## ACROSS

1. Increasing in size
4. Clergyman
7. Presiding jury person
8. Locate
9. Sewing cotton
12. Idle
15. People of no consequence
17. Chinese calculator
18. Fashion flair
21. Full of energy
22. Majestic
23. Garden timepiece

## DOWN

1. Spiral motion
2. Kitchen stirrer, ... spoon
3. Jewels
4. Air duct
5. Made of clay
6. Not commonly found
10. Numeral
11. Light timber
13. Fragile outer casing
14. Complying with
16. Doomed to fail
18. Mast pole
19. Sinister
20. Tropical wading bird

# CROSSWORD 295

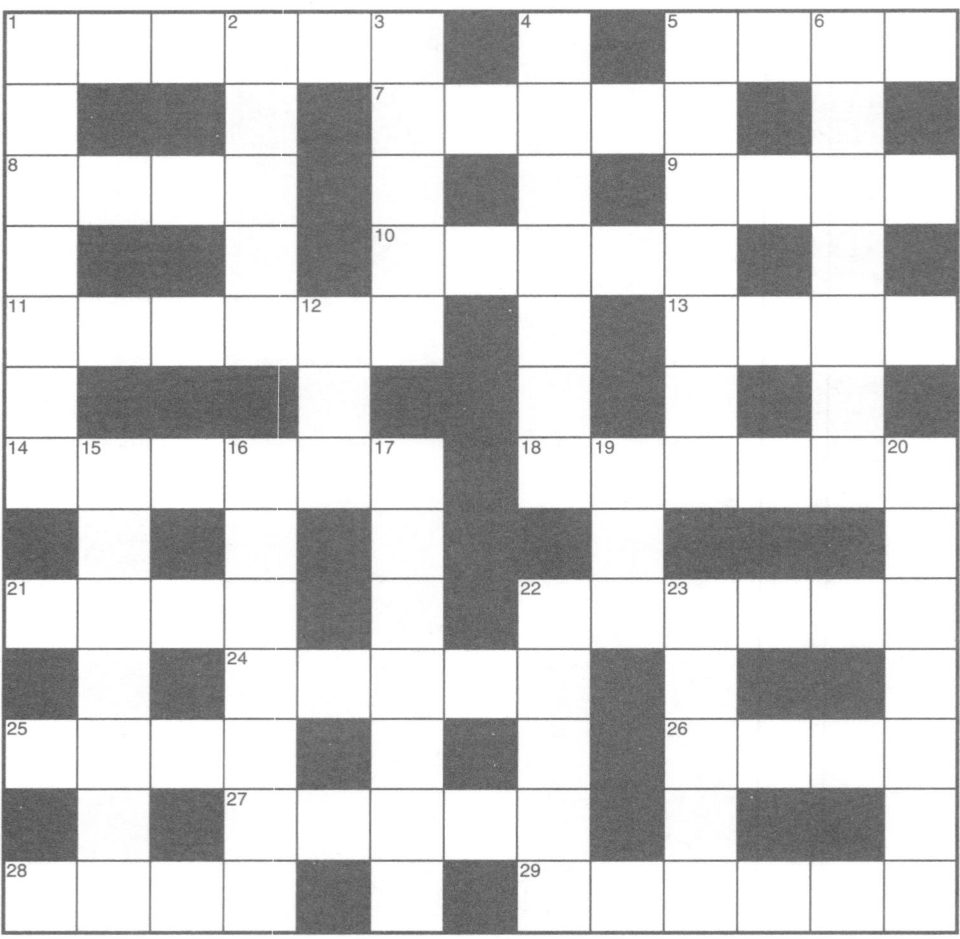

## ACROSS

1. Jewish scholars
5. Taverns
7. Shudder
8. Door frame post
9. Bound along
10. Modify
11. Ran after
13. Eye membrane
14. Raw vegetable dishes
18. Bean or pea
21. Intensive promotion
22. Lessened
24. Nodules
25. Hit parade entry
26. Brass instrument
27. Summon up
28. Tinted
29. Commotion

## DOWN

1. Says no to
2. Infants
3. Police group
4. Sunshade
5. Throwing (stones) at
6. Christening ceremony
12. Conclusion
15. Anyone
16. Retaliated for
17. Movie production companies
19. Flow away
20. Makes beloved
22. Daisy-like flower
23. Loft

# CROSSWORD 296

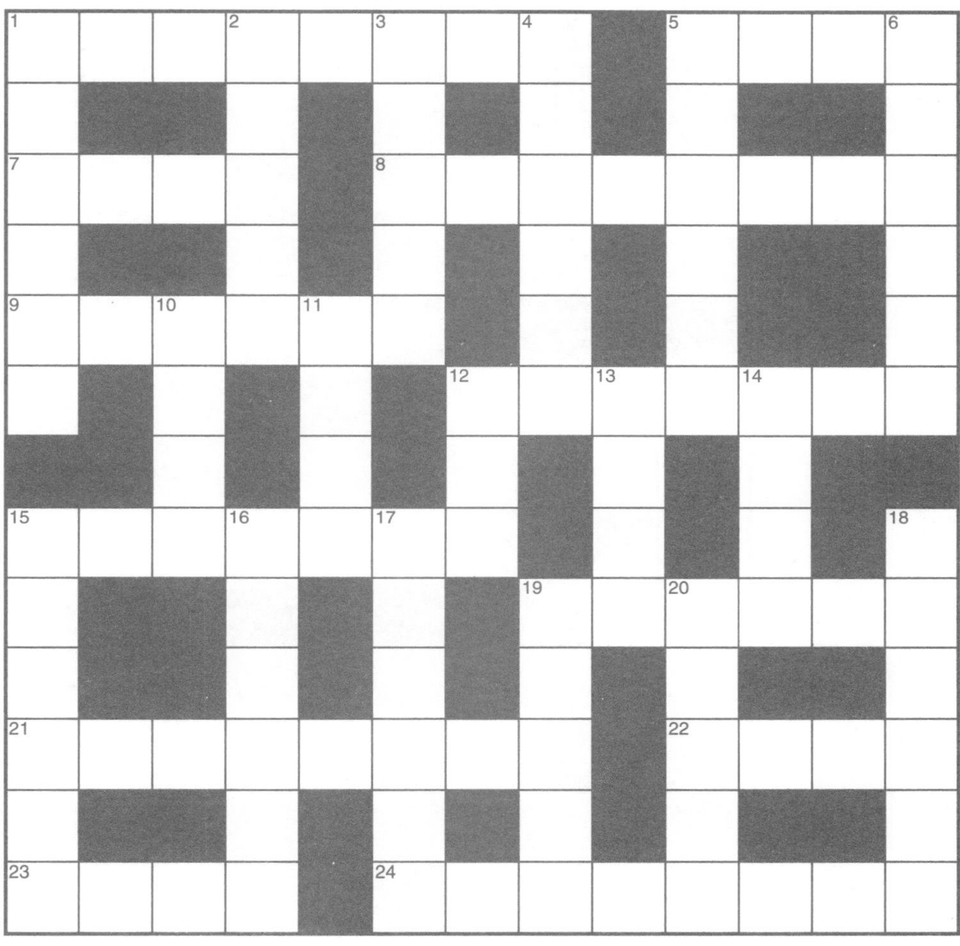

## ACROSS

1. Muddling
5. Rounded thermometer part
7. Sow (with grain)
8. Snag
9. Voice box
12. Wholesomeness
15. Stomach
19. Chemistry flask
21. Internally
22. Political power group
23. Finely ground rocks
24. Was frugal

## DOWN

1. Rightly
2. Severely (hurt)
3. Alphabetical listing
4. Brief look
5. Indistinct speech
6. Bread shop
10. Incursion
11. Average
12. Lair
13. Sweetly appealing
14. Tiny notch
15. Military forces
16. Ahead
17. Mass departure
18. Fortified
19. Purchaser
20. Stamp book

# CROSSWORD 297

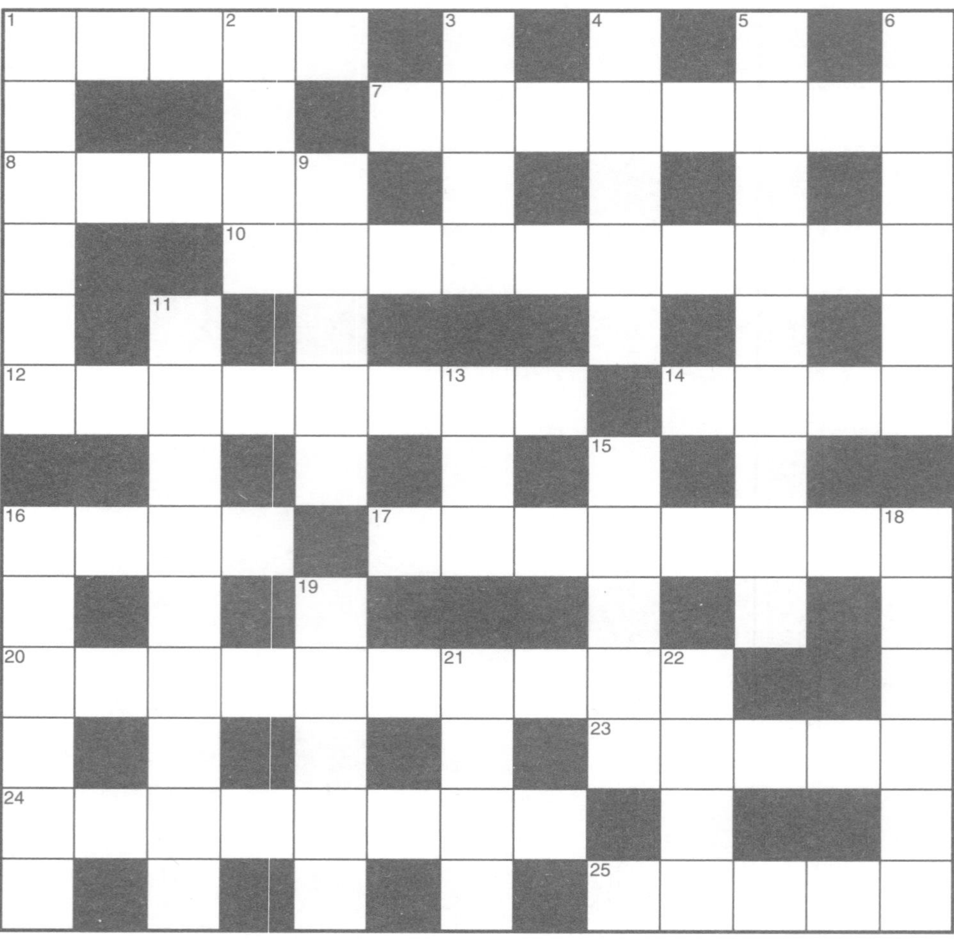

## ACROSS

1. Skirt fold
7. Magic
8. Let
10. Self-absorbed person
12. Nonprofessionals
14. Damage
16. Ticking explosive, ... bomb
17. Revoked
20. Manicured item
23. Innocent
24. Captivates
25. Stayed on one's feet

## DOWN

1. Blood fluid
2. Soon
3. Essential mineral
4. Minor transgression
5. Worthy of praise
6. Method
9. Increases in robberies, crime ...
11. Mouth organ
13. Wild grass
15. Plant secretion
16. Chewy confectionery
18. Shield
19. Flower segment
21. Tennis court barriers
22. Hold out

# CROSSWORD 298

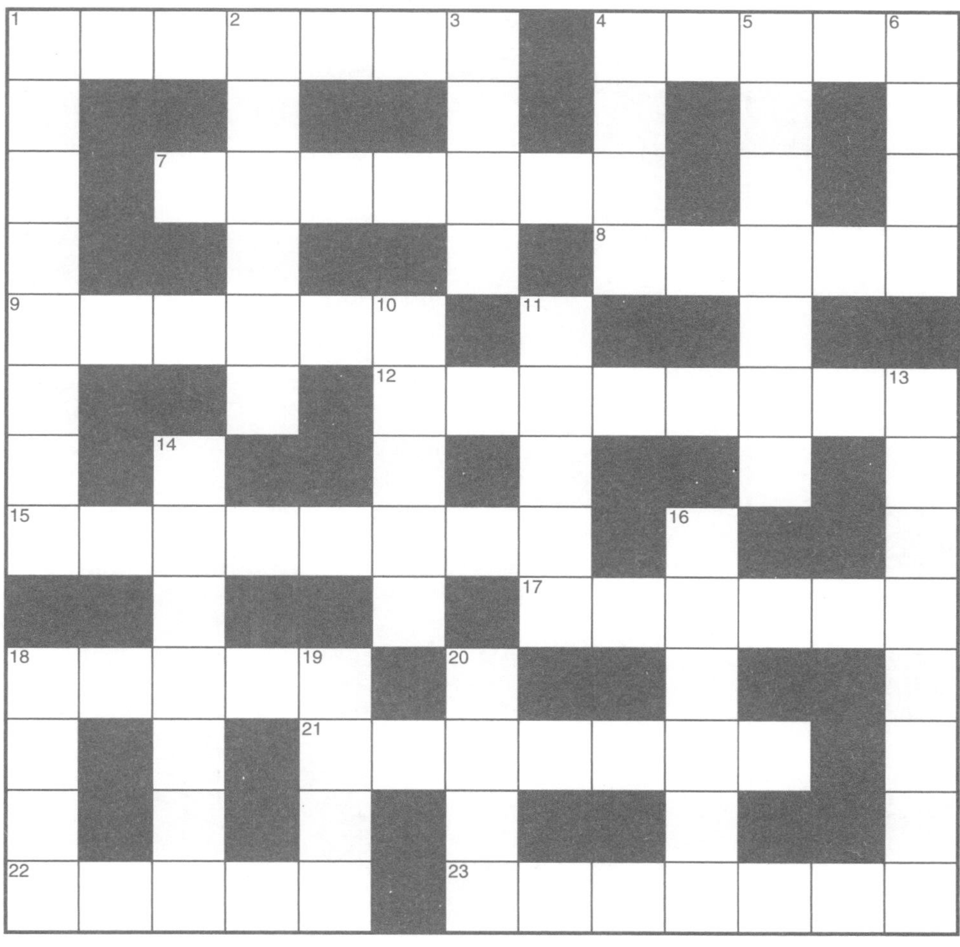

## ACROSS

1. Reveals
4. Assortment
7. Ousted
8. Tests
9. Frozen drop
12. Beauty shows
15. Orbit
17. Downward distances
18. Scenic outlooks
21. Rescued disaster victim
22. Trample, ... on
23. Markets for goods

## DOWN

1. Suitable (bachelor)
2. Take exception
3. Situate
4. Attendant
5. Holds
6. Shrill barks
10. Geological time unit
11. Stared lasciviously at
13. Abates (of noise)
14. Biology or physics
16. Charity launch
18. Sleeveless garment
19. Dispatch
20. Angel's ring

# CROSSWORD 299

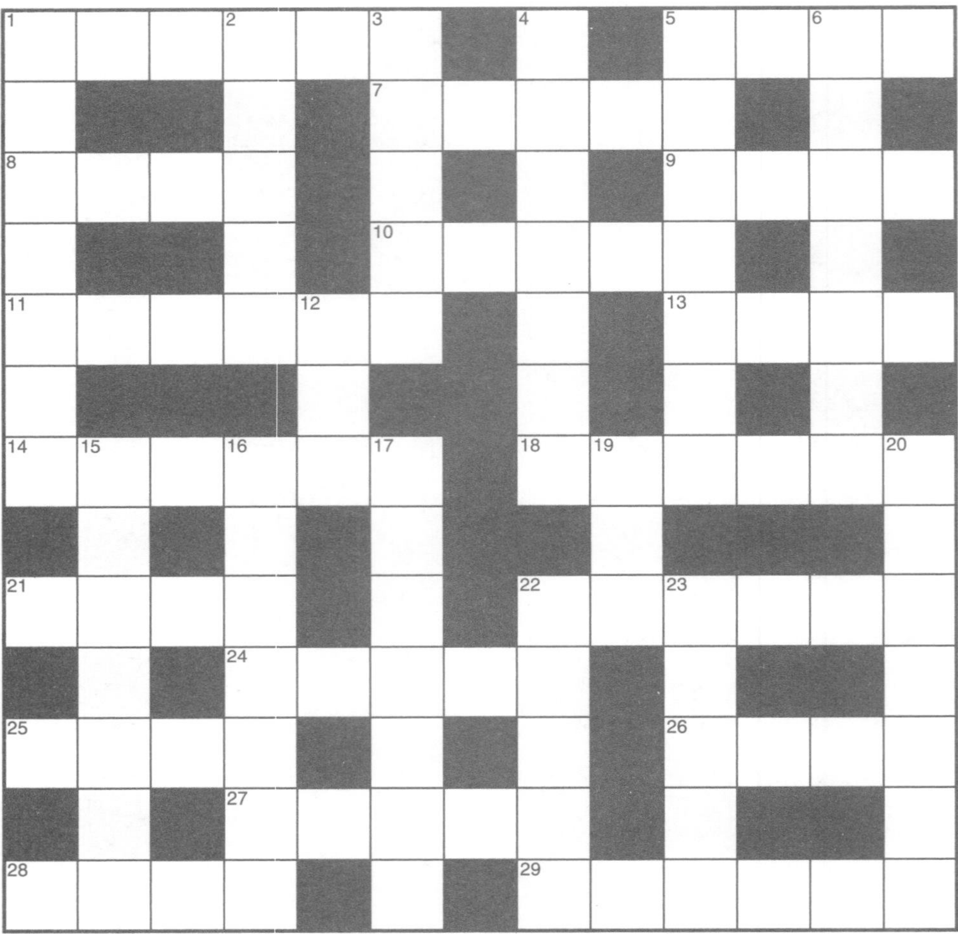

## ACROSS

1. Uncomplicated
5. Pleads with
7. Foolish
8. Medicine portion
9. University faculty head
10. Listened to
11. Most recent
13. Imaginative plan
14. Barbarian
18. Month
21. Floating filth
22. Not in a position (to)
24. Portents
25. King cat
26. Insect larva
27. Interior design
28. Picnic pests
29. Stab

## DOWN

1. Railway shunting tracks
2. Fragment
3. Number of spider's legs
4. Card game
5. Sheets & blankets
6. Pointy beards
12. Slump
15. Christie's & Sotheby's, ... houses
16. Oval nuts
17. Inherent nature
19. Large jar
20. Quiver
22. Wrongfully seize (power)
23. Use fishing rod

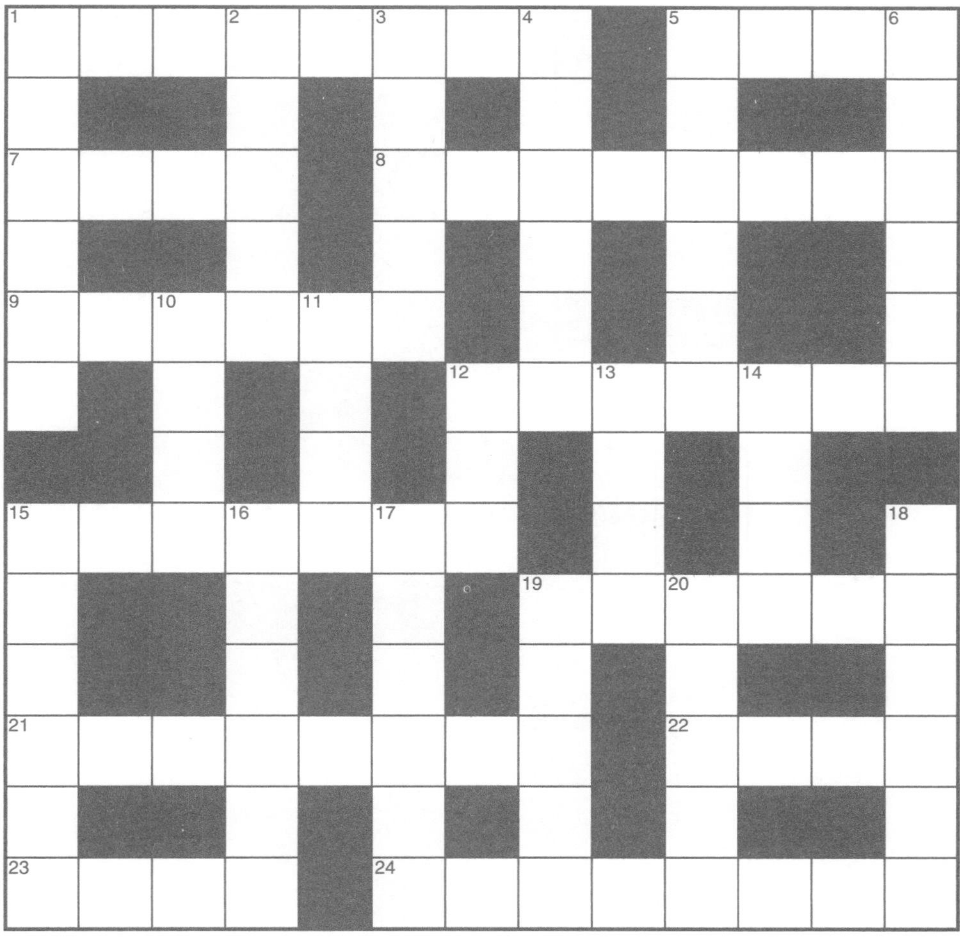

## ACROSS

1. Crowned heads
5. Untamed
7. Join by fusion
8. Straw-roofed (cottage)
9. Impolitely
12. Taunted
15. Made happy
19. Book user
21. Ravager
22. Copied
23. Consider
24. Greatly enjoyed

## DOWN

1. Lawn cutters
2. Confuse
3. Spiteful
4. Attitude
5. Sinful
6. Avoided
10. Jobless benefit
11. Trails (behind)
12. Doze, ... off
13. Margin
14. Burden
15. First paint coat
16. Burning out of control
17. Income cheat, tax ...
18. Corroded
19. Pastoral
20. Collect

# CROSSWORD 301

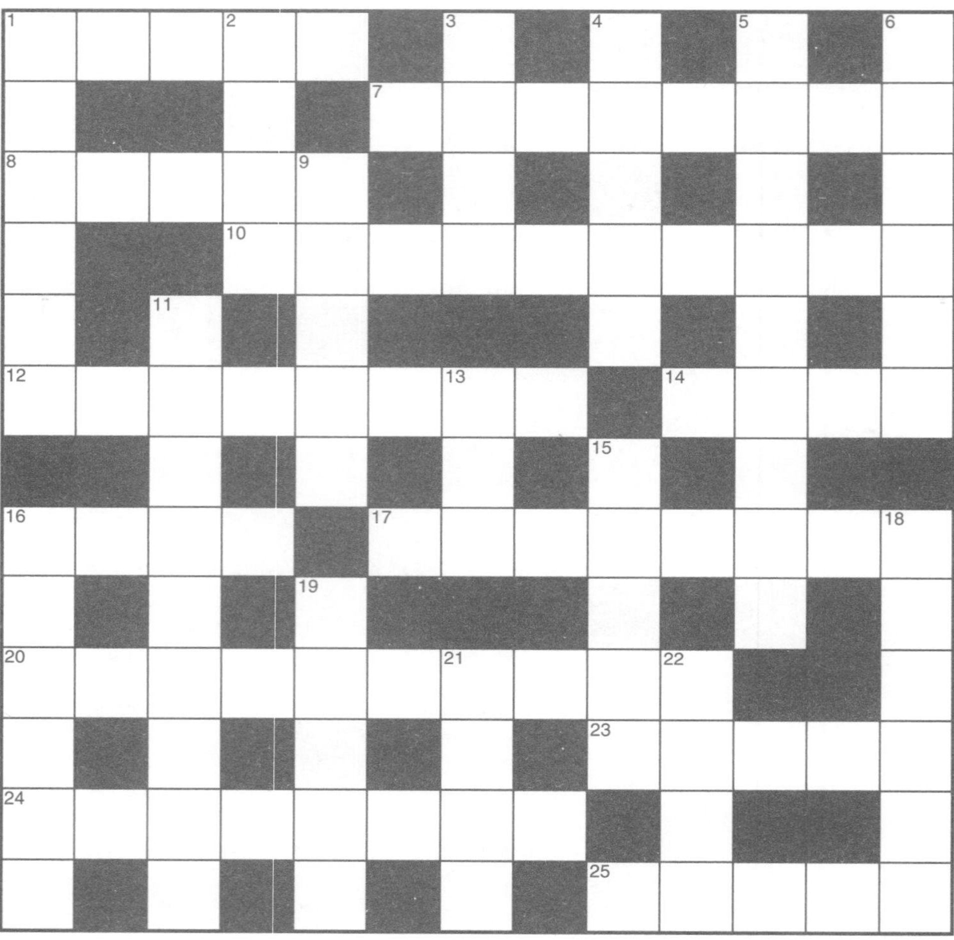

## ACROSS

1. Inuit shelter
7. Not merited
8. Havoc
10. Stealing from employer
12. Grabbed eagerly
14. Little devils
16. Spoken exam
17. Restorer
20. Made assurances
23. Pickle
24. Intestines
25. Wake up

## DOWN

1. Linear units
2. Double-reed instrument
3. Formerly
4. Wound dressing
5. Hospital
6. Proverbs
9. Spank
11. Cloudy eye condition
13. Day before, ... of
15. Stories
16. Wild sprees
18. Subside
19. South American parrot
21. Lean
22. Dead as a ...

# CROSSWORD 302

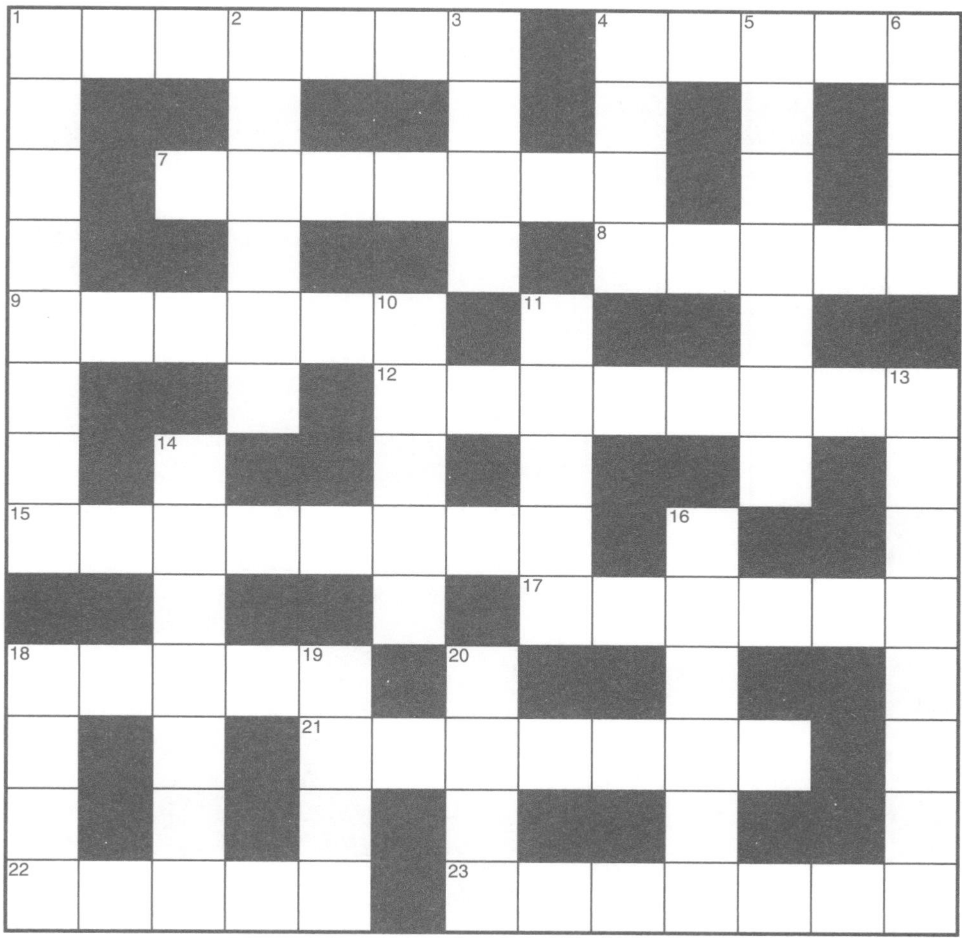

## ACROSS

1. Laundered
4. Furious
7. Reveal
8. Swigged
9. Journey
12. Live monotonous life
15. Search among rubbish
17. Unchanging
18. Drake's call
21. Subtle differences
22. Preliminary copy
23. Demonic

## DOWN

1. Mobile homes
2. Mammal or reptile
3. Blunt (knife)
4. Transfixed
5. Escape vehicle, ... car
6. Tug sharply
10. Squares (up)
11. Giant monsters
13. Highly charged
14. Mosquito fever
16. Photographer's tool
18. Multiple-birth child
19. Tangle
20. Male sheep

# CROSSWORD 303

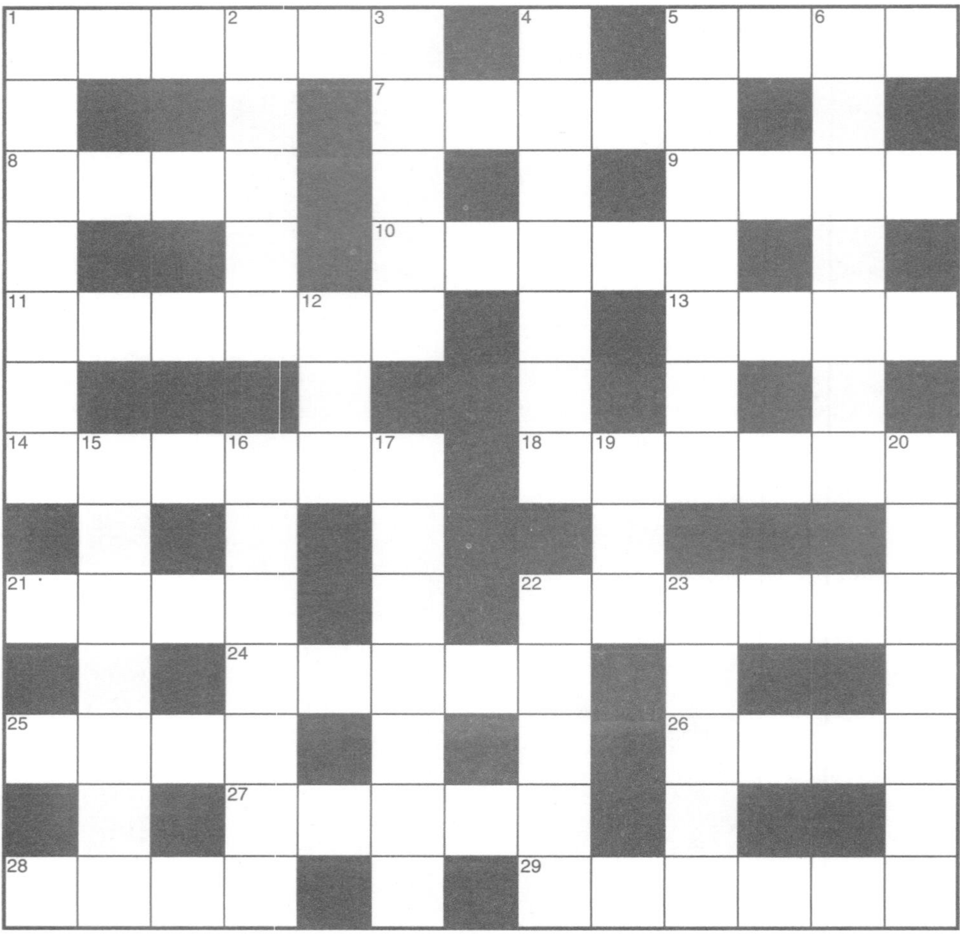

## ACROSS

1. Together, in ...
5. Niggles
7. Unsuitable
8. Weave (one's way)
9. Chinese dog breed
10. 10 percent
11. Cure
13. Very dark
14. Seasoned sausage
18. Bets
21. Disease agent
22. Royal-court clown
24. Prelude
25. Rouse
26. Sentence component
27. Not joined
28. Pop star
29. Parchment roll

## DOWN

1. Towards a higher level
2. Move crabwise
3. Neat (gadget)
4. Sun-shower arc
5. Needing a scratch
6. Door-tapper
12. Faintly-lit
15. Given warning
16. Navy chief
17. As a substitute
19. Snacked
20. Austrian pastry
22. Jogs (memory)
23. Underground waste channel

# CROSSWORD 304

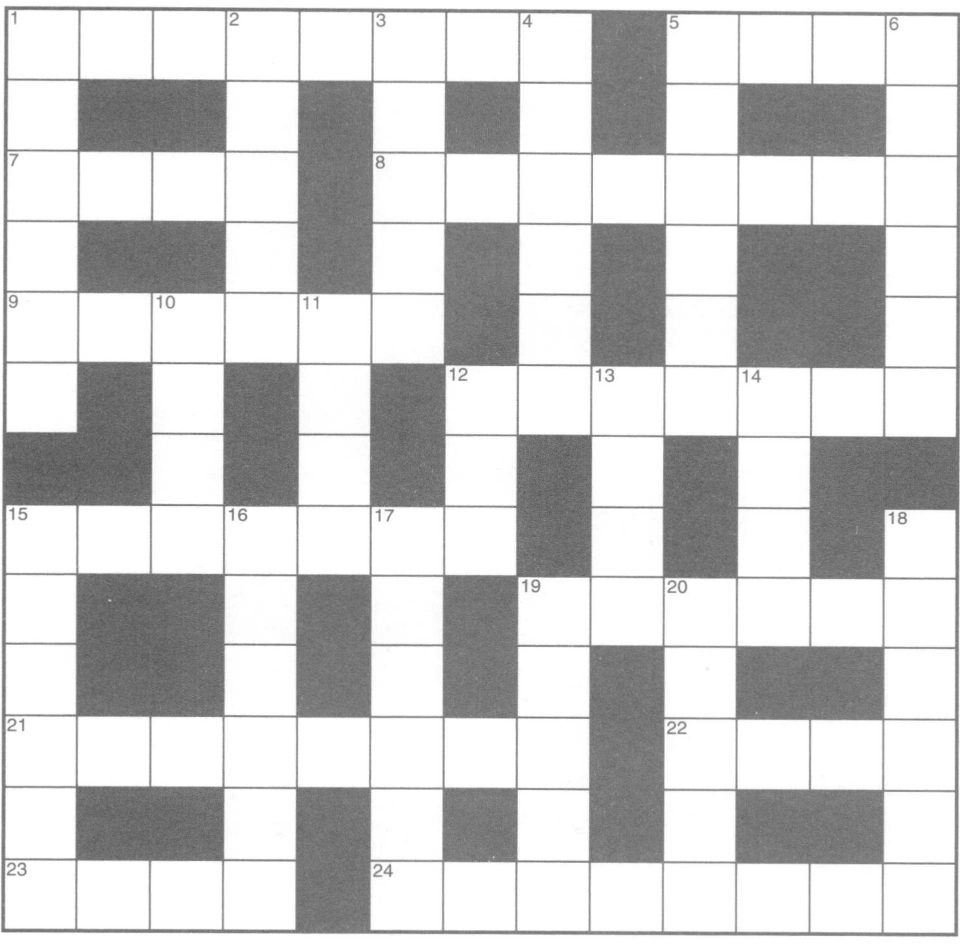

## ACROSS

1. Inappropriate
5. Hawaiian dance
7. Indian garment
8. Ironing
9. Impudent
12. Sloped
15. Route
19. Tidier
21. Runaways
22. Ewe's offspring
23. Root vegetables
24. Calming drug

## DOWN

1. Fly or ant
2. Elevate
3. Opium plant
4. Contrite
5. Hurry
6. Debated
10. Compass point
11. Was familiar with
12. Operative
13. Wheel spindle
14. Written material
15. Only
16. Pester
17. Heavenly spirits
18. High-pitched (instrument)
19. Inched (car) forward
20. Allocate

# CROSSWORD 305

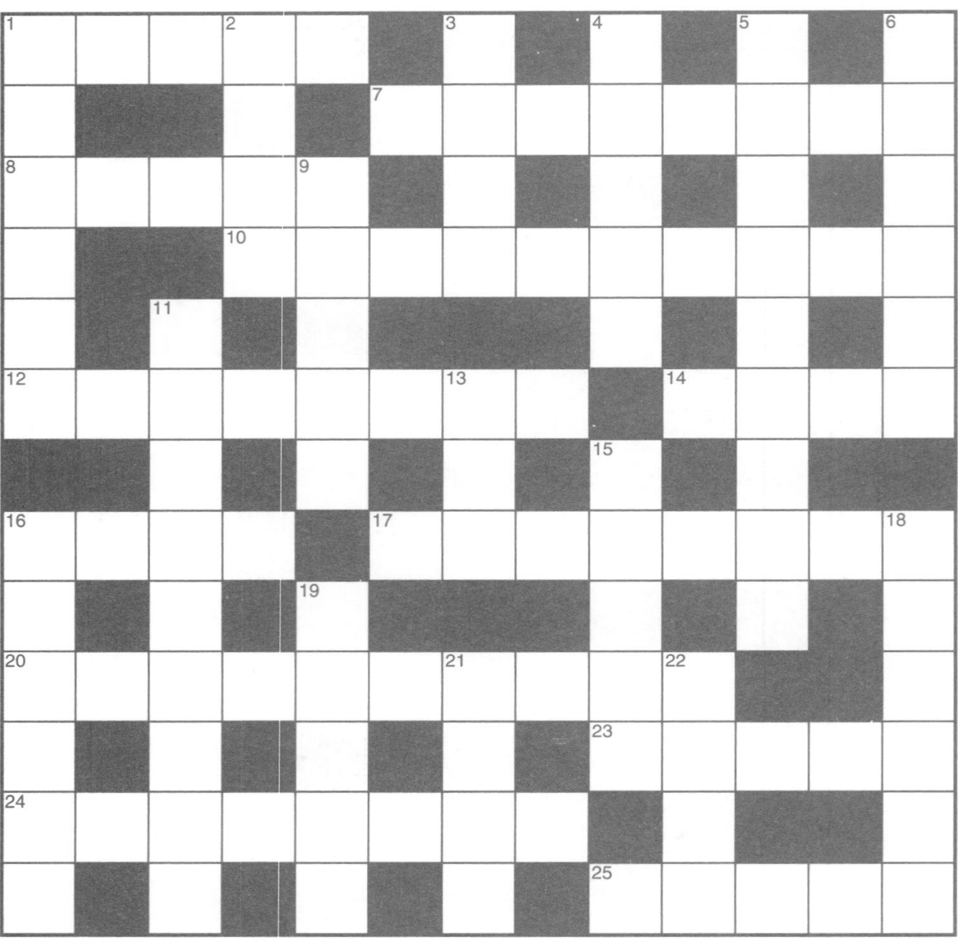

## ACROSS

1. Back tooth
7. Most sugary
8. Cheekily confident
10. Strolling
12. Hearing impairment
14. Treads the boards
16. Ray of light
17. Pullovers
20. Far-reaching
23. Craze
24. Plunders
25. Not given food

## DOWN

1. Derided
2. Makes request
3. Identical sibling
4. Raised river bank
5. Enchanted
6. Periods of growth
9. Involved tales
11. Venturing (guess)
13. Female pig
15. Woman's title
16. Watch out!
18. Wisp
19. Long exam answer
21. Leaf-scraping tool
22. Mend with needle

# CROSSWORD 306

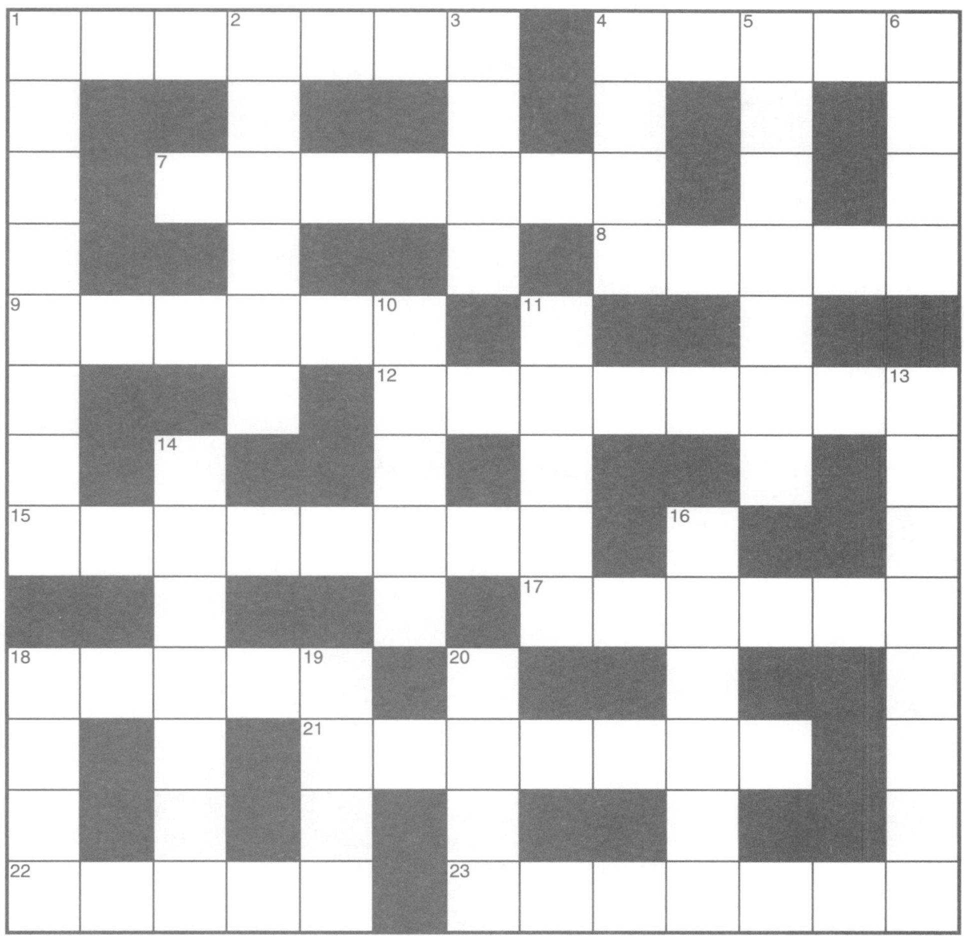

## ACROSS

1. Most complete
4. Theatrical performance
7. Excite
8. Sat for portrait
9. Gentle wind
12. Barely adequate
15. Trainees
17. Warmed up
18. Miniature (animal)
21. Makes contact with
22. Peculiarly
23. Horse enclosures

## DOWN

1. Goldfish home
2. Connected
3. Melt
4. Unfathomable
5. Funny
6. Waterless
10. Entrench
11. Grind
13. Noisiness
14. Supervised
16. Job path
18. Test-drive car, ... model
19. Become ragged
20. Softest-known powder

# CROSSWORD 307

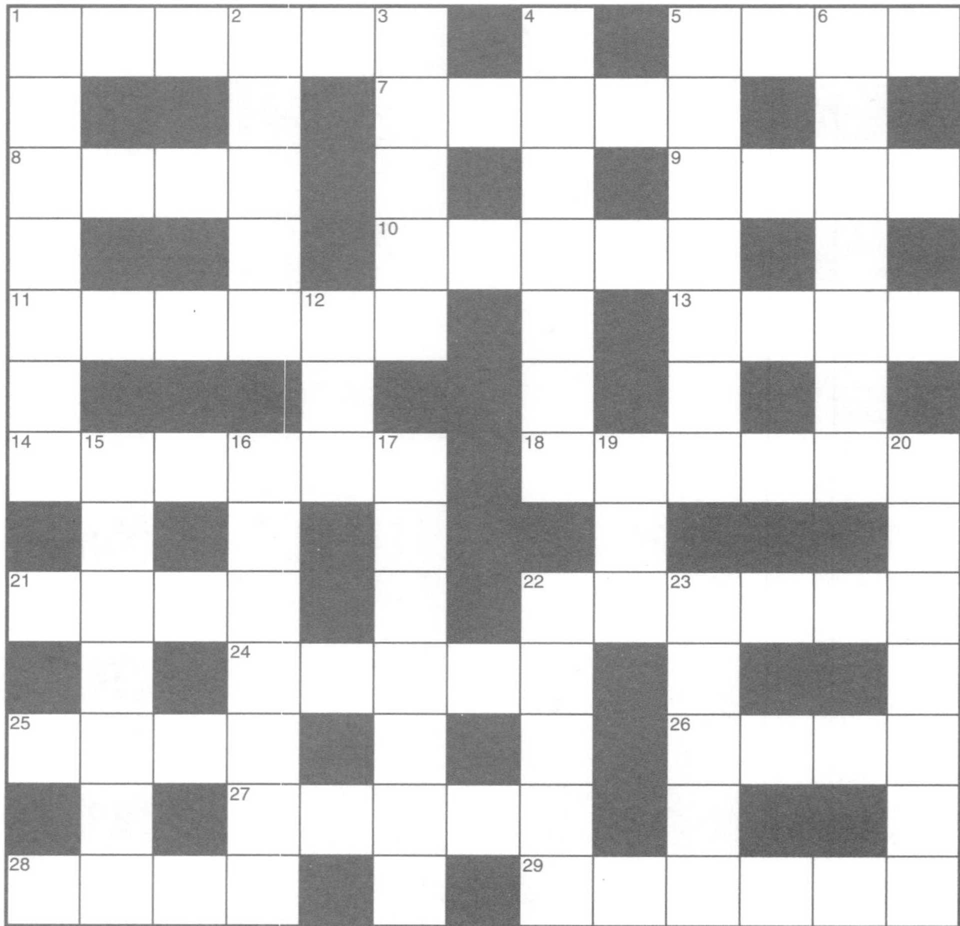

## ACROSS

1. Pie crust
5. Pour with rain
7. Astound
8. Jumping parasite
9. Pen tips
10. Stockpile
11. Have effect (on)
13. Golf club
14. Frolic
18. Highly amuse
21. Arm or leg
22. Pulled strenuously
24. Atmosphere layer
25. Grain storage facility
26. Impartial
27. Well-known
28. Optic organs
29. Seductively

## DOWN

1. Panting
2. Royal headwear
3. Sailing boat
4. Spanish bullfighter
5. Looking after
6. Involve (in dispute)
12. Murmuring sound
15. Sprightliness
16. Long-snouted monkeys
17. Page formats
19. Poet's word for before
20. Mature in years
22. Listens to
23. Attach (to)

# CROSSWORD 308

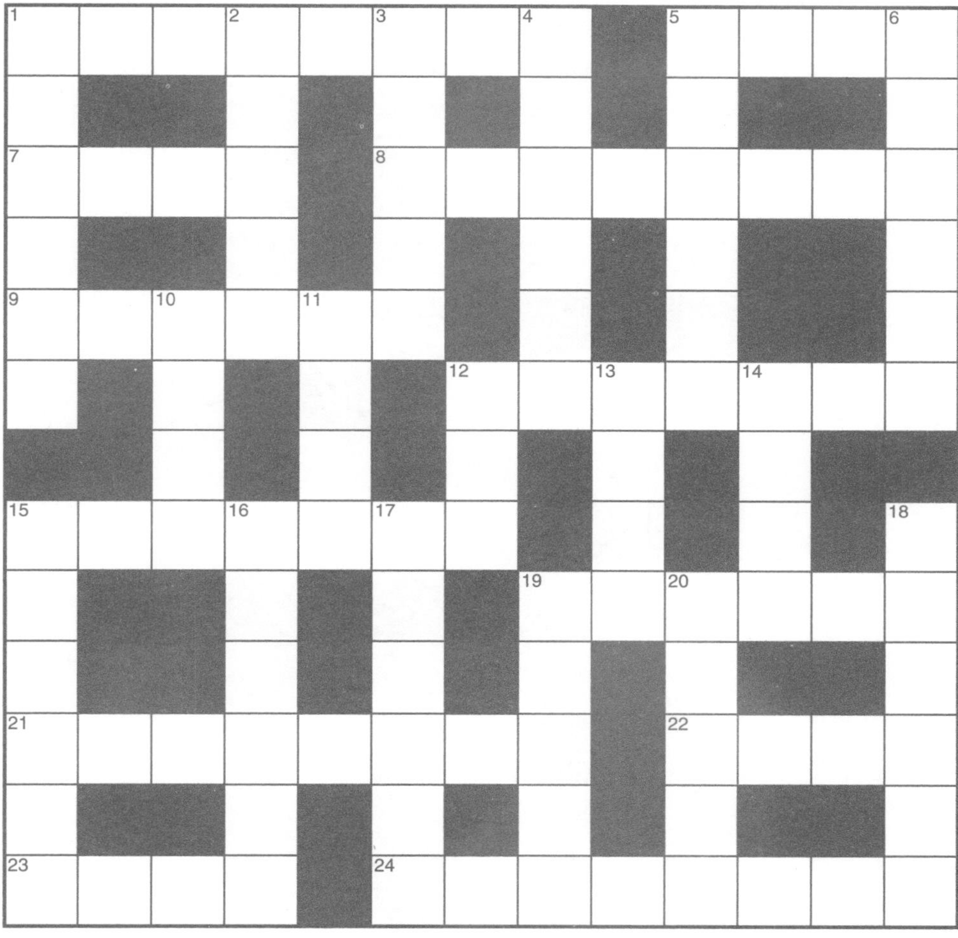

## ACROSS

1. To the point
5. Frog-like animal
7. Narrated
8. Particular
9. Disapproving looks
12. Eerier
15. Peculiarly
19. Rule (country)
21. Bestride
22. Ascend
23. Traded for money
24. Castle prisons

## DOWN

1. Validate (treaty)
2. Provide (with)
3. Beasts of burden
4. One dozen
5. Clothes maker
6. Surgeon
10. Seep out
11. Close
12. Route
13. Towards the inside of
14. Love excessively, ... on
15. Expeditions
16. Enlarge
17. Glorified
18. Buries (corpse)
19. Extract (information)
20. Panache

# CROSSWORD 309

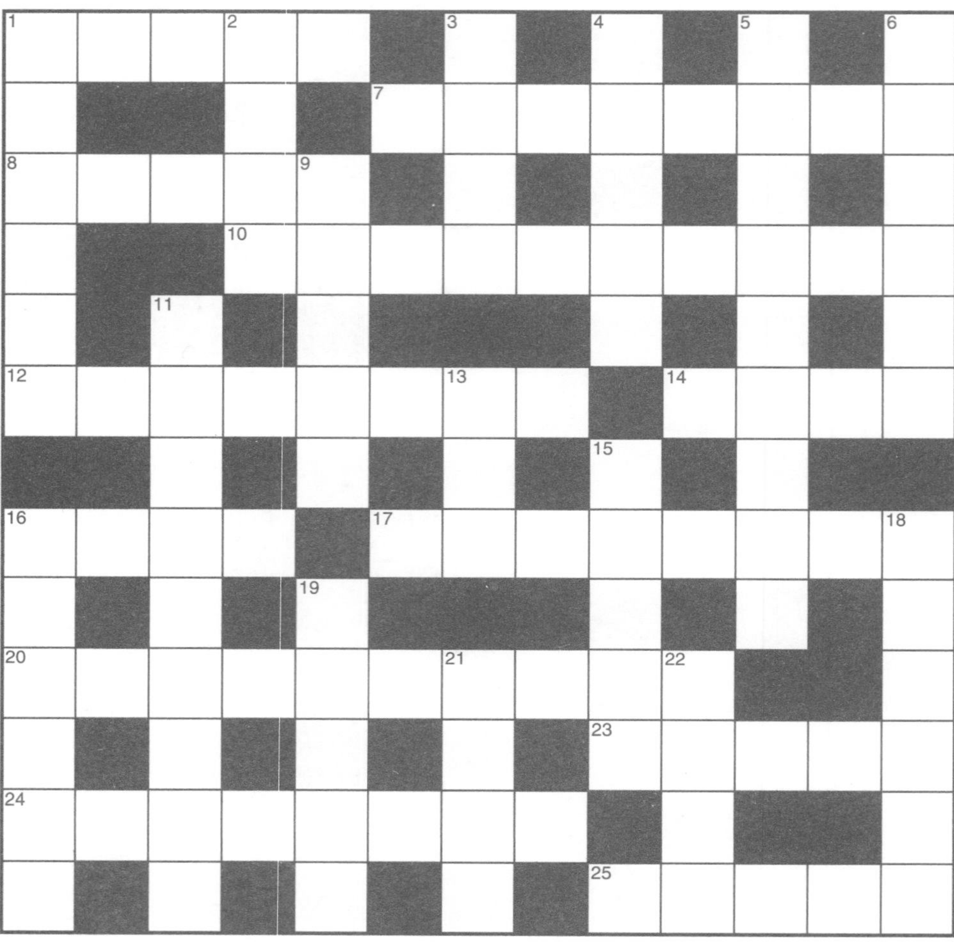

## ACROSS

1. Fizzy drinks
7. Carve in stone
8. Bread cereal
10. Watering at the mouth
12. Seizing
14. Horse breeding farm
16. Wildlife enclosures
17. Smartly
20. Unnecessarily
23. Number of days in a week
24. Raises
25. Inundate

## DOWN

1. Cutting wood
2. Regrettably
3. Opposed to
4. Shoo!
5. Priests
6. Bordered
9. Striped cat
11. Air pressure gauge
13. Zilch
15. Ellipses
16. More eccentric
18. Gaped tiredly
19. Dispel (fears)
21. Cast (skin)
22. Scream

# CROSSWORD 310

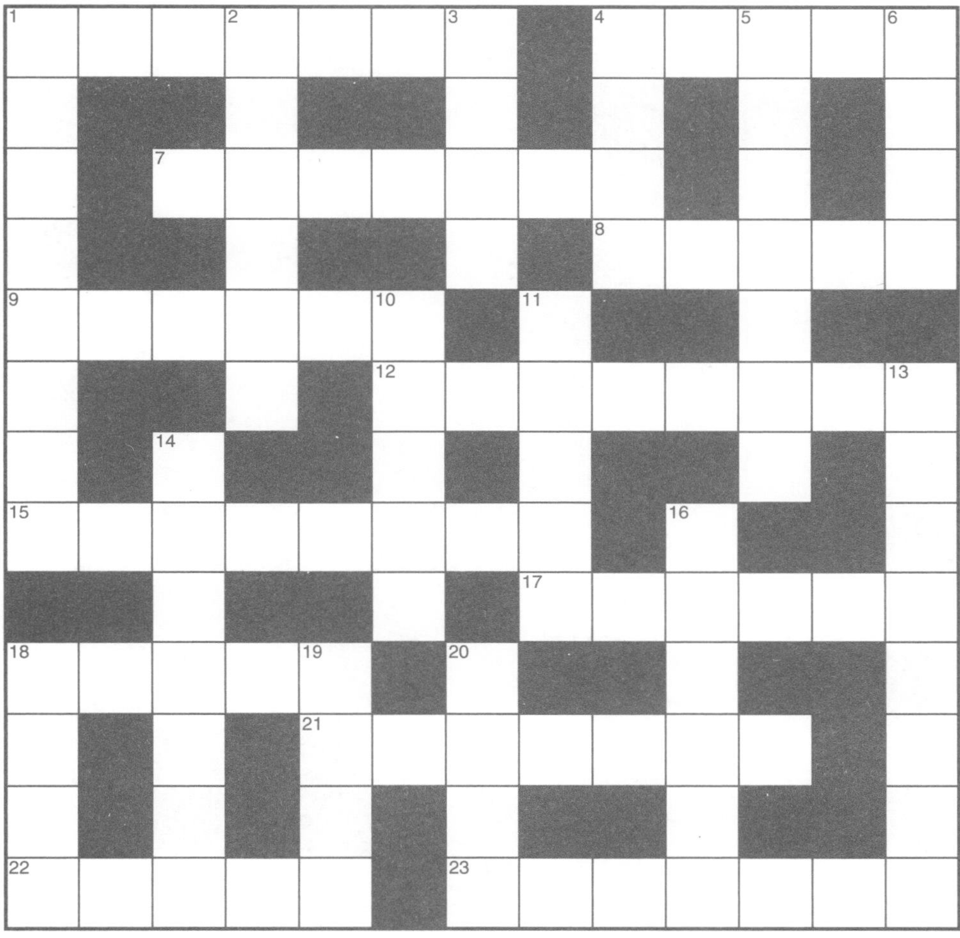

## ACROSS

1. Capitulated
4. Get on (ship)
7. Hail as
8. Furry fruit
9. Accommodation resorts
12. Deduced
15. Clemency
17. Harvested
18. Unexcited
21. Greed
22. Emblem
23. Intimated

## DOWN

1. Girlish or boyish
2. Wanted
3. Twofold
4. Jolt
5. Concerns
6. Morse symbols, dot & ...
10. Signals
11. Following
13. Muffled
14. Made angry
16. Invalidate
18. Shapeless mass
19. Edgy, ill at ...
20. Travel along runway

# CROSSWORD 311

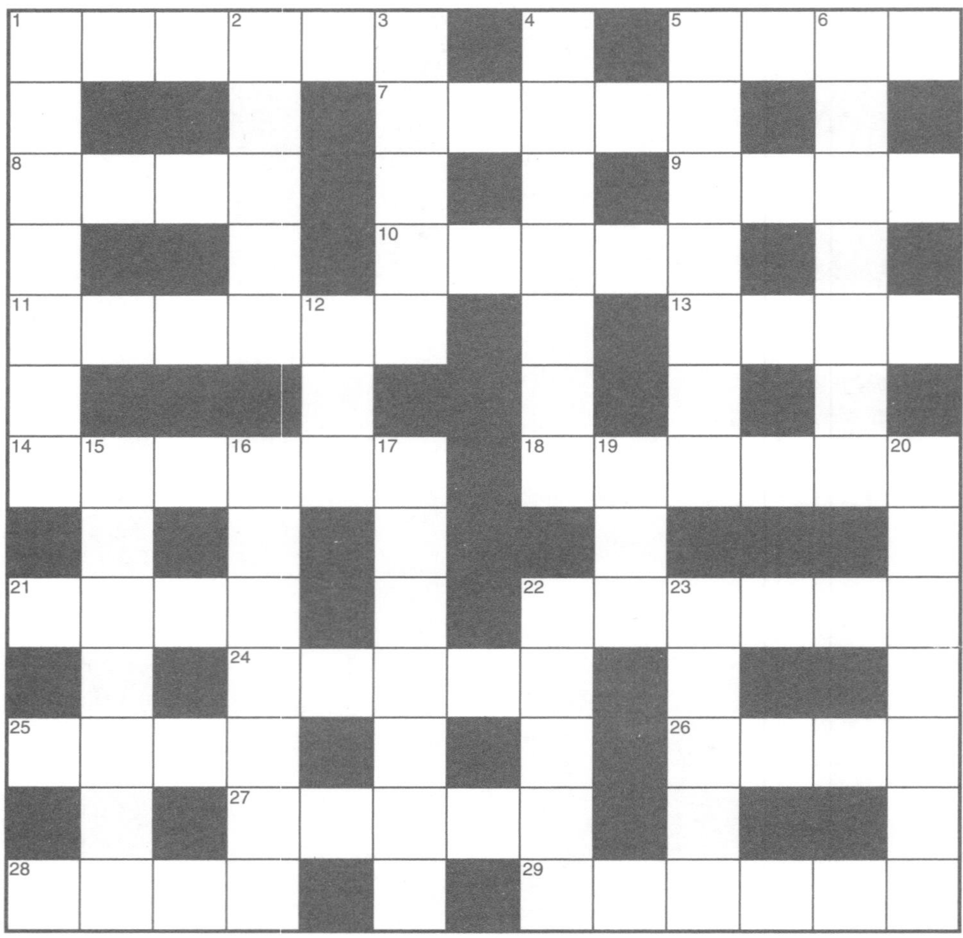

## ACROSS

1. Large Galápagos lizard
5. Unreachable serves
7. Rental agreement
8. Dish
9. True
10. Book leaf
11. Outlaw
13. Wild pig
14. Join in sporadically
18. Booted ball
21. Eagerly expectant
22. Genetic mix
24. Hard to lift
25. Broad
26. Titled lady
27. Beautify
28. Wearing footwear
29. Devious

## DOWN

1. Partook of liquor
2. Troubled
3. Up high
4. Detachable lock
5. Of heart/lung exercises
6. Issue (from)
12. Sick
15. Distress
16. Conceited person
17. Mid-Earth line
19. Creeping vine
20. Frail with age
22. Church songs
23. Shift

# CROSSWORD 312

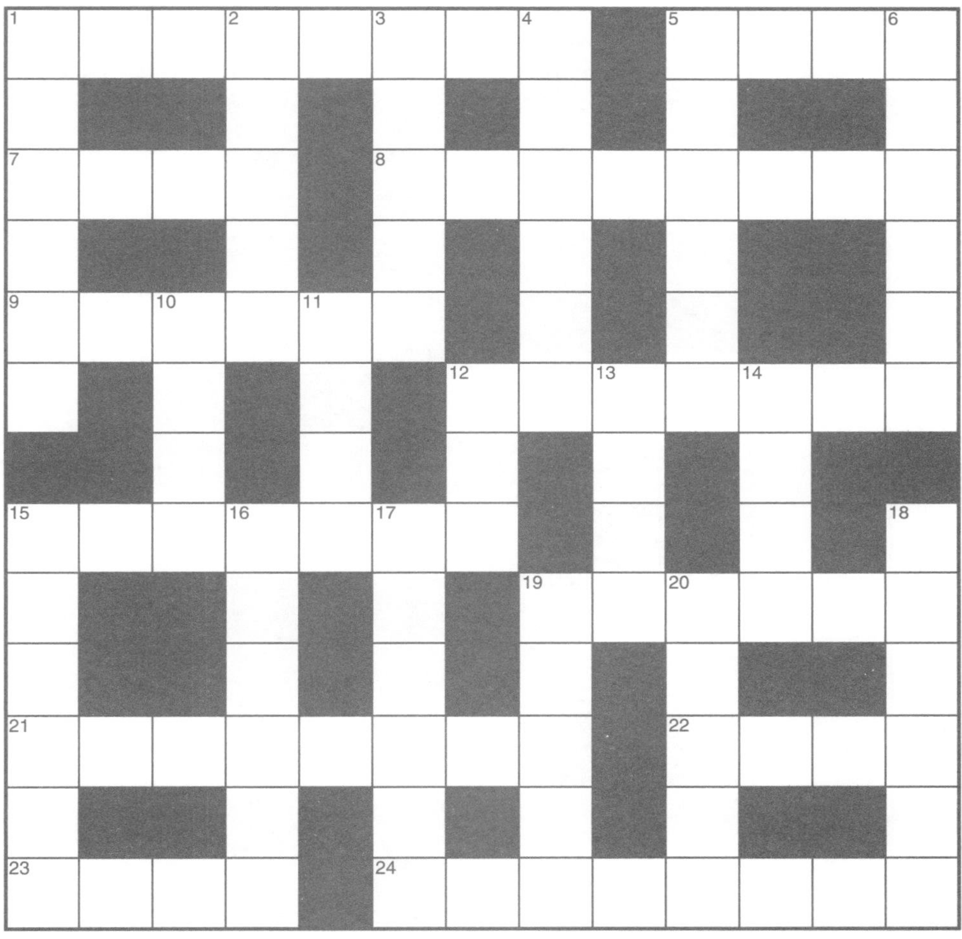

## ACROSS

1. Enjoyable
5. Raised (cattle)
7. Shrub
8. Giving (medal)
9. Movie collie dog
12. Super-chilled storage space
15. Set up (event)
19. Cowardly
21. Delivered sermon
22. Legacy document
23. Dirt
24. Incomes

## DOWN

1. Tiny rock
2. Blaze's remnants
3. Humble (oneself)
4. Merchant
5. Dress top
6. Double-edged knife
10. Burn surface of
11. wHoly picture
12. Enemy
13. Heavy fencing sword
14. Enthusiastic devotion
15. Takes in (child)
16. Besiege
17. Sudden outflows
18. Lives
19. Mountain call
20. Drop (prices)

# CROSSWORD 313

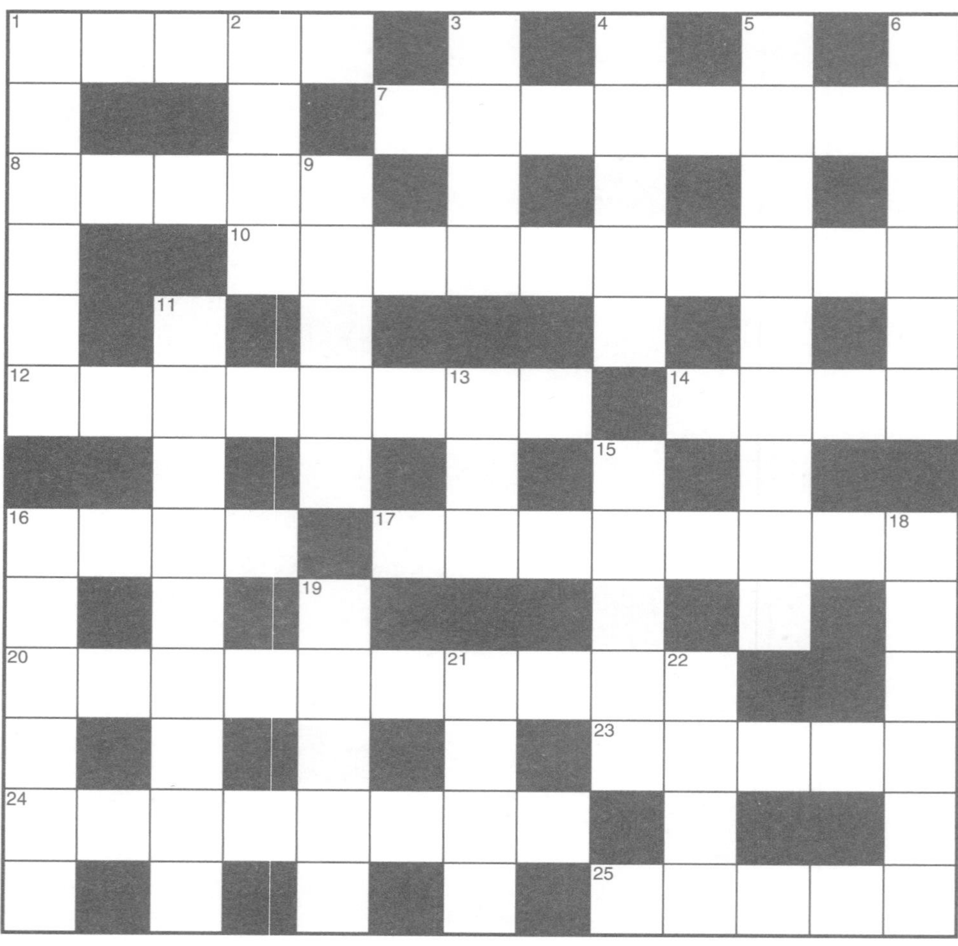

## ACROSS

1. Crime groups
7. Most apparent
8. Rapid
10. Harsh boss
12. Outrageous incidents
14. Action
16. Occupations
17. Unenlightened
20. Caribbean pirates
23. Fork-tongued creature
24. Green gems
25. Tolerate

## DOWN

1. Deep cuts
2. Donation
3. Anti-aircraft fire
4. Of birth
5. Lady's partner
6. Stockpiled
9. Late arriving
11. Cooked outdoors
13. Lower limb
15. Sightseeing trips
16. Chatter wildly
18. Steal
19. Air traffic monitor
21. Whirlpool
22. Social bigot

# CROSSWORD 314

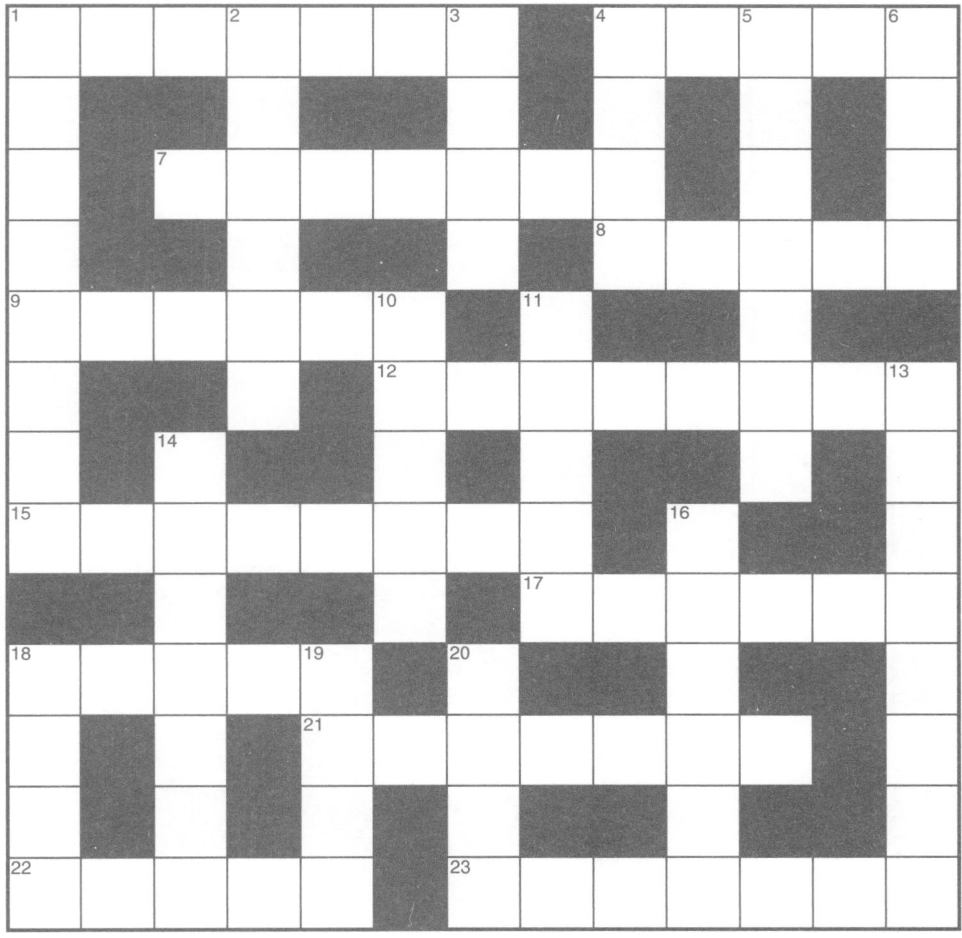

## ACROSS

1. Less loud
4. Rotund
7. Drumming insects
8. S American dance
9. Highest point
12. Never dimming
15. Holder of degree
17. Cause
18. Majestic
21. Frightened
22. Hornet relatives
23. Serious-minded

## DOWN

1. Interrogating
2. Draw forth
3. Purges
4. Throw in air
5. Drinks server
6. Meditation routine
10. Person, ... being
11. Proposal
13. Fencer's glove
14. Struts
16. Inn
18. Radiance
19. Sponges lightly
20. Superman's garment

# CROSSWORD 315

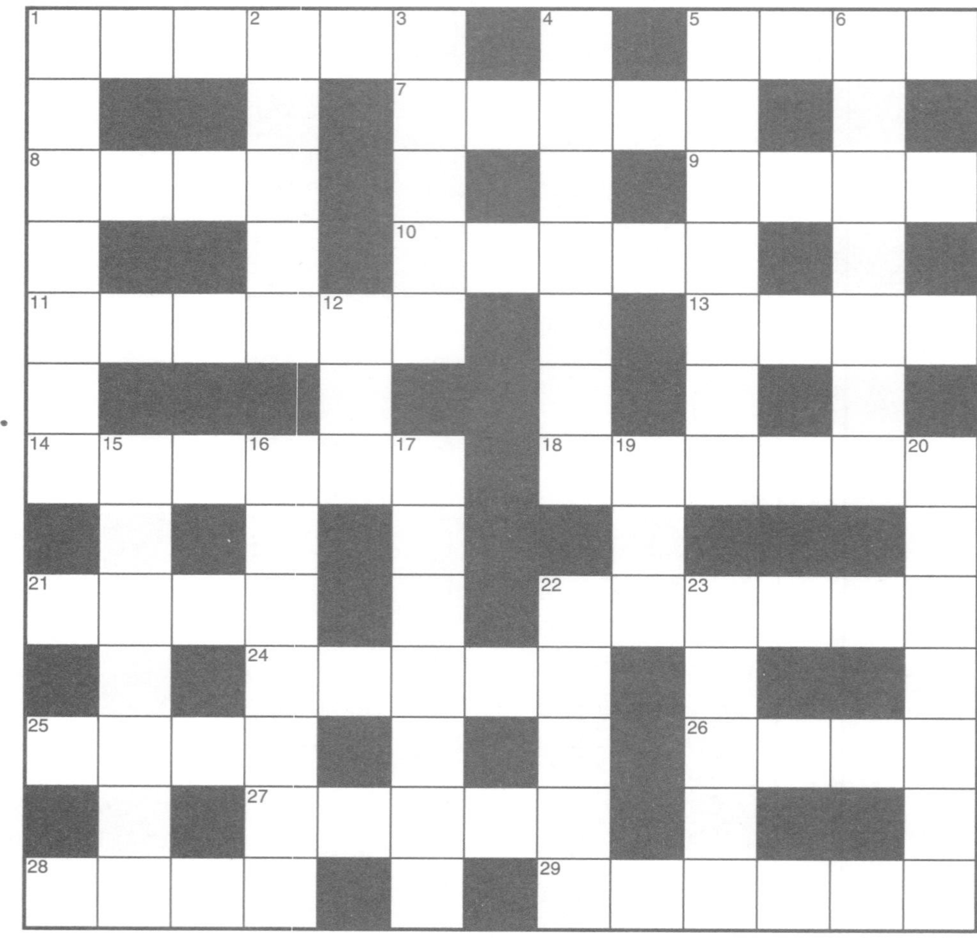


## ACROSS

1. Floral tribute
5. Paper quantity
7. Consumption
8. Cheerless
9. Encryption
10. Drink container
11. Purple flowers
13. Aware of
14. Ballroom performer
18. Light-ray tools
21. Burial chamber
22. Effaced
24. Thump
25. Springboard descent
26. Slothful
27. Intelligence organ
28. Poultry products
29. Shows way

## DOWN

1. Walked like duck
2. Major blood vessel
3. Blusters, ... & puffs
4. Chewy sweet
5. Calculates
6. Accounts examiner
12. Snooker stick
15. Greatly loving
16. Spider traps
17. Absconder
19. Ventilate
20. Melancholy
22. Making last, ... out
23. Elsewhere excuse

# CROSSWORD 316

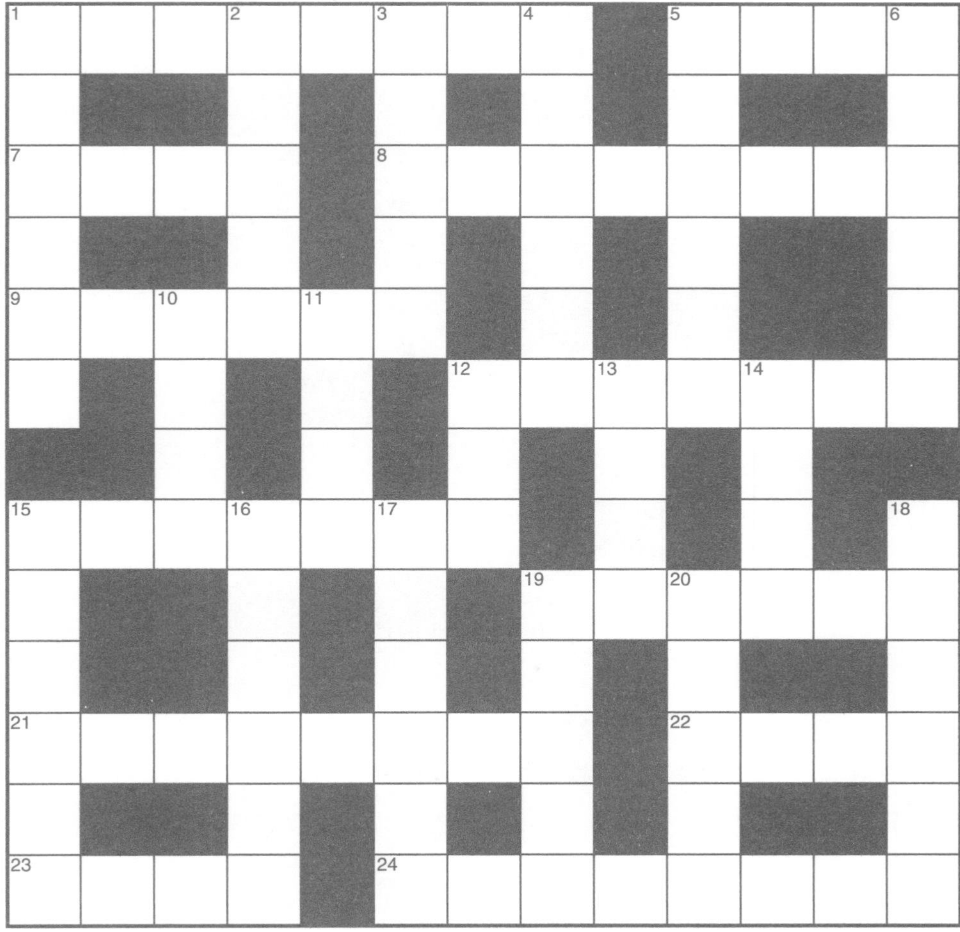

## ACROSS

1. Waste
5. Parsley or mint
7. Greek liquor
8. Simmering (meat)
9. Fascinates
12. Stuck (to)
15. Groomed feathers
19. Halted
21. Protest
22. Long narrative
23. Heavy metal
24. Gentleness

## DOWN

1. Scrubs hard
2. Living quarters
3. Sums owed
4. Thundered
5. Harass
6. Planted microphones in
10. Carpentry clamp
11. Adolescent
12. Include
13. Wish
14. Revolutions
15. Package
16. Ran off to marry
17. Preserve (corpse)
18. Personal values
19. Waterway
20. Fire crime

# CROSSWORD 317

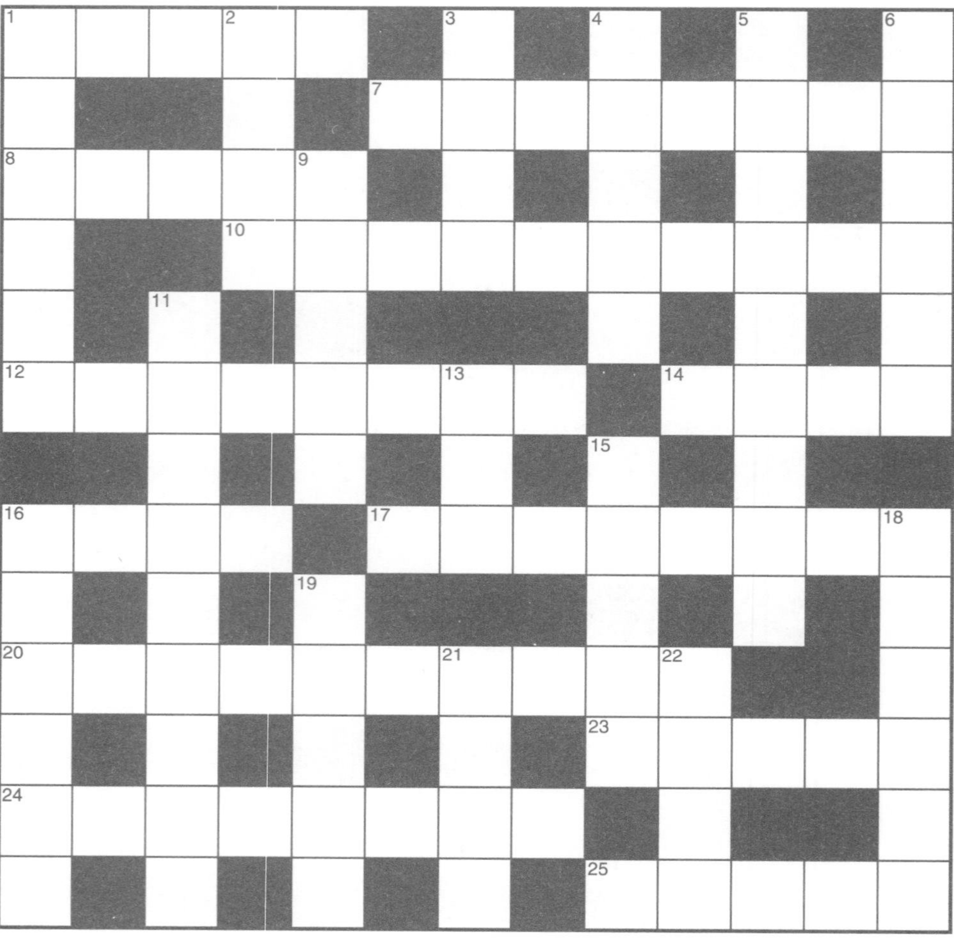

## ACROSS

1. Birds of prey
7. Tutors
8. Bend to pray
10. Woeful
12. Looking quickly
14. ... & foot
16. Constrictor snakes
17. Throw (jockey)
20. Taking away (from)
23. Intended
24. Joined armed forces
25. Relinquished (territory)

## DOWN

1. Country walking
2. Ship's spine
3. Heredity unit
4. Severe (illness)
5. Electric pianos
6. Climb (stairs)
9. Gate fastener
11. Spider
13. Convent dweller
15. Flora & ...
16. Human forms
18. Oozed out
19. Stop briefly
21. Begins golf, ... off
22. Taunt

# CROSSWORD 318

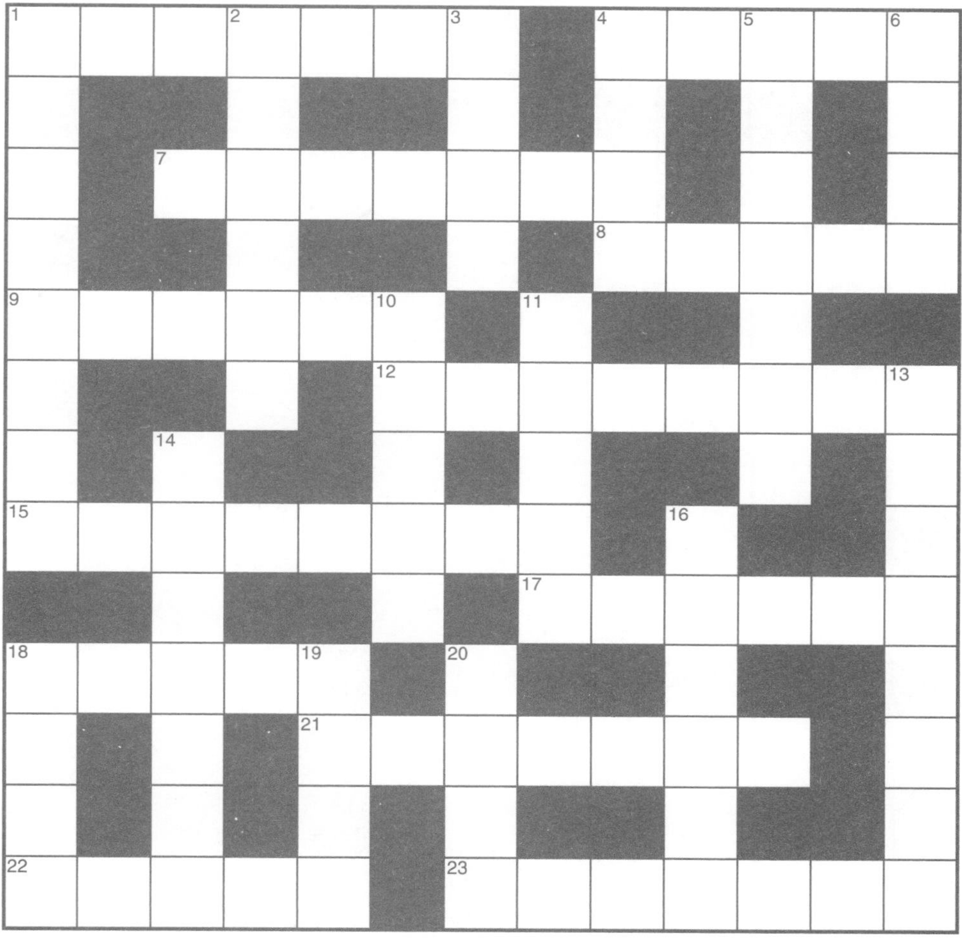

## ACROSS

1. Steals plane
4. Steam burn
7. Patchy (complexion)
8. Unpaid servant
9. Cancel out
12. Pamphlets
15. Hugged
17. Influenced
18. Feeling
21. Of the beach
22. Tropical fruit
23. Announces

## DOWN

1. Address angrily
2. Not sinking
3. Punch forcefully
4. Utters
5. Scraped
6. ... & duchess
10. Vote in
11. Attacks
13. Sports arenas
14. Leave high & dry
16. Dessert, ... split
18. Moved in water
19. Repeat
20. Speed of sound measure

# CROSSWORD 319

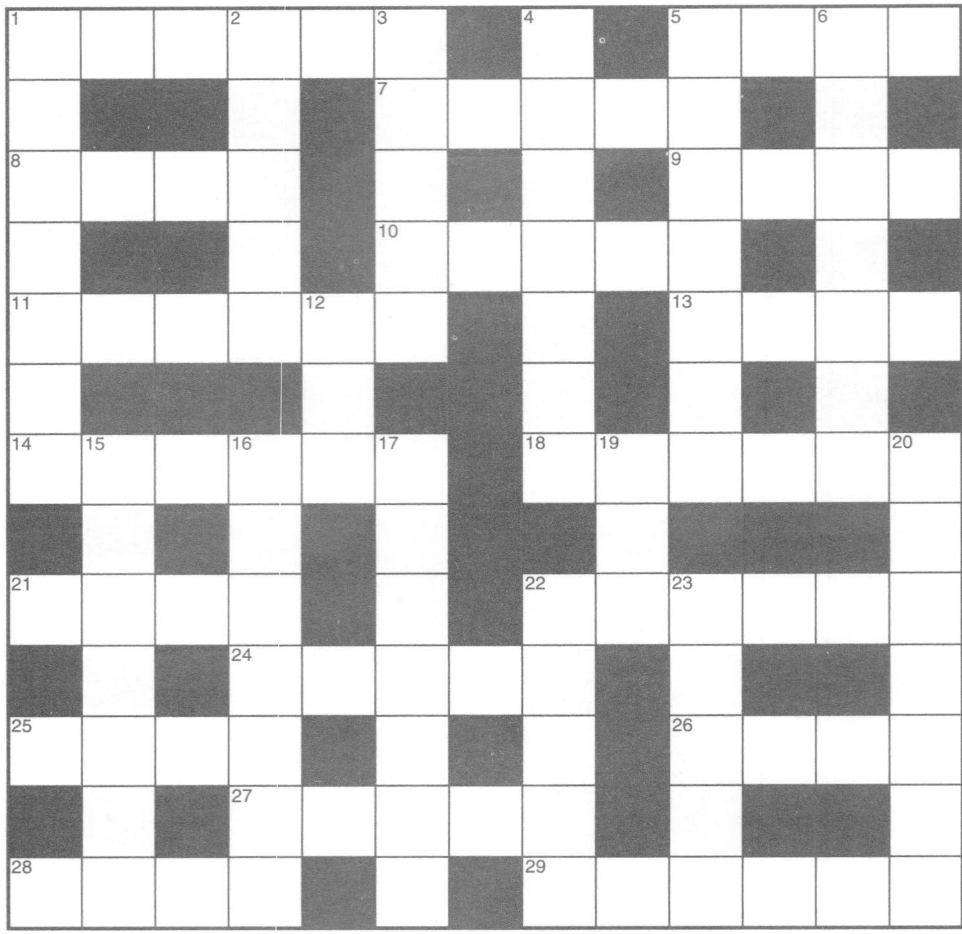

## ACROSS

1. Unsettled (bill)
5. Fittingly
7. Diplomatic messenger
8. Like, ... as
9. Catches (thief)
10. Beetle grub
11. Doctor's ward visits
13. Edible flesh
14. Predatory birds
18. Deceptive traps
21. Trim
22. Lively horse gait
24. Jewish scholar
25. Open (parcel)
26. Once-prized fur
27. Sifting utensil
28. Glimpse
29. Decomposed

## DOWN

1. Rapid rise
2. Pallid
3. Distributes cards
4. Gave too much food to
5. Energetic
6. Collection of books
12. Pass away
15. Window shelters
16. Tropical disease
17. Drool
19. Tip of grain
20. Crept stealthily
22. Bagpipes player
23. Allow in

# CROSSWORD 320

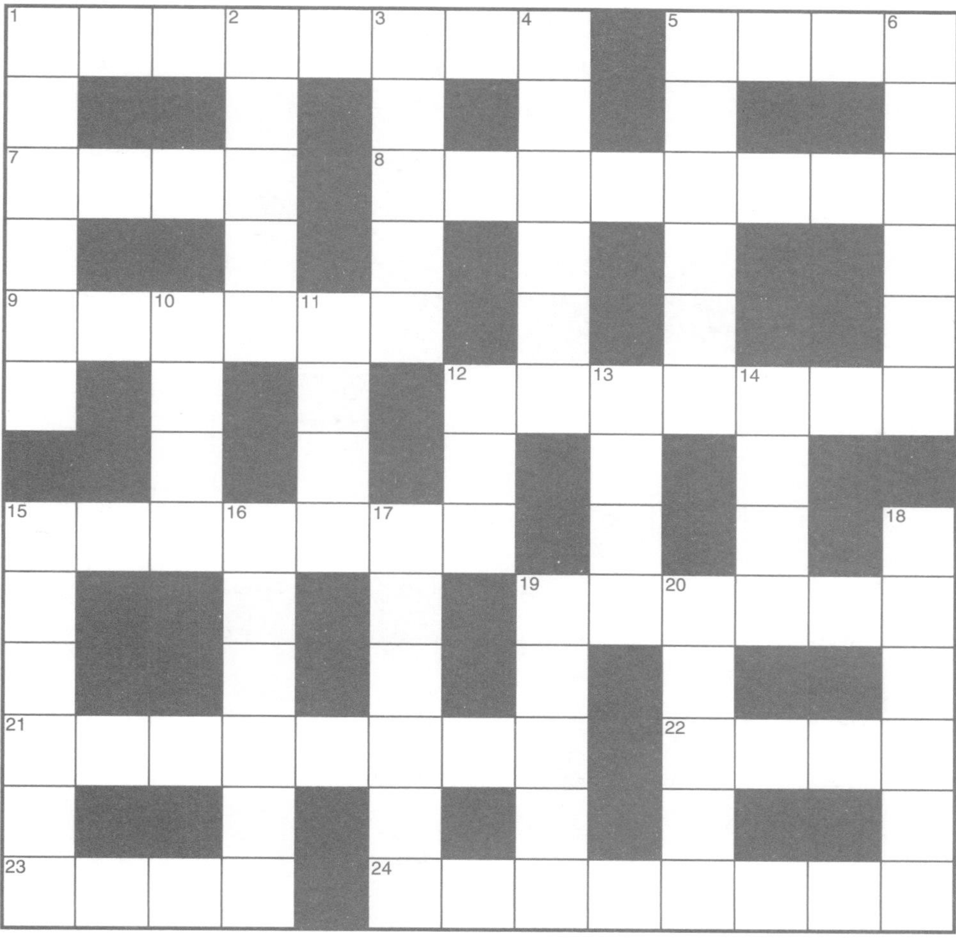

## ACROSS

1. Planned (building)
5. Insincere (of speech)
7. Opening in fence
8. Ribbed cotton velvet
9. Pokes fun at
12. Having (to)
15. Part of book
19. Perceive
21. Signed protest document
22. Mirth
23. Desert hill
24. Seconded

## DOWN

1. Numbers
2. Objects
3. Narrow straits
4. Ridicule
5. Measured
6. Purchasing
10. Vicinity
11. Give off
12. Neither
13. Threat, do it or ...!
14. Tiny island
15. Restricted (of wage increase)
16. Law enforcers
17. Imperial realm
18. Be present at
19. Ate out
20. Striped jungle animal

# CROSSWORD 321

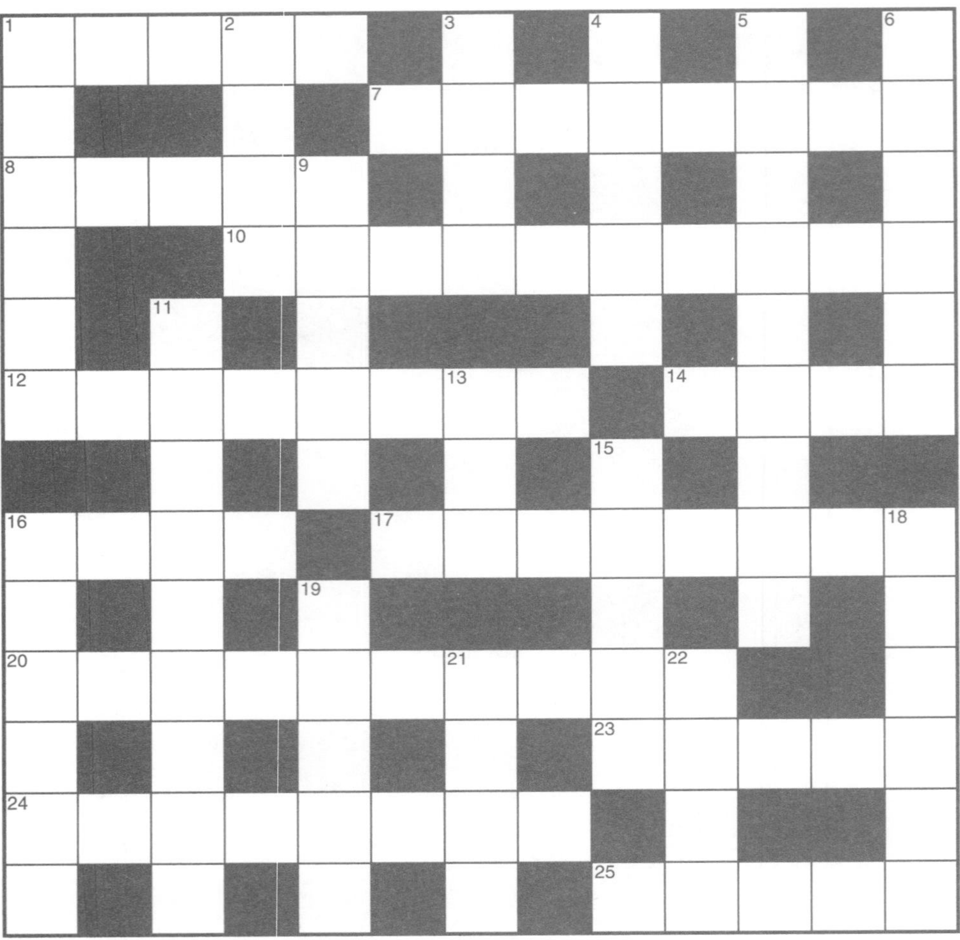

## ACROSS

1. Round door handles
7. Herring-like fish
8. Equivalent
10. Moderation
12. Craving, ... for
14. Infant's bed
16. Arrive at wharf
17. Avoided
20. Castle moat crossing
23. Enclosed areas
24. Serial sessions
25. Synthetic fabric

## DOWN

1. Eagerly
2. Rhythm
3. Speech defect
4. Oak kernel
5. Habitual gesture
6. Verb modifier
9. Rests
11. Artificial sweetener
13. No
15. Lanky
16. Eludes
18. Little plum
19. Monastery superior
21. Freezes, ... over
22. Effortless

# CROSSWORD 322

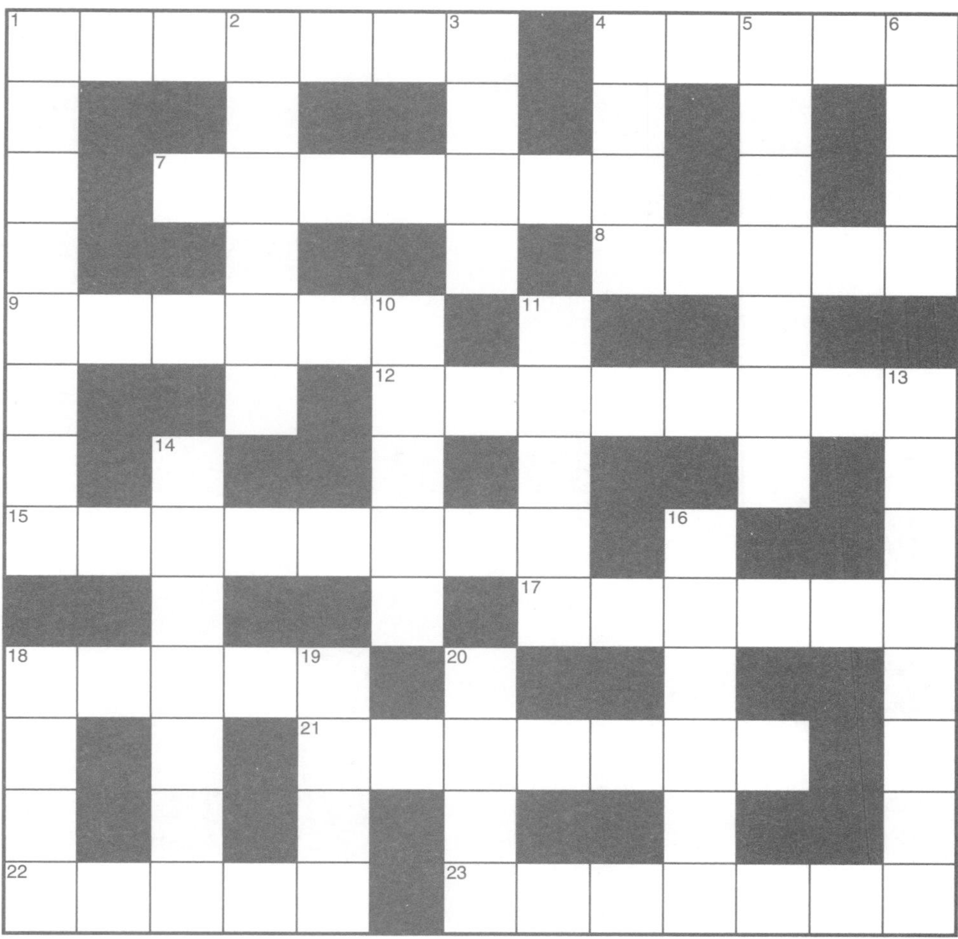

## ACROSS

1. Small chests
4. Larynx, ... box
7. Ravage
8. Reply
9. Marine animal, sea ...
12. Ill-mannered
15. Stiffened (fabric)
17. Shirked
18. Guitar sound
21. Feeling jealous of
22. Keeps us going, ... us over
23. Remodel

## DOWN

1. Seeks advice
2. Chess horse
3. Wound with knife
4. Steer off course
5. Occupy
6. Leave
10. Nocturnal hours
11. Garden tool
13. Proof
14. Parked undercover
16. Middle-age spread
18. Hair dye
19. Receives
20. Always

# CROSSWORD 323

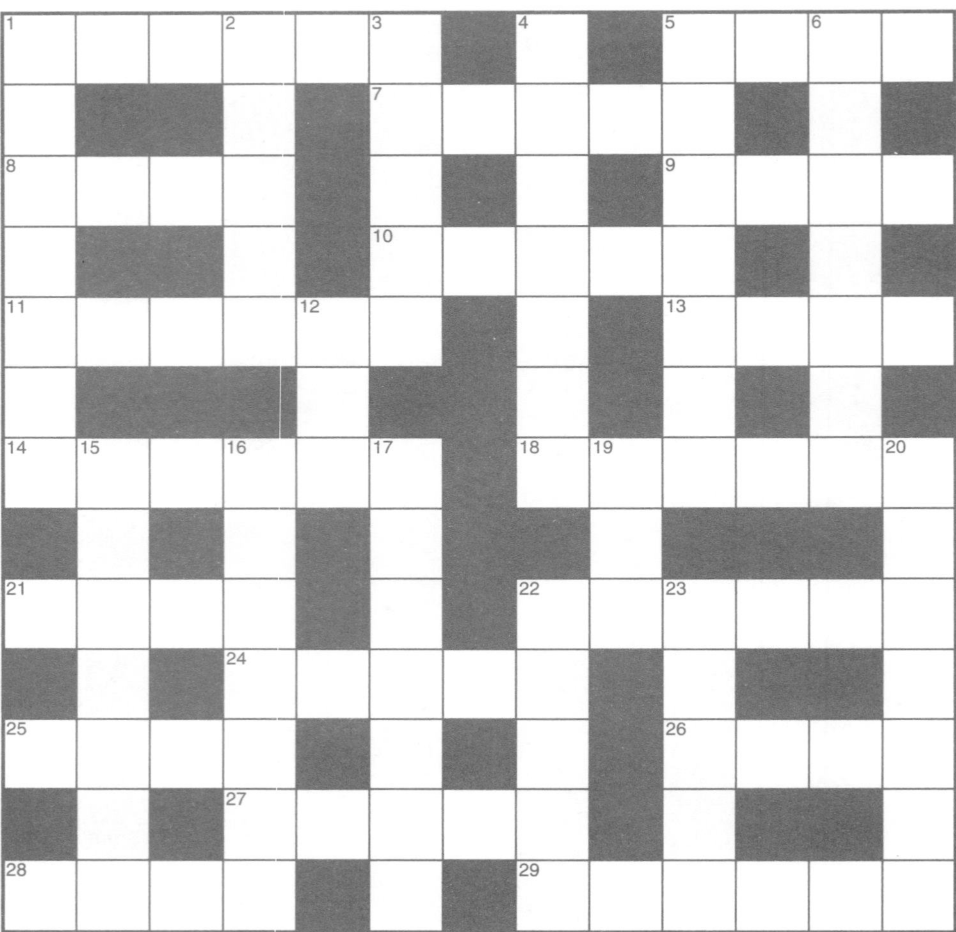

## ACROSS

1. Prodded sharply
5. Forward strategy
7. Roves
8. Pull heavily
9. Dog's cry
10. Meat jelly
11. Certainly
13. Keep secret
14. Jabber
18. 10-year period
21. Becomes mature
22. Encouraging
24. Accurate
25. Ready, willing & ...
26. Girl's plaything
27. Indian class system
28. Phone key
29. Nursery verses

## DOWN

1. Deeming
2. Small trumpet
3. Await with horror
4. Pied
5. Clairvoyant
6. Referred subtly
12. Conger or moray
15. Branch of mathematics
16. Implore
17. Generator emission
19. To ... on the side of caution
20. Inundates
22. Absolute
23. Dizzy

# CROSSWORD 324

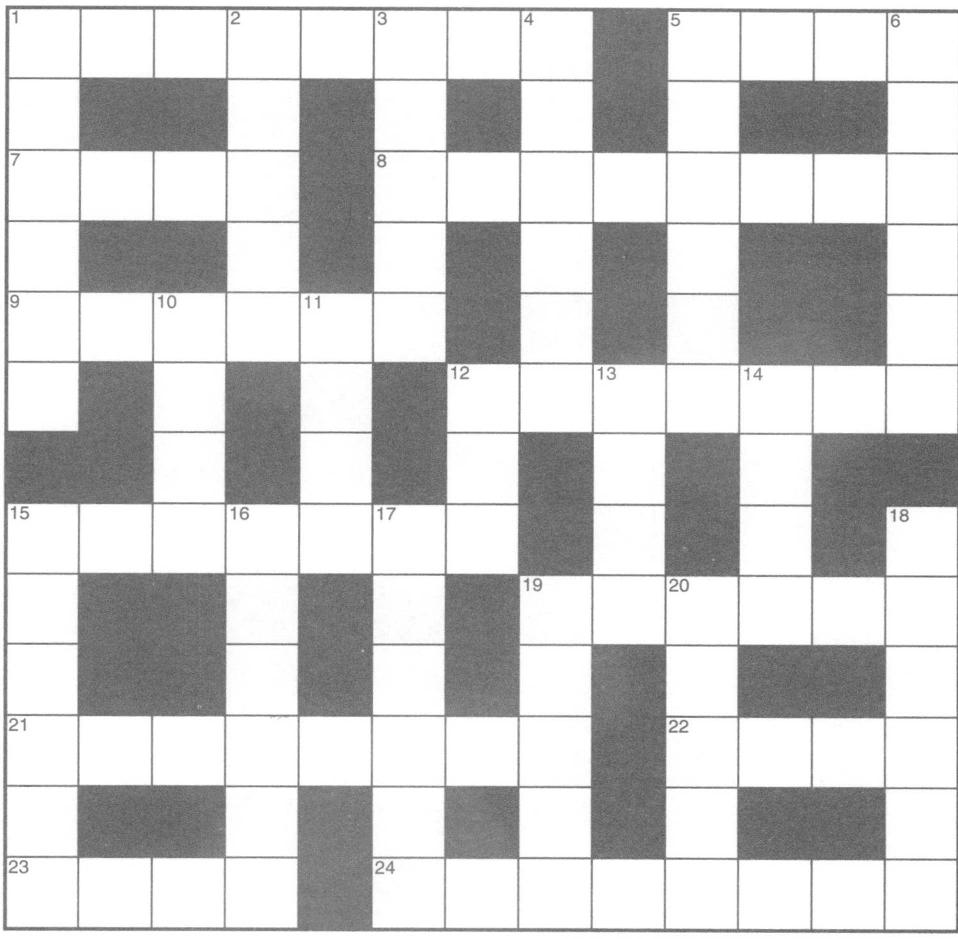

## ACROSS

1. Assailed
5. Swallow nervously
7. Lout
8. Aristocrats
9. Hate
12. Features
15. Lunar-illuminated
19. Martial art
21. Most significant
22. Volcano's flowing rock
23. Light-rail car
24. Preserve as sacred

## DOWN

1. Conflict
2. Gold brick
3. Magic lamp spirit
4. Ledger entries
5. Lubricate
6. Black & white mammals
10. Highest male singing voice
11. Corridor
12. Astern
13. Fervent prayer
14. Unnatural sleep
15. Small (submarine)
16. Incendiary bomb material
17. Hold up
18. Relabel
19. Flying toys
20. Leader

# CROSSWORD 325

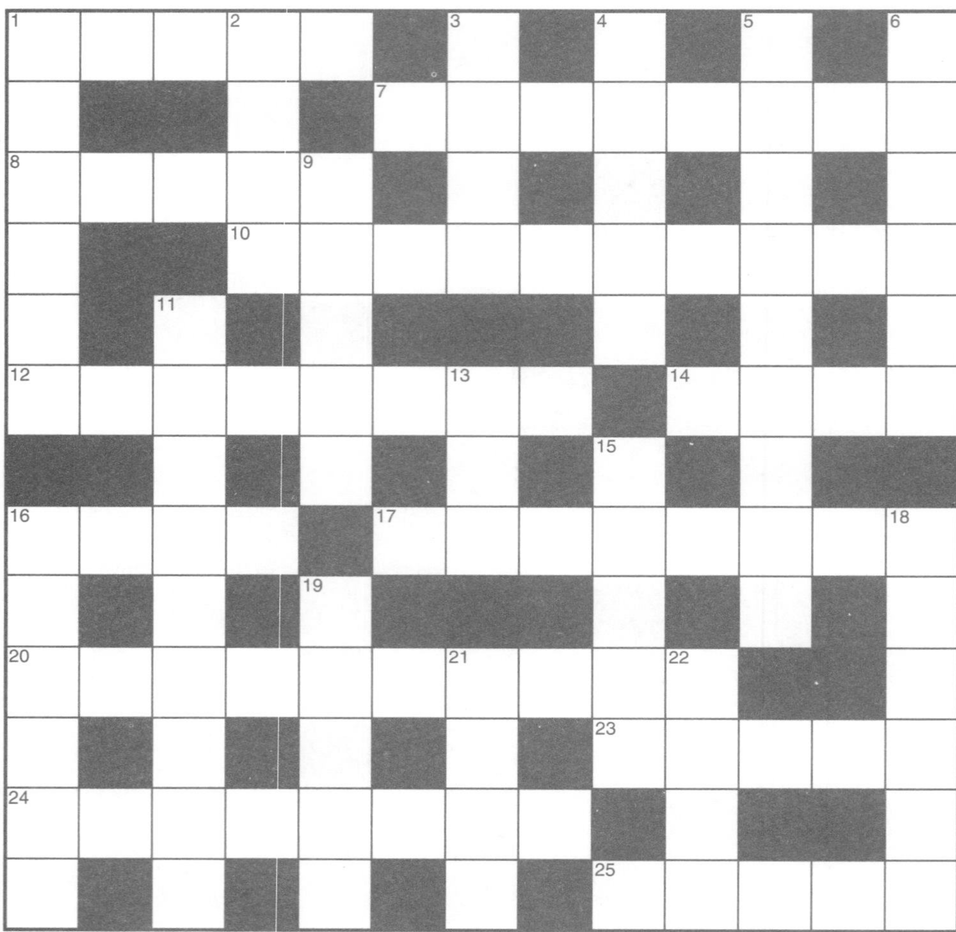

## ACROSS

1. Upright
7. Askew
8. Frog sound
10. Creamy dressing
12. Commanded authoritatively
14. Bottle tops
16. Military subdivision
17. Mental deterioration
20. Without boss
23. Pulls sharply
24. Tightened (fist)
25. Moves lightly (over)

## DOWN

1. Engraved
2. Chowder ingredient
3. Individual performance
4. Animal hides
5. Songwriters
6. Cows' milk sacs
9. Inuit boat
11. Sets (machine) in motion
13. Lamb's mother
15. Cluttered
16. Unlatch
18. Maltreats
19. Tree, copper ...
21. Told falsehood
22. Subsided

# CROSSWORD 326

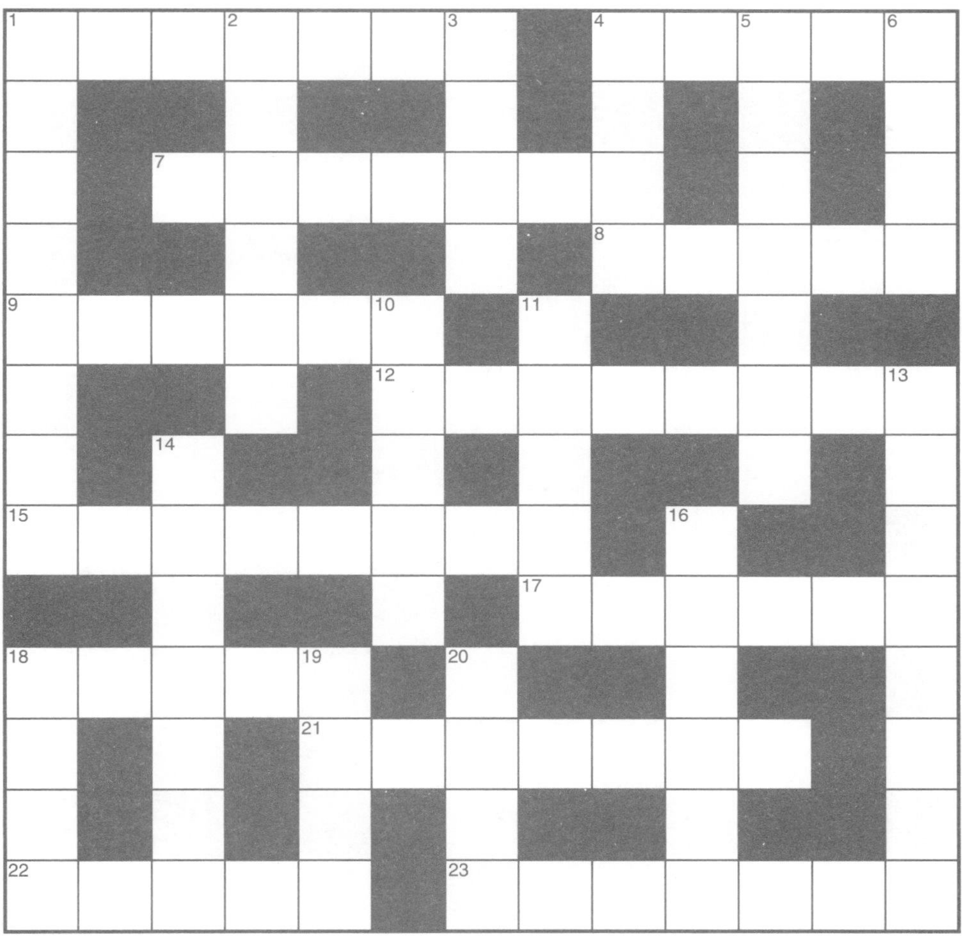

## ACROSS

1. More spacious
4. Make public speech
7. Dissents
8. Instruct
9. Mean
12. Unclogs
15. Treads underfoot
17. Allow
18. Perhaps
21. Young paper-seller
22. Reed instruments
23. Relics galleries

## DOWN

1. Noisiest
2. Crowded in upon
3. Display frame
4. Overthrow
5. Loan, cash ...
6. Merit
10. Unexcitingly
11. Unhealthily overweight
13. Laterally
14. Caribbean music style
16. In abundance
18. Reminder note
19. Terminates
20. Moved through water

# CROSSWORD 327

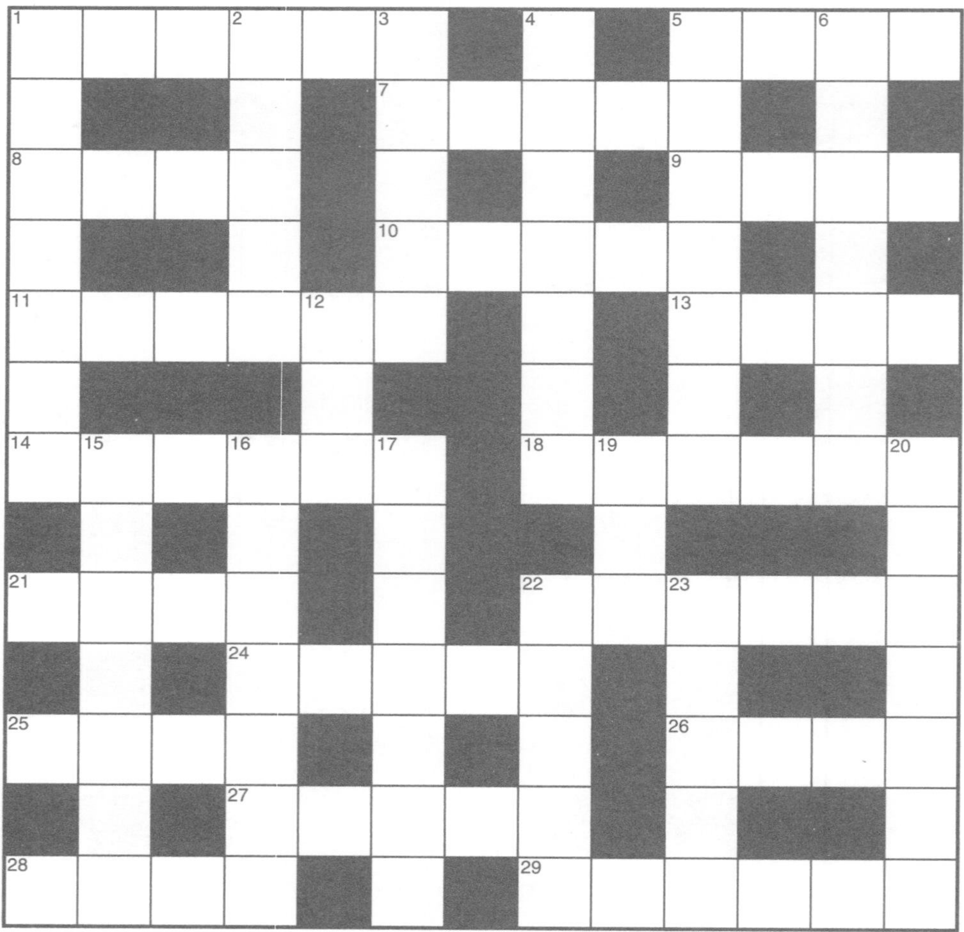

## ACROSS

1. Pressed against with lips
5. Hidden obstacle
7. Cook in oven
8. Pink wine style
9. Consumes food
10. Glowing coal
11. Lodges deeply
13. Imperial length unit
14. Security
18. Roman XI
21. Polluted air
22. Disturbed from slumber
24. Suggestions
25. Gratis
26. Match before final
27. Vary (legislation)
28. Nudge
29. Painting stands

## DOWN

1. Edible nut parts
2. Section of drama
3. Uses towel
4. Trash
5. Uncontaminated
6. Newspaper item
12. Small spot
15. Devotee
16. Intellectual
17. Not as old
19. Established rule
20. Female goats
22. Incidental comment
23. Desert waterholes

# CROSSWORD 328

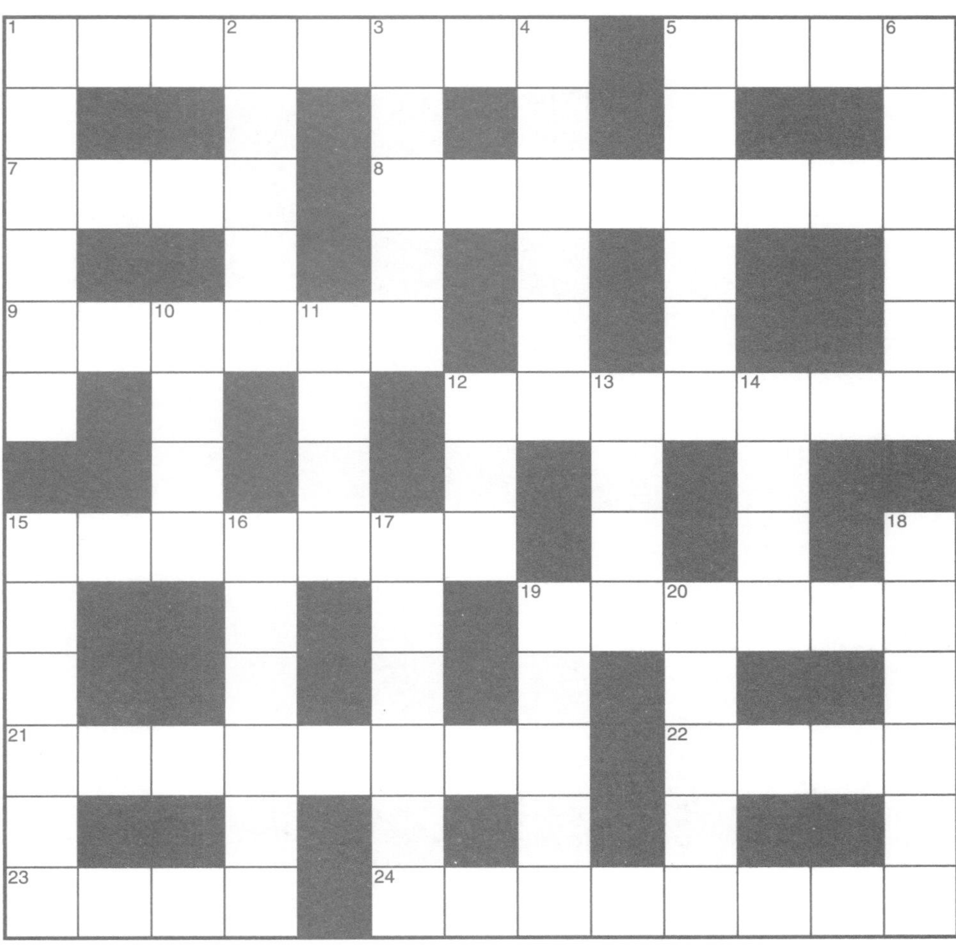

## ACROSS

1. Long-necked animals
5. Mother
7. Throw (dice)
8. Laughs slyly
9. Muscle contractions
12. Unrelenting
15. Closest
19. Butted
21. Official journals
22. Engrossed
23. Wise person
24. Fiddled (with)

## DOWN

1. Overly bright & showy
2. Wheel spindles
3. Clenched hands
4. Went by yacht
5. Large champagne bottle
6. Approval
10. Saintly radiance
11. Inconsiderable
12. Perform
13. Water
14. Nuclear weapon, ... bomb
15. Light pushes
16. Hold in high esteem
17. Group of six
18. Prepared (manuscript)
19. Increased
20. Unite

# CROSSWORD 329

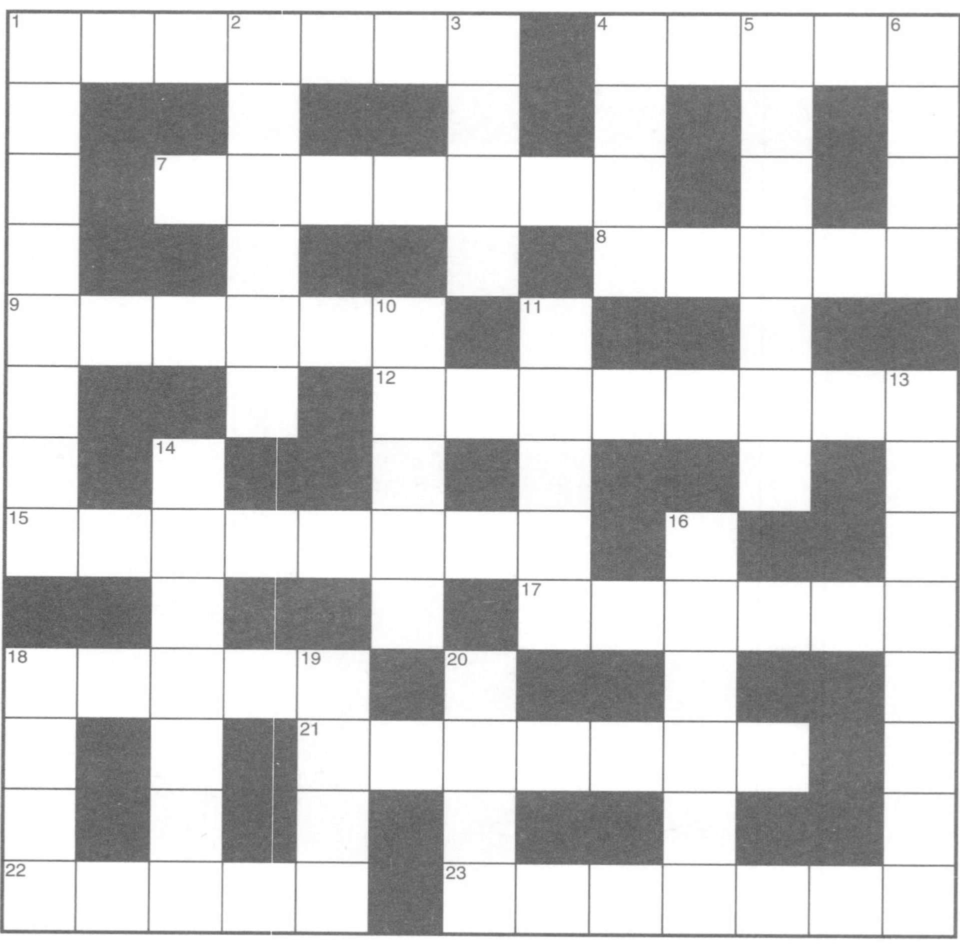

## ACROSS

1. Trivial objection
4. Unsteady
7. Uppermost
8. Pointy-featured
9. Positive electrodes
12. Hunters using snares
15. Rate
17. Pickled
18. Flooded (of decks)
21. Independently
22. Thick slice
23. Take up (cause)

## DOWN

1. Repeatable (of speech)
2. Constructs
3. Stared at
4. Social custom
5. Handmade
6. Open mouth wearily
10. Kettle mist
11. Coffee shops
13. Set of symptoms
14. Pillaged
16. Formal-wear jacket
18. Affirm
19. Massive
20. Hay bundle

# CROSSWORD 330

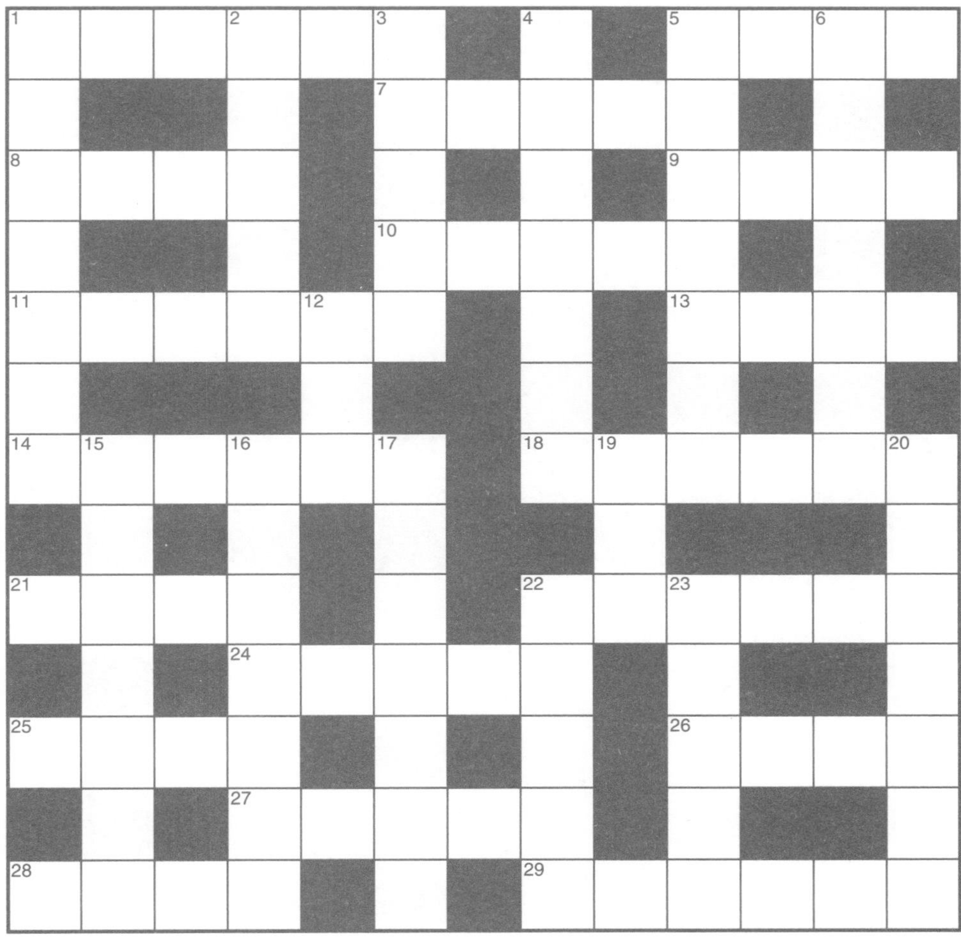

## ACROSS

1. Sight
5. High temperature
7. Musical drama
8. Grassy area
9. Ramble
10. Intends
11. Laments
13. Injure
14. Sound mental health
18. ... & feathered
21. Song of praise
22. Wine flask
24. Different
25. Seaside attraction
26. Group of buffalo
27. Exhilarate
28. Honey liquor
29. Sequence

## DOWN

1. Capacities
2. Hidden
3. Standards
4. Failure to pay
5. More stringent
6. Negative
12. Tennis barrier
15. Whenever
16. Disregarded
17. Muslim woman's veil
19. Trouble
20. Strips of vegetation
22. Cooks in oil
23. Detest

# CROSSWORD 331

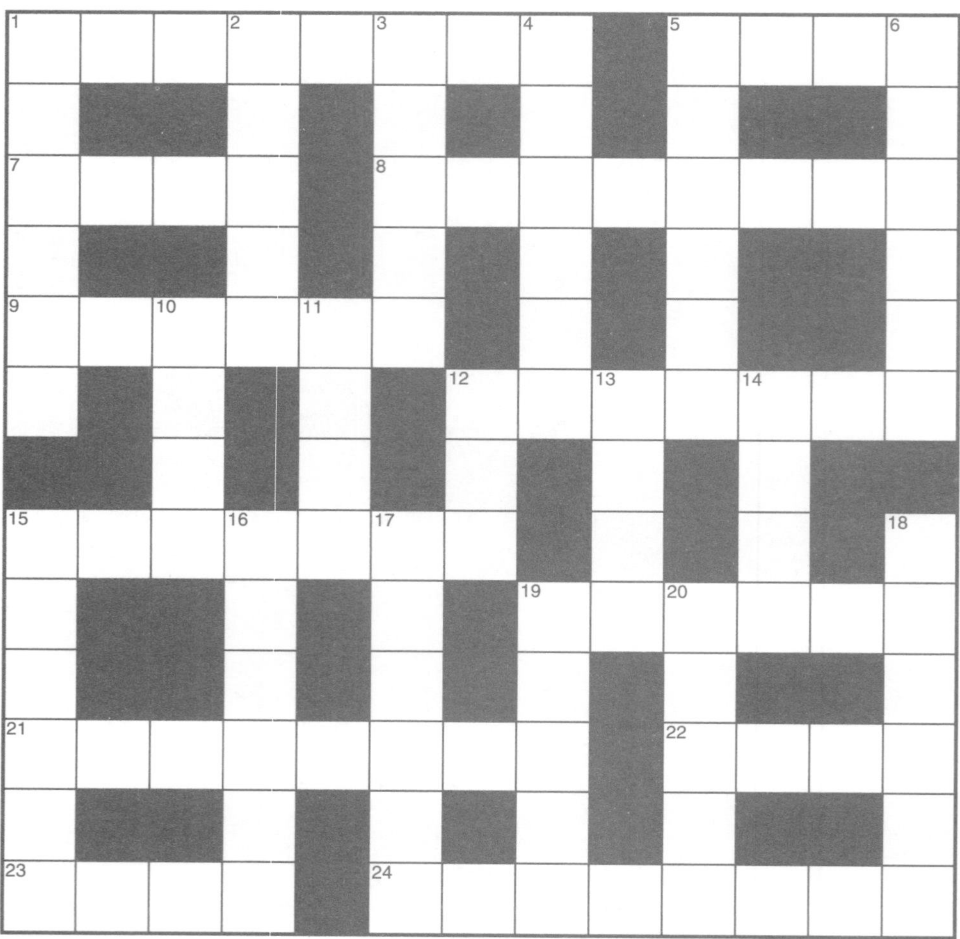

## ACROSS

1. Financial outlays
5. Steals from
7. Loose flesh
8. Sailing
9. Steering device
12. Vigilantly
15. Pure white animals
19. Appreciation
21. Rustic
22. Respected expert
23. Hit with hand
24. Remnants

## DOWN

1. Attempt
2. Flowed away
3. More furtive
4. Networking websites, ... media
5. Prefer to
6. Cloyingly sweet
10. Paint roughly
11. Neatly spaced
12. Donkey
13. Apiece
14. Ruptured
15. Changes to suit conditions
16. Arch of foot
17. Take too far
18. Agenda items
19. Laid ceramic squares
20. Quarrel

# CROSSWORD 332

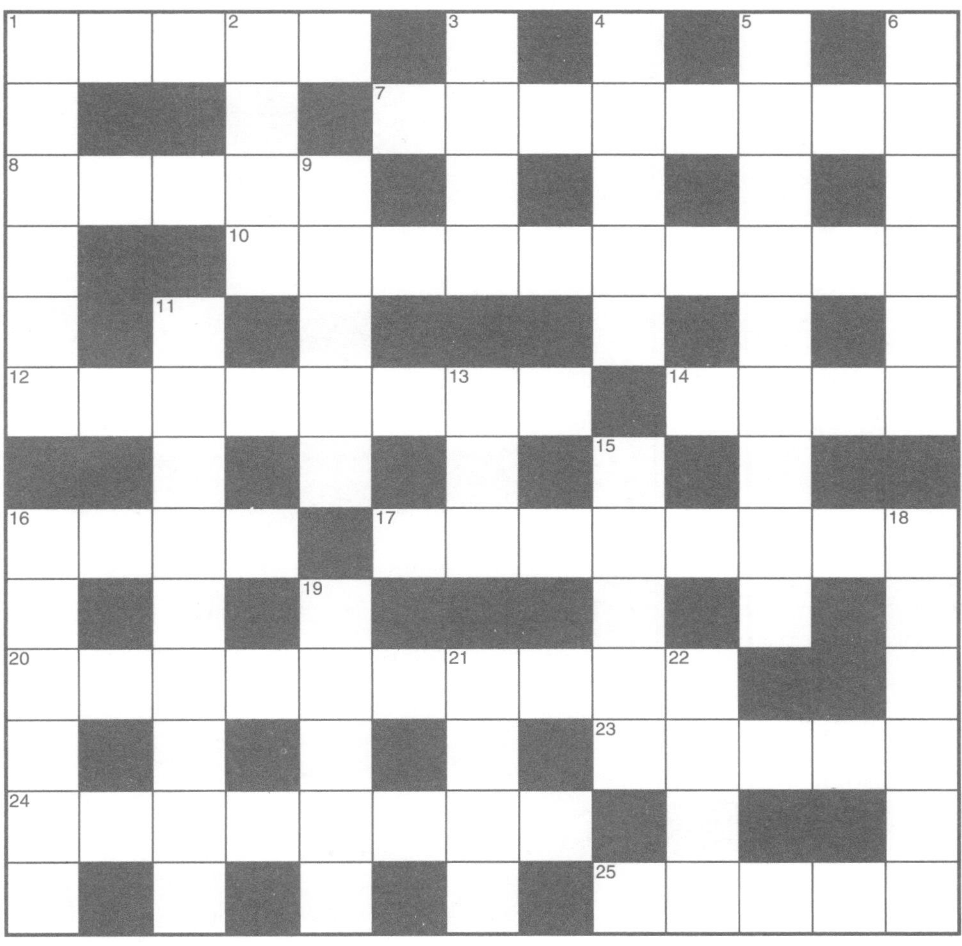

## ACROSS

1. Female relatives
7. Spinning
8. Imperative
10. Plant shop owner
12. Originated
14. Reside
16. Take (baby) off bottle
17. Speared
20. Widening
23. Alleviated
24. Floor covering
25. Orchard fruit

## DOWN

1. Guidance
2. In comparison to
3. Exercise clubs
4. Lions' abodes
5. Circle widths
6. Advertising firm
9. Of the moon
11. Of greatest importance
13. Large antlered animal
15. Hogs & sows
16. Unstable
18. Trawl (riverbed)
19. Cult heroes
21. Subject of a verb
22. Catch breath

# CROSSWORD 333

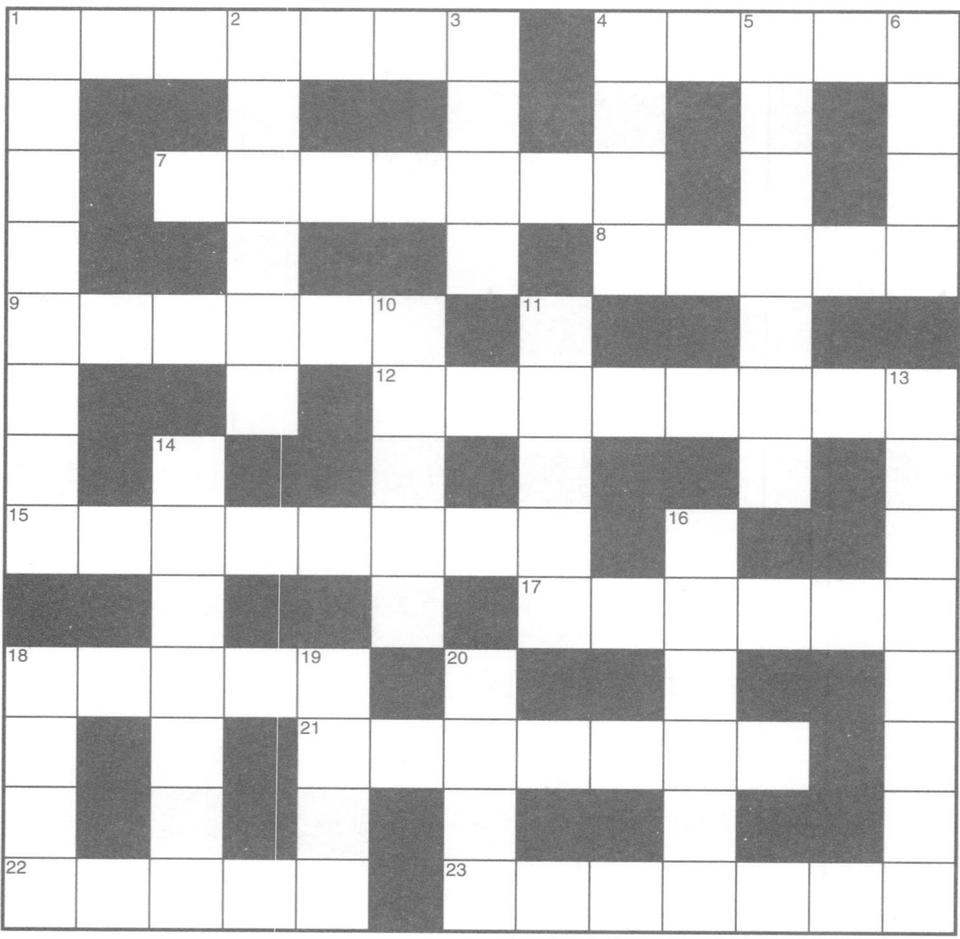

## ACROSS

1. Irregular
4. Dutch bulb flower
7. Four-stringed guitar
8. Laud
9. Venus or Mars
12. Lack of response
15. Withdraw to safe place
17. Cried in pain
18. Feather
21. Straight-faced
22. Smoggy
23. Wadding

## DOWN

1. Caper
2. Requesting, ... for
3. Kitchen professional
4. Mojave Desert plant, Joshua ...
5. Maniac
6. Sphagnum, ... moss
10. Fabled giant
11. Muslim women's quarters
13. Provoking
14. Pricing (properties)
16. Fairway obstacle
18. Swell, ... up
19. Nervous
20. Coarse file

# CROSSWORD 334

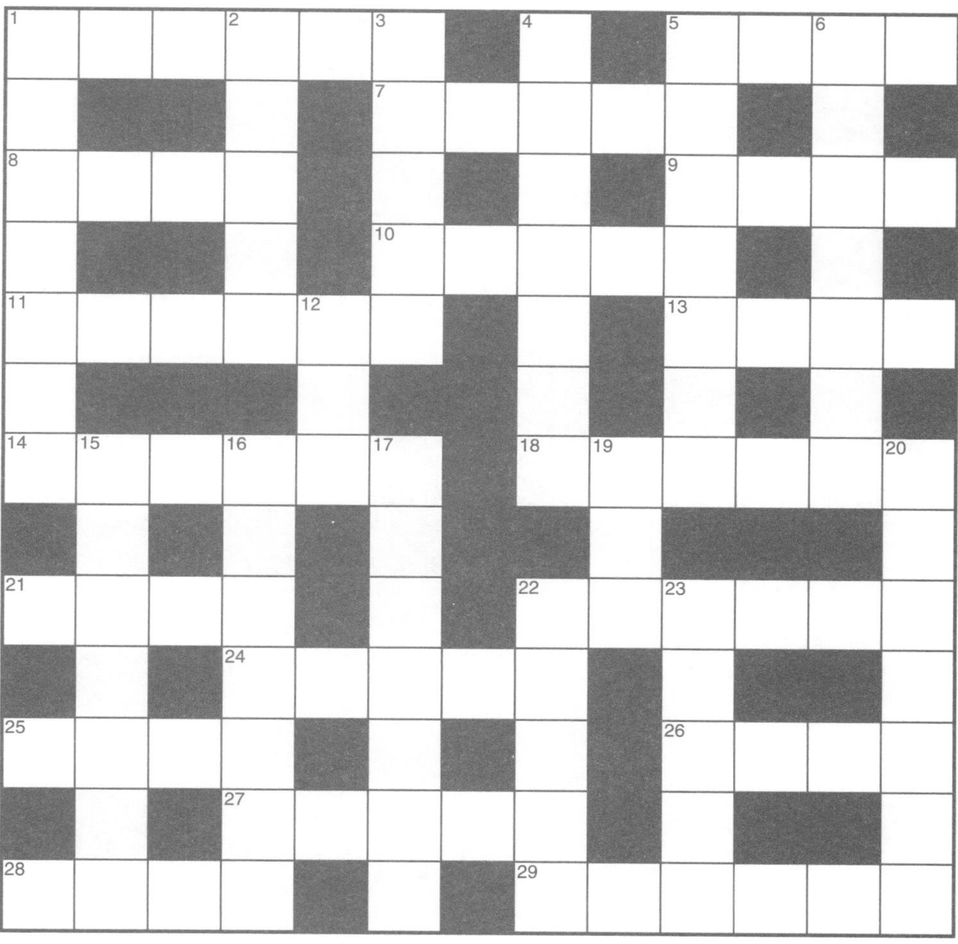

## ACROSS

1. Skewers of meat
5. A distance
7. Alcove
8. Speechless
9. Wealthy
10. Australian native canine
11. Meal course
13. Flank
14. Food toppings
18. Greatly enjoy
21. Honest
22. Striding impatiently
24. Hollywood production
25. Short skirt style
26. Scottish dance
27. Complete (crossword)
28. Insignificant
29. Corrugated

## DOWN

1. Purifying organs
2. Yellowish-brown shade
3. Slyly disparaging
4. Bar-code reader
5. Spray can
6. Shopping walkways
12. Extend, ... out
15. Aircraft company
16. Woman's undergarment
17. Large spades
19. Period
20. Bargained
22. Naval flag, blue ...
23. Was concerned

# CROSSWORD 335

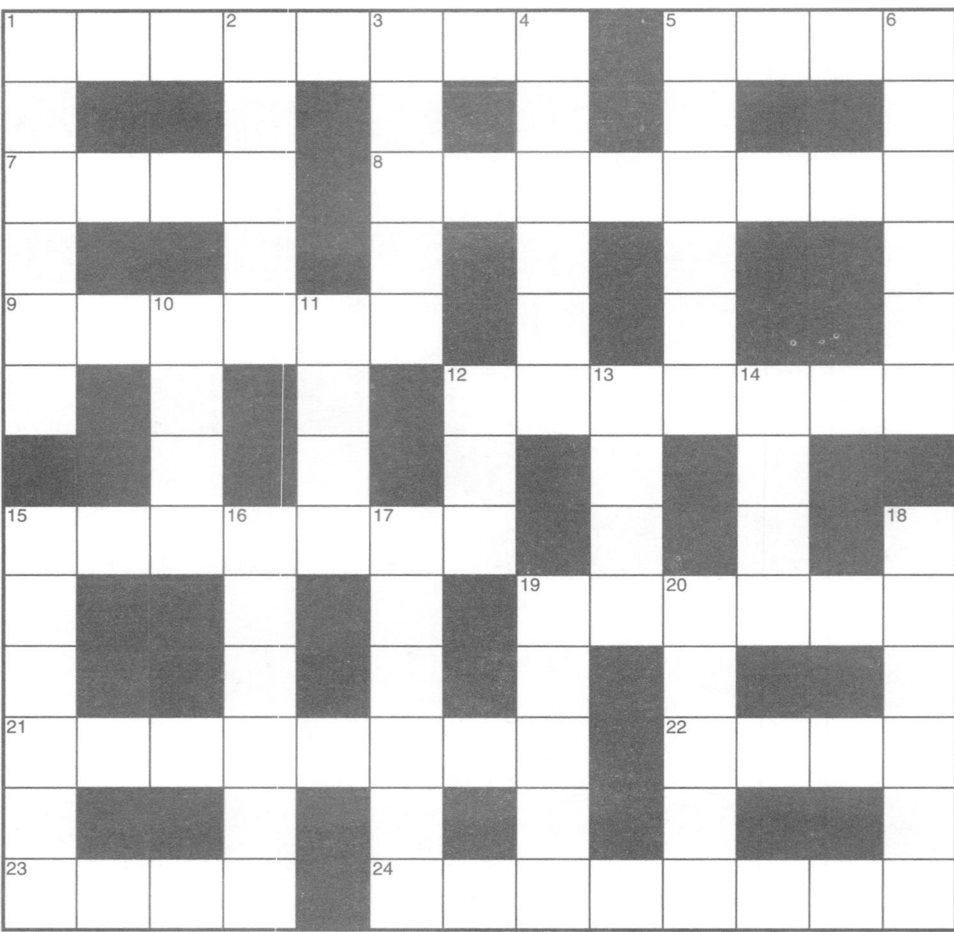

## ACROSS

1. Suggesting
5. Tiny branch
7. Had to repay
8. Shivers with disgust
9. Contaminate
12. Beautified
15. Perspired
19. Greatest in age
21. Small decorative object
22. Close friend
23. Tibetan priest
24. Pungent roots

## DOWN

1. Perversely coincidental
2. Cabin
3. Fabric insert
4. Scratched deeply
5. Neater
6. Poisoned by fumes
10. Number in quintet
11. Jacket
12. In addition
13. Ellipse
14. Inch (car) forward
15. Group (of fish)
16. Spanish fleet
17. Make beloved
18. Stamps with foot
19. Elected
20. Chops in cubes

# CROSSWORD 336

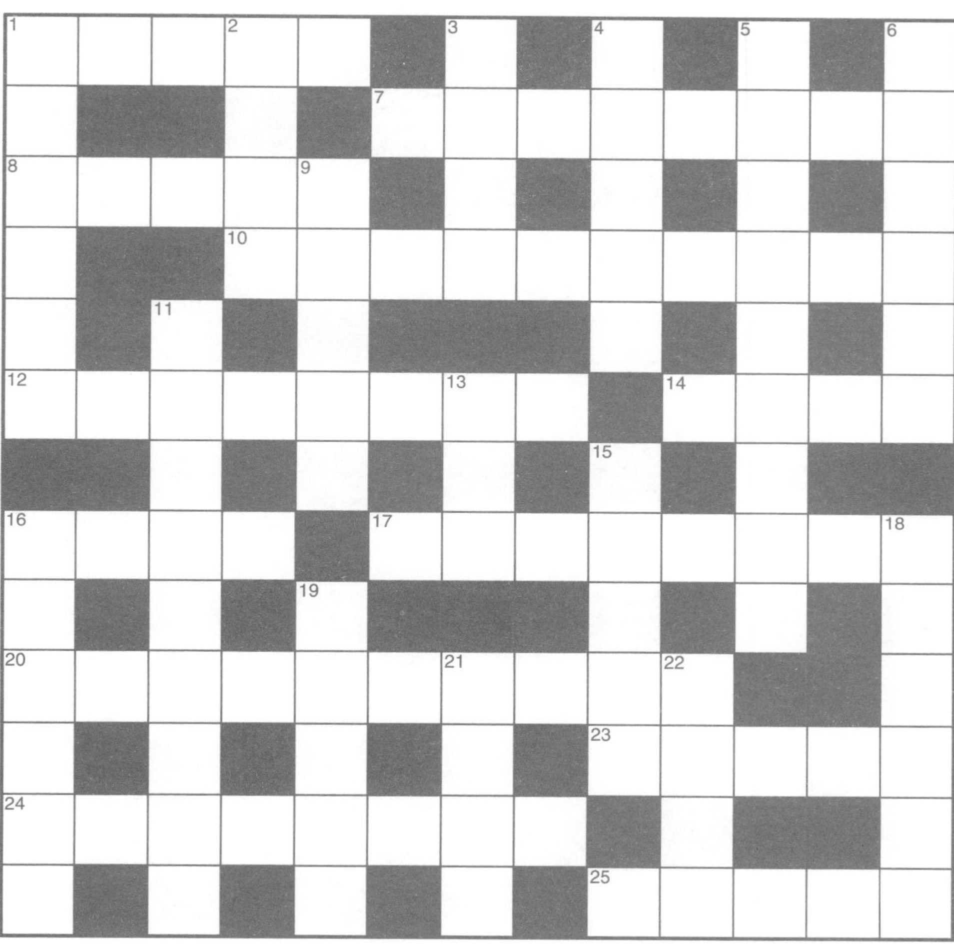

## ACROSS

1. Animal sheds
7. Expressed keenness (over)
8. Double
10. Business venture
12. Small grains
14. Turn towards
16. Contends
17. Heavy fall of rain
20. Distrustful
23. Mixed (with poison)
24. Bewitches
25. Garden statue

## DOWN

1. Nibbling
2. French Riviera resort
3. Poker stake
4. Retail outlets
5. Assessor
6. Hold fast (to)
9. Follow on
11. Canvas shoulder-bag
13. Self-regard
15. Cancel (marriage)
16. Vein, blood ...
18. Puzzle
19. Prima donnas
21. Tiny amount
22. Milled (timber)

# CROSSWORD 337

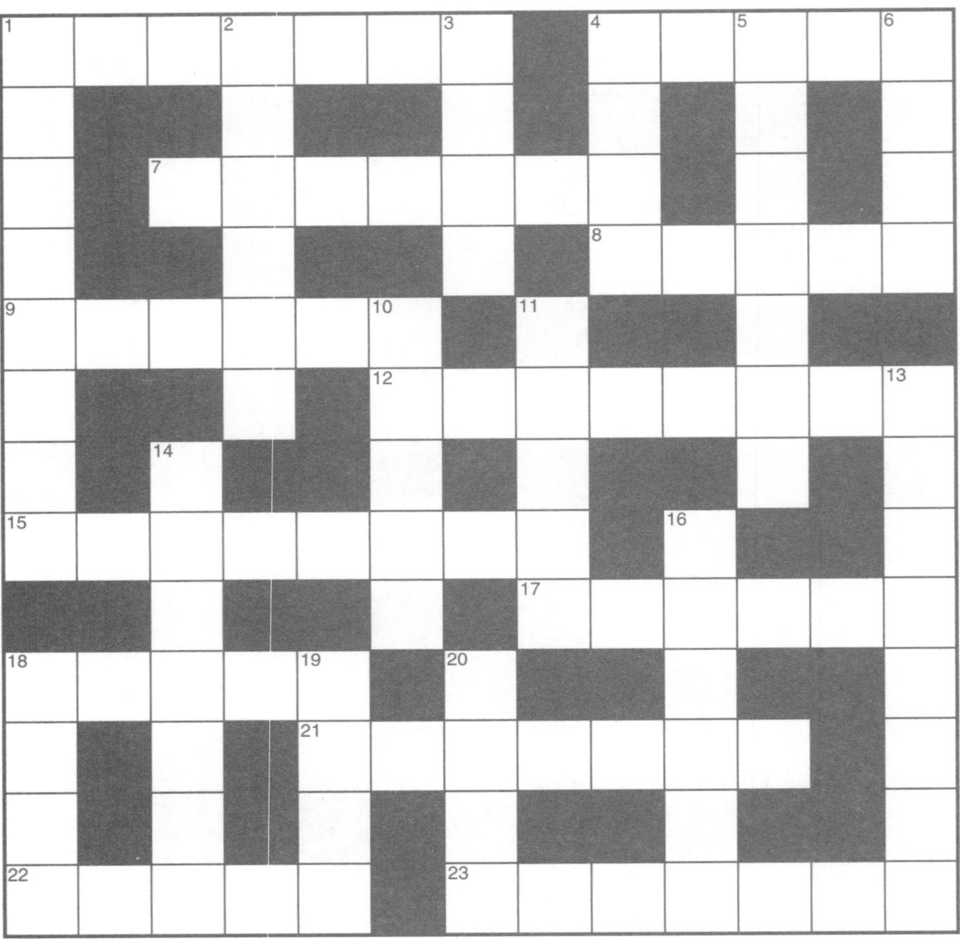

## ACROSS

1. Rod & reel sport
4. Lower leg joint
7. Truncate
8. Country bumpkin
9. Cried in grief
12. Thought of
15. Marine creature's home
17. Go by (of time)
18. Endorses
21. Citrus fruits
22. Small notches
23. Retribution taker

## DOWN

1. Motorways
2. Every 60 minutes
3. Equipment
4. Wartime friend
5. Striking with foot
6. Nobleman
10. Nickels & ...
11. Aesop tale
13. Political deserter
14. Extremist
16. Subterranean chamber
18. Bullocks
19. Scatters (seeds)
20. Carnival

# CROSSWORD 338

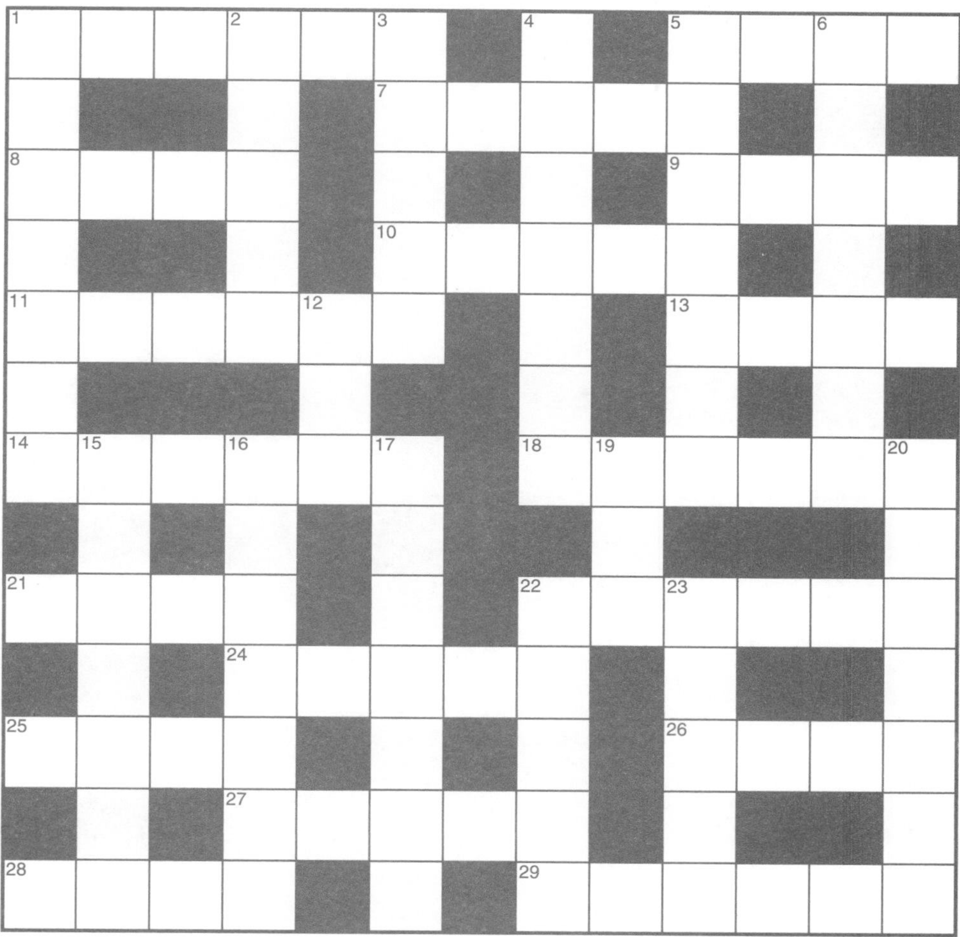

## ACROSS

1. Of the universe
5. Prompted (actor)
7. Peruvian pack animal
8. Rounded roof
9. Fleshy part of ear
10. Concerning ships
11. Obliterates
13. Written test
14. Effluent
18. Sampled
21. Relinquish
22. Stood on hind legs
24. Dining bench
25. River boat
26. Long tale
27. Grind down
28. Curve
29. Zigzagged (through traffic)

## DOWN

1. Stout clubs
2. Intersects
3. Tribal groups
4. Gather (crops)
5. Visitors
6. Hug
12. Unborn chick
15. Legally kill
16. Aided in crime
17. Arch over eye
19. Gorilla or chimpanzee
20. Drew conclusions
22. Reaffirm (promise)
23. Rink

# CROSSWORD 339

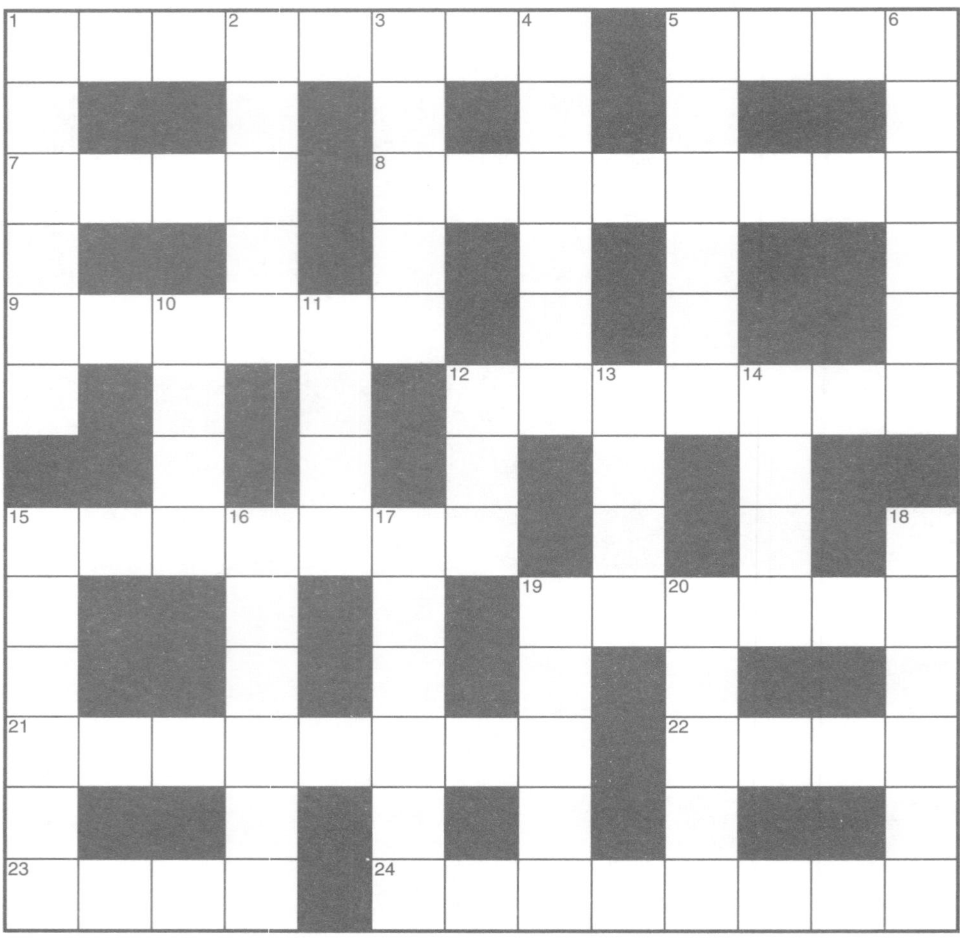

## ACROSS

1. Upbeat person
5. Part of arrow
7. Political takeover
8. Partaking of alcohol
9. Cadence
12. Guided (to seat)
15. Brown skin mark
19. Muffle
21. Military occupiers
22. Foundation
23. Asian sauce bean
24. Anticipation

## DOWN

1. Transpires
2. Computer data
3. Colloquialism
4. Cultural prohibitions
5. Air ball
6. Stuck in mud
10. Harness (oxen)
11. Bird of prey
12. Operation
13. Great dislike
14. Rip violently
15. Non-solids
16. Noisy summer insect
17. Light beers
18. Hay fever reaction
19. Fine powders
20. Saunter

# CROSSWORD 340

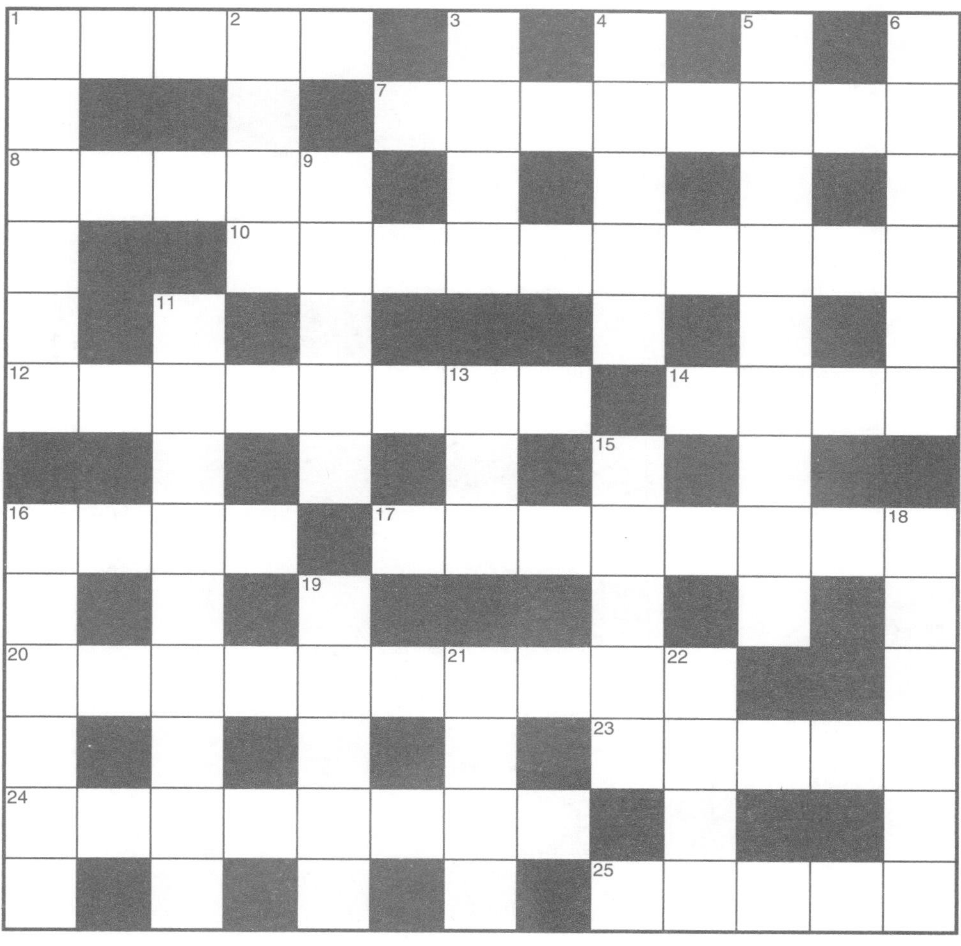

## ACROSS

1. Horse's cry
7. Increased
8. Pale purple
10. Intermediate position
12. Sword holder
14. Ventilates
16. Lose intensity, ... off
17. Commissioned soldiers
20. Calmly
23. Stunned
24. Caressing with nose
25. Unfastened

## DOWN

1. Synthetic fabrics
2. Take rudely
3. Discontinued (project)
4. Loiter
5. Supplements in food
6. Work-shy people
9. Hair grooming tools
11. Celebrity photographers
13. Football arbiter
15. Pasture
16. Rubbing with cloth
18. Ranked in tennis
19. Ships' spines
21. Large jars
22. Wool

# CROSSWORD 341

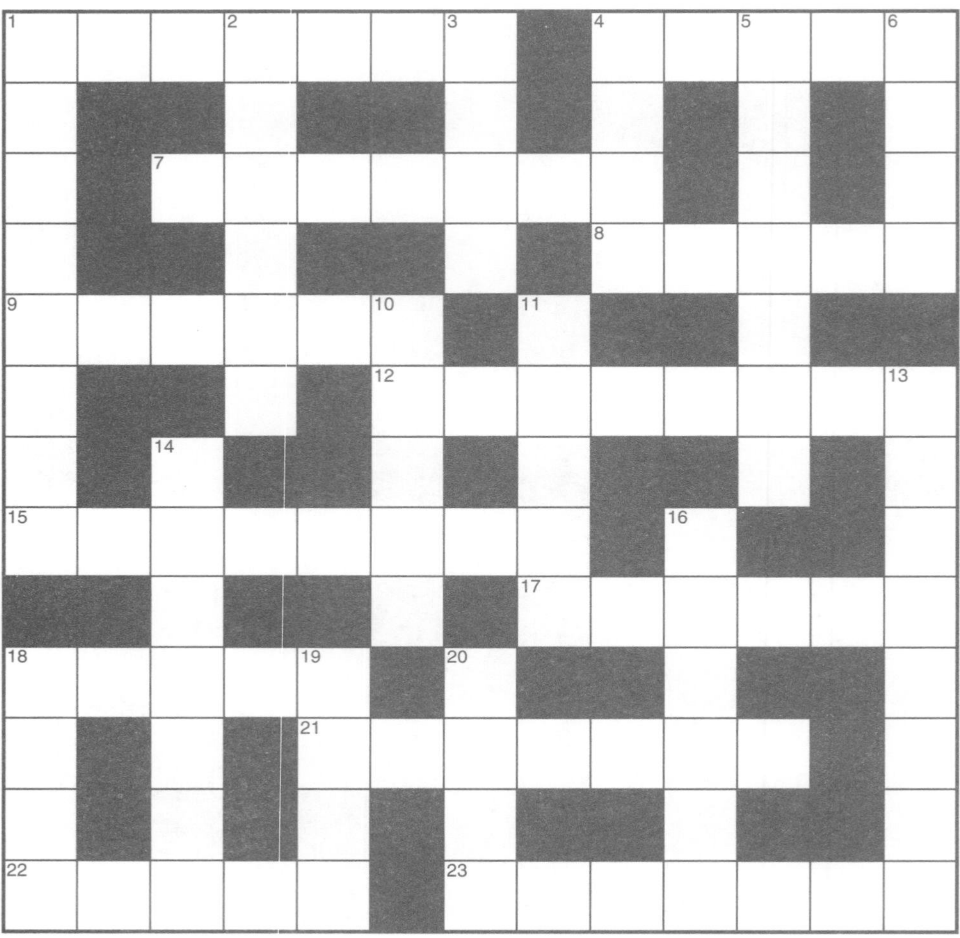

## ACROSS

1. Stomach-settling powder
4. Conscious existence
7. Edible leafstalk
8. Escape
9. Handled roughly
12. 12-month-old horse
15. Tester
17. Gazed fixedly
18. Force out
21. Sloping typeface
22. Fairground attractions
23. Obvious

## DOWN

1. Put together
2. Occasionally, once in ... (1,5)
3. Cope (with)
4. Infant
5. Null & void
6. Clarified butter
10. Perishing
11. Whiskers
13. Incline
14. Tried
16. Rotten
18. Pitcher
19. Facial features
20. Story

# CROSSWORD 342

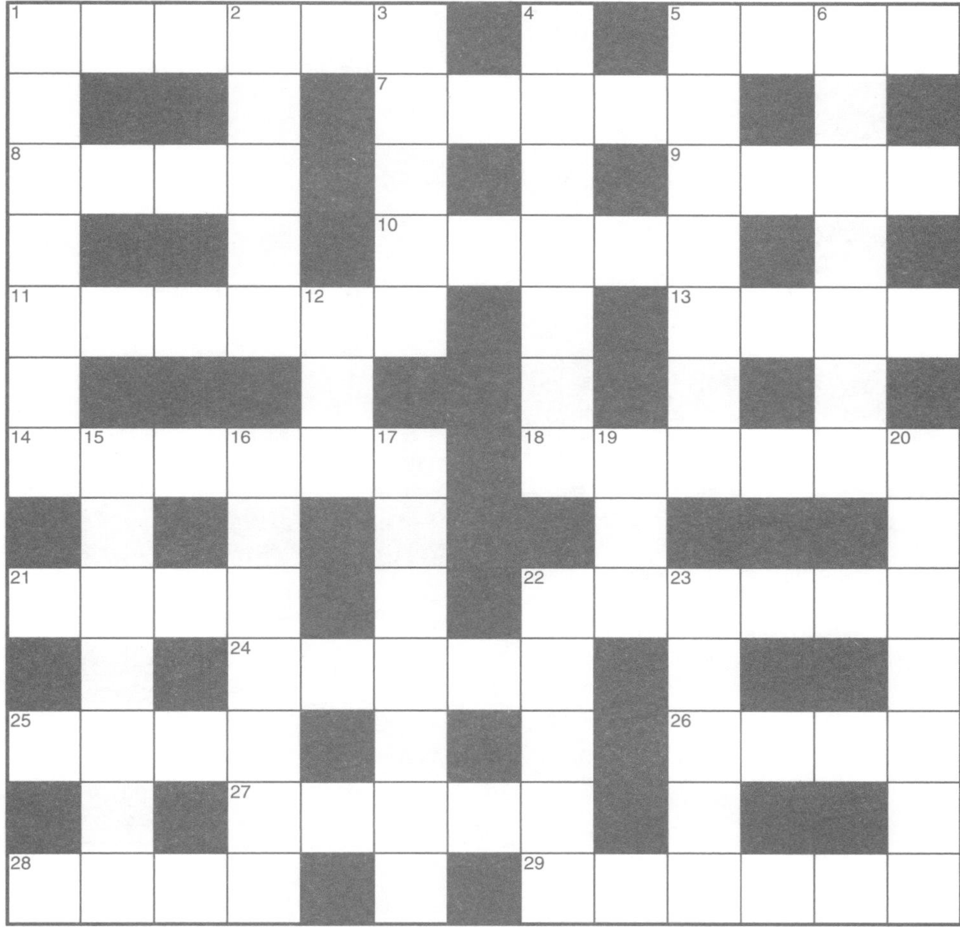

## ACROSS

1. Insist
5. Canoodle
7. Predatory bird
8. Frozen, ... over
9. Conger fish
10. Current (permit)
11. Monarch's seat
13. Company symbol
14. Considered
18. Ornamental ribbons
21. Wound crust
22. Peacock's mate
24. Beyond our planet, outer ...
25. Sculptured likeness
26. Taverns
27. Occasion
28. Movie queen
29. Detects

## DOWN

1. Moved with tide
2. Of sound system
3. Dig
4. Ever youthful
5. Pine tree leaves
6. Perfume
12. Formerly known as
15. Cake (with mud)
16. Gangster
17. Formal arguments
19. Top pilot
20. Nasal bone cavities
22. Vermin
23. Straighten

# CROSSWORD 343

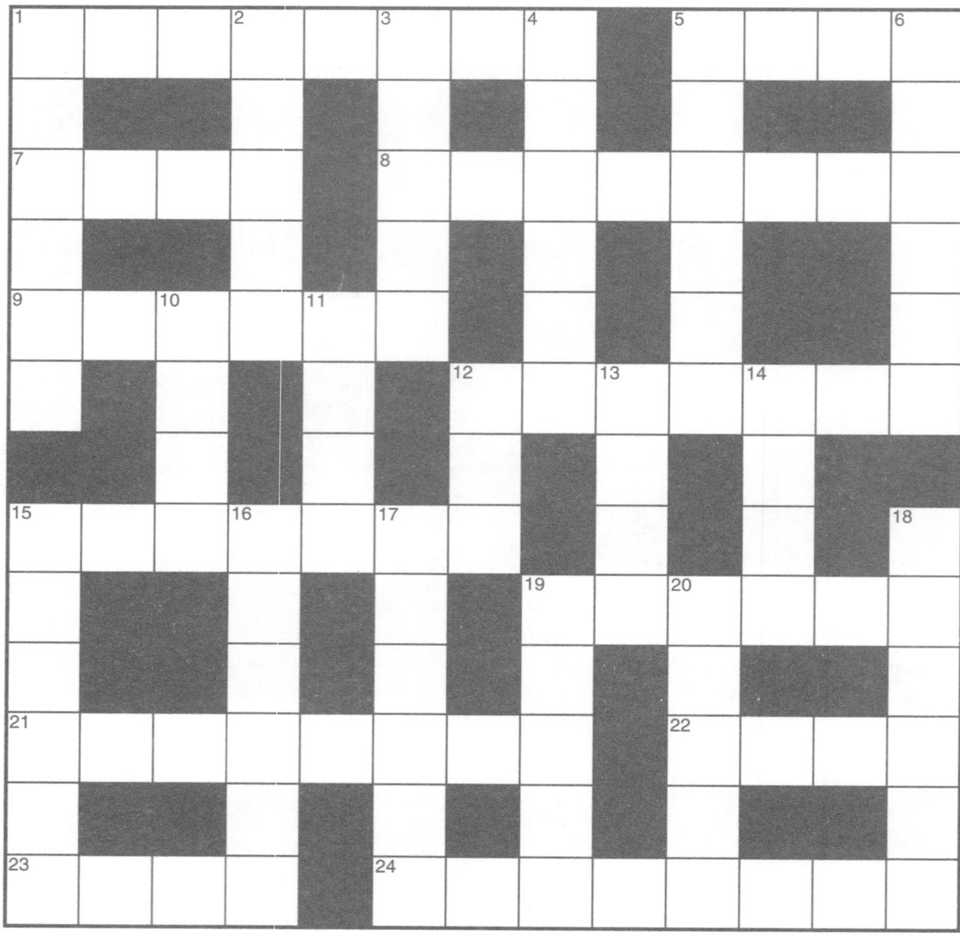

## ACROSS

1. Computer-based inventory
5. Compulsion
7. Canned fish
8. Ship's wall
9. To wit
12. Shellfish
15. Gain
19. Pill
21. Visionaries
22. Eating utensil
23. Dull thump
24. Struggled against

## DOWN

1. Estimating age of
2. In the know
3. London's Westminster ...
4. Funeral service tribute
5. Uninjured
6. Whirlpools
10. Nocturnal insect
11. Similar to
12. An individual
13. Long upholstered seat
14. Diabolical
15. In between
16. ... or outward
17. Thin covering
18. Watched covertly, ... out
19. Chores
20. Polishes

# CROSSWORD 344

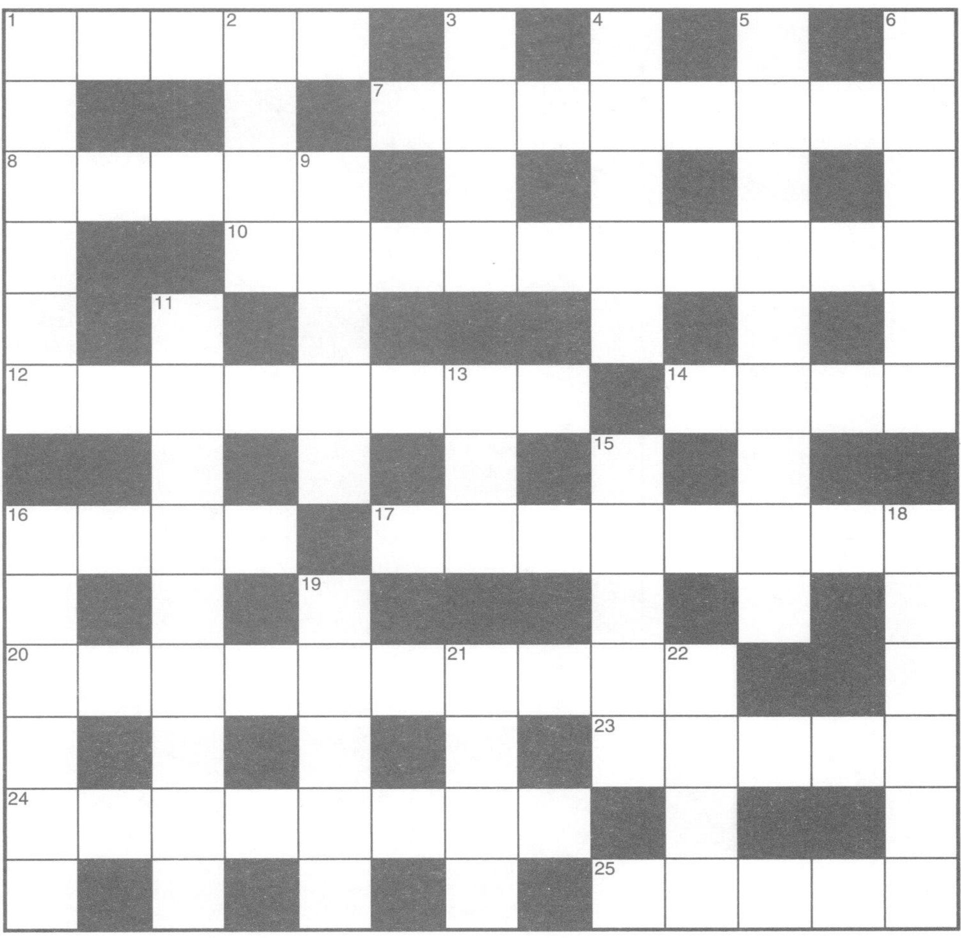

## ACROSS

1. Homeless animal
7. Domestic helpers
8. Thin piece
10. Sixtieth, ..., eightieth
12. Practical people
14. Forearm bone
16. Which?
17. Tropical cyclones
20. Respectful attention
23. Press (dough)
24. Amiably
25. Wrote by machine

## DOWN

1. Female sibling
2. Circle parts
3. Leave hurriedly
4. Prickly desert plants
5. Mutiny
6. Respiratory disorder
9. Ghostly
11. Annoying
13. Attempt
15. Dense
16. Treats unfairly
18. Squalid
19. Opera solos
21. Competently
22. Begrudge

# CROSSWORD 345

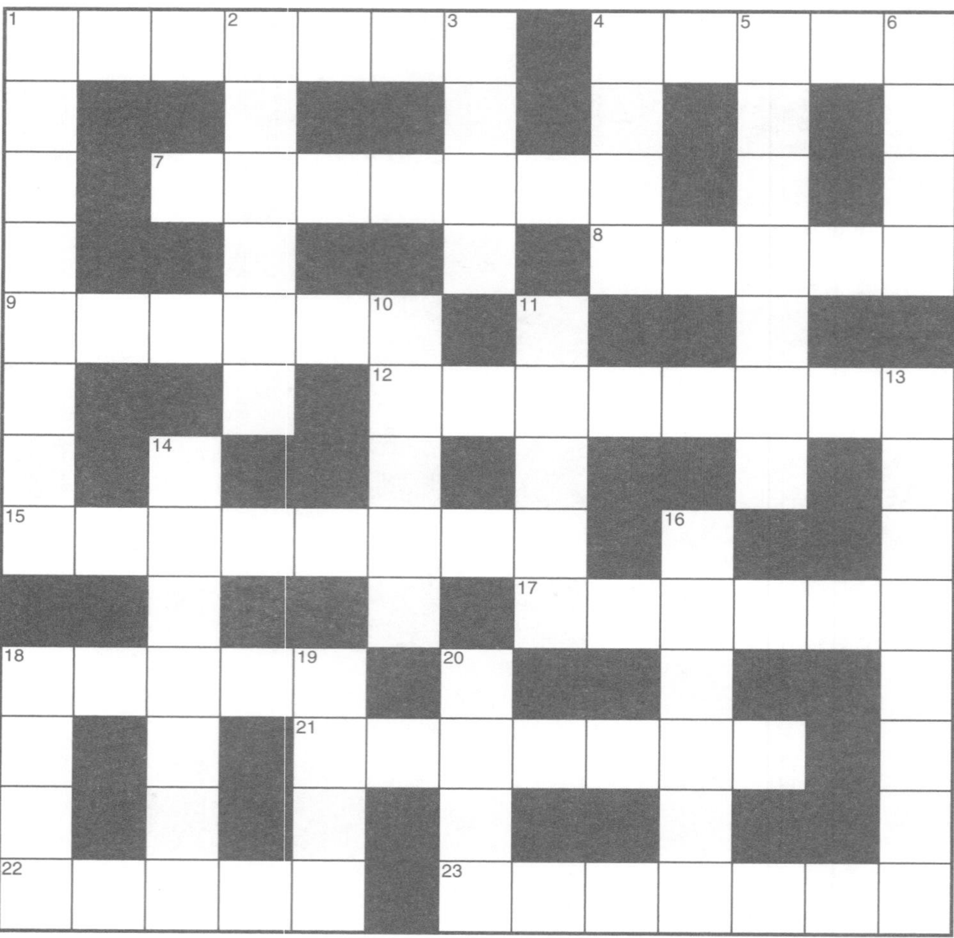

## ACROSS

1. Prehistoric remains
4. Execute (law)
7. Weather characteristics
8. Hired help
9. Flower spores
12. Grow bigger
15. Movie caption
17. Ferret relative
18. Vagrant
21. Prolonged applause
22. Not nice
23. Convent

## DOWN

1. Swimmer's fins
2. Exclusively
3. Clean break
4. Rams' mates
5. Yearbook
6. Slight quarrel
10. Halfway golf hole
11. Wood fastener
13. Convulsions disorder
14. Wears away
16. Large monkey
18. Urban community
19. Small horse
20. Self-regarding

# CROSSWORD 346

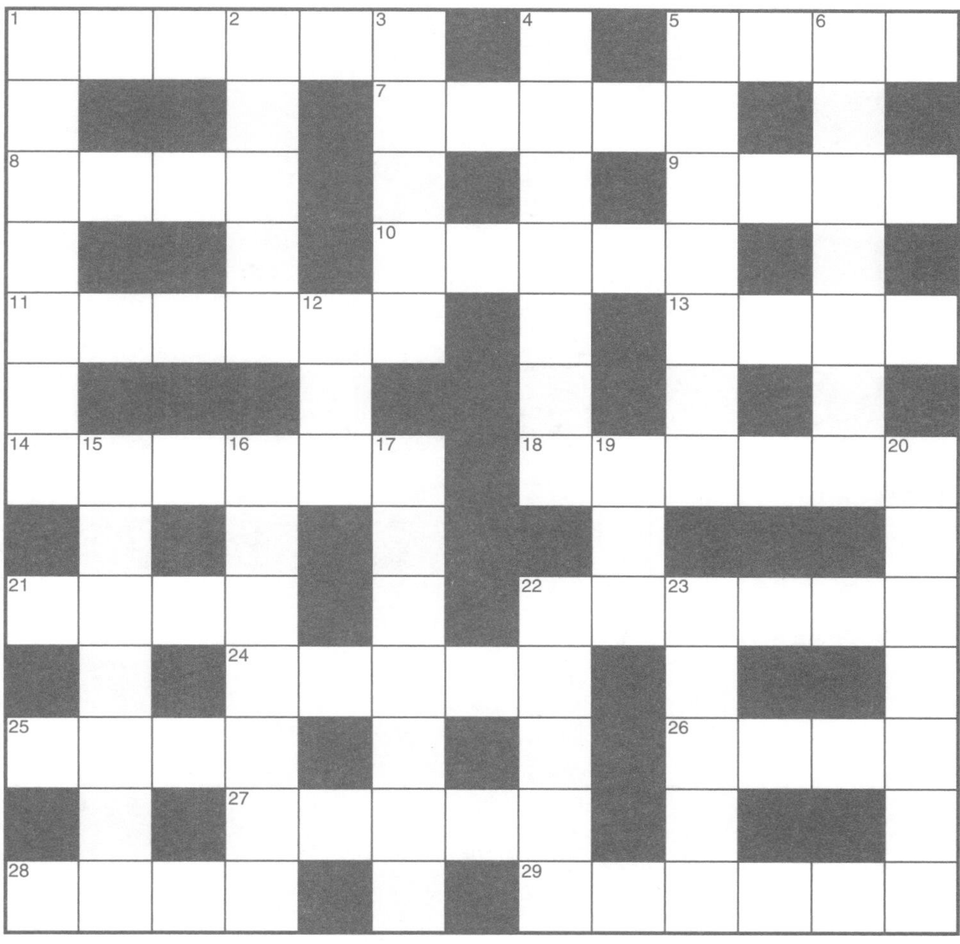

## ACROSS

1. Assortment
5. Irritation
7. Final figure
8. Single sound system
9. Lend to
10. Angry
11. Racial
13. Weight unit
14. Crude huts
18. Wooden hammer
21. Tinted
22. Taken from plane (of photo)
24. Shine (at)
25. Flightless New Zealand bird
26. Horse restraint
27. Sibling's daughter
28. Hand (out)
29. Anxiety condition

## DOWN

1. Hurdlers
2. Carried on breeze
3. Moral principle
4. Level
5. Illicit
6. Farce
12. Annoy
15. Disordered
16. Powerful analgesic
17. Stunned
19. Positive vote
20. Natural skills
22. Foreign
23. Not as common

# CROSSWORD 347

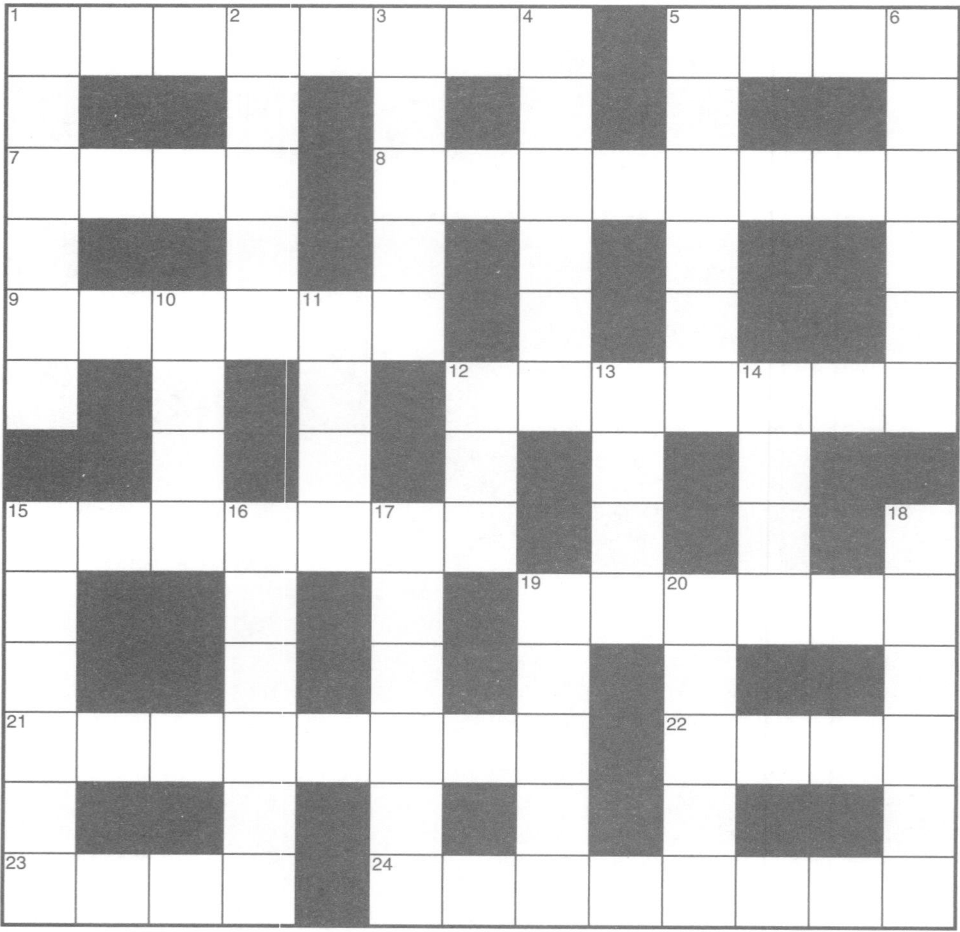

## ACROSS

1. Belief in higher principles
5. Group of three
7. Zodiac crustacean
8. Seepages
9. Signature tunes
12. Held tightly
15. Set up (tent)
19. Retailer
21. Dwells in
22. Radar screen spot
23. Be concerned
24. Bald

## DOWN

1. Provoke
2. CD of songs
3. Small islands
4. More spiteful
5. Grills
6. Unseated
10. Reword
11. Cut (design) with acid
12. Gallivant (about)
13. Pimple rash
14. Ring (of bells)
15. Speaker's platform
16. Faint-hearted person
17. Improve the quality of
18. Petty complaints
19. Japanese snack
20. Clothing tag

# CROSSWORD 348

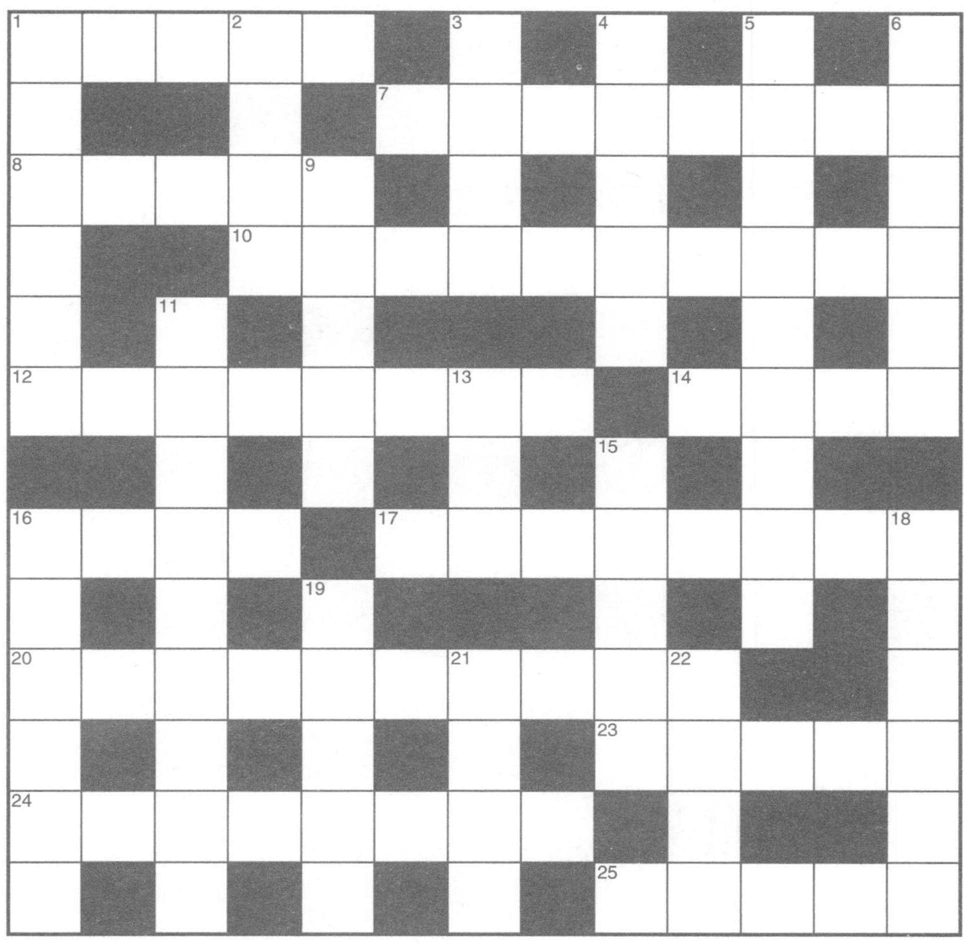

## ACROSS

1. Ethical
7. Orators
8. Ruled (paper)
10. Went without
12. Ambles
14. Ox-like antelopes
16. Unruly crowds
17. Obvious
20. Overly emotional plays
23. Foxtrot or rumba
24. Unnatural
25. Resource

## DOWN

1. Grinding teeth
2. Inspires with reverence
3. Bracing strut
4. Homeless children
5. Revoked
6. Incidental comments
9. Blowpipe missiles
11. Tempestuous
13. Knock sharply
15. Cold side dish
16. Young-suckling animal
18. Most docile
19. Love deeply
21. Leave, go ...
22. Sinks in middle

# CROSSWORD 349

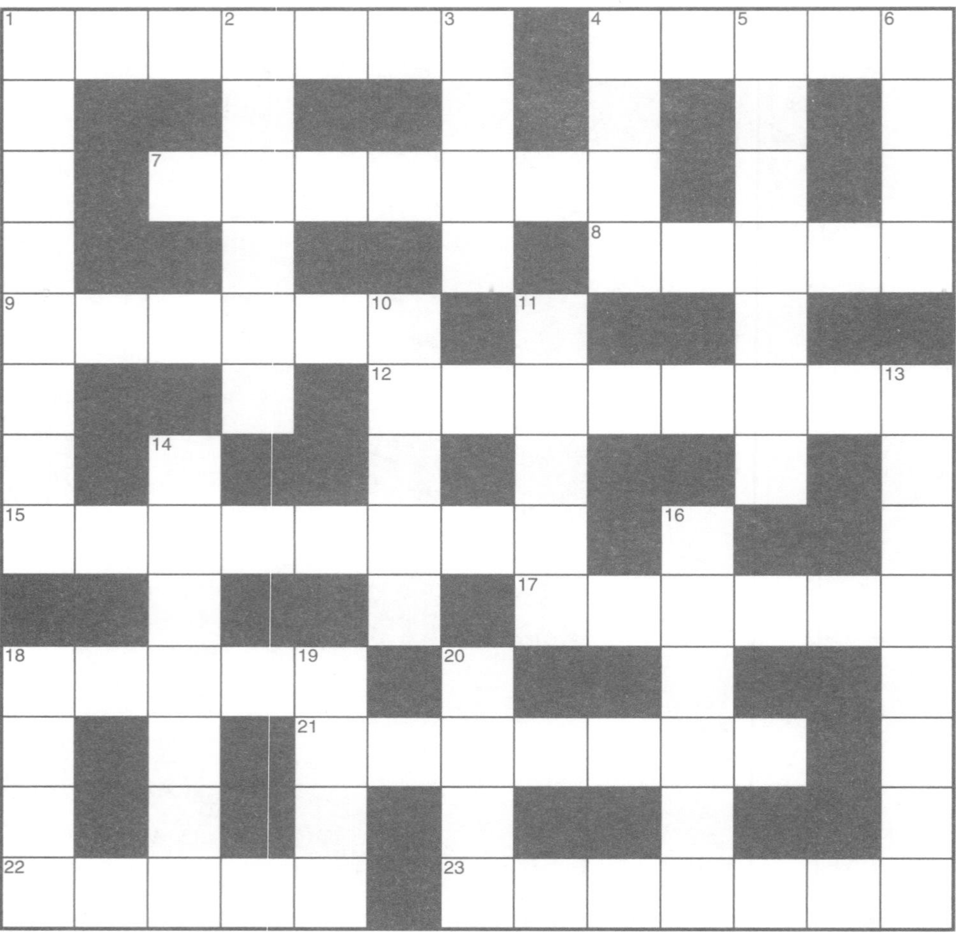

## ACROSS

1. Trainee
4. Opposite of rural
7. Governing body
8. Hanker
9. Pine
12. Proximity
15. Eminence
17. Alpine melodies
18. Open sore
21. Nonprofessional
22. Gentle prod
23. Marked with spots

## DOWN

1. Reclining casually
2. Rampaged
3. Game, ... paper scissors
4. Repulsive
5. Became distended
6. Advertising-light gas
10. Drew to a close
11. Small magical being
13. Fluctuated
14. Very thirsty
16. Modify
18. Onto
19. Hurtle
20. Placid

# CROSSWORD 350

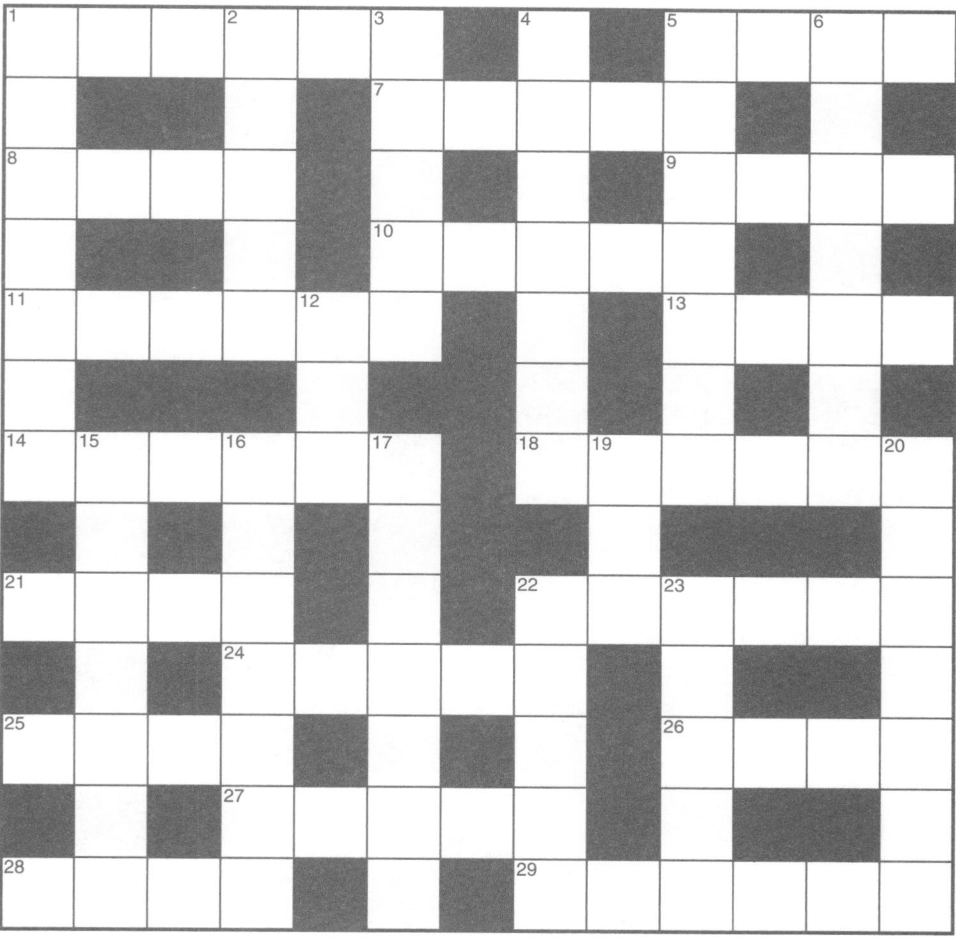

## ACROSS

1. Made insensitive
5. Cleaning bar
7. Diminish
8. Slide violently
9. Hoax
10. Modules
11. Unsystematic
13. Article
14. Speared
18. Exile
21. Sunrise
22. Not transparent
24. Protracted, ... out
25. Of the mouth
26. Bread portion
27. Run off to marry
28. Little terrors
29. Decorative tuft

## DOWN

1. Nasal opening
2. Curved
3. Fact
4. Passenger vehicle
5. Recording period
6. Emerges from sleep
12. Unrefined metal
15. Rearranged word
16. Wax tapers
17. Generators
19. Rock band's sound booster
20. Attentive
22. Beginning (of illness)
23. Collection of charts

# CROSSWORD 351

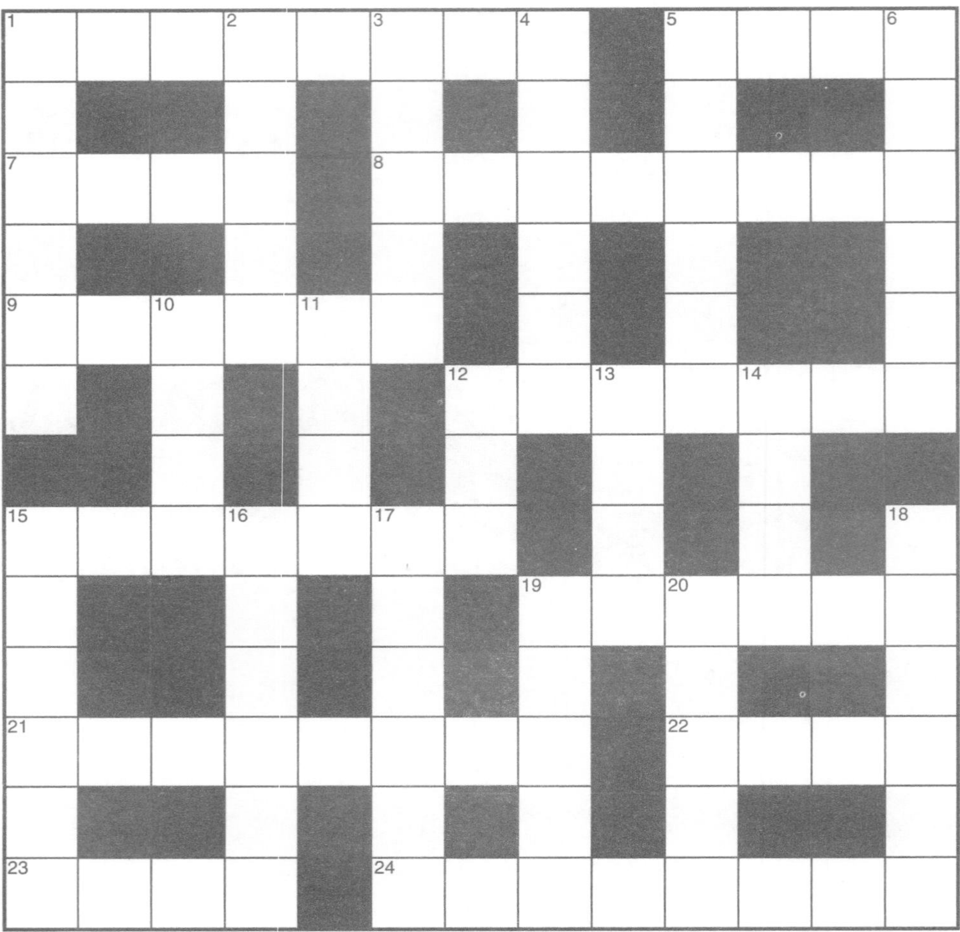

## ACROSS

1. Firearm sounds
5. Hold back
7. Strong cord
8. Tolerable
9. Aside from
12. Medieval farm worker
15. Decomposed
19. Enrages
21. Computer accessory
22. Assistant
23. Trots
24. Vigorous action

## DOWN

1. Stocking band
2. Military blockade
3. Circle (planet)
4. Horse shed
5. Mantras
6. Chicken cut
10. Stylish
11. Hunter's victim
12. Bean container
13. Nameless author
14. Land measure
15. Blacker
16. Courtroom excuses
17. Enclose
18. To the rear
19. Muddle
20. Huge person

# CROSSWORD 352

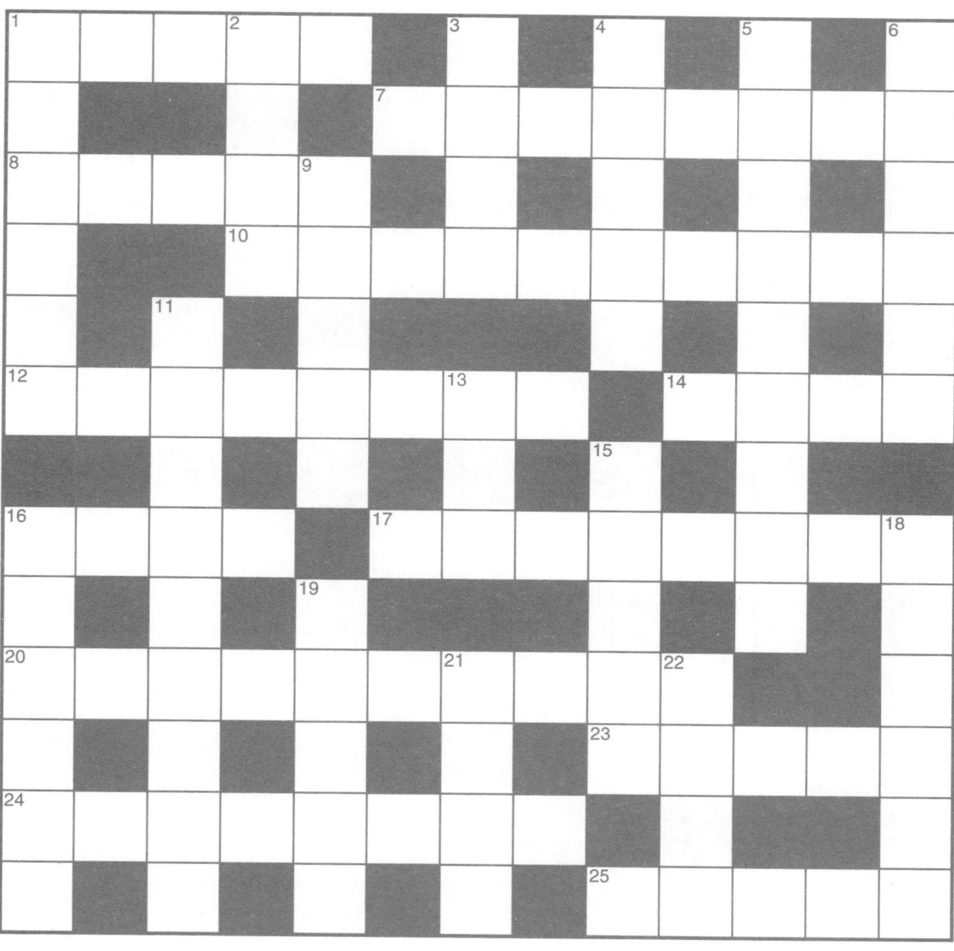

## ACROSS

1. Travel permits
7. Keep apart
8. In the lead
10. Horseracing track
12. Entitling
14. Flabbergast
16. Throb
17. Spread out
20. Unwillingness
23. Fairies
24. Moving (hips)
25. Common

## DOWN

1. Practicable
2. Almost closed
3. This spot
4. Truncheon
5. Bouffant or bob
6. Lower dignity of
9. Loiter
11. Study of body tissue
13. Chill (in the air)
15. Absurdity
16. Feathered darts
18. Main fin
19. Skin of head
21. Father's sister
22. Deer

# CROSSWORD 353

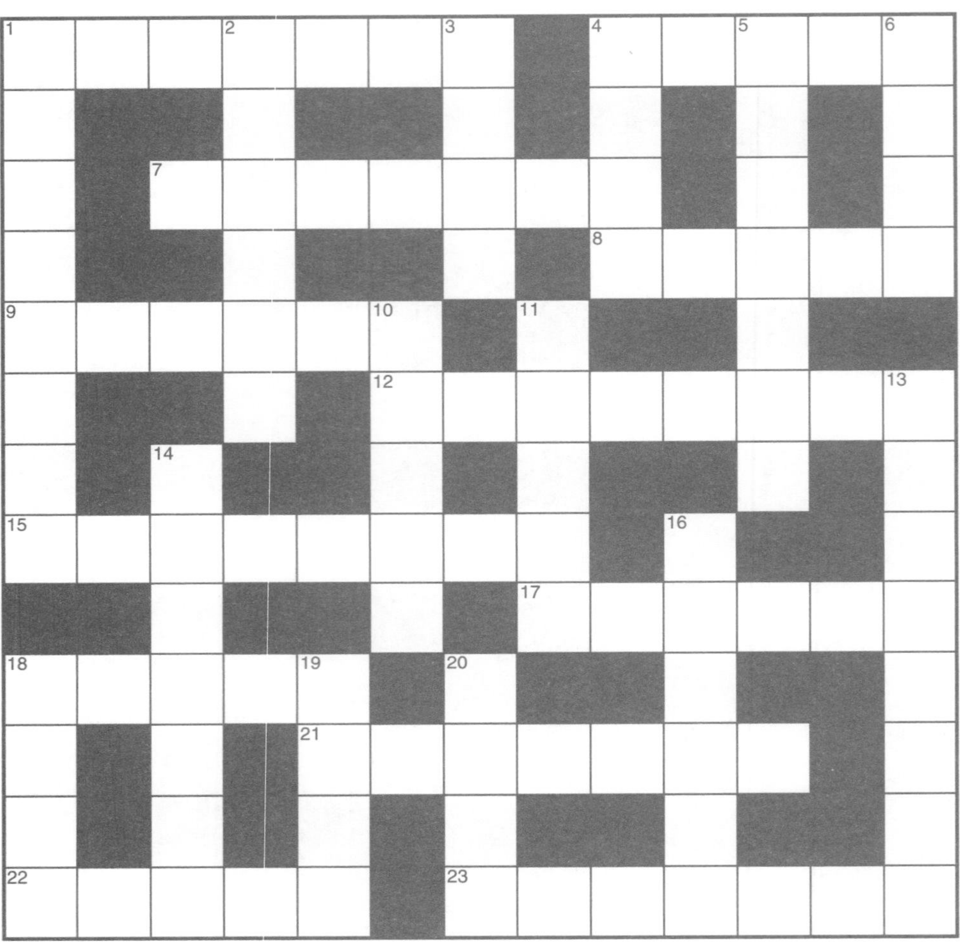

## ACROSS

1. Polar shipping hazard
4. Hang in folds
7. Instruction books
8. Lift with effort
9. Political refuge
12. Conceding
15. Happened repeatedly
17. Wireless crackle
18. Restaurant cooks
21. Holding (party)
22. Shrub border
23. Drains through tube

## DOWN

1. Impersonator
2. Street fights
3. Cattle prod
4. Bowl
5. Water-related
6. Inch (along)
10. One of the Magi's gifts
11. Invasive plants
13. Kind & courteous
14. Conspired
16. Fire (rocket)
18. Notes & coins
19. Footwear item
20. Serpents

# CROSSWORD 354

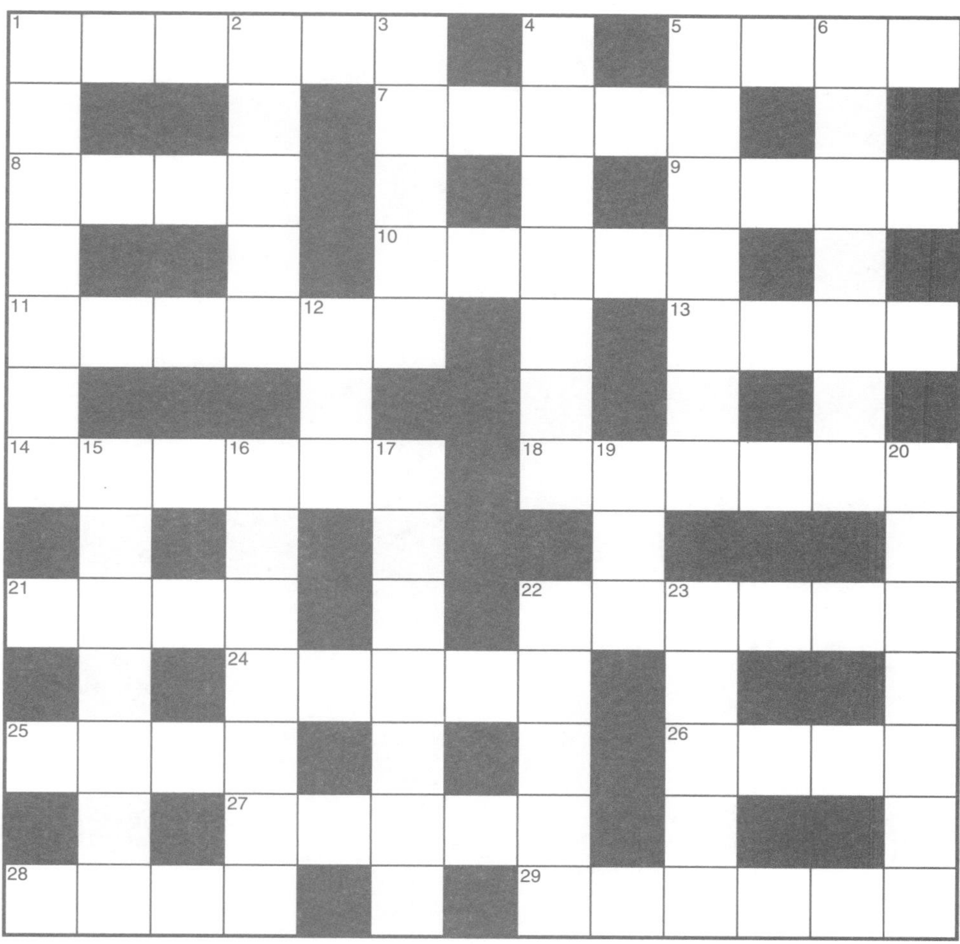

## ACROSS

1. Cooks in oven
5. Assents with head
7. Send abroad in disgrace
8. Large boat
9. Hit sharply
10. Perch
11. Quirks of nature
13. Creative thought
14. Sorrowful poem
18. Illuminates
21. White metal
22. Used fishing rod
24. Written defamation
25. Vagrant
26. Varicose ...
27. Velvety leather
28. Ancient musical instrument
29. Baton races

## DOWN

1. Serene
2. Brown pigment
3. Scorches
4. Of central importance
5. Making twig home
6. Local language
12. Relatives
15. Divorce payment
16. Wrap
17. Topples
19. Charged atom
20. Rail shunting lines
22. Adjust
23. Judge's hammer

# CROSSWORD 355

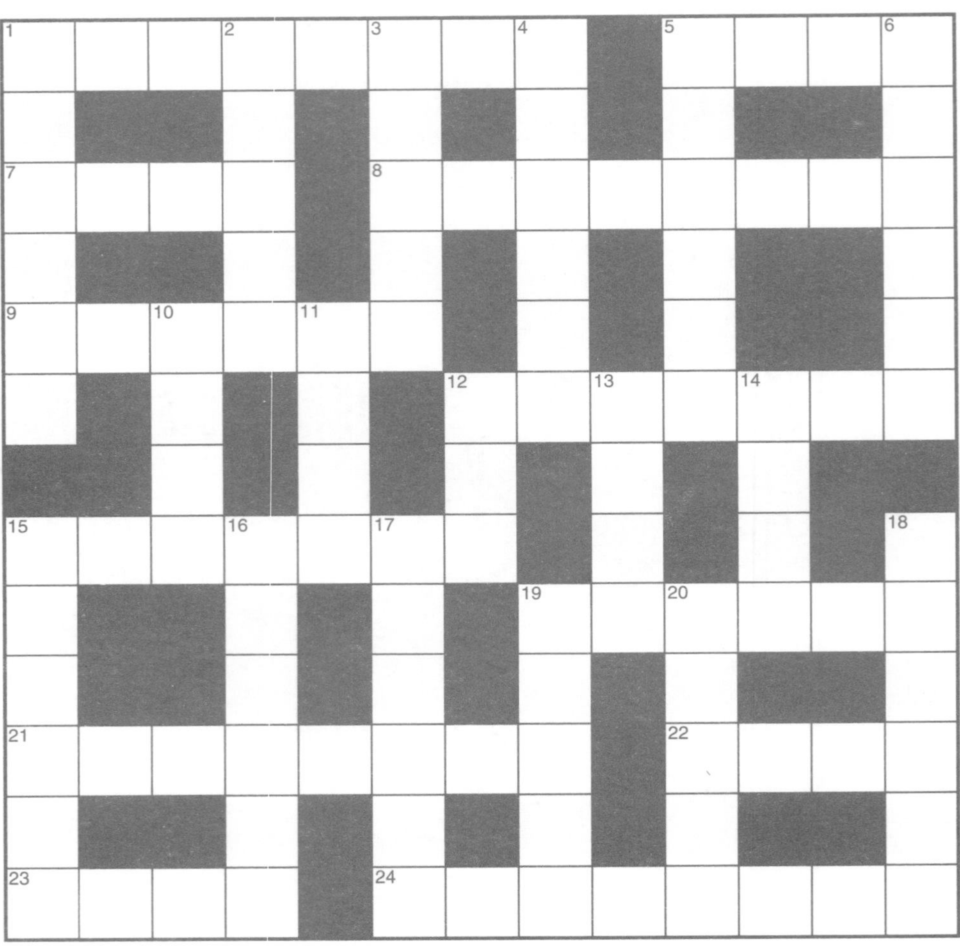

## ACROSS

1. Gathers (troops)
5. Military force
7. Handle
8. Inhibit
9. Fall away
12. Tampered
15. Most indistinct
19. More orderly
21. One million watts
22. Benevolent
23. Want
24. Headfirst descent (4,4)

## DOWN

1. Fabricators
2. Marten fur
3. Be consistent (with)
4. Bun seed
5. Overseas
6. Pulled with a jerk
10. Block (up)
11. Drug (horse)
12. Small floor covering
13. Feast
14. Raise
15. Infestation rodents
16. Unspoken
17. Exert (oneself)
18. Plod
19. Brief letters
20. Invited

# CROSSWORD 356

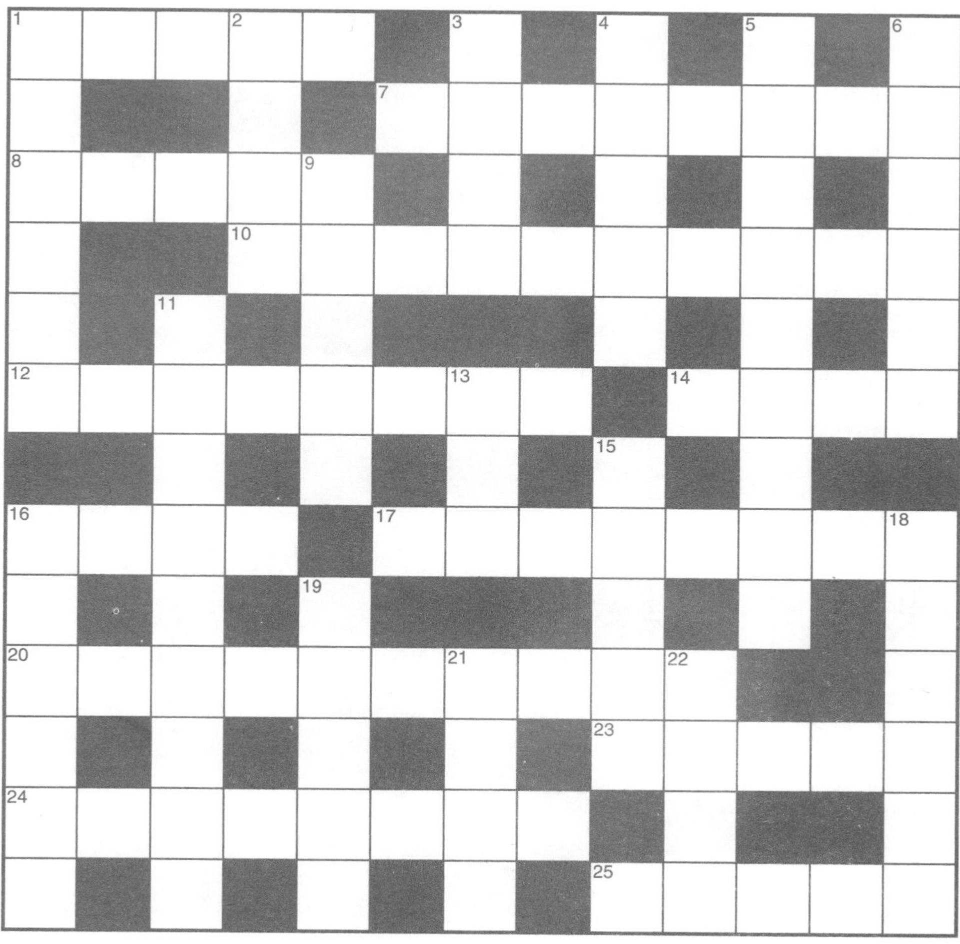

## ACROSS

1. Sailing boat
7. Paltry sum
8. Of hearing
10. Innkeepers
12. Christmas season
14. Tiny insects
16. Shades
17. Held up
20. Corrections
23. Supermarket lane
24. Conscientious
25. Horse

## DOWN

1. Annually
2. Cure
3. Drew
4. Pilfer
5. In a huff
6. Dines well
9. Goes the distance
11. Reportedly
13. Scheduled to arrive
15. Spaghetti or macaroni
16. Amasses stock
18. Rely
19. Proverb
21. Geological eras
22. River sediment

# CROSSWORD 357

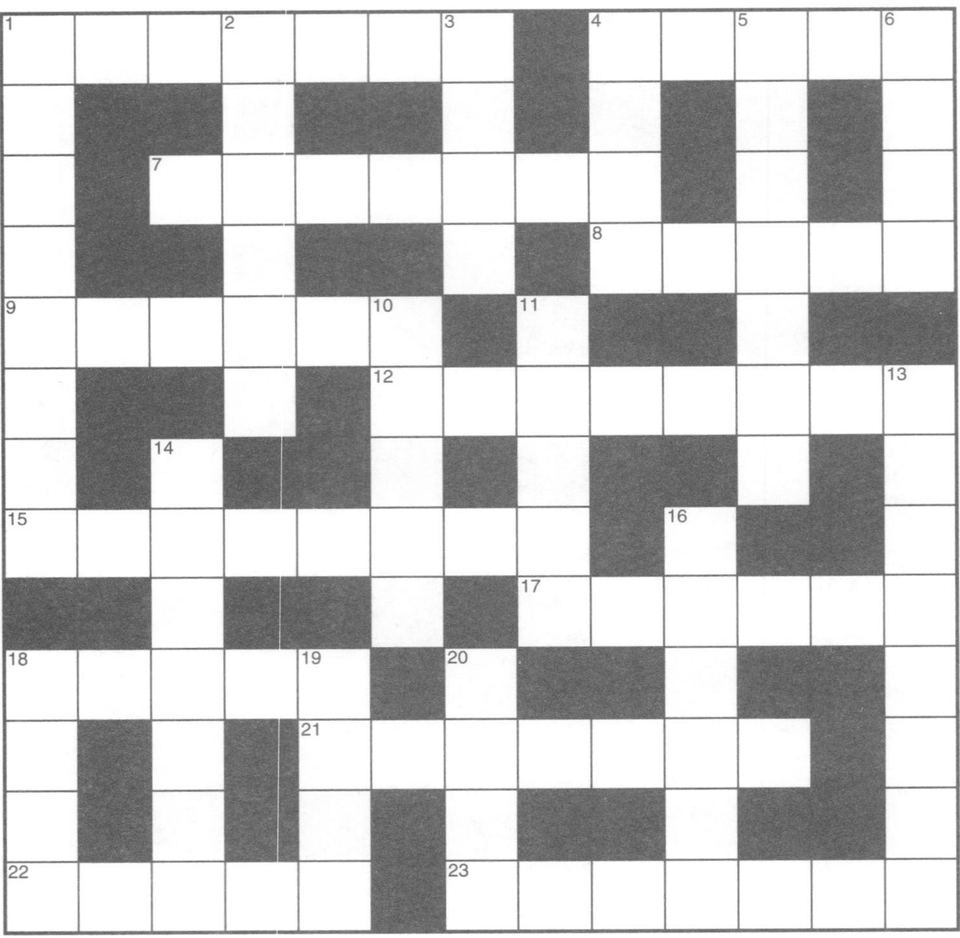

## ACROSS

1. Eddied
4. Sober
7. Generally speaking
8. Depart
9. Amusingly coarse
12. Sold to public
15. Glass fitters
17. Rasping
18. Remove whiskers
21. Stretched (for)
22. Plant stem lumps
23. Go back over (path)

## DOWN

1. Cutting fleece off
2. Disclose
3. Dull
4. Window ledge
5. Genial
6. Valley
10. Dehydrated
11. Stockpile secretly
13. Postponed
14. Attacked viciously
16. Profession
18. Leg bone
19. Makes slip-up
20. Impartial

# CROSSWORD 358

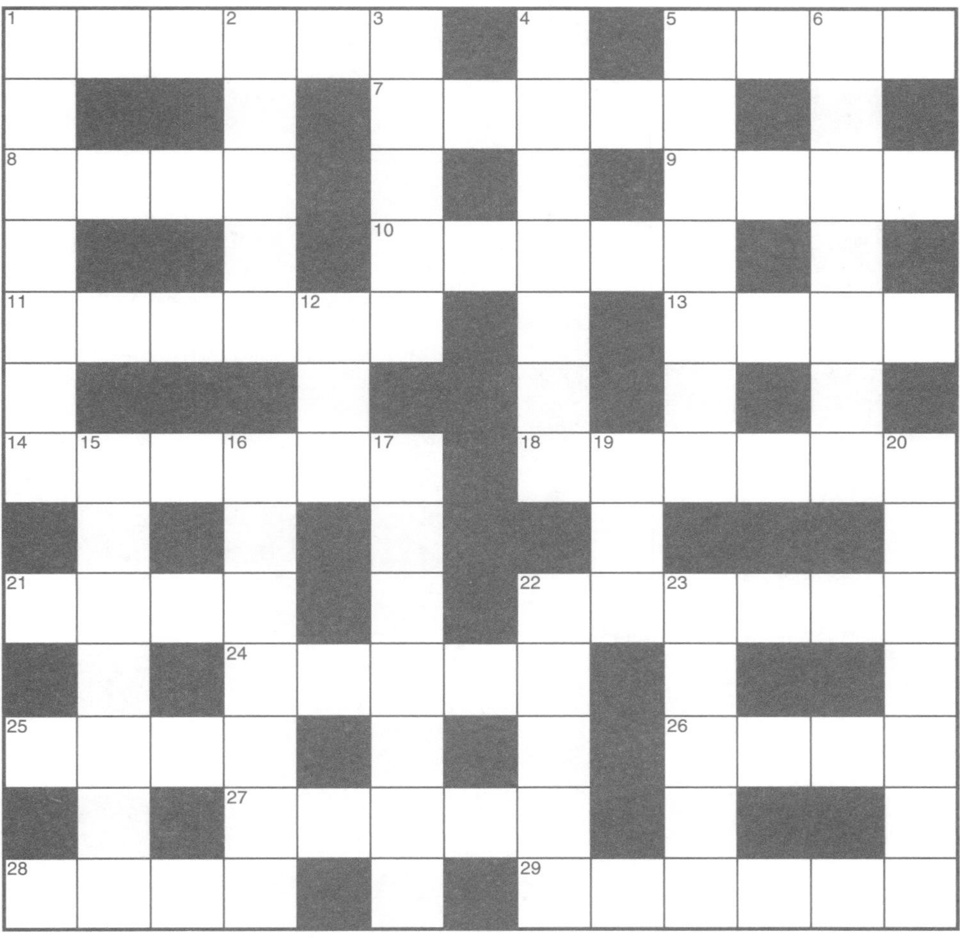

## ACROSS

1. Unfastened
5. Gloom
7. Bring together
8. Insect larva
9. Piece of foliage
10. Solemn ringing of bells
11. Propels
13. Portent
14. Vehicle depot
18. Estimate (damages)
21. Slide
22. Valiant
24. Aunt & ...
25. Saint's disc of light
26. Suitor
27. Dark
28. Lyrical poems
29. Entice

## DOWN

1. Still happening
2. Illustrious
3. Dips into drink
4. Predicament
5. Becomes gentler
6. Magazine subscribers
12. Fallen tree
15. Ungainly
16. Laborious
17. Rigidly
19. Witness (event)
20. Hide
22. Warms
23. Mad (dog)

# CROSSWORD 359

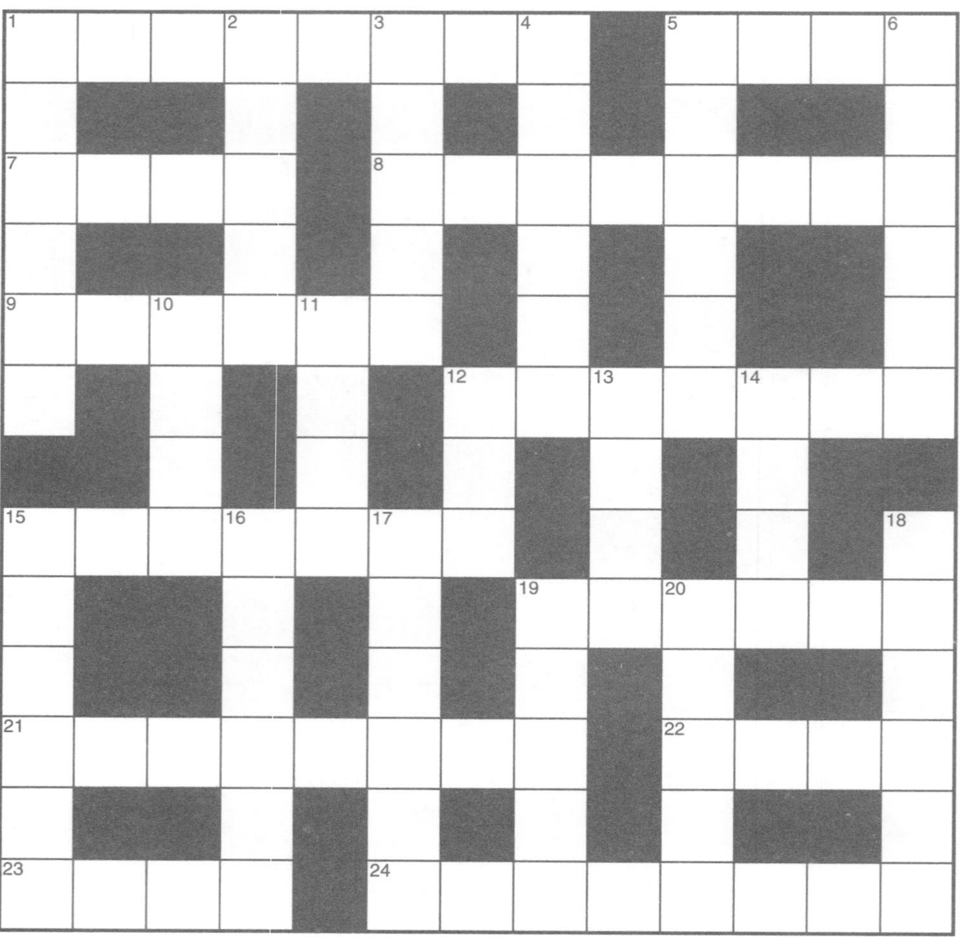

## ACROSS

1. Bird hunted for sport
5. Extinct
7. Pagan statue
8. Vaulting game
9. Talkative
12. Gathered
15. Ruled as monarch
19. Halts
21. Introductory statement
22. Departed
23. Alleviate
24. Sound mufflers

## DOWN

1. Royal offspring
2. Apportion
3. Mixed metal
4. Heartbreaking
5. Sillier
6. Tenacious
10. Against
11. Identical sibling
12. Assistance
13. Baked treat
14. Applications
15. Small wave
16. Spin
17. Able to be eaten
18. Cinema attendants
19. Approving shout
20. Cherub

# CROSSWORD 360

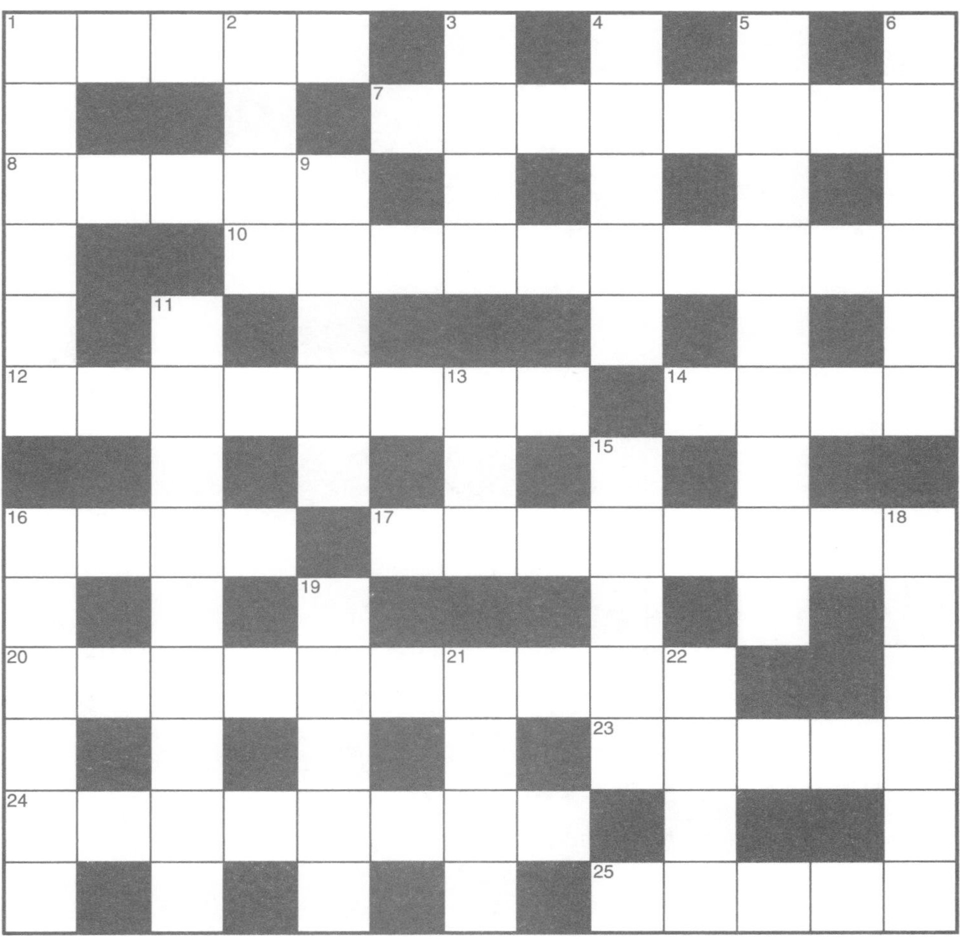

## ACROSS

1. Immerses
7. Contestants
8. Ran in neutral
10. Sealed against moisture
12. Going by (of time)
14. Frozen rain
16. Ship's bottom
17. Pullovers
20. Book custodians
23. Performed play
24. Increase in intensity
25. Ceasefire agreement

## DOWN

1. Repress
2. Was conversant with
3. Largest body joint
4. Holds tightly
5. Introduces new ideas
6. Worthwhile
9. Donald Duck's sweetheart
11. Novel
13. At the present moment
15. Finnish steam bath
16. Orca, ... whale
18. Ice-cream dessert
19. Recover
21. Inside
22. Wound blemish

# CROSSWORD 361

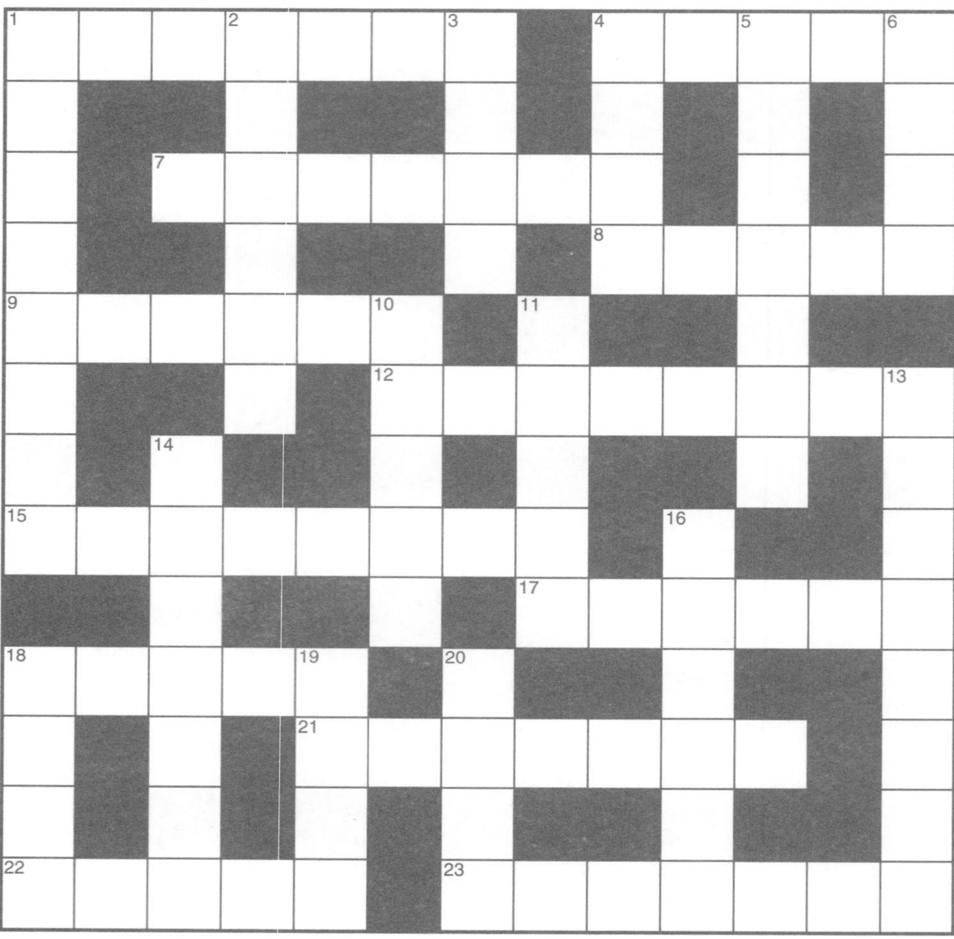

## ACROSS

1. Gland secretion
4. Tremor
7. Recipe
8. Leavening agent
9. Over again
12. Slaughterhouse
15. Rush headlong (of herd)
17. Citrus fruit
18. Cutting utensil
21. Ball-filled seat
22. Frog-like animals
23. Luxury (food)

## DOWN

1. Kidnap victims
2. Tied up (boat)
3. Australian birds
4. Loading wharf
5. Pilot
6. Compass direction
10. Rabbit relatives
11. Small but significant role
13. Respectful
14. Chocolate, strawberry or ...
16. Persian market
18. Make with wool
19. Tide movements, ... & flows
20. Crooned

# CROSSWORD 362

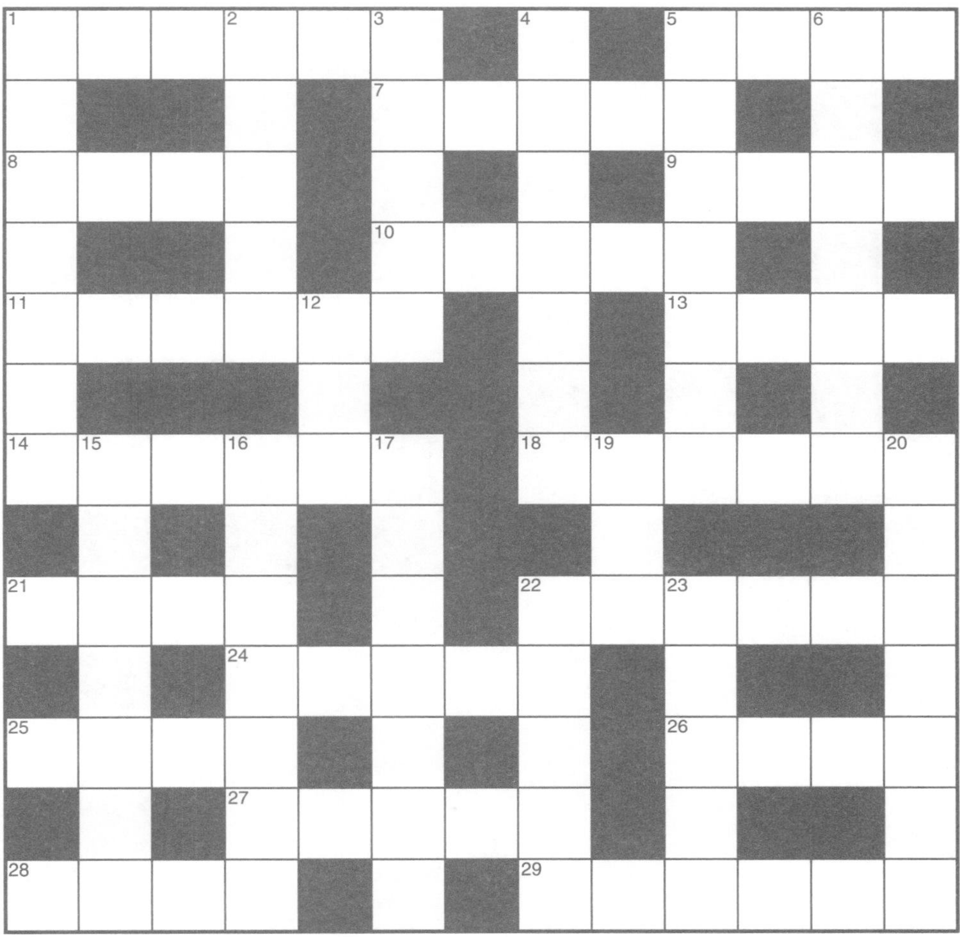

## ACROSS

1. Large Galápagos lizard
5. Theirs & ...
7. Get on (ship)
8. Short-term worker
9. Yellow part of egg
10. Defrosts
11. Sums up
13. Glide aloft
14. Hunting expedition
18. Non-professionals
21. Steamship fuel
22. Sitting down
24. Signified
25. Languish
26. Fewer
27. Hospital sister
28. Membranous sac
29. Oarsmen

## DOWN

1. Keeps as POW
2. ..., beta, gamma
3. Touches at one end
4. Sun shield
5. Eventful trip
6. Liberate
12. For each
15. Expression of regret
16. Affliction
17. Harms
19. Snacked
20. Naturists
22. Guide
23. Entitle

# CROSSWORD 363

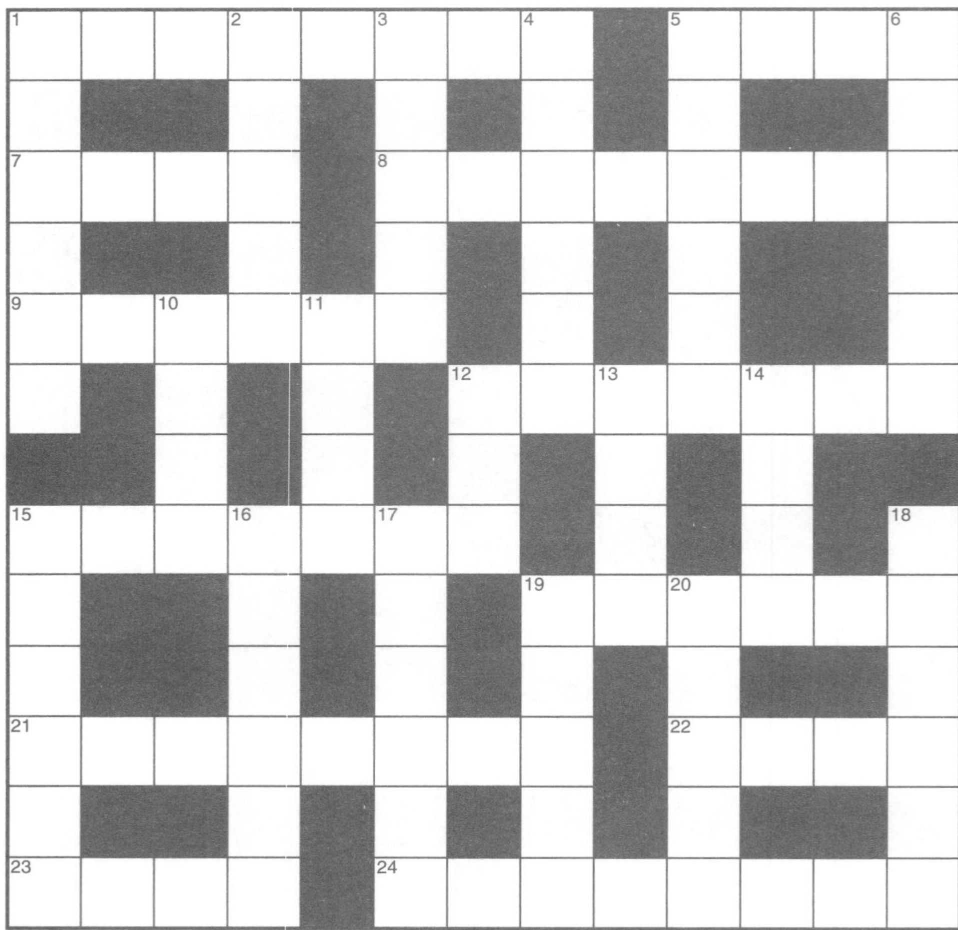

## ACROSS

1. Fibrous tissue
5. Uterus
7. Male pig
8. Straw-roofed
9. Delicate
12. Held tenderly
15. Untitled
19. Go after
21. Intestinal cleanser
22. Medicine amount
23. Hyphen
24. Orderliness

## DOWN

1. Sexual drive
2. Kitchen smock
3. Diary record
4. Merchant
5. Sinful
6. Began to flower
10. Pressing appliance
11. Those people
12. Masticated cow fodder
13. In addition
14. Pause (in storm)
15. Bare
16. Fasten
17. Recruit
18. Chirps
19. Liberated
20. Loaded down

# CROSSWORD 364

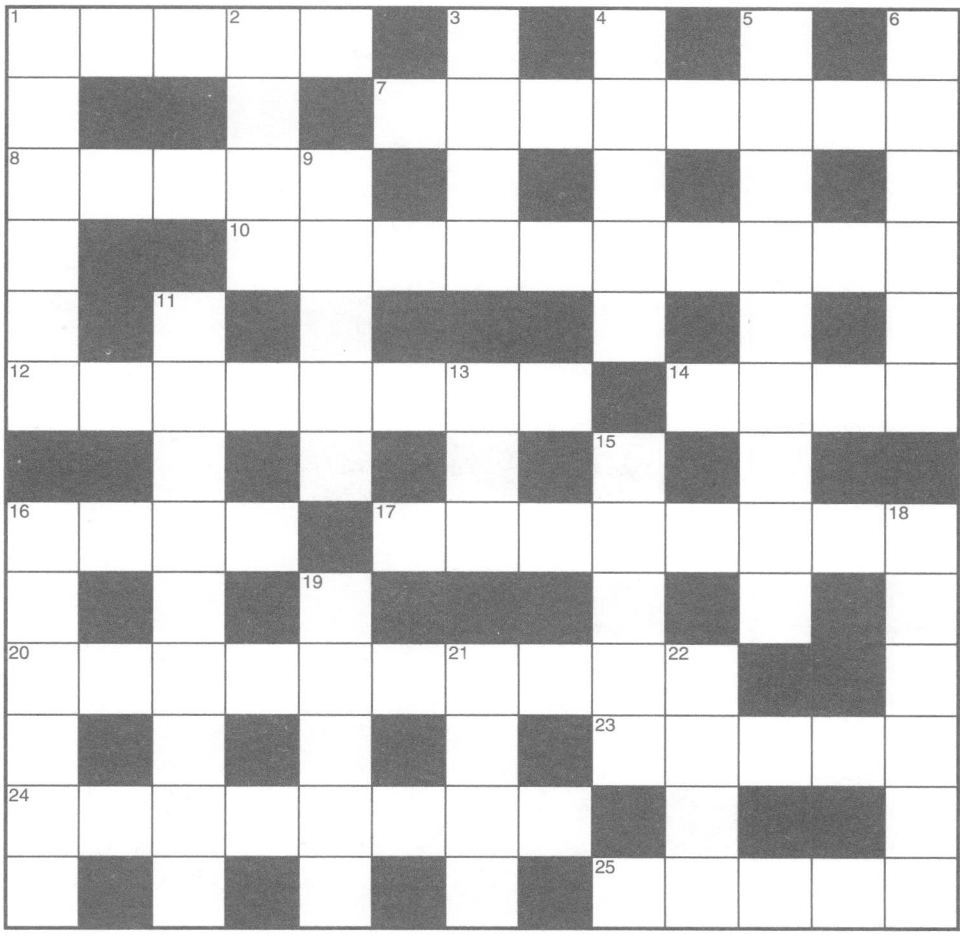

## ACROSS

1. Of birth
7. Strangest
8. Articulate
10. Convalescent home
12. Disgraces
14. Tiny bird
16. ... & queen
17. Hottest (curry)
20. Planning (future events)
23. Stared fixedly
24. Anticipated
25. Biblical prayer

## DOWN

1. Works of fiction
2. Woe!
3. Deep-pitched instrument
4. Citrus fruit
5. Family-lines
6. Flower part
9. Exalts
11. Pawnbrokers' premises
13. Remove branches from
15. Freezing over
16. Affectionate gestures
18. Bicycle for two
19. Official decree
21. Lascivious smirk
22. Practical jokes

# CROSSWORD 365

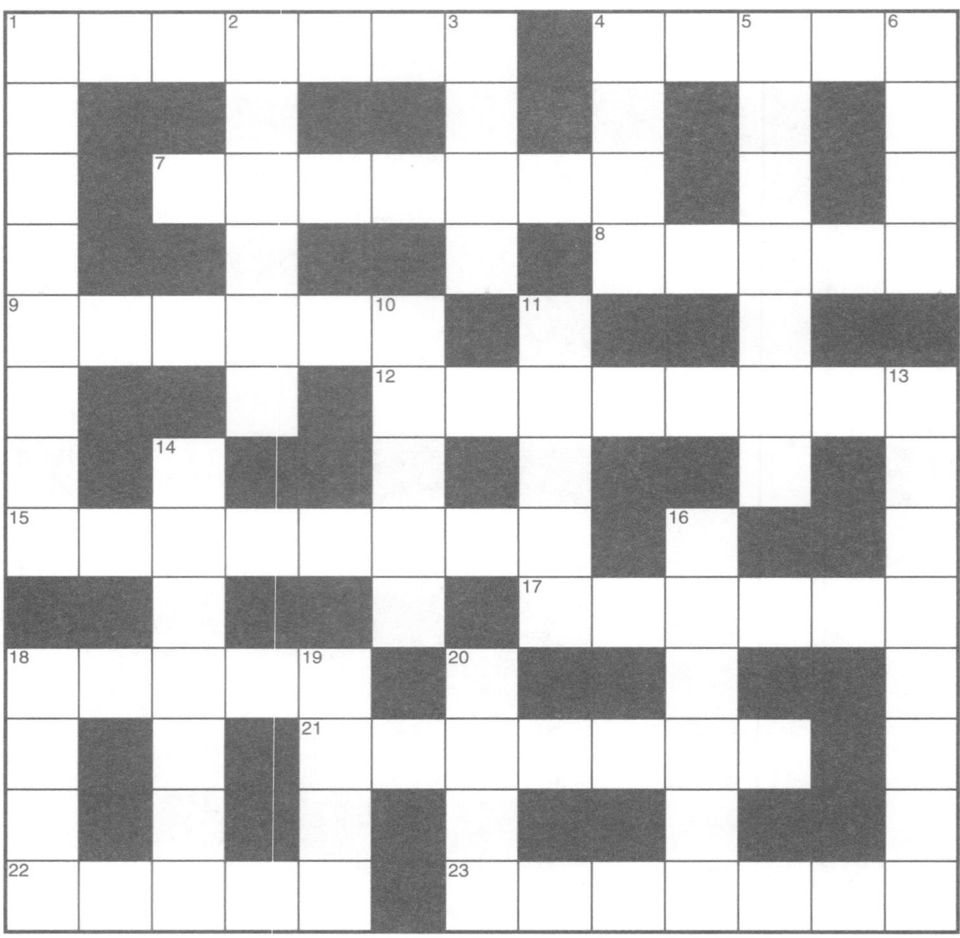

## ACROSS

1. Wandering (tribe)
4. Disobey (rules)
7. Banner
8. Eradicate
9. Channel
12. Re-emerge
15. Passages from text
17. Cried in pain
18. Australian marsupial
21. More tired
22. Ahead of time
23. Snuggled

## DOWN

1. Steer
2. In blossom
3. Cajole
4. Become dim
5. Eight-note intervals
6. Cylinder
10. Explode (of volcano)
11. Fizzy
13. Blushed
14. Paint-removing tool
16. Most cunning
18. Flying toy
19. Askew
20. Young deer

# SOLUTIONS

# SOLUTIONS

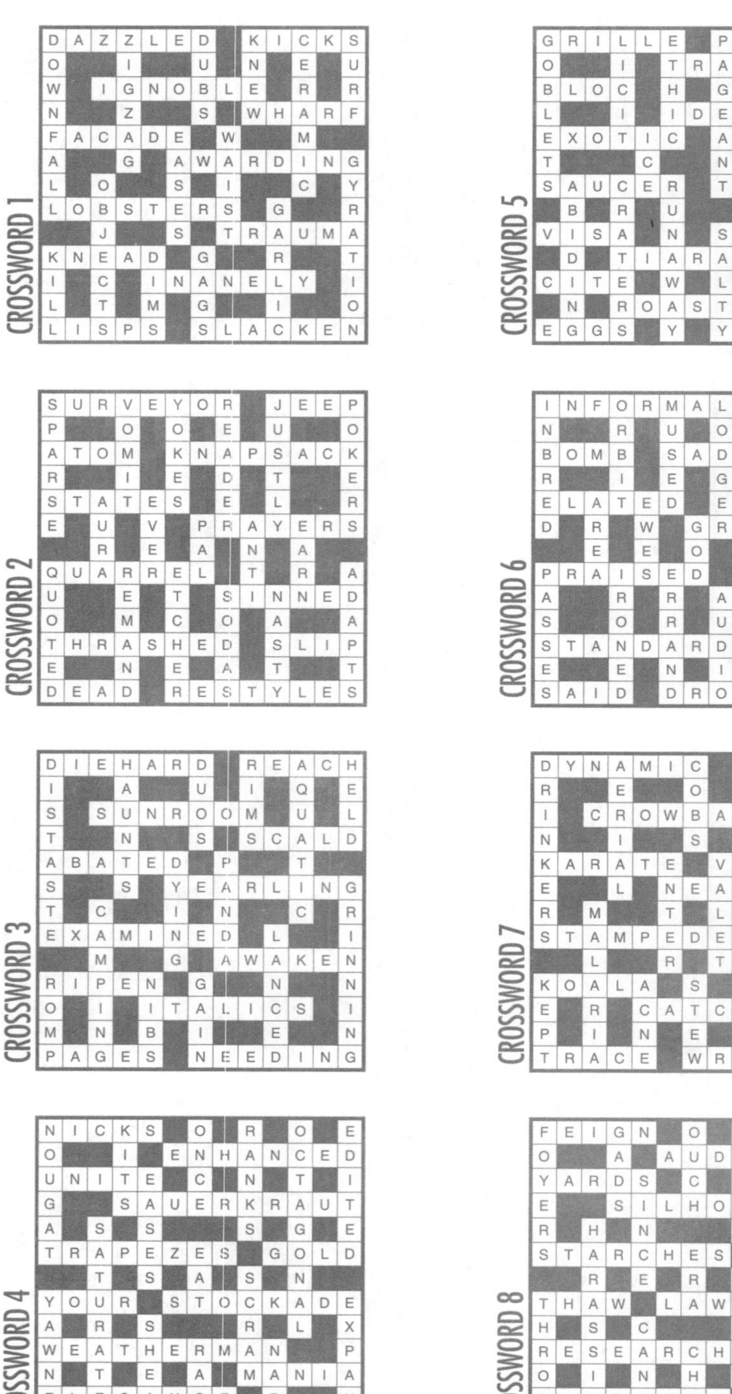
CROSSWORD 1
CROSSWORD 5
CROSSWORD 2
CROSSWORD 6
CROSSWORD 3
CROSSWORD 7
CROSSWORD 4
CROSSWORD 8

# SOLUTIONS

## CROSSWORD 9

H A Z A R D # G # S I T E
A # # M # W H A L E # I #
N U M B # A # M # R I L E
G # # L # R A B B I # L #
M Y S E L F # L # A W E D
A # # # I # # E # L # R #
N A B B E D # D E S I S T
# N # I # O # # Y # # # O
K N I T # U # G E L D E D
# U # U R B A N # E # # D
F I L M # L # A # G I L L
# T # E W E R S # A # # E
H Y M N # S # H E L P E R

## CROSSWORD 10

U L T I M A T E # H U L A
N # # T # R # C # A # # L
F I R E # C O L E S L A W
O # # M # E # A # S # # A
L E A S E D # I # L # # Y
D # G # P # B R E E Z E S
# # O # E # U # C # O # #
J O G G E R S # H # N # I
A # # Y # E # M O D E R N
C # # R # F # O # E # # L
K N E A D I N G # S O Y A
A # # T # N # U # K # # N
L A T E # E N L I S T E D

## CROSSWORD 11

I M P A L E D # O R A T E
N # # N # # E # V # B # L
S # I S O L A T E # S # M
O # # W # # N # N E C K S
L E G E N D # A # # E # #
E # # R # U N B I A S E D
N # C # # M # E # # S # I
T R A N S M I T # T # # T
# # P # # Y # S T A T I C
O V A R Y # T # # V # # H
N # B # O R A N G E S # I
T # L # G # P # # R # # N
O P E R A # S I G N I N G

## CROSSWORD 12

L O O K S # A # S # D # A
O # # I # E J E C T I O N
A B O D E # A # O # S # O
N # # S A C R I F I C E D
E # F # R # # # F # U # E
D A I N T I E R # A S P S
# # R # H # L # L # S # #
B A S H # O F F I C E R S
A # T # V # # # L # S # E
N O B L E W O M A N # # E
D # O # R # A # C A K E D
I R R I G A T E # M # # E
T # N # E # S # R E D I D

## CROSSWORD 13

R E G G A E # A # R A F T
E # # O # V O D K A # A #
H E I R # I # V # I N C H
O # # G # C R A W L # T #
U R G E N T # N # I R I S
S # # # I # # C # N # O #
E A S E L S # E G G I N G
# V # S # E # # N # # # I
H O S T # T # C U B I N G
# I # E M B E R # R # # G
I D L E # A # O # O V A L
# E # M A C H O # A # # E
A D D S # K # N O D D E D

## CROSSWORD 14

C A L A M A R I # P U F F
Y # # N # P # N # L # # L
G R I N # P A S S A B L E
N # # U # L # T # S # # X
E V O L V E # E # M # # E
T # X # A # U P D A T E D
# # E # N # R # A # H # #
V E N I S O N # T # U # A
O # # S # C # N A G G E D
I # # L # C # I # A # # D
C R E A T U R E # B E L L
E # # N # R # C # L # # E
D Y E D # S K E W E R E D

## CROSSWORD 15

S A F A R I S # D O V E S
T # # B # # O # A # O # U
R # N O T A B L Y # Y # R
A # # A # # S # S T A F F
Y E A R N S # P # # G # #
I # # D # T R A I N E R S
N # M # # E # Y # # S # H
G R A D U A T E # C # # A
# # T # # M # E V A D E D
E X A M S # L # # N # # O
L # D # E V E N I N G # W
S # O # A # I # # E # # E
E R R O R # S T U D I E D

## CROSSWORD 16

Q U A Y S # S # L # A # T
U # # E # S T R A D D L E
E Q U A L # U # S # O # N
U # # R A I N S T O R M S
E # C # M # # # S # A # E
D R A M A T I C # S T U D
# # T # S # R # P # I # #
F L A T # S E N A T O R S
U # R # S # # # S # N # U
S T A L A G M I T E # # P
I # C # U # I # E A G L E
N O T I C I N G # R # # R
G # S # E # I # B L U R B

# SOLUTIONS

## CROSSWORD 17

| N | A | T | I | O | N |  | S |  | K | I | C | K |
|---|---|---|---|---|---|---|---|---|---|---|---|---|
| E |  |  | N |  | U | N | C | L | E |  | O |  |
| U | L | N | A |  | D |  | O |  | E | B | B | S |
| T |  |  | N |  | E | Q | U | I | P |  | W |  |
| R | U | P | E | E | S |  | R |  | E | K | E | S |
| A |  |  |  | R |  |  | E |  | R |  | B |  |
| L | A | N | D | E | D |  | R | E | S | I | S | T |
|  | G |  | O |  | O |  |  | G |  |  |  | E |
| G | I | R | L |  | M |  | I | O | D | I | N | E |
|  | T |  | P | L | A | I | N |  | O |  |  | T |
| L | A | S | H |  | I |  | T |  | U | R | G | E |
|  | T |  | I | N | N | E | R |  | G |  |  | R |
| V | E | I | N |  | S |  | O | T | H | E | R | S |

## CROSSWORD 18

| T | H | A | T | C | H | E | D |  | G | A | L | A |
|---|---|---|---|---|---|---|---|---|---|---|---|---|
| I |  |  | A |  | I |  | I |  | O |  |  | N |
| G | A | R | B |  | D | E | R | I | S | I | O | N |
| E |  |  | L |  | E |  | E |  | S |  |  | A |
| R | E | B | E | L | S |  | C |  | I |  |  | L |
| S |  | O |  | O |  | S | T | A | P | L | E | S |
|  |  | A |  | A |  | K |  | R |  | O |  |  |
| T | H | R | I | F | T | Y |  | I |  | I |  | U |
| E |  |  | N |  | W |  | P | A | I | N | E | D |
| N |  |  | W |  | E |  | E |  | N |  |  | D |
| D | E | T | A | I | L | E | D |  | F | L | E | E |
| E |  |  | R |  | V |  | A |  | E |  |  | R |
| R | A | I | D |  | E | N | L | A | R | G | E | S |

## CROSSWORD 19

| G | R | O | V | E | L | S |  | Y | E | A | S | T |
|---|---|---|---|---|---|---|---|---|---|---|---|---|
| Y |  |  | I |  |  | C |  | A |  | E |  | O |
| M |  | A | C | C | L | A | I | M |  | R |  | E |
| K |  |  | T |  |  | R |  | S | L | O | P | S |
| H | E | L | I | U | M |  | T |  |  | B |  |  |
| A |  |  | M |  | I | N | A | C | T | I | V | E |
| N |  | N |  |  | M |  | N |  |  | C |  | M |
| A | M | A | S | S | I | N | G |  | S |  |  | I |
|  |  | I |  |  | C |  | Y | A | C | H | T | S |
| R | O | V | E | D |  | H |  |  | E |  |  | S |
| O |  | E |  | I | M | A | G | I | N | E |  | I |
| O |  | L |  | R |  | L |  |  | T |  |  | O |
| M | A | Y | B | E |  | O | A | R | S | M | A | N |

## CROSSWORD 20

| L | O | C | A | L |  | N |  | S |  | S |  | A |
|---|---|---|---|---|---|---|---|---|---|---|---|---|
| O |  |  | N |  | P | A | D | L | O | C | K | S |
| F | L | O | O | R |  | I |  | O |  | A |  | C |
| T |  |  | N | E | G | L | I | G | I | B | L | E |
| E |  | P |  | N |  |  |  | S |  | B |  | N |
| D | E | A | F | E | N | E | D |  | H | A | R | D |
|  |  | C |  | W |  | M |  | A |  | R |  |  |
| W | O | K | S |  | O | U | T | M | O | D | E | D |
| A |  | A |  | A |  |  |  | B |  | S |  | A |
| V | I | G | I | L | A | N | T | E | S |  |  | W |
| E |  | I |  | P |  | O |  | R | A | T | E | D |
| R | A | N | C | H | E | R | S |  | G |  |  | L |
| S |  | G |  | A |  | M |  | I | S | S | U | E |

## CROSSWORD 21

| P | R | E | A | C | H |  | L |  | R | O | A | D |
|---|---|---|---|---|---|---|---|---|---|---|---|---|
| L |  |  | L |  | A | W | A | S | H |  | N |  |
| E | V | I | L |  | T |  | Z |  | U | N | I | T |
| A |  |  | O |  | C | L | I | M | B |  | M |  |
| T | W | I | T | C | H |  | E |  | A | W | A | Y |
| E |  |  |  | U |  |  | S |  | R |  | T |  |
| D | U | S | T | E | R |  | T | A | B | L | E | T |
|  | N |  | H |  | E |  |  | Y |  |  |  | I |
| E | N | V | Y |  | M |  | S | E | E | I | N | G |
|  | E |  | R | E | A | L | M |  | R |  |  | H |
| T | R | I | O |  | T |  | A |  | A | B | U | T |
|  | V |  | I | N | C | U | R |  | S |  |  | E |
| S | E | N | D |  | H |  | T | R | E | M | O | R |

## CROSSWORD 22

| V | O | L | A | T | I | L | E |  | Q | U | A | D |
|---|---|---|---|---|---|---|---|---|---|---|---|---|
| O |  |  | W |  | D |  | N |  | U |  |  | E |
| T | U | N | A |  | I | N | C | R | E | A | S | E |
| I |  |  | R |  | O |  | A |  | S |  |  | P |
| N | E | W | E | S | T |  | S |  | T |  |  | L |
| G |  | O |  | E |  | B | E | A | S | T | L | Y |
|  |  | M |  | M |  | I |  | L |  | U |  |  |
| F | I | B | B | I | N | G |  | S |  | S |  | S |
| L |  |  | R |  | A |  | P | O | C | K | E | T |
| O |  |  | A |  | T |  | O |  | U |  |  | A |
| O | U | T | C | R | I | E | S |  | T | O | M | B |
| D |  |  | E |  | V |  | E |  | E |  |  | L |
| S | L | I | D |  | E | N | S | H | R | I | N | E |

## CROSSWORD 23

| O | R | G | A | N | I | C |  | M | O | P | E | S |
|---|---|---|---|---|---|---|---|---|---|---|---|---|
| B |  |  | F |  |  | O |  | U |  | I |  | O |
| L |  | E | F | F | E | C | T | S |  | R |  | R |
| I |  |  | R |  |  | K |  | K | N | A | V | E |
| V | A | C | A | T | E |  | D |  |  | T |  |  |
| I |  |  | Y |  | M | E | A | N | D | E | R | S |
| O |  | C |  |  | B |  | I |  |  | S |  | Y |
| N | E | A | T | N | E | S | S |  | G |  |  | N |
|  |  | P |  |  | D |  | Y | E | L | P | E | D |
| K | N | E | E | S |  | S |  |  | I |  |  | R |
| N |  | R |  | T | R | A | G | E | D | Y |  | O |
| E |  | E |  | O |  | G |  |  | E |  |  | M |
| W | I | D | O | W |  | O | U | T | D | O | N | E |

## CROSSWORD 24

| H | U | M | A | N |  | S |  | L |  | S |  | A |
|---|---|---|---|---|---|---|---|---|---|---|---|---|
| A |  |  | I |  | E | M | B | A | R | K | E | D |
| G | E | A | R | S |  | O |  | I |  | E |  | O |
| G |  |  | S | O | N | G | W | R | I | T | E | R |
| I |  | J |  | L |  |  |  | S |  | C |  | N |
| S | E | A | F | A | R | E | R |  | T | H | U | S |
|  |  | Y |  | R |  | E |  | W |  | I |  |  |
| D | O | W | N |  | A | L | L | I | A | N | C | E |
| E |  | A |  | A |  |  |  | N |  | G |  | X |
| B | I | L | L | B | O | A | R | D | S |  |  | I |
| R |  | K |  | A |  | C |  | Y | A | N | K | S |
| I | D | E | N | T | I | T | Y |  | G |  |  | T |
| S |  | D |  | E |  | S |  | F | A | W | N | S |

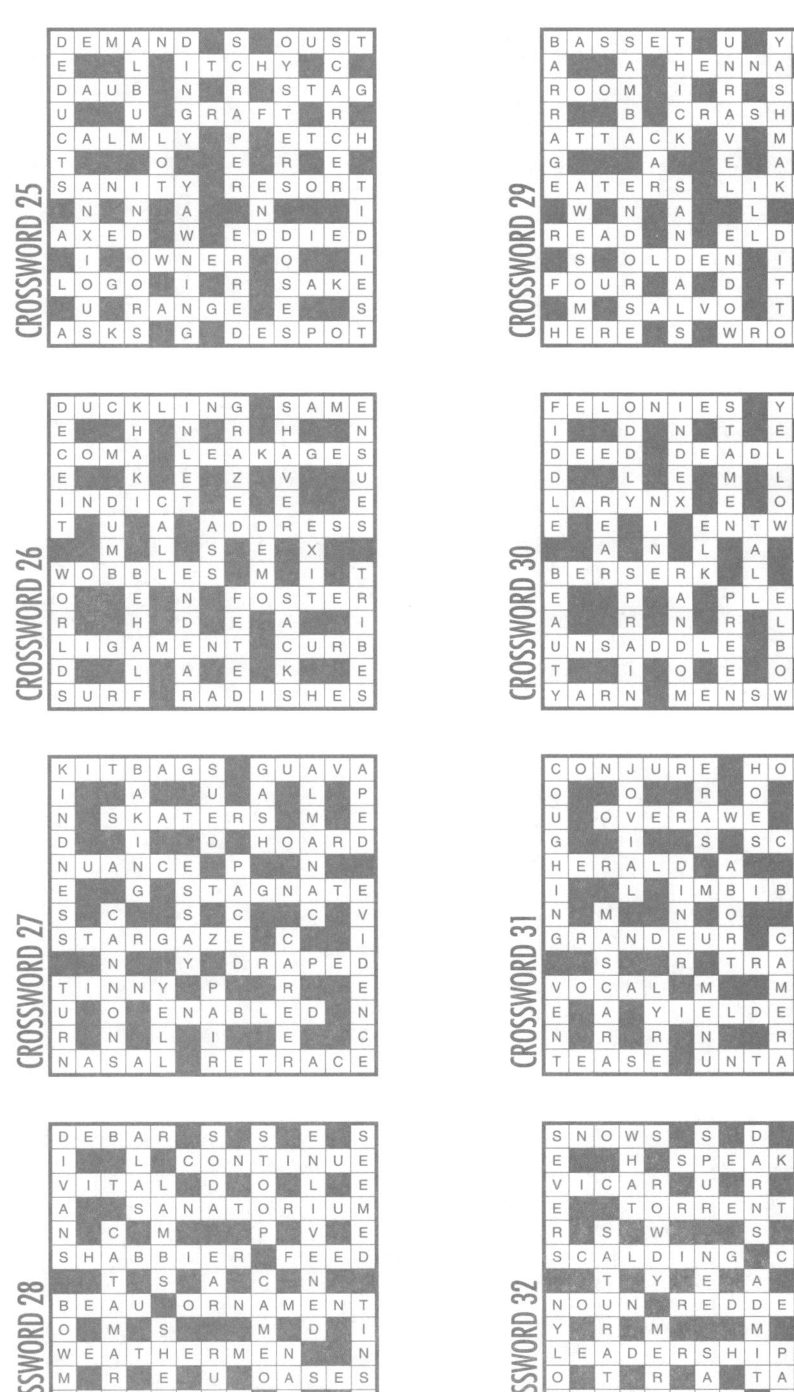
CROSSWORD 25
CROSSWORD 26
CROSSWORD 27
CROSSWORD 28
CROSSWORD 29
CROSSWORD 30
CROSSWORD 31
CROSSWORD 32

# SOLUTIONS

## CROSSWORD 33

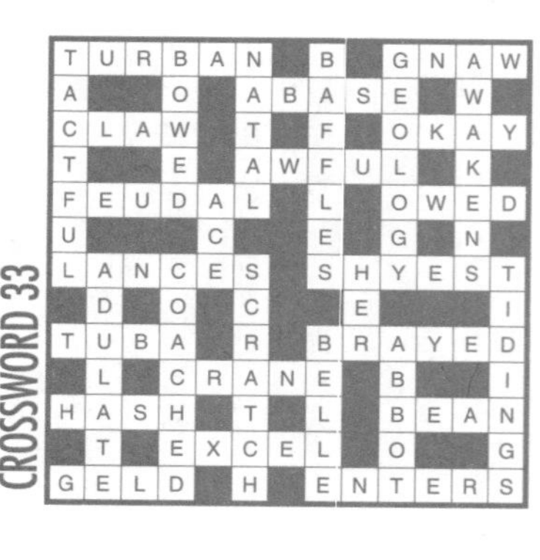

| T | U | R | B | A | N |  | B |  | G | N | A | W |
|---|---|---|---|---|---|---|---|---|---|---|---|---|
| A |  |  | O |  | A | B | A | S | E |  | W |  |
| C | L | A | W |  | T |  | F |  | O | K | A | Y |
| T |  |  | E |  | A | W | F | U | L |  | K |  |
| F | E | U | D | A | L |  | L |  | O | W | E | D |
| U |  |  |  | C |  |  | E |  | G |  | N |  |
| L | A | N | C | E | S |  | S | H | Y | E | S | T |
|  | D |  | O |  | C |  |  | E |  |  |  | I |
| T | U | B | A |  | R |  | B | R | A | Y | E | D |
|  | L |  | C | R | A | N | E |  | B |  |  | I |
| H | A | S | H |  | T |  | L |  | B | E | A | N |
|  | T |  | E | X | C | E | L |  | O |  |  | G |
| G | E | L | D |  | H |  | E | N | T | E | R | S |

## CROSSWORD 34

| N | O | W | A | D | A | Y | S |  | P | L | E | A |
|---|---|---|---|---|---|---|---|---|---|---|---|---|
| O |  |  | I |  | L |  | E |  | U |  |  | M |
| D | I | E | D |  | I | N | C | U | B | A | T | E |
| U |  |  | E |  | E |  | U |  | L |  |  | N |
| L | E | A | D | E | N |  | R |  | I |  |  | D |
| E |  | Q |  | A |  | R | E | A | C | H | E | S |
|  |  | U |  | C |  | O |  | L |  | U |  |  |
| P | O | A | C | H | E | D |  | T |  | N |  | E |
| I |  |  | U |  | D |  | P | O | E | T | R | Y |
| C |  |  | R |  | G |  | I |  | X |  |  | E |
| N | E | G | A | T | I | V | E |  | P | O | O | L |
| I |  |  | T |  | E |  | T |  | E |  |  | E |
| C | A | M | E |  | R | O | Y | A | L | I | S | T |

## CROSSWORD 35

| H | U | R | T | F | U | L |  | S | T | A | I | D |
|---|---|---|---|---|---|---|---|---|---|---|---|---|
| E |  |  | Y |  |  | E |  | E |  | T |  | R |
| A |  | U | P | S | T | A | R | T |  | T |  | U |
| D |  |  | I |  |  | N |  | S | L | A | N | G |
| A | T | O | N | E | D |  | I |  |  | I |  |  |
| C |  |  | G |  | R | E | M | N | A | N | T | S |
| H |  | W |  |  | E |  | P |  |  | S |  | A |
| E | V | A | C | U | A | T | E |  | S |  |  | N |
|  |  | G |  |  | D |  | L | E | A | F | E | D |
| B | L | E | N | D |  | F |  |  | L |  |  | W |
| R |  | R |  | E | L | A | S | T | I | C |  | I |
| A |  | E |  | N |  | R |  |  | V |  |  | C |
| S | I | D | E | S |  | M | O | N | A | R | C | H |

## CROSSWORD 36

| W | H | E | A | T |  | F |  | I |  | H |  | E |
|---|---|---|---|---|---|---|---|---|---|---|---|---|
| A |  |  | F |  | T | R | I | G | G | E | R | S |
| F | L | E | A | S |  | E |  | L |  | I |  | T |
| F |  |  | R | A | C | E | C | O | U | R | S | E |
| L |  | D |  | R |  |  |  | O |  | L |  | E |
| E | X | A | M | I | N | E | S |  | L | O | O | M |
|  |  | T |  | S |  | T |  | A |  | O |  |  |
| D | R | A | B |  | H | A | N | D | Y | M | A | N |
| A |  | B |  | O |  |  |  | A |  | S |  | O |
| B | L | A | N | C | M | A | N | G | E |  |  | O |
| B |  | S |  | E |  | G |  | E | A | S | E | D |
| E | L | E | V | A | T | E | S |  | S |  |  | L |
| D |  | S |  | N |  | D |  | C | Y | C | L | E |

## CROSSWORD 37

| H | O | M | A | G | E |  | C |  | C | O | A | T |
|---|---|---|---|---|---|---|---|---|---|---|---|---|
| O |  |  | D |  | B | R | A | S | H |  | R |  |
| B | A | L | D |  | O |  | J |  | A | R | M | Y |
| B |  |  | E |  | N | O | O | K | S |  | R |  |
| L | O | U | D | L | Y |  | L |  | T | I | E | R |
| E |  |  |  | A |  |  | E |  | E |  | S |  |
| S | A | L | A | D | S |  | D | E | N | O | T | E |
|  | I |  | B |  | E |  |  | K |  |  |  | N |
| B | R | E | D |  | V |  | N | E | A | R | E | D |
|  | S |  | O | B | E | S | E |  | D |  |  | U |
| T | H | E | M |  | R |  | S |  | D | E | A | R |
|  | I |  | E | N | A | C | T |  | L |  |  | E |
| S | P | U | N |  | L |  | S | T | E | W | E | D |

## CROSSWORD 38

| K | E | Y | B | O | A | R | D |  | M | A | M | A |
|---|---|---|---|---|---|---|---|---|---|---|---|---|
| I |  |  | I |  | G |  | A |  | A |  |  | N |
| M | E | A | D |  | I | N | W | A | R | D | L | Y |
| O |  |  | E |  | L |  | N |  | I |  |  | W |
| N | E | E | D | L | E |  | E |  | N |  |  | A |
| O |  | V |  | U |  | I | D | E | A | L | L | Y |
|  |  | E |  | L |  | C |  | W |  | U |  |  |
| F | I | N | A | L | L | Y |  | E |  | S |  | U |
| L |  |  | B |  | O |  | U | R | C | H | I | N |
| A |  |  | A |  | W |  | P |  | O |  |  | B |
| K | I | T | C | H | E | N | S |  | M | A | D | E |
| E |  |  | U |  | R |  | E |  | M |  |  | N |
| S | A | P | S |  | S | I | T | U | A | T | E | D |

## CROSSWORD 39

| O | U | T | P | A | C | E |  | C | R | A | Z | E |
|---|---|---|---|---|---|---|---|---|---|---|---|---|
| R |  |  | O |  |  | Y |  | A |  | P |  | D |
| I |  | U | S | E | L | E | S | S |  | P |  | I |
| G |  |  | T |  |  | D |  | E | X | A | L | T |
| I | G | U | A | N | A |  | C |  |  | R |  |  |
| N |  |  | L |  | B | O | A | R | D | E | R | S |
| A |  | C |  |  | H |  | U |  |  | L |  | T |
| L | I | A | I | S | O | N | S |  | B |  |  | Y |
|  |  | N |  |  | R |  | E | N | A | M | E | L |
| C | H | A | F | F |  | B |  |  | N |  |  | I |
| H |  | S |  | A | N | A | G | R | A | M |  | S |
| I |  | T |  | M |  | T |  |  | N |  |  | T |
| C | H | A | S | E |  | H | I | J | A | C | K | S |

## CROSSWORD 40

| A | V | E | R | T |  | P |  | G |  | S |  | A |
|---|---|---|---|---|---|---|---|---|---|---|---|---|
| U |  |  | O |  | F | I | N | A | N | C | E | D |
| G | R | O | U | P |  | C |  | L |  | A |  | O |
| U |  |  | T | A | S | K | M | A | S | T | E | R |
| S |  | P |  | T |  |  |  | S |  | T |  | E |
| T | H | A | T | C | H | E | S |  | R | E | N | D |
|  |  | L |  | H |  | L |  | P |  | R |  |  |
| H | E | A | D |  | I | M | M | I | N | E | N | T |
| A |  | T |  | S |  |  |  | E |  | D |  | E |
| P | R | A | N | K | S | T | E | R | S |  |  | N |
| P |  | B |  | I |  | E |  | S | A | U | N | A |
| E | C | L | I | P | S | E | S |  | N |  |  | N |
| N |  | E |  | S |  | N |  | S | K | I | R | T |

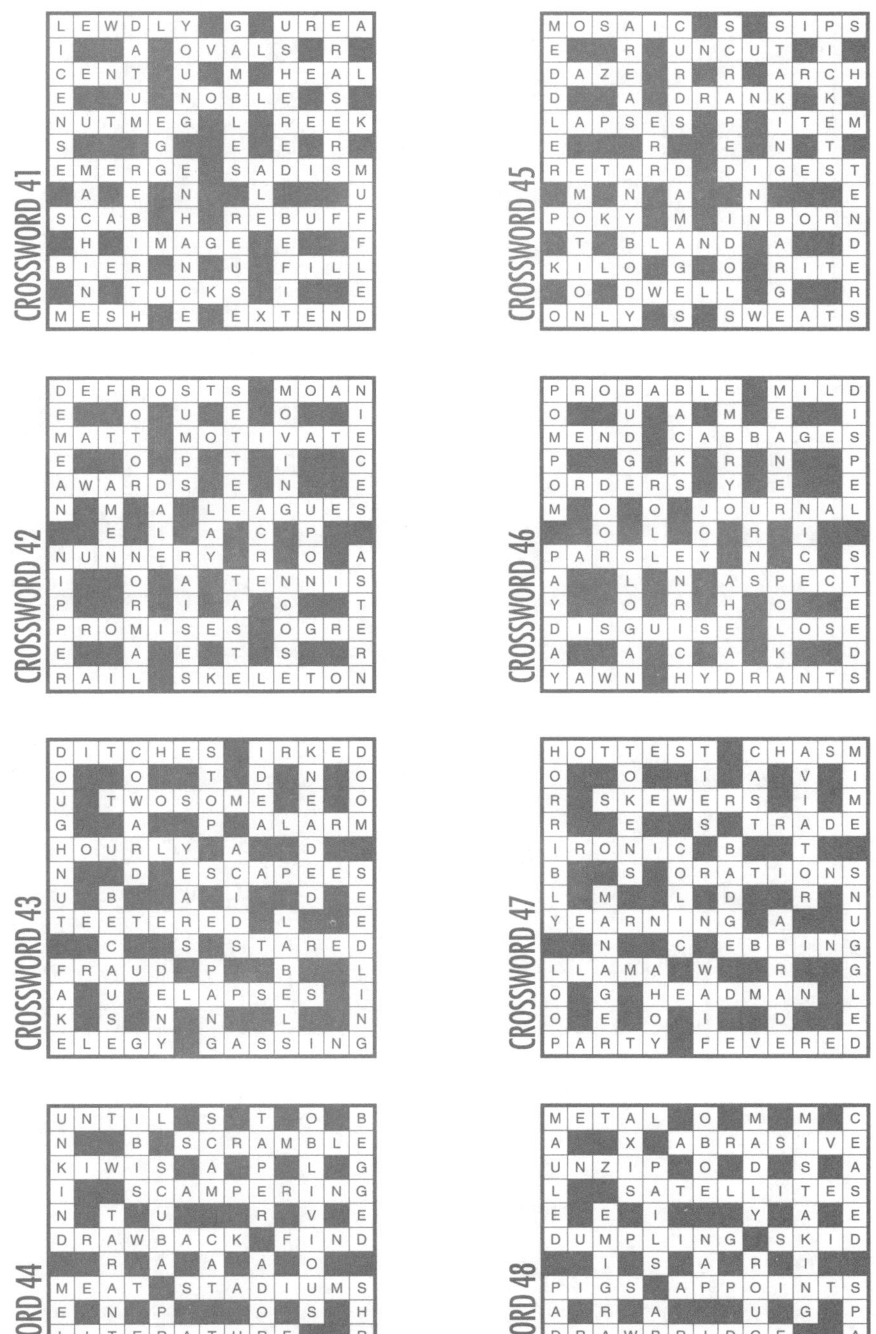
CROSSWORD 41
CROSSWORD 45
CROSSWORD 42
CROSSWORD 46
CROSSWORD 43
CROSSWORD 47
CROSSWORD 44
CROSSWORD 48

# SOLUTIONS

## CROSSWORD 49

| C | I | C | A | D | A | | C | | V | I | C | E |
|---|---|---|---|---|---|---|---|---|---|---|---|---|
| R | | | S | | F | L | O | R | A | | O | |
| O | A | T | H | | F | | M | | R | E | A | P |
| Q | | | E | | I | M | P | L | Y | | S | |
| U | N | I | S | E | X | | I | | I | N | T | O |
| E | | | | W | | | L | | N | | A | |
| T | A | N | D | E | M | | E | N | G | U | L | F |
| | N | | R | | O | | | O | | | | E |
| T | Y | P | E | | T | | C | R | A | D | L | E |
| | T | | S | L | O | S | H | | B | | | L |
| D | I | G | S | | R | | O | | O | G | L | E |
| | M | | E | P | E | E | S | | U | | | R |
| H | E | M | S | | D | | E | X | T | R | A | S |

## CROSSWORD 50

| A | T | T | O | R | N | E | Y | | R | A | I | N |
|---|---|---|---|---|---|---|---|---|---|---|---|---|
| C | | | T | | E | | E | | E | | | I |
| C | A | S | H | | V | O | L | C | A | N | I | C |
| E | | | E | | E | | L | | S | | | H |
| P | O | O | R | E | R | | E | | O | | | E |
| T | | P | | M | | O | D | D | N | E | S | S |
| | | A | | I | | U | | O | | P | | |
| H | O | L | S | T | E | R | | D | | I | | E |
| U | | | H | | M | | V | O | I | C | E | S |
| S | | | A | | B | | I | | D | | | T |
| H | A | N | D | B | A | G | S | | L | A | M | A |
| E | | | E | | R | | O | | E | | | T |
| S | L | E | D | | K | E | R | O | S | E | N | E |

## CROSSWORD 51

| S | H | E | R | I | F | F | | N | I | G | H | T |
|---|---|---|---|---|---|---|---|---|---|---|---|---|
| I | | | E | | | E | | O | | R | | O |
| D | | B | O | M | B | A | R | D | | E | | A |
| E | | | P | | | T | | S | T | A | N | D |
| W | H | E | E | L | S | | C | | | S | | |
| A | | | N | | H | E | A | R | T | E | N | S |
| Y | | P | | | O | | R | | | S | | H |
| S | C | A | B | B | A | R | D | | D | | | O |
| | | R | | | L | | S | H | A | M | E | D |
| H | E | A | R | D | | C | | | H | | | D |
| I | | G | | I | R | A | T | E | L | Y | | I |
| G | | O | | P | | L | | | I | | | E |
| H | U | N | K | S | | F | O | R | A | G | E | R |

## CROSSWORD 52

| I | N | S | E | T | | A | | B | | D | | A |
|---|---|---|---|---|---|---|---|---|---|---|---|---|
| D | | | O | | I | N | V | A | D | E | R | S |
| I | R | O | N | S | | T | | I | | V | | T |
| O | | | S | E | V | E | N | T | I | E | T | H |
| T | | L | | N | | | | S | | L | | M |
| S | L | A | N | D | E | R | S | | T | O | G | A |
| | | N | | S | | E | | F | | P | | |
| N | A | G | S | | E | F | F | L | U | E | N | T |
| U | | U | | R | | | | E | | D | | O |
| R | E | A | W | A | K | E | N | E | D | | | R |
| S | | G | | D | | D | | T | A | M | E | R |
| E | M | E | R | A | L | D | S | | S | | | I |
| S | | S | | R | | Y | | C | H | I | L | D |

## CROSSWORD 53

| R | E | M | A | N | D | | S | | B | E | A | K |
|---|---|---|---|---|---|---|---|---|---|---|---|---|
| U | | | D | | I | N | T | E | R | | R | |
| M | I | N | D | | G | | A | | A | R | C | S |
| P | | | E | | I | D | I | O | M | | H | |
| L | E | A | R | N | T | | N | | B | R | A | Y |
| E | | | | U | | | E | | L | | I | |
| S | A | I | N | T | S | | D | R | E | N | C | H |
| | L | | O | | T | | | A | | | | A |
| H | I | N | T | | R | | C | Y | N | I | C | S |
| | M | | C | O | A | C | H | | Y | | | T |
| G | O | S | H | | N | | A | | L | U | T | E |
| | N | | E | L | D | E | R | | O | | | N |
| G | Y | M | S | | S | | M | I | N | E | R | S |

## CROSSWORD 54

| S | E | N | T | R | I | E | S | | L | U | N | G |
|---|---|---|---|---|---|---|---|---|---|---|---|---|
| E | | | O | | C | | U | | A | | | O |
| Q | U | I | P | | O | R | B | I | T | I | N | G |
| U | | | I | | N | | D | | E | | | G |
| E | L | E | C | T | S | | U | | N | | | L |
| L | | A | | R | | F | E | A | T | U | R | E |
| | | R | | A | | A | | U | | G | | |
| R | E | N | A | M | E | D | | R | | L | | I |
| E | | | F | | N | | C | A | N | Y | O | N |
| V | | | R | | L | | I | | E | | | U |
| V | A | C | A | T | I | N | G | | R | O | A | R |
| E | | | I | | S | | A | | V | | | E |
| D | E | A | D | | T | A | R | G | E | T | E | D |

## CROSSWORD 55

| K | N | O | C | K | E | D | | D | I | N | G | O |
|---|---|---|---|---|---|---|---|---|---|---|---|---|
| I | | | L | | | O | | O | | O | | N |
| L | | P | I | V | O | T | A | L | | M | | C |
| L | | | M | | | S | | L | E | A | S | E |
| J | A | B | B | E | D | | S | | | D | | |
| O | | | S | | O | C | C | U | P | I | E | D |
| Y | | H | | | P | | A | | | C | | I |
| S | E | A | S | H | E | L | L | | E | | | S |
| | | R | | | D | | Y | O | D | E | L | S |
| L | O | D | E | S | | H | | | I | | | U |
| O | | I | | I | T | A | L | I | C | S | | A |
| P | | E | | R | | R | | | T | | | D |
| S | E | R | V | E | | P | E | N | S | I | V | E |

## CROSSWORD 56

| J | U | M | B | O | | L | | K | | C | | A |
|---|---|---|---|---|---|---|---|---|---|---|---|---|
| E | | | E | | V | I | T | A | M | I | N | S |
| E | V | E | N | T | | M | | P | | V | | L |
| R | | | T | A | M | B | O | U | R | I | N | E |
| E | | S | | R | | | | T | | L | | E |
| D | A | U | N | T | I | N | G | | W | I | S | P |
| | | P | | S | | A | | P | | A | | |
| I | M | P | S | | O | B | T | A | I | N | E | D |
| N | | L | | C | | | | R | | S | | O |
| G | U | I | T | A | R | I | S | T | S | | | O |
| O | | E | | C | | L | | S | A | V | E | D |
| T | H | R | O | T | T | L | E | | N | | | L |
| S | | S | | I | | S | | A | G | R | E | E |

# SOLUTIONS

## CROSSWORD 57

| S | E | N | T | R | Y |  | B |  | D | E | B | T |
|---|---|---|---|---|---|---|---|---|---|---|---|---|
| E |  |  | H |  | A | M | A | Z | E |  | U |  |
| E | A | S | E |  | C |  | B |  | N | I | B | S |
| T |  |  | M |  | H | O | B | O | S |  | B |  |
| H | O | N | E | S | T |  | L |  | E | E | L | S |
| E |  |  |  | U |  |  | E |  | S |  | E |  |
| D | A | U | B | E | D |  | D | E | T | E | S | T |
|  | P |  | E |  | E |  |  | A |  |  |  | E |
| S | P | E | D |  | C |  | S | T | A | G | E | D |
|  | E |  | R | E | A | C | H |  | R |  |  | I |
| T | A | C | O |  | N |  | O |  | O | U | Z | O |
|  | S |  | O | U | T | D | O |  | M |  |  | U |
| T | E | R | M |  | S |  | T | E | A | S | E | S |

## CROSSWORD 58

| M | E | G | A | W | A | T | T |  | S | N | A | P |
|---|---|---|---|---|---|---|---|---|---|---|---|---|
| A |  |  | L |  | N |  | R |  | Q |  |  | E |
| J | U | D | O |  | V | I | A | D | U | C | T | S |
| O |  |  | O |  | I |  | U |  | A |  |  | T |
| R | U | E | F | U | L |  | M |  | S |  |  | L |
| S |  | D |  | N |  | M | A | C | H | E | T | E |
|  |  | G |  | D |  | U |  | O |  | V |  |  |
| P | L | Y | W | O | O | D |  | P |  | E |  | P |
| L |  |  | I |  | U |  | D | E | A | R | E | R |
| U |  |  | Z |  | N |  | O |  | N |  |  | O |
| M | O | N | A | R | C | H | S |  | K | N | O | B |
| E |  |  | R |  | E |  | E |  | L |  |  | E |
| S | O | L | D |  | S | A | D | D | E | N | E | D |

## CROSSWORD 59

| A | Q | U | A | T | I | C |  | Y | I | E | L | D |
|---|---|---|---|---|---|---|---|---|---|---|---|---|
| C |  |  | D |  |  | H |  | A |  | X |  | A |
| T |  | E | D | I | T | I | O | N |  | P |  | R |
| I |  |  | L |  |  | T |  | K | N | A | C | K |
| V | E | N | E | E | R |  | F |  |  | N |  |  |
| I |  |  | S |  | H | E | A | T | E | D | L | Y |
| S |  | A |  |  | Y |  | U |  |  | S |  | A |
| T | A | L | I | S | M | A | N |  | A |  |  | S |
|  |  | B |  |  | E |  | A | M | B | U | S | H |
| B | R | I | C | K |  | P |  |  | B |  |  | M |
| O |  | N |  | N | U | A | N | C | E | S |  | A |
| O |  | O |  | O |  | P |  |  | S |  |  | K |
| R | E | S | E | T |  | A | M | A | S | S | E | S |

## CROSSWORD 60

| B | R | E | A | D |  | A |  | K |  | D |  | I |
|---|---|---|---|---|---|---|---|---|---|---|---|---|
| A |  |  | I |  | I | G | N | I | T | I | O | N |
| S | N | I | D | E |  | O |  | T |  | S |  | D |
| I |  |  | E | X | A | G | G | E | R | A | T | E |
| N |  | O |  | I |  |  |  | S |  | B |  | E |
| G | O | B | B | L | I | N | G |  | F | L | E | D |
|  |  | S |  | E |  | O |  | H |  | I |  |  |
| I | T | C | H |  | S | T | R | A | I | N | E | D |
| N |  | E |  | G |  |  |  | U |  | G |  | I |
| S | U | N | B | A | T | H | I | N | G |  |  | N |
| A |  | I |  | F |  | O |  | T | A | K | E | N |
| N | O | T | I | F | I | E | D |  | I |  |  | E |
| E |  | Y |  | E |  | D |  | O | T | T | E | R |

## CROSSWORD 61

| I | N | L | A | N | D |  | M |  | D | I | R | T |
|---|---|---|---|---|---|---|---|---|---|---|---|---|
| L |  |  | G |  | U | S | A | G | E |  | E |  |
| L | A | V | A |  | L |  | L |  | M | E | L | T |
| E |  |  | I |  | L | E | A | V | E |  | E |  |
| G | R | I | N | D | S |  | R |  | R | E | A | M |
| A |  |  |  | U |  |  | I |  | I |  | S |  |
| L | A | D | D | E | R |  | A | N | T | H | E | M |
|  | S |  | U |  | O |  |  | A |  |  |  | O |
| S | T | A | R |  | B |  | H | Y | B | R | I | D |
|  | O |  | A | M | B | L | E |  | A |  |  | U |
| B | U | L | B |  | I |  | W |  | R | E | A | L |
|  | N |  | L | U | N | G | E |  | E |  |  | E |
| E | D | G | E |  | G |  | D | O | D | G | E | S |

## CROSSWORD 62

| R | O | M | A | N | C | E | D |  | H | U | L | A |
|---|---|---|---|---|---|---|---|---|---|---|---|---|
| U |  |  | C |  | A |  | R |  | O |  |  | D |
| N | E | A | R |  | S | H | A | M | B | L | E | D |
| W |  |  | E |  | E |  | W |  | B |  |  | I |
| A | B | A | S | E | S |  | E |  | L |  |  | N |
| Y |  | J |  | P |  | F | R | E | E | I | N | G |
|  |  | A |  | E |  | E |  | C |  | C |  |  |
| W | A | R | H | E | A | D |  | H |  | E |  | G |
| E |  |  | E |  | R |  | M | O | R | S | E | L |
| A |  |  | R |  | R |  | A |  | I |  |  | O |
| L | A | I | D | B | A | C | K |  | N | U | M | B |
| T |  |  | E |  | Y |  | E |  | S |  |  | E |
| H | I | N | D |  | S | U | R | G | E | O | N | S |

## CROSSWORD 63

| J | U | M | B | L | E | D |  | M | O | V | I | E |
|---|---|---|---|---|---|---|---|---|---|---|---|---|
| A |  |  | O |  |  | A |  | O |  | E |  | S |
| I |  | O | V | E | R | R | U | N |  | R |  | P |
| L |  |  | I |  |  | E |  | O | V | A | R | Y |
| B | A | N | N | E | D |  | S |  |  | N |  |  |
| I |  |  | E |  | W | I | C | K | E | D | L | Y |
| R |  | O |  |  | A |  | A |  |  | A |  | U |
| D | E | F | E | R | R | A | L |  | P |  |  | L |
|  |  | F |  |  | F |  | P | L | A | G | U | E |
| O | P | E | R | A |  | S |  |  | U |  |  | T |
| V |  | N |  | K | I | C | K | I | N | G |  | I |
| E |  | D |  | I |  | U |  |  | C |  |  | D |
| R | I | S | E | N |  | M | A | N | H | O | L | E |

## CROSSWORD 64

| N | I | C | K | S |  | T |  | S |  | M |  | S |
|---|---|---|---|---|---|---|---|---|---|---|---|---|
| E |  |  | I |  | L | A | N | K | I | E | S | T |
| A | B | I | D | E |  | L |  | E |  | D |  | U |
| T |  |  | S | A | N | C | T | I | F | I | E | D |
| L |  | P |  | R |  |  |  | N |  | C |  | I |
| Y | E | A | R | L | I | N | G |  | S | I | L | O |
|  |  | P |  | Y |  | I |  | R |  | N |  |  |
| F | L | A | N |  | P | L | E | A | S | A | N | T |
| A |  | R |  | T |  |  |  | I |  | L |  | R |
| C | H | A | R | I | T | A | B | L | Y |  |  | U |
| A |  | Z |  | T |  | U |  | S | A | W | E | D |
| D | A | Z | Z | L | I | N | G |  | P |  |  | G |
| E |  | I |  | E |  | T |  | A | S | I | D | E |

# SOLUTIONS

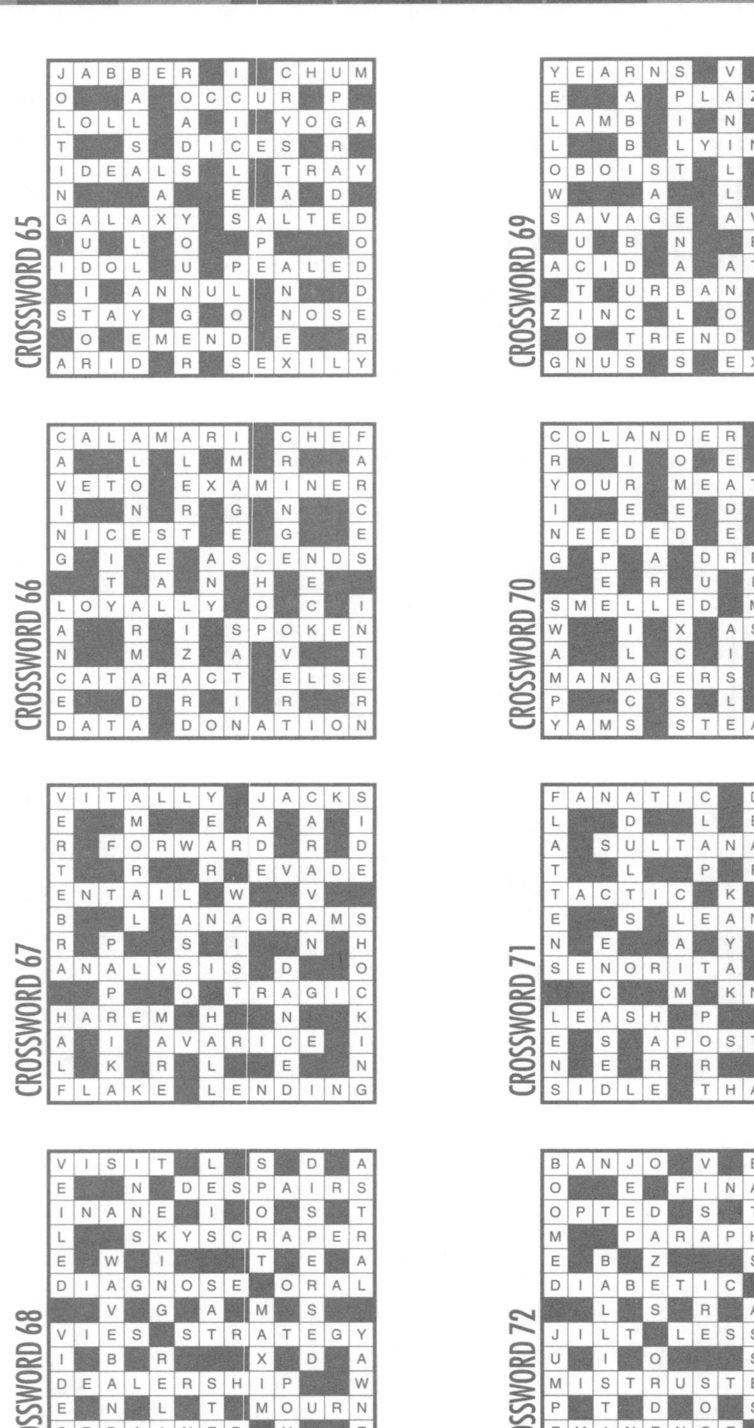
CROSSWORD 65
CROSSWORD 69
CROSSWORD 66
CROSSWORD 70
CROSSWORD 67
CROSSWORD 71
CROSSWORD 68
CROSSWORD 72

# SOLUTIONS

## CROSSWORD 73

| M | A | D | D | E | N |  | A |  | W | R | A | P |
|---|---|---|---|---|---|---|---|---|---|---|---|---|
| E |  |  | E |  | O | L | D | E | R |  | U |  |
| E | V | I | L |  | B |  | V |  | E | N | D | S |
| T |  |  | T |  | L | O | A | D | S |  | I |  |
| I | N | F | A | M | Y |  | N |  | T | A | B | S |
| N |  |  |  | U |  |  | C |  | L |  | L |  |
| G | A | R | A | G | E |  | E | L | E | V | E | N |
|  | M |  | N |  | R |  |  | I |  |  |  | E |
| S | M | U | G |  | R |  | K | E | B | A | B | S |
|  | O |  | L | E | A | R | N |  | U |  |  | T |
| A | N | T | I |  | N |  | E |  | M | I | L | L |
|  | I |  | N | U | D | G | E |  | P |  |  | E |
| R | A | N | G |  | S |  | L | I | S | T | E | D |

## CROSSWORD 74

| T | R | A | C | T | O | R | S |  | G | R | A | B |
|---|---|---|---|---|---|---|---|---|---|---|---|---|
| A |  |  | A |  | F |  | A |  | L |  |  | U |
| M | I | N | T |  | F | A | T | H | O | M | E | D |
| E |  |  | E |  | A |  | I |  | A |  |  | G |
| S | P | I | R | A | L |  | R |  | T |  |  | E |
| T |  | S |  | M |  | P | E | A | S | A | N | T |
|  |  | L |  | O |  | I |  | L |  | C |  |  |
| F | R | E | C | K | L | E |  | S |  | T |  | A |
| O |  |  | A |  | O |  | C | O | A | S | T | S |
| A |  |  | R |  | O |  | A |  | N |  |  | S |
| M | O | L | A | S | S | E | S |  | N | O | N | E |
| E |  |  | F |  | E |  | K |  | O |  |  | S |
| D | O | Z | E |  | R | E | S | T | Y | L | E | S |

## CROSSWORD 75

| N | E | G | A | T | E | D |  | A | W | A | R | D |
|---|---|---|---|---|---|---|---|---|---|---|---|---|
| O |  |  | C |  |  | I |  | W |  | B |  | Y |
| M |  | S | T | O | R | A | G | E |  | R |  | E |
| I |  |  | U |  |  | L |  | S | C | A | L | D |
| N | A | P | A | L | M |  | S |  |  | D |  |  |
| A |  |  | L |  | A | C | C | I | D | E | N | T |
| T |  | B |  |  | C |  | R |  |  | S |  | W |
| E | V | A | L | U | A | T | E |  |  | H |  | I |
|  |  | L |  |  | W |  | W | E | A | V | E | D |
| A | W | A | K | E |  | D |  |  | Z |  |  | D |
| R |  | N |  | G | R | A | D | U | A | L |  | L |
| E |  | C |  | G |  | R |  |  | R |  |  | E |
| A | B | E | T | S |  | N | E | E | D | L | E | D |

## CROSSWORD 76

| T | U | B | A | S |  | L |  | B |  | M |  | H |
|---|---|---|---|---|---|---|---|---|---|---|---|---|
| O |  |  | V |  | S | E | P | A | R | A | T | E |
| T | O | N | I | C |  | W |  | K |  | R |  | A |
| T |  |  | D | A | Y | D | R | E | A | M | E | D |
| E |  | C |  | N |  |  |  | S |  | A |  | E |
| D | R | A | M | A | T | I | C |  | B | L | E | D |
|  |  | V |  | L |  | O |  | B |  | A |  |  |
| F | E | A | R |  | U | N | H | E | E | D | E | D |
| L |  | L |  | M |  |  |  | I |  | E |  | E |
| U | N | C | H | A | N | G | I | N | G |  |  | A |
| I |  | A |  | T |  | L |  | G | A | P | E | D |
| D | E | D | U | C | T | E | D |  | S |  |  | L |
| S |  | E |  | H |  | E |  | S | P | R | A | Y |

## CROSSWORD 77

| V | I | C | A | R | S |  | C |  | P | O | K | E |
|---|---|---|---|---|---|---|---|---|---|---|---|---|
| I |  |  | R |  | Q | U | A | K | E |  | N |  |
| R | I | P | E |  | U |  | S |  | A | M | I | D |
| U |  |  | N |  | A | S | H | E | N |  | F |  |
| S | T | R | A | N | D |  | I |  | U | N | I | T |
| E |  |  |  | E |  |  | E |  | T |  | N |  |
| S | A | N | I | T | Y |  | R | E | S | I | G | N |
|  | V |  | N |  | E |  |  | Y |  |  |  | U |
| C | E | D | E |  | L |  | W | E | A | K | E | R |
|  | R |  | P | U | L | S | E |  | S |  |  | S |
| C | A | S | T |  | I |  | A |  | K | I | W | I |
|  | G |  | L | I | N | E | N |  | E |  |  | N |
| D | E | F | Y |  | G |  | S | E | W | I | N | G |

## CROSSWORD 78

| C | O | W | A | R | D | L | Y |  | K | I | S | S |
|---|---|---|---|---|---|---|---|---|---|---|---|---|
| L |  |  | G |  | E |  | A |  | E |  |  | E |
| I | D | L | E |  | C | O | C | K | E | Y | E | D |
| E |  |  | N |  | O |  | H |  | P |  |  | U |
| N | E | C | T | A | R |  | T |  | E |  |  | C |
| T |  | O |  | X |  | A | S | T | R | I | D | E |
|  |  | B |  | L |  | R |  | U |  | C |  |  |
| N | O | S | I | E | S | T |  | N |  | O |  | U |
| A |  |  | R |  | T |  | J | A | U | N | T | S |
| R |  |  | O |  | R |  | E |  | N |  |  | E |
| R | E | I | N | D | E | E | R |  | D | O | F | F |
| O |  |  | E |  | A |  | K |  | E |  |  | U |
| W | I | N | D |  | M | I | S | T | R | I | A | L |

## CROSSWORD 79

| T | E | R | R | A | I | N |  | E | N | T | E | R |
|---|---|---|---|---|---|---|---|---|---|---|---|---|
| R |  |  | I |  |  | U |  | A |  | E |  | O |
| A |  | C | O | C | O | N | U | T |  | N |  | B |
| M |  |  | T |  |  | S |  | S | H | A | V | E |
| P | H | L | E | G | M |  | B |  |  | N |  |  |
| L |  |  | R |  | O | V | E | R | A | C | T | S |
| E |  | T |  |  | U |  | L |  |  | Y |  | E |
| D | I | A | G | O | N | A | L |  | K |  |  | N |
|  |  | X |  |  | D |  | Y | I | E | L | D | S |
| R | U | I | N | G |  | G |  |  | E |  |  | I |
| E |  | C |  | I | M | A | G | I | N | E |  | B |
| D |  | A |  | F |  | R |  |  | L |  |  | L |
| O | R | B | I | T |  | B | I | C | Y | C | L | E |

## CROSSWORD 80

| W | O | M | A | N |  | A |  | R |  | P |  | L |
|---|---|---|---|---|---|---|---|---|---|---|---|---|
| I |  |  | I |  | E | S | C | A | P | A | D | E |
| S | K | I | L | L |  | P |  | N |  | R |  | S |
| E |  |  | S | E | N | S | A | T | I | O | N | S |
| S |  | P |  | E |  |  |  | S |  | D |  | E |
| T | H | A | T | C | H | E | D |  | H | Y | P | E |
|  |  | R |  | H |  | E |  | S |  | I |  |  |
| S | N | A | G |  | F | L | A | M | I | N | G | O |
| A |  | G |  | L |  |  |  | I |  | G |  | N |
| F | O | R | E | I | G | N | E | R | S |  |  | W |
| A |  | A |  | M |  | A |  | K | A | R | M | A |
| R | E | P | U | B | L | I | C |  | G |  |  | R |
| I |  | H |  | O |  | L |  | V | O | T | E | D |

# SOLUTIONS

CROSSWORD 85

| D | R | I | L | L | S |  | E |  | T | O | O | L |
|---|---|---|---|---|---|---|---|---|---|---|---|---|
| A |  |  | A |  | W | I | N | C | E |  | R |  |
| W | E | E | P |  | A |  | T |  | A | W | A | Y |
| N |  |  | S |  | T | O | W | E | R |  | T |  |
| I | M | P | E | L | S |  | I |  | I | R | I | S |
| N |  |  |  | I |  |  | N |  | N |  | O |  |
| G | A | I | E | T | Y |  | E | D | G | I | N | G |
|  | M |  | A |  | E |  |  | I |  |  |  | O |
| S | P | A | R |  | L |  | V | E | R | G | E | D |
|  | L |  | S | E | P | I | A |  | E |  |  | S |
| P | I | T | H |  | I |  | N |  | B | O | D | E |
|  | F |  | O | U | N | C | E |  | E |  |  | N |
| C | Y | S | T |  | G |  | S | U | L | K | E | D |

CROSSWORD 86

| S | Q | U | A | N | D | E | R |  | E | L | K | S |
|---|---|---|---|---|---|---|---|---|---|---|---|---|
| P |  |  | D |  | U |  | E |  | D |  |  | A |
| R | U | S | E |  | M | E | A | N | D | E | R | S |
| I |  |  | P |  | M |  | P |  | I |  |  | H |
| G | E | N | T | L | Y |  | E |  | E |  |  | E |
| S |  | O |  | O |  | T | R | A | D | E | R | S |
|  |  | U |  | N |  | A |  | F |  | B |  |  |
| V | I | N | E | G | A | R |  | A |  | B |  | E |
| O |  |  | C |  | R |  | G | R | A | S | P | S |
| C |  |  | Z |  | M |  | U |  | B |  |  | C |
| A | D | H | E | S | I | V | E |  | U | L | N | A |
| L |  |  | M |  | E |  | S |  | S |  |  | P |
| S | O | D | A |  | S | U | S | P | E | N | S | E |

CROSSWORD 87

| T | R | E | A | T | E | D |  | M | E | A | L | S |
|---|---|---|---|---|---|---|---|---|---|---|---|---|
| R |  |  | N |  |  | E |  | U |  | N |  | O |
| O |  | C | Y | M | B | A | L | S |  | O |  | F |
| U |  |  | O |  |  | N |  | E | X | T | R | A |
| S | I | N | N | E | D |  | R |  |  | H |  |  |
| E |  |  | E |  | W | E | A | R | I | E | S | T |
| R |  | P |  |  | E |  | I |  |  | R |  | R |
| S | T | A | R | T | L | E | D |  | C |  |  | I |
|  |  | R |  |  | T |  | S | T | A | T | I | C |
| M | E | A | N | T |  | T |  |  | M |  |  | K |
| A |  | D |  | R | O | A | S | T | E | D |  | E |
| I |  | E |  | U |  | C |  |  | R |  |  | R |
| M | I | D | G | E |  | T | Y | R | A | N | N | Y |

CROSSWORD 88

| J | A | M | B | S |  | E |  | P |  | D |  | K |
|---|---|---|---|---|---|---|---|---|---|---|---|---|
| E |  |  | R |  | A | V | I | A | T | I | O | N |
| T | R | E | A | D |  | E |  | V |  | L |  | I |
| S |  |  | S | A | U | N | T | E | R | I | N | G |
| A |  | C |  | U |  |  |  | D |  | G |  | H |
| M | E | A | N | N | E | S | S |  | D | E | N | T |
|  |  | R |  | T |  | H |  | S |  | N |  |  |
| U | S | E | R |  | M | Y | T | H | I | C | A | L |
| N |  | T |  | L |  |  |  | E |  | E |  | O |
| P | E | A | C | E | F | U | L | L | Y |  |  | C |
| A |  | K |  | V |  | R |  | L | A | R | V | A |
| I | C | E | B | E | R | G | S |  | R |  |  | L |
| D |  | R |  | R |  | E |  | I | D | E | A | S |

# SOLUTIONS

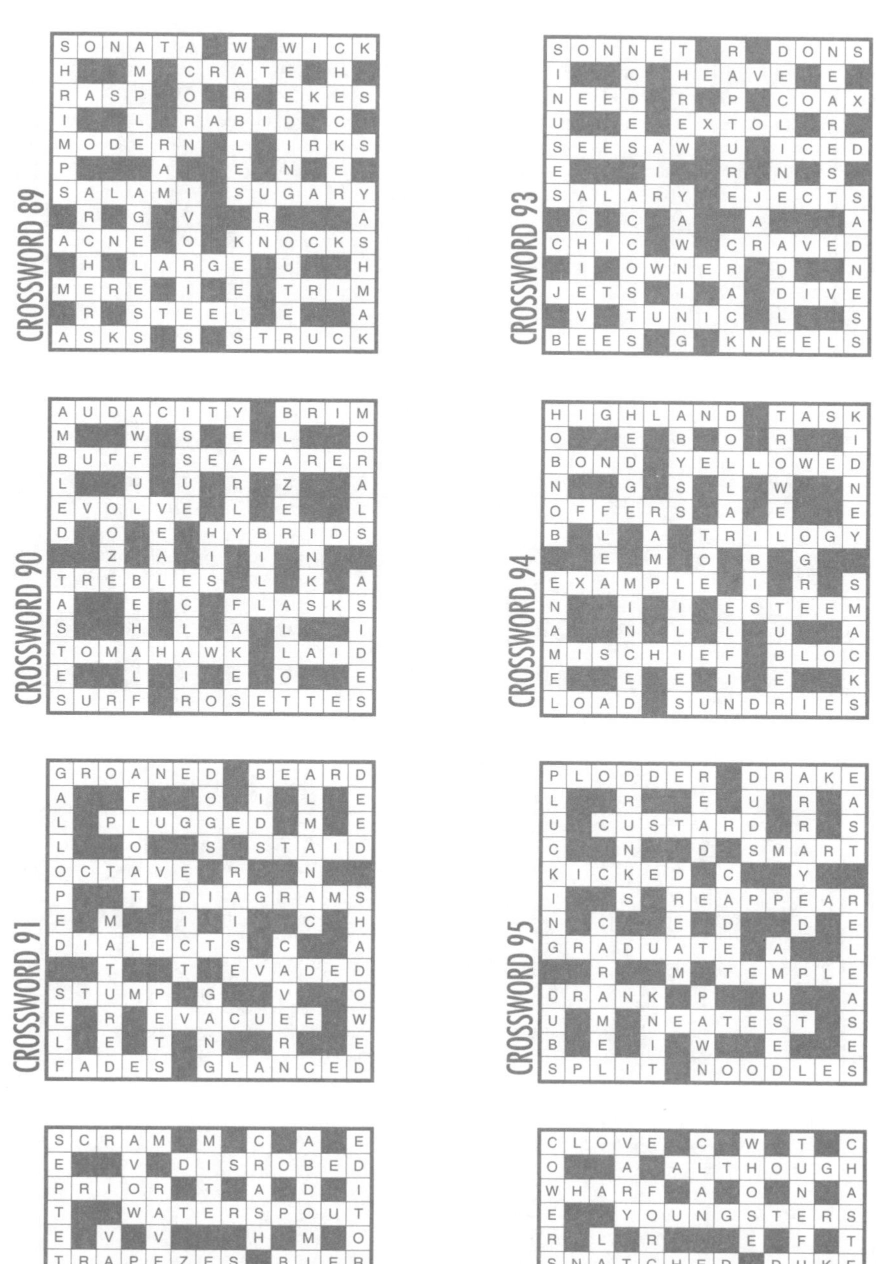
CROSSWORD 89
CROSSWORD 93
CROSSWORD 90
CROSSWORD 94
CROSSWORD 91
CROSSWORD 95
CROSSWORD 92
CROSSWORD 96

# SOLUTIONS

## CROSSWORD 97

| P | R | E | A | C | H |  | E |  | G | R | A | M |
|---|---|---|---|---|---|---|---|---|---|---|---|---|
| L |  |  | M |  | Y | O | D | E | L |  | R |  |
| A | R | I | A |  | E |  | U |  | O | U | C | H |
| N |  |  | S |  | N | E | C | K | S |  | H |  |
| N | A | U | S | E | A |  | A |  | S | L | I | T |
| E |  |  |  | N |  |  | T |  | E |  | N |  |
| R | A | P | I | D | S |  | E | N | S | I | G | N |
|  | I |  | M |  | C |  |  | E |  |  |  | A |
| C | R | A | B |  | R |  | D | E | A | C | O | N |
|  | C |  | I | M | A | G | E |  | I |  |  | N |
| C | R | I | B |  | T |  | A |  | M | I | N | I |
|  | E |  | E | X | C | E | L |  | E |  |  | E |
| A | W | E | D |  | H |  | S | E | D | A | N | S |

## CROSSWORD 98

| D | O | O | R | B | E | L | L |  | S | A | I | D |
|---|---|---|---|---|---|---|---|---|---|---|---|---|
| I |  |  | A |  | W |  | O |  | C |  |  | E |
| R | I | N | K |  | E | M | P | T | Y | I | N | G |
| E |  |  | E |  | R |  | P |  | T |  |  | R |
| C | H | A | S | M | S |  | E |  | H |  |  | E |
| T |  | X |  | A |  | A | D | V | E | R | S | E |
|  |  | E |  | L |  | I |  | A |  | O |  |  |
| F | I | D | D | L | E | D |  | S |  | L |  | E |
| E |  |  | E |  | N |  | S | E | A | L | E | D |
| E |  |  | M |  | R |  | A |  | S |  |  | I |
| B | E | H | A | V | I | N | G |  | S | L | A | B |
| L |  |  | N |  | C |  | A |  | E |  |  | L |
| E | Y | E | D |  | H | E | S | I | T | A | T | E |

## CROSSWORD 99

| G | I | R | A | F | F | E |  | S | O | P | P | Y |
|---|---|---|---|---|---|---|---|---|---|---|---|---|
| R |  |  | N |  |  | R |  | A |  | I |  | E |
| O |  | E | Y | E | B | R | O | W |  | G |  | L |
| U |  |  | H |  |  | S |  | N | A | T | A | L |
| N | Y | L | O | N | S |  | L |  |  | A |  |  |
| D |  |  | W |  | I | D | E | N | T | I | F | Y |
| E |  | R |  |  | D |  | A |  |  | L |  | I |
| D | E | A | F | N | E | S | S |  | R |  |  | E |
|  |  | D |  |  | S |  | T | R | I | B | A | L |
| T | H | I | R | D |  | O |  |  | F |  |  | D |
| A |  | O |  | A | N | G | R | I | L | Y |  | I |
| L |  | E |  | M |  | L |  |  | E |  |  | N |
| L | E | D | G | E |  | E | X | U | D | I | N | G |

## CROSSWORD 100

| A | T | L | A | S |  | S |  | A |  | M |  | A |
|---|---|---|---|---|---|---|---|---|---|---|---|---|
| L |  |  | X |  | S | K | I | D | D | I | N | G |
| B | A | S | I | C |  | I |  | O |  | N |  | R |
| U |  |  | S | U | M | M | E | R | T | I | M | E |
| M |  | J |  | R |  |  |  | E |  | S |  | E |
| S | H | A | B | B | I | E | R |  | S | T | U | D |
|  |  | I |  | S |  | W |  | J |  | E |  |  |
| C | U | L | T |  | R | E | H | E | A | R | S | E |
| O |  | B |  | U |  |  |  | S |  | S |  | R |
| F | O | R | T | N | I | G | H | T | S |  |  | R |
| F |  | E |  | P |  | O |  | S | A | U | N | A |
| E | X | A | M | I | N | E | S |  | L |  |  | N |
| E |  | K |  | N |  | S |  | S | T | O | O | D |

## CROSSWORD 101

| I | N | L | A | I | D |  | O |  | A | L | A | S |
|---|---|---|---|---|---|---|---|---|---|---|---|---|
| N |  |  | I |  | E | M | B | E | D |  | M |  |
| N | U | L | L |  | U |  | T |  | A | T | O | M |
| I |  |  | E |  | C | H | A | M | P |  | U |  |
| N | E | E | D | L | E |  | I |  | T | I | N | Y |
| G |  |  |  | I |  |  | N |  | E |  | T |  |
| S | A | L | A | D | S |  | S | A | D | I | S | M |
|  | W |  | M |  | E |  |  | Y |  |  |  | I |
| S | K | I | N |  | T |  | C | E | A | S | E | S |
|  | W |  | E | M | B | E | R |  | L |  |  | T |
| D | A | M | S |  | A |  | A |  | P | L | E | A |
|  | R |  | T | A | C | K | S |  | H |  |  | K |
| I | D | L | Y |  | K |  | S | T | A | B | L | E |

## CROSSWORD 102

| P | H | E | A | S | A | N | T |  | L | O | O | T |
|---|---|---|---|---|---|---|---|---|---|---|---|---|
| U |  |  | P |  | D |  | O |  | E |  |  | O |
| P | U | M | A |  | D | E | P | O | S | I | T | S |
| I |  |  | R |  | E |  | P |  | S |  |  | S |
| L | O | F | T | E | D |  | L |  | E |  |  | E |
| S |  | L |  | M |  | B | E | A | R | E | R | S |
|  |  | O |  | I |  | O |  | L |  | O |  |  |
| N | I | G | H | T | L | Y |  | T |  | N |  | A |
| A |  |  | U |  | I |  | N | O | I | S | E | S |
| P |  |  | M |  | A |  | I |  | N |  |  | T |
| P | R | E | A | M | B | L | E |  | G | A | Z | E |
| E |  |  | N |  | L |  | C |  | O |  |  | R |
| D | I | M | E |  | E | X | E | R | T | I | O | N |

## CROSSWORD 103

| N | E | R | V | O | U | S |  | S | P | U | R | N |
|---|---|---|---|---|---|---|---|---|---|---|---|---|
| E |  |  | E |  |  | A |  | E |  | N |  | U |
| G |  | E | T | H | I | C | A | L |  | S |  | T |
| L |  |  | O |  |  | K |  | L | I | C | K | S |
| I | N | T | E | N | D |  | O |  |  | R |  |  |
| G |  |  | D |  | O | F | F | I | C | E | R | S |
| E |  | O |  |  | W |  | T |  |  | W |  | T |
| E | X | C | H | A | N | G | E |  | F |  |  | E |
|  |  | E |  |  | S |  | N | U | A | N | C | E |
| F | R | A | U | D |  | M |  |  | B |  |  | P |
| L |  | N |  | U | N | A | W | A | R | E |  | L |
| A |  | I |  | E |  | M |  |  | I |  |  | E |
| B | U | C | K | S |  | A | B | S | C | E | S | S |

## CROSSWORD 104

| M | A | D | A | M |  | A |  | B |  | A |  | M |
|---|---|---|---|---|---|---|---|---|---|---|---|---|
| O |  |  | R |  | S | C | R | A | M | B | L | E |
| M | A | R | C | H |  | R |  | R |  | R |  | L |
| E |  |  | S | A | U | E | R | K | R | A | U | T |
| N |  | T |  | C |  |  |  | S |  | S |  | E |
| T | R | E | K | K | I | N | G |  | F | I | N | D |
|  |  | R |  | S |  | A |  | H |  | V |  |  |
| E | A | R | N |  | U | G | L | I | N | E | S | S |
| X |  | O |  | S |  |  |  | R |  | S |  | A |
| C | E | R | E | M | O | N | I | E | S |  |  | C |
| E |  | I |  | O |  | O |  | R | A | N | C | H |
| P | O | S | T | C | A | R | D |  | G |  |  | E |
| T |  | T |  | K |  | M |  | I | S | L | E | T |

# SOLUTIONS

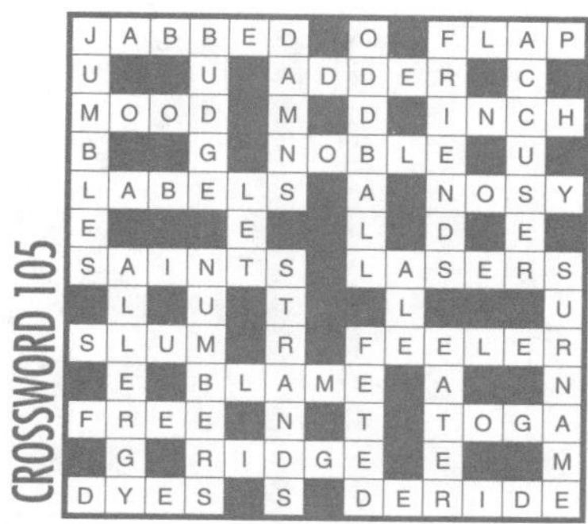

CROSSWORD 105

| J | A | B | B | E | D |  | O |  | F | L | A | P |
|---|---|---|---|---|---|---|---|---|---|---|---|---|
| U |  |  | U |  | A | D | D | E | R |  | C |  |
| M | O | O | D |  | M |  | D |  | I | N | C | H |
| B |  |  | G |  | N | O | B | L | E |  | U |  |
| L | A | B | E | L | S |  | A |  | N | O | S | Y |
| E |  |  |  | E |  |  | L |  | D |  | E |  |
| S | A | I | N | T | S |  | L | A | S | E | R | S |
|  | L |  | U |  | T |  |  | L |  |  |  | U |
| S | L | U | M |  | R |  | F | E | E | L | E | R |
|  | E |  | B | L | A | M | E |  | A |  |  | N |
| F | R | E | E |  | N |  | T |  | T | O | G | A |
|  | G |  | R | I | D | G | E |  | E |  |  | M |
| D | Y | E | S |  | S |  | D | E | R | I | D | E |

CROSSWORD 106

| A | D | V | A | N | C | E | D |  | E | N | V | Y |
|---|---|---|---|---|---|---|---|---|---|---|---|---|
| V |  |  | R |  | R |  | E |  | N |  |  | A |
| E | A | R | S |  | O | C | C | A | S | I | O | N |
| R |  |  | O |  | N |  | I |  | U |  |  | K |
| T | R | A | N | C | E |  | D |  | E |  |  | E |
| S |  | P |  | A |  | F | E | A | S | T | E | D |
|  |  | E |  | L |  | A |  | L |  | R |  |  |
| R | I | D | D | L | E | D |  | L |  | I |  | O |
| E |  |  | W |  | L |  | M | Y | O | P | I | C |
| S |  |  | A |  | O |  | A |  | R |  |  | T |
| C | O | R | R | U | P | T | S |  | A | U | R | A |
| U |  |  | F |  | E |  | O |  | T |  |  | N |
| E | M | U | S |  | S | E | N | T | E | N | C | E |

CROSSWORD 107

| J | A | B | B | E | R | S |  | N | I | C | H | E |
|---|---|---|---|---|---|---|---|---|---|---|---|---|
| O |  |  | E |  |  | W |  | O |  | L |  | A |
| D |  | E | M | E | R | A | L | D |  | E |  | S |
| H |  |  | O |  |  | Y |  | S | H | A | R | E |
| P | H | R | A | S | E |  | B |  |  | N |  |  |
| U |  |  | N |  | P | L | A | Y | P | E | N | S |
| R |  | P |  |  | E |  | G |  |  | R |  | H |
| S | T | A | M | P | E | D | E |  | P |  |  | E |
|  |  | R |  |  | S |  | L | E | A | F | E | D |
| N | I | C | E | R |  | H |  |  | N |  |  | D |
| O |  | H |  | O | K | A | Y | I | N | G |  | I |
| O |  | E |  | T |  | W |  |  | E |  |  | N |
| N | U | D | E | S |  | K | I | D | D | I | N | G |

CROSSWORD 108

| M | U | M | M | Y |  | L |  | H |  | C |  | A |
|---|---|---|---|---|---|---|---|---|---|---|---|---|
| A |  |  | U |  | P | O | L | E | C | A | T | S |
| C | O | N | G | A |  | G |  | E |  | P |  | Y |
| A |  |  | S | C | H | O | O | L | G | I | R | L |
| W |  | S |  | I |  |  |  | S |  | L |  | U |
| S | C | A | N | D | A | L | S |  | S | L | A | M |
|  |  | C |  | S |  | O |  | S |  | A |  |  |
| J | A | C | K |  | S | T | E | W | A | R | D | S |
| E |  | H |  | C |  |  |  | E |  | Y |  | E |
| W | E | A | T | H | E | R | M | A | N |  |  | P |
| E |  | R |  | I |  | U |  | R | E | L | I | T |
| L | O | I | T | E | R | E | D |  | T |  |  | I |
| S |  | N |  | F |  | S |  | A | S | P | I | C |

CROSSWORD 109

| G | Y | R | A | T | E |  | D |  | U | N | D | O |
|---|---|---|---|---|---|---|---|---|---|---|---|---|
| A |  |  | D |  | E | V | E | N | S |  | E |  |
| T | A | C | O |  | R |  | F |  | H | E | A | L |
| E |  |  | P |  | I | R | A | T | E |  | R |  |
| W | R | I | T | H | E |  | C |  | R | E | E | L |
| A |  |  |  | O |  |  | E |  | E |  | S |  |
| Y | E | L | P | E | D |  | S | E | D | A | T | E |
|  | N |  | A |  | E |  |  | K |  |  |  | N |
| U | S | E | D |  | L |  | N | E | I | G | H | S |
|  | N |  | D | R | A | P | E |  | N |  |  | U |
| W | A | I | L |  | Y |  | S |  | T | I | E | R |
|  | R |  | E | L | E | C | T |  | R |  |  | E |
| S | E | E | D |  | D |  | S | L | O | P | E | D |

CROSSWORD 110

| R | E | O | P | E | N | E | D |  | U | P | O | N |
|---|---|---|---|---|---|---|---|---|---|---|---|---|
| E |  |  | U |  | I |  | R |  | S |  |  | U |
| S | O | U | R |  | F | E | A | T | U | R | E | D |
| I |  |  | S |  | T |  | W |  | R |  |  | G |
| S | O | L | E | L | Y |  | E |  | P |  |  | E |
| T |  | A |  | O |  | D | R | E | S | S | E | S |
|  |  | R |  | O |  | E |  | D |  | U |  |  |
| K | I | D | S | K | I | N |  | G |  | M |  | O |
| I |  |  | Q |  | M |  | T | Y | C | O | O | N |
| M |  |  | U |  | P |  | O |  | I |  |  | I |
| O | R | N | A | M | E | N | T |  | D | E | M | O |
| N |  |  | R |  | D |  | A |  | E |  |  | N |
| O | B | O | E |  | E | N | L | A | R | G | E | S |

CROSSWORD 111

| T | R | A | M | P | E | D |  | M | I | N | E | R |
|---|---|---|---|---|---|---|---|---|---|---|---|---|
| H |  |  | E |  |  | R |  | E |  | O |  | O |
| I |  | E | M | B | R | A | C | E |  | M |  | L |
| N |  |  | B |  |  | G |  | T | R | A | D | E |
| N | O | V | E | L | S |  | M |  |  | D |  |  |
| E |  |  | R |  | A | L | A | R | M | I | S | T |
| S |  | C |  |  | V |  | R |  |  | C |  | W |
| T | O | A | S | T | E | R | S |  | V |  |  | I |
|  |  | N |  |  | D |  | H | E | A | T | E | D |
| B | O | A | R | D |  | P |  |  | L |  |  | D |
| L |  | S |  | U | R | A | N | I | U | M |  | L |
| O |  | T |  | N |  | C |  |  | E |  |  | E |
| B | R | A | C | E |  | K | I | N | D | L | E | S |

CROSSWORD 112

| A | T | T | I | C |  | O |  | M |  | S |  | O |
|---|---|---|---|---|---|---|---|---|---|---|---|---|
| L |  |  | T |  | E | X | P | O | R | T | E | R |
| T | R | I | C | E |  | E |  | U |  | R |  | I |
| E |  |  | H | A | R | N | E | S | S | I | N | G |
| R |  | C |  | V |  |  |  | Y |  | C |  | I |
| S | P | A | C | E | M | A | N |  | S | T | U | N |
|  |  | T |  | S |  | L |  | O |  | E |  |  |
| P | E | A | S |  | G | L | I | M | P | S | E | D |
| U |  | M |  | R |  |  |  | I |  | T |  | E |
| S | T | A | L | A | G | M | I | T | E |  |  | P |
| H |  | R |  | D |  | E |  | S | A | B | L | E |
| E | M | A | N | A | T | E | D |  | S |  |  | N |
| D |  | N |  | R |  | K |  | T | Y | P | E | D |

# SOLUTIONS

## CROSSWORD 113

| F | O | R | M | A | L |  | M |  | H | E | A | R |
|---|---|---|---|---|---|---|---|---|---|---|---|---|
| O |  |  | A |  | A | M | A | Z | E |  | D |  |
| N | I | C | K |  | C |  | C |  | C | A | V | E |
| D |  |  | E |  | K | N | A | C | K |  | E |  |
| L | E | A | R | N | S |  | B |  | L | O | R | E |
| E |  |  |  | U |  |  | R |  | E |  | B |  |
| D | A | R | I | N | G |  | E | L | D | E | S | T |
|  | W |  | N |  | I |  |  | E |  |  |  | R |
| L | A | I | R |  | R |  | S | I | C | K | L | E |
|  | R |  | O | L | D | E | N |  | I |  |  | S |
| I | D | E | A |  | L |  | I |  | V | A | N | S |
|  | E |  | D | R | E | A | D |  | I |  |  | E |
| O | D | E | S |  | S |  | E | T | C | H | E | S |

## CROSSWORD 114

| W | O | B | B | L | I | N | G |  | J | A | M | B |
|---|---|---|---|---|---|---|---|---|---|---|---|---|
| I |  |  | A |  | C |  | R |  | O |  |  | O |
| G | A | W | K |  | I | M | A | G | I | N | E | D |
| G |  |  | E |  | E |  | T |  | S |  |  | I |
| L | E | A | D | E | R |  | E |  | T |  |  | C |
| E |  | J |  | D |  | B | R | I | S | T | L | E |
|  |  | A |  | I |  | U |  | N |  | E |  |  |
| C | U | R | A | T | E | S |  | T |  | A |  | B |
| E |  |  | U |  | X |  | H | O | A | R | S | E |
| L |  |  | N |  | T |  | A |  | U |  |  | D |
| L | E | C | T | U | R | E | S |  | D | A | U | B |
| O |  |  | I |  | A |  | T |  | I |  |  | U |
| S | I | Z | E |  | S | W | E | A | T | I | N | G |

## CROSSWORD 115

| P | I | R | A | N | H | A |  | C | H | A | I | N |
|---|---|---|---|---|---|---|---|---|---|---|---|---|
| U |  |  | R |  |  | P |  | U |  | V |  | E |
| R |  | A | C | T | R | E | S | S |  | I |  | O |
| I |  |  | A |  |  | X |  | P | R | A | W | N |
| F | O | L | D | E | D |  | P |  |  | T |  |  |
| I |  |  | E |  | A | B | A | T | T | O | I | R |
| E |  | T |  |  | L |  | S |  |  | R |  | E |
| S | C | A | R | I | E | S | T |  | O |  |  | V |
|  |  | S |  |  | S |  | A | L | B | I | N | O |
| T | I | T | A | N |  | P |  |  | J |  |  | L |
| H |  | I |  | U | N | A | R | M | E | D |  | V |
| A |  | E |  | M |  | I |  |  | C |  |  | E |
| T | H | R | O | B |  | R | A | T | T | L | E | D |

## CROSSWORD 116

| H | O | B | B | Y |  | T |  | W |  | S |  | A |
|---|---|---|---|---|---|---|---|---|---|---|---|---|
| I |  |  | A |  | R | O | M | A | N | C | E | D |
| J | U | I | C | E |  | W |  | R |  | R |  | A |
| A |  |  | K | I | D | N | A | P | P | I | N | G |
| C |  | P |  | G |  |  |  | S |  | M |  | E |
| K | N | I | G | H | T | E | D |  | O | P | T | S |
|  |  | L |  | T |  | G |  | E |  | I |  |  |
| K | I | C | K |  | C | O | M | B | I | N | E | D |
| O |  | H |  | S |  |  |  | B |  | G |  | R |
| A | V | A | L | A | N | C | H | E | S |  |  | E |
| L |  | R |  | U |  | L |  | D | A | T | E | D |
| A | D | D | I | C | T | E | D |  | I |  |  | G |
| S |  | S |  | Y |  | F |  | B | L | A | D | E |

## CROSSWORD 117

| B | A | N | A | N | A |  | P |  | M | U | C | H |
|---|---|---|---|---|---|---|---|---|---|---|---|---|
| E |  |  | L |  | F | O | L | I | O |  | I |  |
| F | O | A | L |  | F |  | E |  | R | A | P | T |
| A |  |  | E |  | I | N | A | P | T |  | H |  |
| L | A | R | Y | N | X |  | S |  | I | T | E | M |
| L |  |  |  | I |  |  | E |  | F |  | R |  |
| S | A | F | E | T | Y |  | S | H | Y | E | S | T |
|  | B |  | N |  | E |  |  | U |  |  |  | E |
| B | A | T | H |  | A |  | P | E | L | V | I | S |
|  | S |  | A | O | R | T | A |  | I |  |  | T |
| T | H | E | N |  | N |  | N |  | F | U | S | E |
|  | E |  | C | R | E | E | D |  | T |  |  | R |
| E | D | G | E |  | D |  | A | I | S | L | E | S |

## CROSSWORD 118

| T | H | U | D | D | I | N | G |  | V | O | I | D |
|---|---|---|---|---|---|---|---|---|---|---|---|---|
| U |  |  | I |  | R |  | A |  | O |  |  | E |
| B | A | G | S |  | K | I | L | O | W | A | T | T |
| E |  |  | C |  | E |  | O |  | E |  |  | A |
| R | E | C | O | R | D |  | R |  | L |  |  | I |
| S |  | H |  | U |  | N | E | W | S | M | A | N |
|  |  | A |  | N |  | O |  | A |  | O |  |  |
| F | O | R | A | G | E | R |  | V |  | P |  | A |
| L |  |  | R |  | L |  | T | E | A | S | E | D |
| A |  |  | M |  | U |  | W |  | N |  |  | H |
| U | N | S | A | D | D | L | E |  | V | I | N | E |
| N |  |  | D |  | E |  | E |  | I |  |  | R |
| T | U | B | A |  | S | I | D | E | L | I | N | E |

## CROSSWORD 119

| P | E | R | F | E | C | T |  | P | L | A | Z | A |
|---|---|---|---|---|---|---|---|---|---|---|---|---|
| R |  |  | O |  |  | R |  | I |  | L |  | C |
| I |  | A | G | I | T | A | T | E |  | L |  | H |
| M |  |  | G |  |  | Y |  | S | L | A | V | E |
| R | E | N | E | G | E |  | N |  |  | Y |  |  |
| O |  |  | D |  | P | L | A | N | N | E | R | S |
| S |  | S |  |  | I |  | V |  |  | D |  | C |
| E | N | C | I | R | C | L | E |  | S |  |  | A |
|  |  | R |  |  | S |  | L | I | Q | U | O | R |
| P | E | A | C | H |  | T |  |  | U |  |  | R |
| A |  | W |  | U | N | I | F | I | E | S |  | I |
| D |  | N |  | G |  | F |  |  | A |  |  | N |
| S | T | Y | L | E |  | F | L | A | K | I | N | G |

## CROSSWORD 120

| M | O | P | E | S |  | T |  | F |  | D |  | A |
|---|---|---|---|---|---|---|---|---|---|---|---|---|
| E |  |  | W |  | B | R | E | A | K | E | R | S |
| R | I | L | E | D |  | E |  | S |  | V |  | T |
| I |  |  | S | E | V | E | N | T | I | E | T | H |
| T |  | D |  | F |  |  |  | S |  | L |  | M |
| S | H | O | W | E | R | E | D |  | C | O | M | A |
|  |  | W |  | R |  | L |  | F |  | P |  |  |
| U | R | N | S |  | E | F | F | L | U | E | N | T |
| P |  | W |  | V |  |  |  | U |  | R |  | H |
| S | E | A | M | A | N | S | H | I | P |  |  | R |
| E |  | R |  | U |  | A |  | D | A | N | C | E |
| T | O | D | D | L | E | R | S |  | T |  |  | A |
| S |  | S |  | T |  | I |  | A | S | K | E | D |

## CROSSWORD 121

| R | E | G | A | R | D | | G | | T | O | Y | S |
|---|---|---|---|---|---|---|---|---|---|---|---|---|
| E | | | I | | A | W | A | S | H | | I | |
| F | E | N | D | | R | | M | | W | E | E | D |
| U | | | E | | T | I | B | I | A | | L | |
| S | P | A | D | E | S | | L | | R | O | D | E |
| E | | | | G | | | E | | T | | E | |
| D | A | M | A | G | E | | R | E | S | I | D | E |
| | L | | M | | Y | | | R | | | | N |
| S | E | M | I | | E | | P | R | A | Y | E | D |
| | R | | A | M | B | L | E | | M | | | L |
| S | T | A | B | | A | | A | | E | L | S | E |
| | E | | L | I | L | A | C | | N | | | S |
| E | D | D | Y | | L | | E | N | D | O | W | S |

## CROSSWORD 122

| A | F | F | R | A | Y | | P | | G | R | A | B |
|---|---|---|---|---|---|---|---|---|---|---|---|---|
| L | | | O | | E | L | A | T | E | | M | |
| G | L | I | B | | L | | L | | L | A | B | S |
| E | | | I | | P | L | E | A | D | | L | |
| B | L | I | N | D | S | | T | | I | B | I | S |
| R | | | | U | | | T | | N | | N | |
| A | B | O | D | E | S | | E | N | G | A | G | E |
| | O | | O | | C | | A | | | | | N |
| A | P | E | D | | R | | H | Y | B | R | I | D |
| | P | | G | U | A | V | A | | U | | | L |
| M | I | N | I | | T | | V | | G | O | R | E |
| | N | | N | I | C | H | E | | L | | | S |
| A | G | O | G | | H | | N | I | E | C | E | S |

## CROSSWORD 123

| F | I | N | A | N | C | E | S | | R | A | I | N |
|---|---|---|---|---|---|---|---|---|---|---|---|---|
| I | | | D | | H | | I | | O | | | E |
| E | Y | E | D | | A | R | G | U | A | B | L | E |
| S | | | L | | N | | N | | S | | | D |
| T | A | M | E | S | T | | A | | T | | | L |
| A | | I | | E | | C | L | O | S | U | R | E |
| | | L | | M | | O | | U | | N | | |
| L | O | D | G | I | N | G | | C | | D | | R |
| O | | | A | | E | | T | H | R | O | N | E |
| A | | | R | | W | | I | | I | | | P |
| F | I | L | A | M | E | N | T | | F | L | E | A |
| E | | | G | | S | | L | | L | | | I |
| R | I | S | E | | T | E | E | T | E | R | E | D |

## CROSSWORD 124

| Y | E | A | S | T | | B | | S | | C | | P |
|---|---|---|---|---|---|---|---|---|---|---|---|---|
| A | | | A | | P | L | A | T | O | O | N | S |
| C | R | A | G | S | | O | | O | | N | | A |
| H | | | E | L | E | C | T | R | I | C | A | L |
| T | | L | | A | | | | Y | | E | | M |
| S | H | A | B | B | I | E | R | | A | I | L | S |
| | | B | | S | | G | | O | | V | | |
| P | A | Y | S | | S | O | M | B | R | E | R | O |
| L | | R | | R | | | | O | | D | | N |
| E | L | I | M | I | N | A | T | E | D | | | W |
| A | | N | | V | | W | | S | A | M | B | A |
| S | I | T | U | A | T | E | D | | M | | | R |
| E | | H | | L | | D | | S | P | I | E | D |

## CROSSWORD 125

| F | L | O | A | T | E | D | | H | O | L | L | Y |
|---|---|---|---|---|---|---|---|---|---|---|---|---|
| O | | | D | | | E | | U | | O | | A |
| R | | E | D | U | C | A | T | E | | C | | N |
| E | | | I | | | R | | S | H | A | R | K |
| H | I | C | C | U | P | | S | | | T | | |
| A | | | T | | I | N | C | I | D | E | N | T |
| N | | M | | | X | | R | | | D | | W |
| D | E | A | D | L | I | N | E | | P | | | I |
| | | T | | | E | | W | E | A | V | E | D |
| S | L | A | N | G | | M | | | N | | | D |
| I | | D | | Y | E | A | R | N | E | D | | L |
| G | | O | | M | | C | | | L | | | E |
| H | E | R | B | S | | H | A | S | S | L | E | S |

## CROSSWORD 126

| T | O | M | A | T | O | | S | | O | R | B | S |
|---|---|---|---|---|---|---|---|---|---|---|---|---|
| H | | | I | | B | A | T | O | N | | A | |
| W | E | A | R | | E | | U | | E | A | C | H |
| A | | | E | | S | O | B | E | R | | K | |
| R | I | D | D | L | E | | B | | O | B | E | Y |
| T | | | | I | | | E | | U | | R | |
| S | T | U | R | D | Y | | D | E | S | I | S | T |
| | R | | E | | E | | | M | | | | H |
| V | I | S | A | | L | | V | U | L | G | A | R |
| | V | | D | E | L | V | E | | A | | | I |
| K | I | W | I | | I | | X | | T | O | L | L |
| | A | | L | A | N | C | E | | H | | | L |
| P | L | O | Y | | G | | D | R | E | A | M | S |

## CROSSWORD 127

| L | A | X | A | T | I | V | E | | E | D | G | E |
|---|---|---|---|---|---|---|---|---|---|---|---|---|
| E | | | B | | C | | N | | L | | | X |
| G | R | U | B | | I | N | C | U | B | A | T | E |
| U | | | O | | E | | A | | O | | | R |
| M | E | N | T | O | R | | S | | W | | | T |
| E | | O | | N | | C | E | N | S | O | R | S |
| | | O | | C | | U | | O | | R | | |
| C | O | N | T | E | S | T | | S | | A | | T |
| O | | | E | | E | | D | E | A | L | E | R |
| N | | | T | | C | | O | | L | | | A |
| F | I | S | H | B | O | W | L | | L | A | N | D |
| E | | | E | | N | | L | | O | | | E |
| R | O | A | R | | D | I | S | O | W | N | E | D |

## CROSSWORD 128

| V | O | I | C | E | | S | | P | | S | | P |
|---|---|---|---|---|---|---|---|---|---|---|---|---|
| I | | | H | | C | O | W | O | R | K | E | R |
| S | P | L | I | T | | N | | U | | I | | I |
| I | | | T | A | N | G | E | R | I | N | E | S |
| O | | A | | R | | | | S | | N | | O |
| N | O | B | O | D | I | E | S | | L | I | O | N |
| | | R | | Y | | B | | H | | E | | |
| B | O | A | T | | O | B | S | E | S | S | E | D |
| L | | S | | H | | | | N | | T | | E |
| I | M | I | T | A | T | I | O | N | S | | | F |
| N | | V | | I | | N | | A | C | U | T | E |
| K | N | E | E | L | I | N | G | | A | | | A |
| S | | S | | S | | S | | I | N | E | P | T |

# SOLUTIONS

CROSSWORD 133

CROSSWORD 134

CROSSWORD 135

CROSSWORD 136

# SOLUTIONS

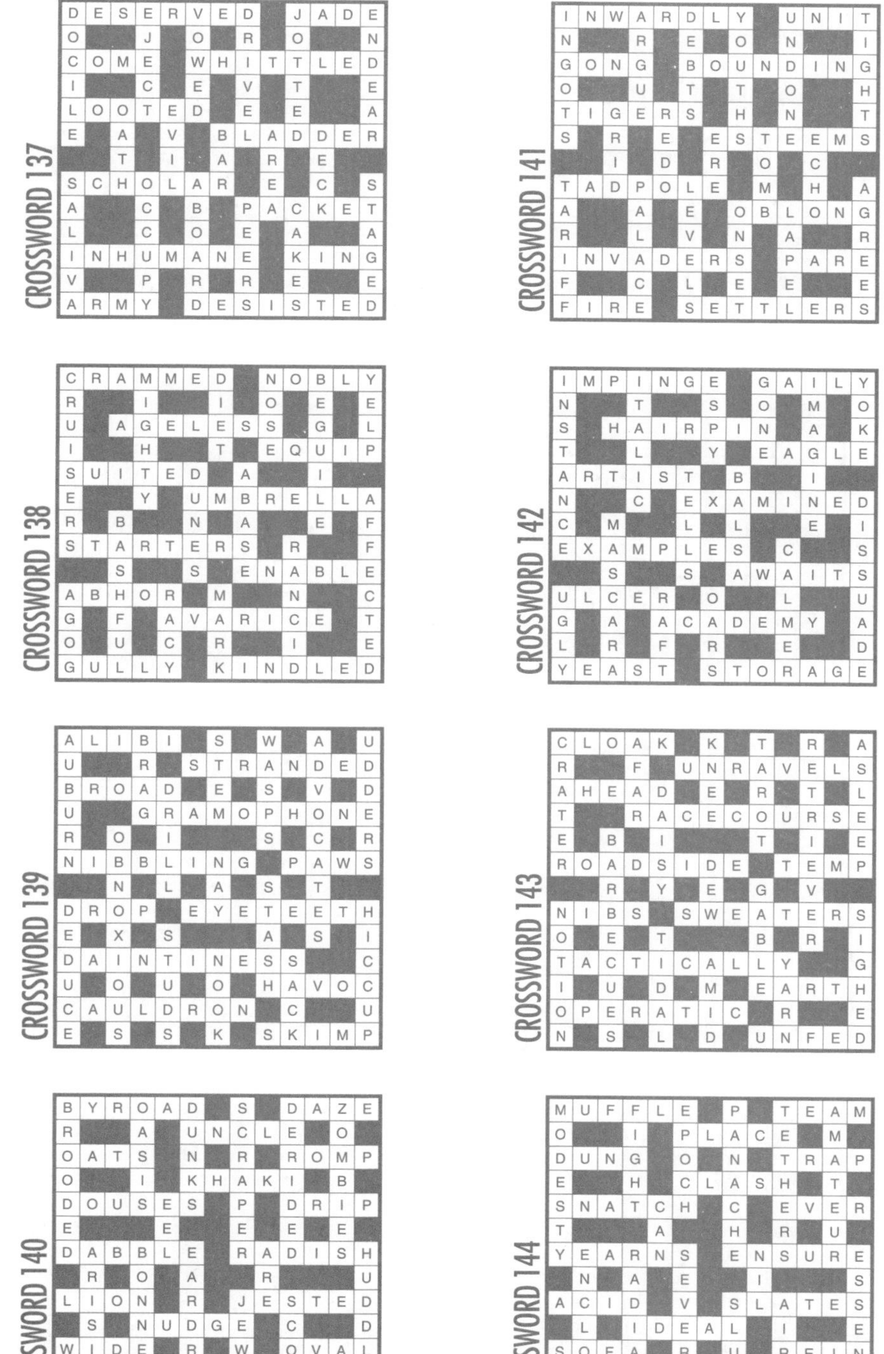
CROSSWORD 137
CROSSWORD 141
CROSSWORD 138
CROSSWORD 142
CROSSWORD 139
CROSSWORD 143
CROSSWORD 140
CROSSWORD 144

# SOLUTIONS

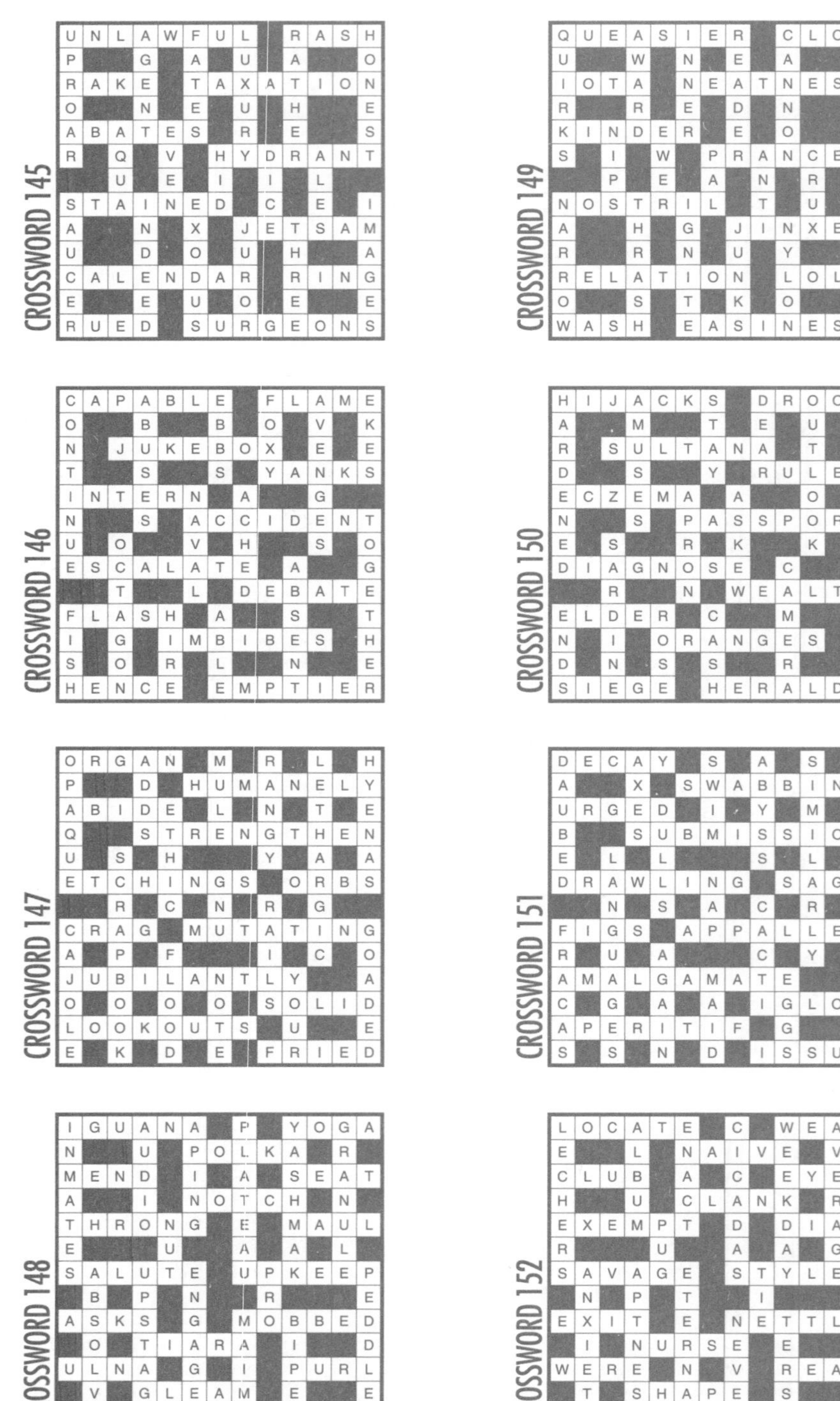

CROSSWORD 145
CROSSWORD 146
CROSSWORD 147
CROSSWORD 148
CROSSWORD 149
CROSSWORD 150
CROSSWORD 151
CROSSWORD 152

# SOLUTIONS

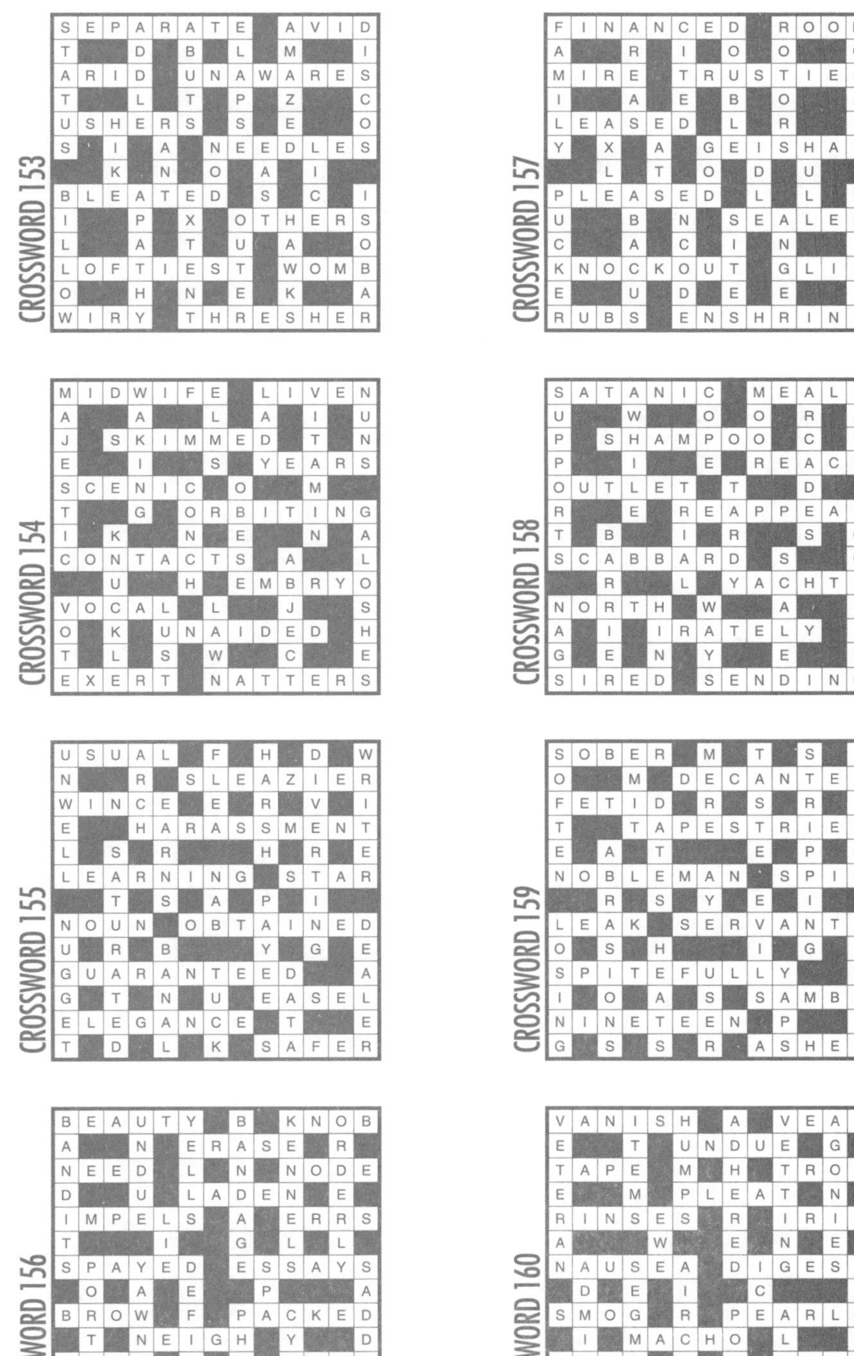
CROSSWORD 153
CROSSWORD 157
CROSSWORD 154
CROSSWORD 158
CROSSWORD 155
CROSSWORD 159
CROSSWORD 156
CROSSWORD 160

# SOLUTIONS

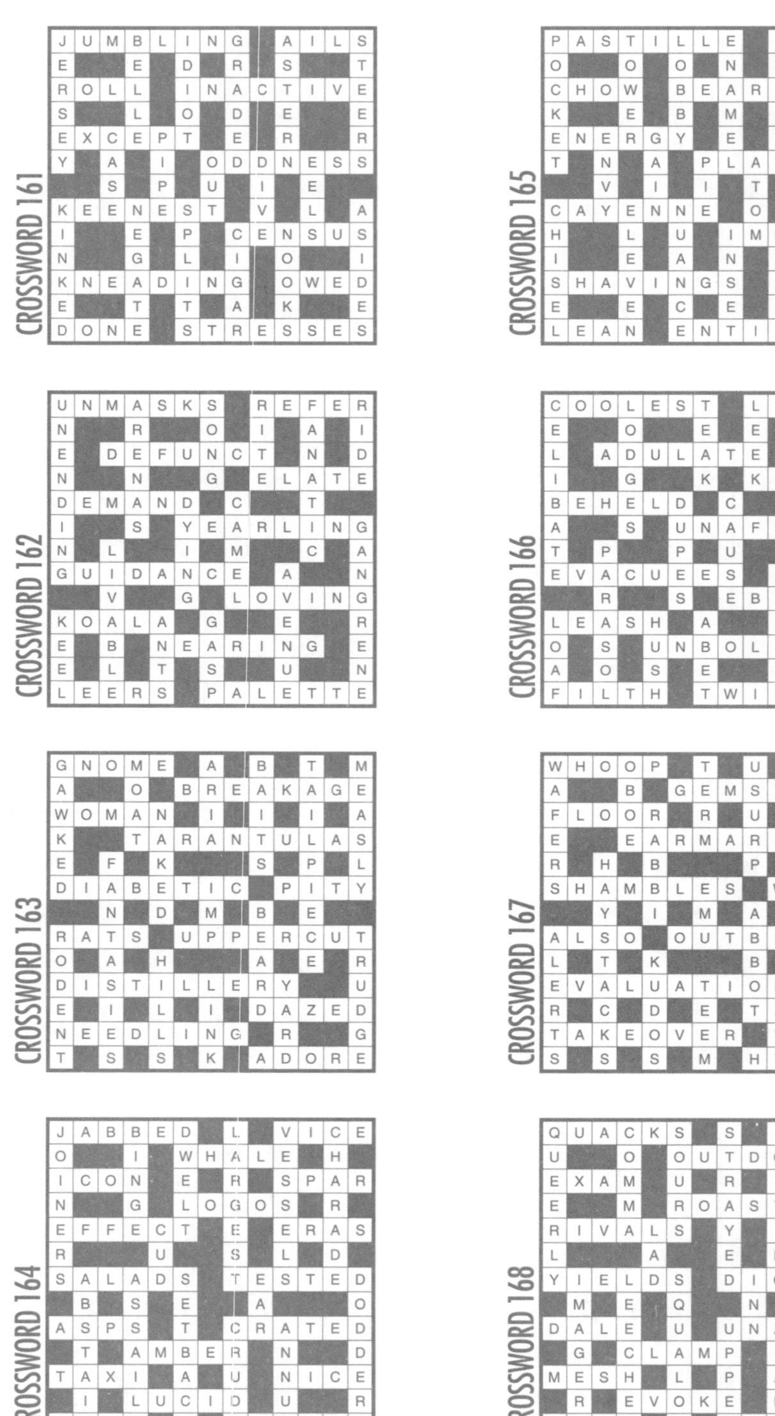
CROSSWORD 161
CROSSWORD 165
CROSSWORD 162
CROSSWORD 166
CROSSWORD 163
CROSSWORD 167
CROSSWORD 164
CROSSWORD 168

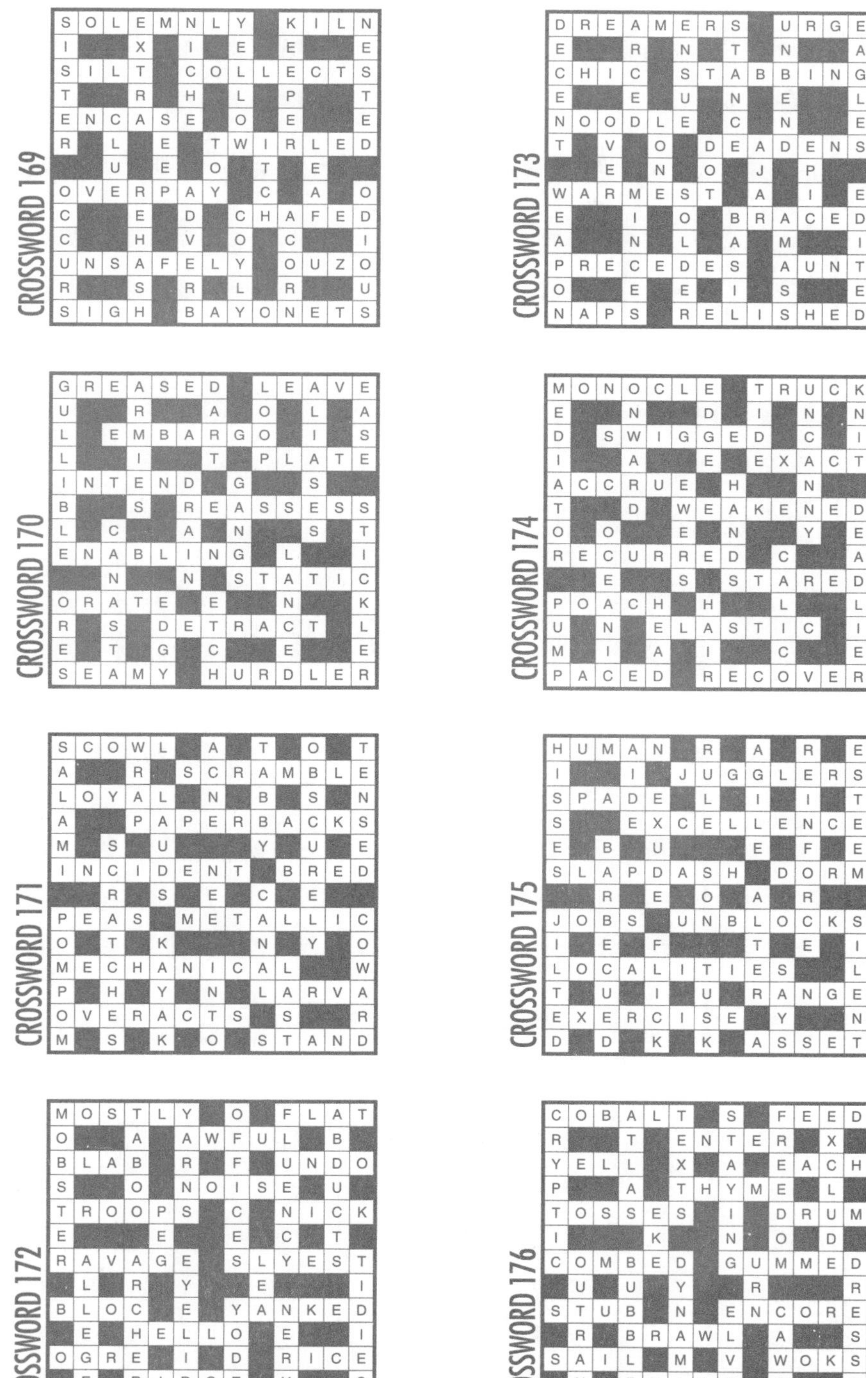
CROSSWORD 169
CROSSWORD 173
CROSSWORD 170
CROSSWORD 174
CROSSWORD 171
CROSSWORD 175
CROSSWORD 172
CROSSWORD 176

# SOLUTIONS

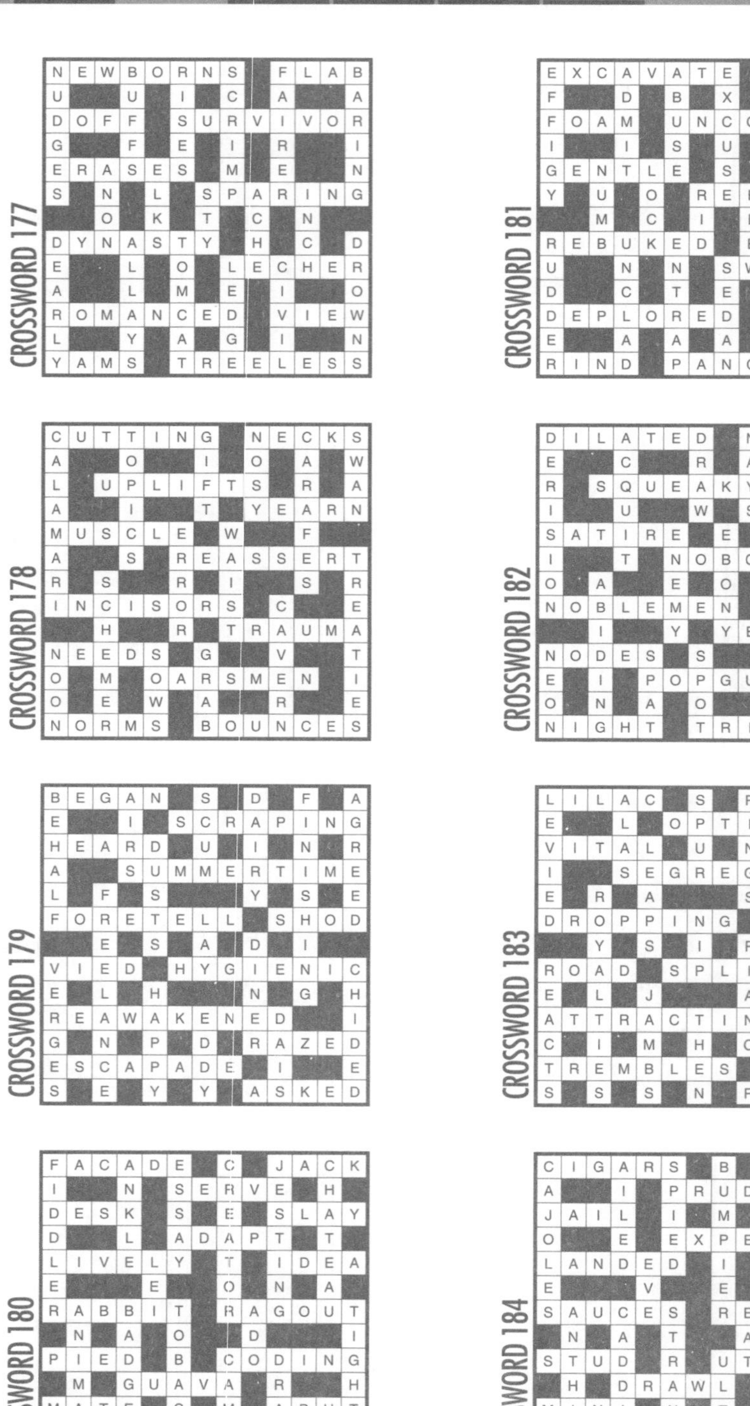

CROSSWORD 177
CROSSWORD 181
CROSSWORD 178
CROSSWORD 182
CROSSWORD 179
CROSSWORD 183
CROSSWORD 180
CROSSWORD 184

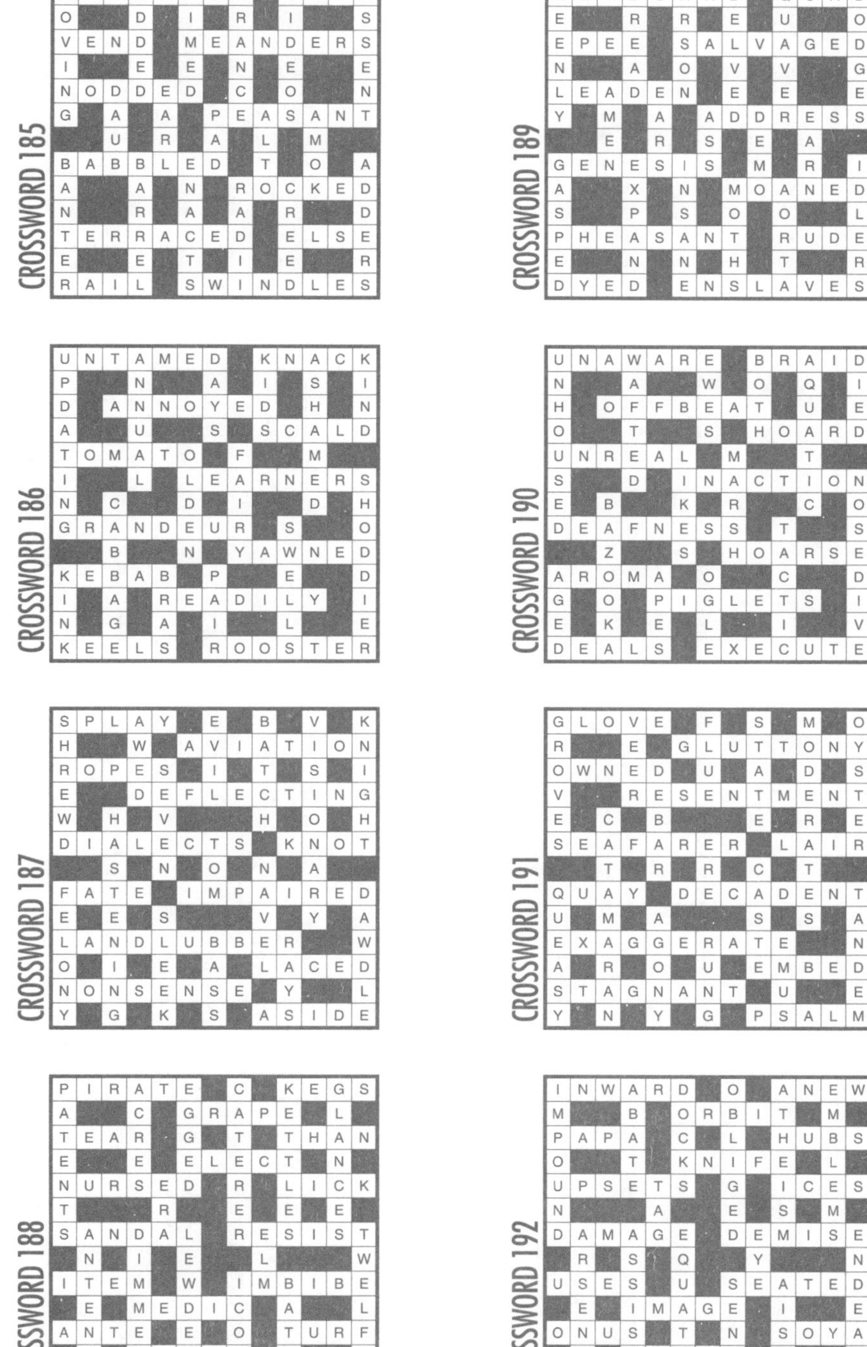
CROSSWORD 185
CROSSWORD 189
CROSSWORD 186
CROSSWORD 190
CROSSWORD 187
CROSSWORD 191
CROSSWORD 188
CROSSWORD 192

# SOLUTIONS

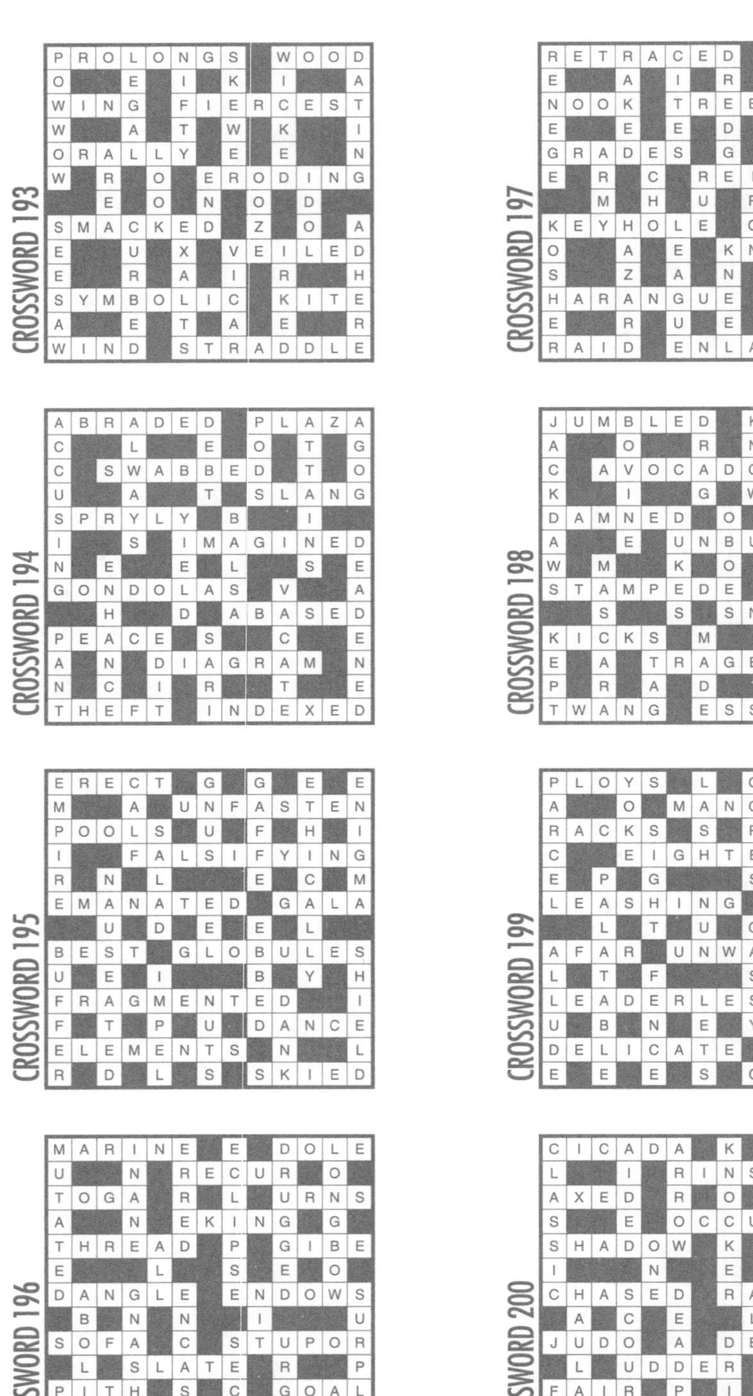
CROSSWORD 193
CROSSWORD 197
CROSSWORD 194
CROSSWORD 198
CROSSWORD 195
CROSSWORD 199
CROSSWORD 196
CROSSWORD 200

CROSSWORD 201

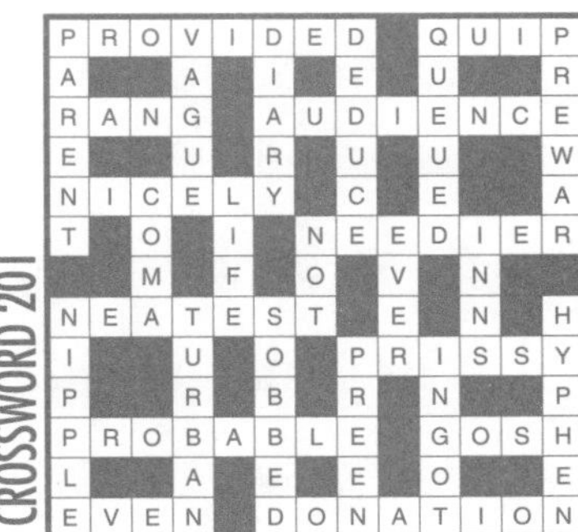

CROSSWORD 205

CROSSWORD 202

CROSSWORD 206

CROSSWORD 203

CROSSWORD 207

CROSSWORD 204

CROSSWORD 208

# SOLUTIONS

## CROSSWORD 209

| G | R | E | A | T | E | S | T |  | G | O | R | Y |
|---|---|---|---|---|---|---|---|---|---|---|---|---|
| I |  |  | L |  | X |  | E |  | U |  |  | O |
| G | A | L | A |  | A | D | M | I | T | T | E | D |
| O |  |  | R |  | M |  | P |  | T |  |  | E |
| L | L | A | M | A | S |  | L |  | E |  |  | L |
| O |  | B |  | I |  | G | E | N | D | E | R | S |
|  |  | L |  | D |  | A |  | A |  | V |  |  |
| B | R | E | W | E | R | S |  | M |  | E |  | U |
| E |  |  | I |  | O |  | Z | E | B | R | A | S |
| A |  |  | Z |  | U |  | O |  | U |  |  | A |
| U | N | F | A | S | T | E | N |  | G | A | R | B |
| T |  |  | R |  | E |  | E |  | L |  |  | L |
| Y | A | R | D |  | D | I | S | P | E | N | S | E |

## CROSSWORD 210

| M | O | G | U | L |  | I |  | E |  | C |  | M |
|---|---|---|---|---|---|---|---|---|---|---|---|---|
| O |  |  | N |  | N | O | R | M | A | L | L | Y |
| B | R | I | D | E |  | T |  | E |  | U |  | S |
| B |  |  | O | B | T | A | I | N | A | B | L | E |
| E |  | S |  | O |  |  |  | D |  | H |  | L |
| D | E | C | A | N | T | E | D |  | W | O | O | F |
|  |  | R |  | Y |  | R |  | S |  | U |  |  |
| R | O | A | R |  | P | R | O | M | I | S | E | D |
| E |  | M |  | S |  |  |  | E |  | E |  | O |
| N | O | B | L | E | W | O | M | A | N |  |  | O |
| E |  | L |  | D |  | N |  | R | A | C | E | D |
| G | R | E | N | A | D | E | S |  | I |  |  | L |
| E |  | D |  | N |  | S |  | C | L | O | S | E |

## CROSSWORD 211

| U | T | T | E | R | L | Y |  | L | E | V | E | E |
|---|---|---|---|---|---|---|---|---|---|---|---|---|
| N |  |  | L |  |  | O |  | O |  | I |  | M |
| W |  | L | O | U | N | G | E | D |  | S |  | I |
| A |  |  | P |  |  | A |  | E | D | I | C | T |
| N | O | V | E | L | S |  | B |  |  | B |  |  |
| T |  |  | S |  | U | S | E | F | U | L | L | Y |
| E |  | C |  |  | G |  | A |  |  | Y |  | U |
| D | R | A | W | B | A | C | K |  | B |  |  | L |
|  |  | N |  |  | R |  | S | C | A | R | C | E |
| D | R | A | M | A |  | H |  |  | N |  |  | T |
| I |  | S |  | P | L | A | T | E | A | U |  | I |
| E |  | T |  | E |  | I |  |  | N |  |  | D |
| D | R | A | M | S |  | R | E | L | A | P | S | E |

## CROSSWORD 212

| I | N | D | E | E | D |  | H |  | D | E | A | R |
|---|---|---|---|---|---|---|---|---|---|---|---|---|
| M |  |  | X |  | E | R | A | S | E |  | V |  |
| A | T | O | P |  | C |  | P |  | V | I | E | D |
| G |  |  | E |  | R | U | P | E | E |  | R |  |
| E | M | P | L | O | Y |  | I |  | L | O | A | D |
| R |  |  |  | A |  |  | E |  | O |  | G |  |
| Y | A | C | H | T | S |  | R | A | P | P | E | D |
|  | L |  | E |  | C |  |  | S |  |  |  | A |
| B | L | O | C |  | R |  | A | P | A | T | H | Y |
|  | U |  | K | H | A | K | I |  | T |  |  | C |
| I | D | O | L |  | T |  | S |  | T | O | G | A |
|  | E |  | E | X | C | E | L |  | I |  |  | R |
| O | D | D | S |  | H |  | E | X | C | U | S | E |

## CROSSWORD 213

| V | O | L | A | T | I | L | E |  | N | U | M | B |
|---|---|---|---|---|---|---|---|---|---|---|---|---|
| A |  |  | U |  | D |  | N |  | E |  |  | A |
| N | E | E | D |  | L | E | A | K | A | G | E | S |
| D |  |  | I |  | E |  | B |  | R |  |  | I |
| A | B | A | T | E | D |  | L |  | E |  |  | N |
| L |  | Q |  | A |  | S | E | A | R | I | N | G |
|  |  | U |  | C |  | A |  | R |  | S |  |  |
| C | O | A | C | H | E | D |  | I |  | L |  | A |
| U |  |  | O |  | X |  | L | A | B | E | L | S |
| R |  |  | B |  | C |  | O |  | U |  |  | T |
| B | R | O | W | B | E | A | T |  | L | A | S | H |
| E |  |  | E |  | E |  | U |  | G |  |  | M |
| D | U | M | B |  | D | Y | S | L | E | X | I | A |

## CROSSWORD 214

| N | E | R | V | E |  | K |  | F |  | D |  | K |
|---|---|---|---|---|---|---|---|---|---|---|---|---|
| A |  |  | E |  | I | N | C | I | S | I | O | N |
| B | R | O | A | D |  | E |  | N |  | V |  | I |
| B |  |  | L | A | C | E | R | A | T | I | N | G |
| E |  | C |  | L |  |  |  | L |  | D |  | H |
| D | E | A | D | E | N | E | D |  | C | E | N | T |
|  |  | T |  | S |  | K |  | D |  | N |  |  |
| D | R | A | G |  | H | E | R | A | L | D | E | D |
| O |  | M |  | G |  |  |  | I |  | S |  | R |
| C | H | A | R | A | C | T | E | R | S |  |  | E |
| I |  | R |  | F |  | O |  | Y | E | A | R | N |
| L | E | A | P | F | R | O | G |  | C |  |  | C |
| E |  | N |  | E |  | L |  | S | T | A | S | H |

## CROSSWORD 215

| J | U | M | B | L | E | D |  | P | L | A | Z | A |
|---|---|---|---|---|---|---|---|---|---|---|---|---|
| O |  |  | U |  |  | E |  | O |  | L |  | N |
| Y |  | A | C | C | L | A | I | M |  | M |  | T |
| S |  |  | K |  |  | L |  | P | E | A | C | E |
| T | H | R | E | A | D |  | B |  |  | N |  |  |
| I |  |  | D |  | U | N | A | F | R | A | I | D |
| C |  | T |  |  | P |  | L |  |  | C |  | R |
| K | E | E | N | N | E | S | S |  | D |  |  | E |
|  |  | M |  |  | S |  | A | B | A | S | E | D |
| R | I | P | E | R |  | Y |  |  | N |  |  | G |
| O |  | T |  | I | T | A | L | I | C | S |  | I |
| M |  | E |  | F |  | R |  |  | E |  |  | N |
| P | A | D | R | E |  | N | U | R | S | I | N | G |

## CROSSWORD 216

| C | R | A | T | E | S |  | S |  | G | O | A | D |
|---|---|---|---|---|---|---|---|---|---|---|---|---|
| O |  |  | A |  | T | A | P | E | R |  | M |  |
| M | A | I | M |  | E |  | E |  | A | W | A | Y |
| P |  |  | E |  | E | N | A | C | T |  | T |  |
| O | U | T | D | I | D |  | K |  | I | C | E | D |
| S |  |  |  | L |  |  | E |  | N |  | U |  |
| E | A | S | E | L | S |  | R | E | G | A | R | D |
|  | W |  | N |  | I |  |  | R |  |  |  | E |
| S | K | I | D |  | G |  | D | A | U | N | T | S |
|  | W |  | U | S | H | E | R |  | N |  |  | P |
| F | A | I | R |  | T |  | E |  | L | A | V | A |
|  | R |  | E | P | E | E | S |  | I |  |  | I |
| O | D | E | S |  | D |  | S | I | T | T | E | R |

# SOLUTIONS

## CROSSWORD 217

| F | I | N | A | N | C | E | D | | F | O | A | M |
|---|---|---|---|---|---|---|---|---|---|---|---|---|
| R | | | G | | A | | O | | O | | | O |
| U | L | N | A | | S | Q | U | I | R | R | E | L |
| M | | | I | | T | | B | | C | | | A |
| P | R | A | N | C | E | | L | | E | | | R |
| S | | R | | O | | V | E | N | D | O | R | S |
| | | E | | R | | E | | O | | V | | |
| W | E | A | K | E | S | T | | D | | E | | I |
| A | | | E | | C | | F | E | A | R | E | D |
| F | | | B | | R | | A | | I | | | E |
| F | I | L | A | M | E | N | T | | M | A | M | A |
| L | | | B | | A | | A | | E | | | L |
| E | N | D | S | | M | A | L | A | D | I | E | S |

## CROSSWORD 218

| R | E | L | A | Y | | P | | A | | N | | M |
|---|---|---|---|---|---|---|---|---|---|---|---|---|
| O | | | L | | P | R | A | C | T | I | C | E |
| C | R | E | A | K | | O | | R | | G | | S |
| K | | | S | A | N | D | W | I | C | H | E | S |
| E | | M | | Y | | | | D | | T | | E |
| T | E | E | N | A | G | E | R | | E | G | G | S |
| | | N | | K | | A | | E | | O | | |
| M | E | A | L | | D | R | I | V | E | W | A | Y |
| A | | G | | B | | | | I | | N | | A |
| N | E | E | D | L | E | S | S | L | Y | | | W |
| A | | R | | E | | U | | S | A | T | I | N |
| G | U | I | D | A | N | C | E | | P | | | E |
| E | | E | | K | | H | | A | S | K | E | D |

## CROSSWORD 219

| P | I | R | A | N | H | A | | B | R | A | N | D |
|---|---|---|---|---|---|---|---|---|---|---|---|---|
| H | | | M | | | C | | U | | R | | A |
| Y | | B | U | N | C | H | E | S | | C | | T |
| S | | | S | | | E | | T | I | A | R | A |
| I | N | T | E | N | D | | C | | | D | | |
| C | | | D | | W | R | A | P | P | E | R | S |
| A | | O | | | A | | D | | | S | | E |
| L | E | C | T | U | R | E | D | | B | | | E |
| | | E | | | F | | Y | I | E | L | D | S |
| B | L | A | N | D | | C | | | H | | | A |
| O | | N | | R | E | A | C | T | E | D | | W |
| O | | I | | A | | M | | | A | | | E |
| M | A | C | A | W | | P | E | D | D | L | E | D |

## CROSSWORD 220

| A | T | T | A | C | H | | P | | G | O | A | L |
|---|---|---|---|---|---|---|---|---|---|---|---|---|
| D | | | R | | E | V | A | D | E | | L | |
| J | A | W | S | | W | | N | | N | I | B | S |
| U | | | O | | E | L | A | T | E | | I | |
| S | T | O | N | E | D | | C | | T | O | N | S |
| T | | | | L | | | H | | I | | O | |
| S | T | I | G | M | A | | E | N | C | A | S | E |
| | A | | A | | D | | | E | | | | L |
| S | T | I | R | | V | | D | E | B | A | S | E |
| | T | | L | E | A | V | E | | U | | | C |
| S | O | Y | A | | N | | T | | M | I | T | T |
| | O | | N | I | C | H | E | | P | | | E |
| U | S | E | D | | E | | R | A | S | P | E | D |

## CROSSWORD 221

| F | L | O | A | T | I | N | G | | U | R | N | S |
|---|---|---|---|---|---|---|---|---|---|---|---|---|
| I | | | S | | M | | O | | N | | | E |
| N | E | T | S | | P | L | A | Y | B | O | Y | S |
| I | | | E | | L | | T | | O | | | A |
| N | E | A | T | L | Y | | E | | L | | | M |
| G | | U | | O | | R | E | S | T | A | T | E |
| | | R | | O | | A | | O | | M | | |
| R | E | A | D | M | I | T | | D | | O | | A |
| A | | | E | | M | | J | A | C | K | A | L |
| M | | | M | | P | | U | | I | | | I |
| M | A | C | A | R | O | N | I | | G | O | N | G |
| E | | | N | | R | | C | | A | | | N |
| D | Y | E | D | | T | H | E | O | R | I | E | S |

## CROSSWORD 222

| H | U | M | U | S | | P | | C | | S | | A |
|---|---|---|---|---|---|---|---|---|---|---|---|---|
| E | | | R | | H | I | J | A | C | K | E | D |
| A | D | A | G | E | | P | | B | | I | | H |
| R | | | E | X | P | E | R | I | E | N | C | E |
| S | | P | | I | | | | N | | N | | R |
| E | L | A | P | S | I | N | G | | J | I | V | E |
| | | N | | T | | U | | F | | E | | |
| B | O | O | T | | U | N | D | E | R | S | E | A |
| E | | R | | A | | | | A | | T | | B |
| H | E | A | D | L | I | G | H | T | S | | | O |
| O | | M | | P | | E | | S | A | U | N | A |
| L | E | A | T | H | E | R | Y | | L | | | R |
| D | | S | | A | | M | | S | T | O | O | D |

## CROSSWORD 223

| V | O | Y | A | G | E | D | | T | W | E | A | K |
|---|---|---|---|---|---|---|---|---|---|---|---|---|
| I | | | R | | | E | | A | | N | | I |
| C | | R | E | B | U | F | F | S | | T | | T |
| I | | | N | | | T | | K | N | A | V | E |
| N | E | G | A | T | E | | G | | | I | | |
| I | | | S | | E | X | A | M | P | L | E | S |
| T | | R | | | R | | N | | | S | | H |
| Y | E | A | R | L | I | N | G | | B | | | A |
| | | L | | | E | | S | T | A | T | I | C |
| M | A | L | E | S | | G | | | Z | | | K |
| O | | I | | A | N | A | G | R | A | M | | L |
| O | | E | | F | | S | | | A | | | E |
| D | O | D | G | E | | H | O | A | R | D | E | D |

## CROSSWORD 224

| Y | A | N | K | E | D | | A | | N | I | C | E |
|---|---|---|---|---|---|---|---|---|---|---|---|---|
| E | | | O | | E | A | G | L | E | | H | |
| L | A | M | A | | M | | E | | E | P | I | C |
| L | | | L | | O | G | L | E | D | | S | |
| O | R | D | A | I | N | | E | | L | I | E | D |
| W | | | | N | | | S | | E | | L | |
| S | I | R | E | N | S | | S | A | D | I | S | M |
| | N | | X | | E | | | G | | | | I |
| C | H | I | C | | T | | F | O | L | I | O | S |
| | A | | E | M | B | E | R | | A | | | E |
| F | L | I | P | | A | | E | | Y | O | U | R |
| | E | | T | U | C | K | S | | E | | | L |
| A | D | D | S | | K | | H | E | R | E | S | Y |

# SOLUTIONS

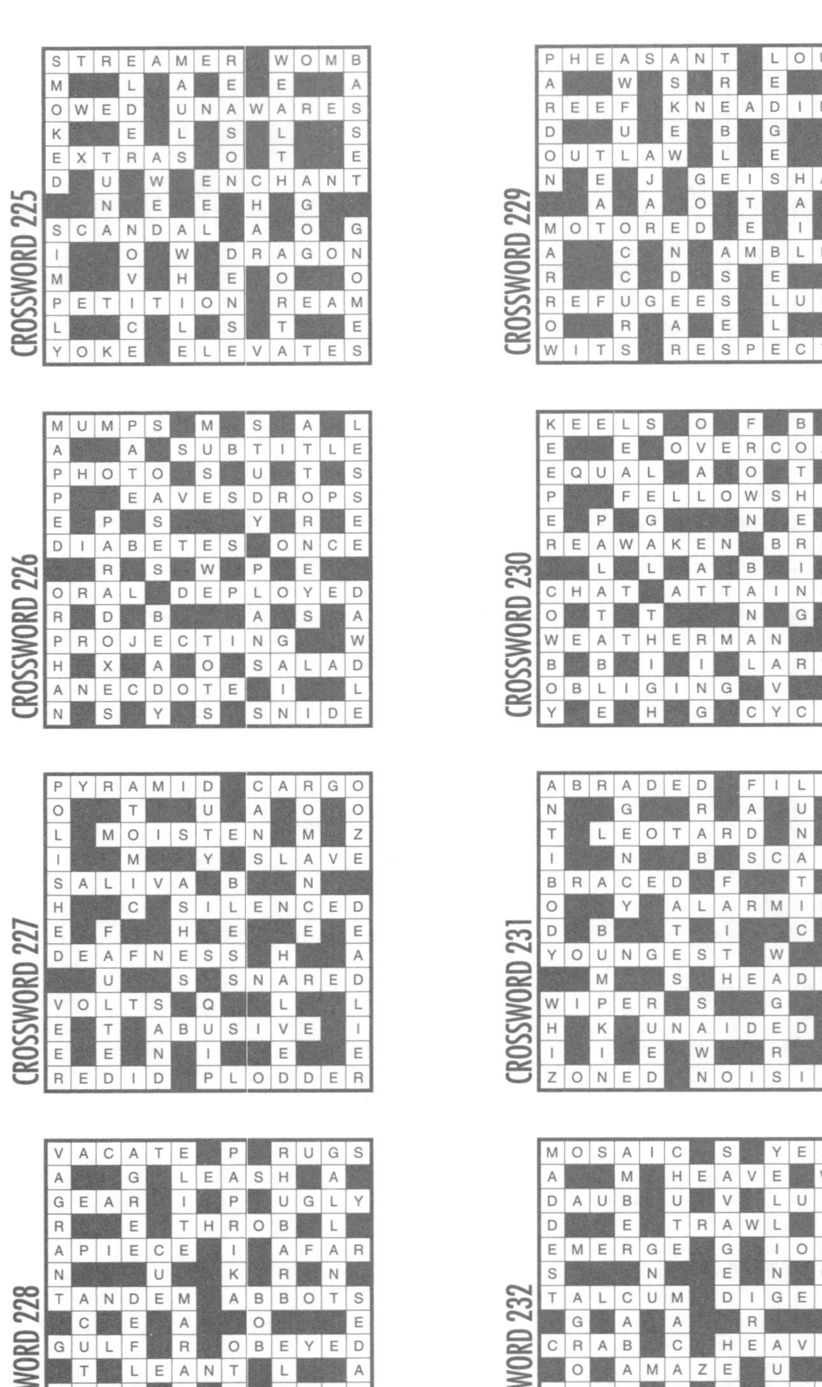
CROSSWORD 225
CROSSWORD 229
CROSSWORD 226
CROSSWORD 230
CROSSWORD 227
CROSSWORD 231
CROSSWORD 228
CROSSWORD 232

## CROSSWORD 233

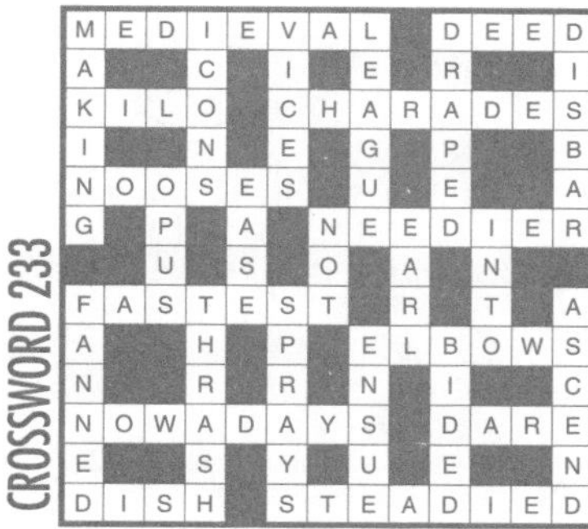

| M | E | D | I | E | V | A | L |  | D | E | E | D |
|---|---|---|---|---|---|---|---|---|---|---|---|---|
| A |  |  | C |  | I |  | E |  | R |  |  | I |
| K | I | L | O |  | C | H | A | R | A | D | E | S |
| I |  |  | N |  | E |  | G |  | P |  |  | B |
| N | O | O | S | E | S |  | U |  | E |  |  | A |
| G |  | P |  | A |  | N | E | E | D | I | E | R |
|  |  | U |  | S |  | O |  | A |  | N |  |  |
| F | A | S | T | E | S | T |  | R |  | T |  | A |
| A |  |  | H |  | P |  | E | L | B | O | W | S |
| N |  |  | R |  | R |  | N |  | I |  |  | C |
| N | O | W | A | D | A | Y | S |  | D | A | R | E |
| E |  |  | S |  | Y |  | U |  | E |  |  | N |
| D | I | S | H |  | S | T | E | A | D | I | E | D |

## CROSSWORD 234

| O | C | E | A | N |  | W |  | H |  | L |  | H |
|---|---|---|---|---|---|---|---|---|---|---|---|---|
| P |  |  | U |  | D | E | M | U | R | E | L | Y |
| P | R | I | N | T |  | R |  | M |  | N |  | E |
| O |  |  | T | E | L | E | V | I | S | I | O | N |
| S |  | S |  | P |  |  |  | D |  | E |  | A |
| E | X | A | M | I | N | E | R |  | A | N | T | S |
|  |  | U |  | D |  | M |  | A |  | T |  |  |
| D | U | C | T |  | Q | U | I | B | B | L | E | D |
| E |  | E |  | R |  |  |  | O |  | Y |  | E |
| A | P | P | R | E | H | E | N | D | S |  |  | G |
| R |  | A |  | M |  | A |  | E | A | G | E | R |
| L | A | N | K | I | E | S | T |  | S |  |  | E |
| Y |  | S |  | T |  | Y |  | S | H | A | M | E |

## CROSSWORD 235

| S | U | B | J | E | C | T |  | W | E | A | R | Y |
|---|---|---|---|---|---|---|---|---|---|---|---|---|
| H |  |  | I |  |  | H |  | E |  | L |  | A |
| R |  | P | L | A | C | A | R | D |  | L |  | M |
| I |  |  | T |  |  | N |  | S | O | A | R | S |
| V | E | N | E | E | R |  | R |  |  | Y |  |  |
| E |  |  | D |  | E | V | A | C | U | E | E | S |
| L |  | W |  |  | L |  | I |  |  | D |  | C |
| S | C | A | B | B | A | R | D |  | C |  |  | H |
|  |  | D |  |  | X |  | S | E | A | N | C | E |
| K | U | D | O | S |  | Z |  |  | M |  |  | D |
| N |  | L |  | T | W | I | R | L | E | D |  | U |
| E |  | E |  | A |  | N |  |  | R |  |  | L |
| W | I | D | E | R |  | C | A | P | A | B | L | E |

## CROSSWORD 236

| H | A | Z | A | R | D |  | R |  | L | E | A | P |
|---|---|---|---|---|---|---|---|---|---|---|---|---|
| O |  |  | V |  | I | M | A | G | E |  | V |  |
| W | O | R | E |  | A |  | V |  | M | O | A | N |
| E |  |  | R |  | R | E | A | L | M |  | R |  |
| V | A | S | T | L | Y |  | G |  | I | R | I | S |
| E |  |  |  | E |  |  | E |  | N |  | C |  |
| R | A | S | C | A | L |  | D | A | G | G | E | R |
|  | V |  | L |  | E |  |  | N |  |  |  | E |
| S | O | F | A |  | E |  | B | Y | P | A | S | S |
|  | C |  | I | N | C | U | R |  | O |  |  | I |
| F | A | R | M |  | H |  | I |  | S | T | A | G |
|  | D |  | E | V | E | N | S |  | S |  |  | N |
| F | O | L | D |  | S |  | K | N | E | E | L | S |

## CROSSWORD 237

| S | E | A | S | H | E | L | L |  | H | U | L | A |
|---|---|---|---|---|---|---|---|---|---|---|---|---|
| C |  |  | A |  | N |  | E |  | O |  |  | B |
| H | E | R | B |  | V | I | A | D | U | C | T | S |
| E |  |  | L |  | O |  | D |  | S |  |  | U |
| M | E | R | E | L | Y |  | E |  | E |  |  | R |
| E |  | I |  | E |  | G | N | A | S | H | E | D |
|  |  | C |  | A |  | A |  | X |  | E |  |  |
| S | N | E | A | K | E | D |  | L |  | A |  | F |
| O |  |  | N |  | C |  | D | E | A | L | E | R |
| U |  |  | G |  | H |  | O |  | B |  |  | E |
| G | A | L | L | E | O | N | S |  | A | N | O | N |
| H |  |  | E |  | E |  | E |  | T |  |  | Z |
| T | E | N | D |  | S | U | D | D | E | N | L | Y |

## CROSSWORD 238

| H | U | F | F | S |  | S |  | F |  | I |  | A |
|---|---|---|---|---|---|---|---|---|---|---|---|---|
| I |  |  | I |  | S | T | R | A | N | D | E | D |
| G | U | A | V | A |  | A |  | I |  | E |  | V |
| H |  |  | E | X | U | B | E | R | A | N | C | E |
| E |  | O |  | I |  |  |  | S |  | T |  | R |
| R | E | C | E | N | T | L | Y |  | L | I | M | B |
|  |  | T |  | G |  | O |  | S |  | C |  |  |
| L | O | A | N |  | S | T | O | C | K | A | D | E |
| I |  | G |  | S |  |  |  | A |  | L |  | R |
| A | D | O | L | E | S | C | E | N | T |  |  | O |
| B |  | N |  | P |  | A |  | T | A | X | E | D |
| L | E | A | N | I | N | G | S |  | C |  |  | E |
| E |  | L |  | A |  | E |  | H | O | W | L | S |

## CROSSWORD 239

| S | U | B | S | I | D | Y |  | Y | E | A | S | T |
|---|---|---|---|---|---|---|---|---|---|---|---|---|
| H |  |  | E |  |  | A |  | E |  | R |  | I |
| A |  | R | E | N | E | W | A | L |  | R |  | M |
| M |  |  | S |  |  | N |  | P | L | A | C | E |
| B | E | H | A | V | E |  | A |  |  | Y |  |  |
| L |  |  | W |  | N | O | S | I | N | E | S | S |
| E |  | A |  |  | T |  | I |  |  | D |  | Y |
| D | E | B | A | R | R | E | D |  | C |  |  | N |
|  |  | I |  |  | Y |  | E | R | A | S | E | D |
| O | L | D | E | N |  | C |  |  | V |  |  | R |
| U |  | I |  | O | R | A | N | G | E | S |  | O |
| S |  | N |  | D |  | L |  |  | R |  |  | M |
| T | O | G | A | S |  | F | U | R | N | A | C | E |

## CROSSWORD 240

| W | R | E | A | T | H |  | E |  | E | V | I | L |
|---|---|---|---|---|---|---|---|---|---|---|---|---|
| I |  |  | L |  | E | X | A | L | T |  | M |  |
| G | L | I | B |  | E |  | R |  | C | L | A | N |
| W |  |  | U |  | L | U | N | C | H |  | G |  |
| A | R | O | M | A | S |  | E |  | I | B | I | S |
| M |  |  |  | R |  |  | S |  | N |  | N |  |
| S | A | L | A | M | I |  | T | A | G | G | E | D |
|  | V |  | U |  | N |  |  | I |  |  |  | E |
| W | E | L | D |  | S |  | I | R | O | N | I | C |
|  | N |  | I | C | I | N | G |  | N |  |  | E |
| J | U | S | T |  | S |  | L |  | S | P | U | N |
|  | E |  | O | U | T | D | O |  | E |  |  | C |
| U | S | E | R |  | S |  | O | U | T | L | A | Y |

# SOLUTIONS

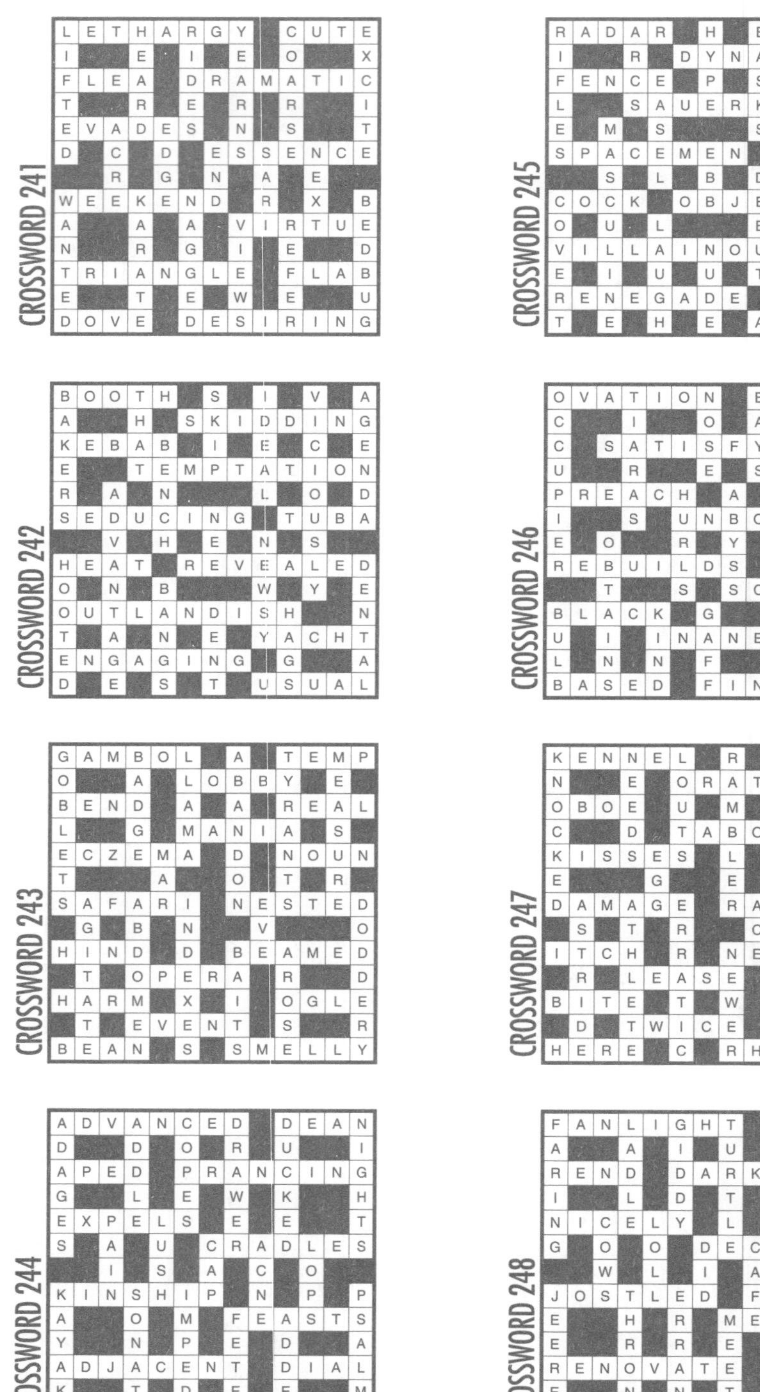

CROSSWORD 241
CROSSWORD 245
CROSSWORD 242
CROSSWORD 246
CROSSWORD 243
CROSSWORD 247
CROSSWORD 244
CROSSWORD 248

# SOLUTIONS

## CROSSWORD 249

| O | V | A | L | S |  | E |  | S |  | S |  | O |
|---|---|---|---|---|---|---|---|---|---|---|---|---|
| U |  |  | I |  | E | D | U | C | A | T | E | D |
| N | O | M | A | D |  | G |  | O |  | A |  | D |
| C |  |  | R | E | C | Y | C | L | A | B | L | E |
| E |  | J |  | C |  |  |  | D |  | I |  | S |
| S | E | A | F | A | R | E | R |  | C | L | O | T |
|  |  | Y |  | Y |  | Y |  | M |  | I |  |  |
| F | O | W | L |  | P | E | D | A | N | T | I | C |
| O |  | A |  | O |  |  |  | P |  | Y |  | A |
| O | B | L | I | G | I | N | G | L | Y |  |  | N |
| L |  | K |  | R |  | U |  | E | A | T | E | N |
| E | L | E | V | E | N | T | H |  | N |  |  | E |
| D |  | R |  | S |  | S |  | S | K | I | E | D |

## CROSSWORD 250

| S | A | F | A | R | I | S |  | H | O | P | E | D |
|---|---|---|---|---|---|---|---|---|---|---|---|---|
| P |  |  | P |  |  | T |  | I |  | H |  | E |
| O |  | A | P | P | L | A | U | D |  | O |  | A |
| R |  |  | E |  |  | Y |  | E | M | B | E | D |
| A | R | M | A | D | A |  | A |  |  | I |  |  |
| D |  |  | R |  | V | I | G | I | L | A | N | T |
| I |  | M |  |  | O |  | O |  |  | S |  | O |
| C | H | A | M | P | I | O | N |  | S |  |  | A |
|  |  | L |  |  | D |  | Y | O | U | T | H | S |
| O | P | A | L | S |  | S |  |  | P |  |  | T |
| P |  | R |  | N | U | A | N | C | E | S |  | I |
| T |  | I |  | U |  | C |  |  | R |  |  | N |
| S | L | A | N | G |  | S | O | B | B | I | N | G |

## CROSSWORD 251

| E | X | P | A | N | D |  | G |  | C | H | I | P |
|---|---|---|---|---|---|---|---|---|---|---|---|---|
| N |  |  | S |  | W | H | A | L | E |  | N |  |
| I | N | C | H |  | E |  | M |  | L | E | I | S |
| G |  |  | E |  | L | A | B | E | L |  | T |  |
| M | A | G | N | E | T |  | L |  | A | R | I | D |
| A |  |  |  | R |  |  | E |  | R |  | A |  |
| S | A | U | C | E | R |  | R | A | S | H | L | Y |
|  | I |  | R |  | I |  |  | G |  |  |  | I |
| P | L | E | A |  | D |  | R | E | M | O | T | E |
|  | M |  | W | E | D | G | E |  | I |  |  | L |
| K | E | E | L |  | L |  | U |  | S | A | I | D |
|  | N |  | E | W | E | R | S |  | E |  |  | E |
| S | T | U | D |  | D |  | E | A | R | N | E | D |

## CROSSWORD 252

| H | A | M | M | O | C | K | S |  | L | A | M | B |
|---|---|---|---|---|---|---|---|---|---|---|---|---|
| O |  |  | E |  | O |  | U |  | A |  |  | I |
| L | E | W | D |  | O | R | B | I | T | I | N | G |
| D |  |  | I |  | K |  | T |  | T |  |  | W |
| E | N | A | C | T | S |  | L |  | E |  |  | I |
| R |  | V |  | A |  | T | E | A | R | I | N | G |
|  |  | O |  | X |  | A |  | L |  | C |  |  |
| R | O | W | D | I | E | R |  | T |  | O |  | A |
| U |  |  | O |  | E |  | B | O | N | N | E | T |
| F |  |  | N |  | R |  | A |  | Y |  |  | T |
| F | O | R | A | G | I | N | G |  | L | I | K | E |
| L |  |  | T |  | E |  | E |  | O |  |  | N |
| E | P | E | E |  | R | E | L | E | N | T | E | D |

## CROSSWORD 253

| W | A | R | N | S |  | S |  | A |  | A |  | T |
|---|---|---|---|---|---|---|---|---|---|---|---|---|
| A |  |  | U |  | S | K | Y | D | I | V | E | R |
| Y | E | L | L | S |  | I |  | D |  | A |  | A |
| L |  |  | L | A | U | N | D | E | R | I | N | G |
| A |  | C |  | L |  |  |  | D |  | L |  | I |
| Y | E | L | L | O | W | E | D |  | T | A | L | C |
|  |  | E |  | N |  | G |  | S |  | B |  |  |
| Q | U | A | Y |  | S | O | C | I | A | L | L | Y |
| U |  | R |  | A |  |  |  | F |  | E |  | E |
| A | M | A | L | G | A | M | A | T | E |  |  | A |
| R |  | N |  | E |  | A |  | S | A | N | E | R |
| R | I | C | H | N | E | S | S |  | S |  |  | L |
| Y |  | E |  | T |  | S |  | S | T | R | A | Y |

## CROSSWORD 254

| D | A | Z | Z | L | E | D |  | H | O | A | R | D |
|---|---|---|---|---|---|---|---|---|---|---|---|---|
| I |  |  | O |  |  | O |  | U |  | N |  | I |
| S |  | I | M | P | A | C | T | S |  | T |  | R |
| O |  |  | B |  |  | K |  | H | E | A | R | T |
| W | A | N | I | N | G |  | M |  |  | C |  |  |
| N |  |  | E |  | A | D | A | P | T | I | N | G |
| E |  | G |  |  | L |  | R |  |  | D |  | E |
| D | I | A | G | R | A | M | S |  | T |  |  | N |
|  |  | S |  |  | S |  | H | O | A | R | S | E |
| W | I | T | C | H |  | F |  |  | V |  |  | T |
| I |  | R |  | E | L | A | P | S | E | D |  | I |
| T |  | I |  | W |  | W |  |  | R |  |  | C |
| H | A | C | K | S |  | N | A | N | N | I | E | S |

## CROSSWORD 255

| E | N | T | A | I | L |  | C |  | S | O | W | S |
|---|---|---|---|---|---|---|---|---|---|---|---|---|
| L |  |  | L |  | A | B | A | S | E |  | E |  |
| A | N | T | I |  | I |  | N |  | A | I | D | S |
| S |  |  | K |  | R | E | A | R | S |  | L |  |
| T | O | W | E | L | S |  | P |  | I | R | O | N |
| I |  |  |  | E |  |  | E |  | D |  | C |  |
| C | A | D | E | T | S |  | S | T | E | A | K | S |
|  | L |  | M |  | U |  |  | E |  |  |  | L |
| S | C | A | B |  | B |  | R | A | B | B | L | E |
|  | O |  | R | I | D | G | E |  | O |  |  | N |
| A | H | O | Y |  | U |  | I |  | A | V | I | D |
|  | O |  | O | C | E | A | N |  | R |  |  | E |
| E | L | K | S |  | S |  | S | A | D | D | E | R |

## CROSSWORD 256

| C | A | L | A | M | A | R | I |  | S | I | T | S |
|---|---|---|---|---|---|---|---|---|---|---|---|---|
| L |  |  | D |  | M |  | T |  | T |  |  | I |
| A | T | O | M |  | E | M | A | N | A | T | E | D |
| U |  |  | I |  | N |  | L |  | T |  |  | L |
| S | E | A | T | E | D |  | I |  | U |  |  | E |
| E |  | L |  | L |  | A | C | C | E | P | T | S |
|  |  | L |  | S |  | S |  | L |  | U |  |  |
| J | O | Y | L | E | S | S |  | A |  | M |  | A |
| U |  |  | I |  | Q |  | A | D | O | P | T | S |
| I |  |  | Z |  | U |  | S |  | V |  |  | H |
| C | A | T | A | R | A | C | T |  | E | C | H | O |
| E |  |  | R |  | S |  | I |  | R |  |  | R |
| S | P | E | D |  | H | E | R | I | T | A | G | E |

# SOLUTIONS

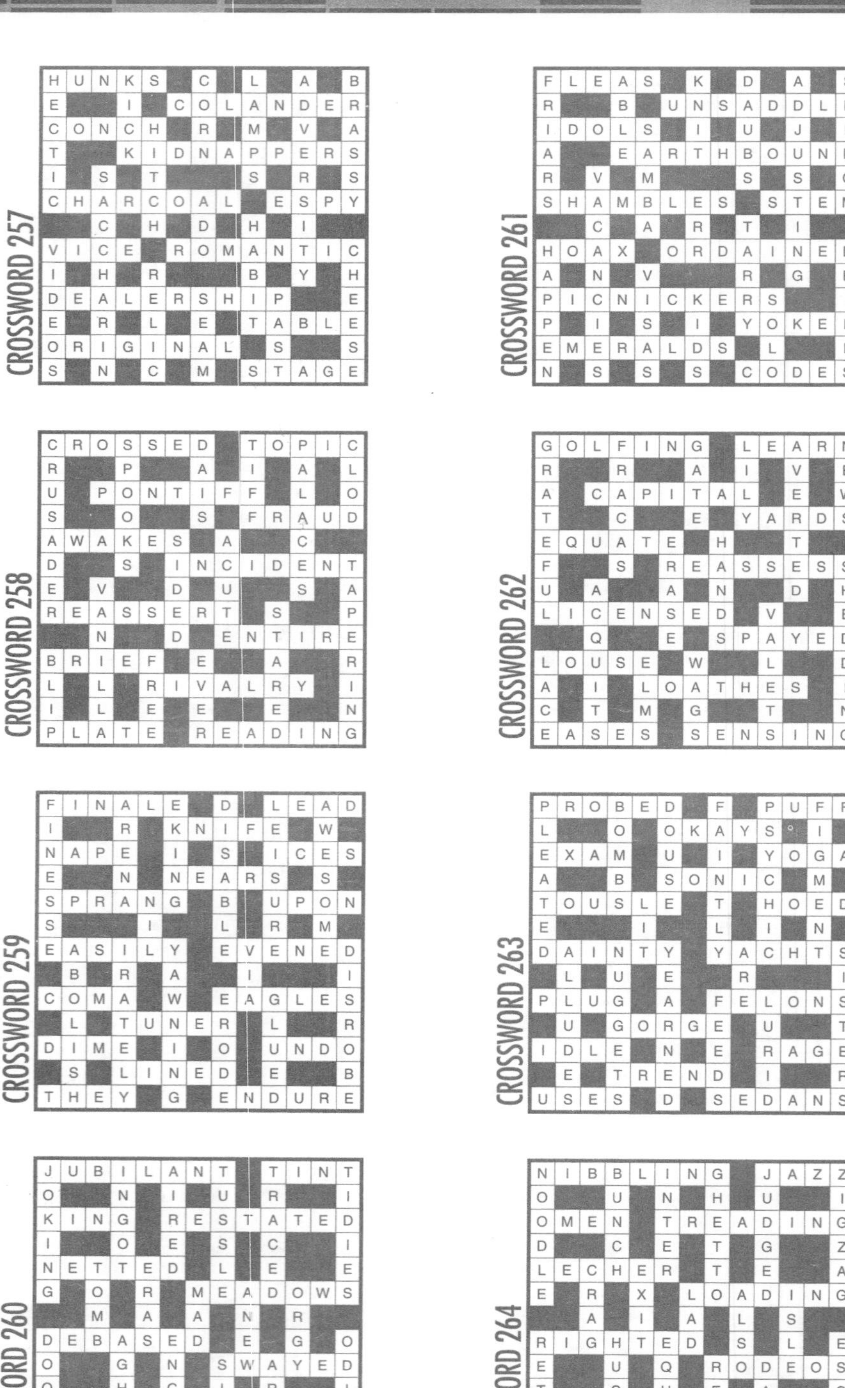
CROSSWORD 257
CROSSWORD 261
CROSSWORD 258
CROSSWORD 262
CROSSWORD 259
CROSSWORD 263
CROSSWORD 260
CROSSWORD 264

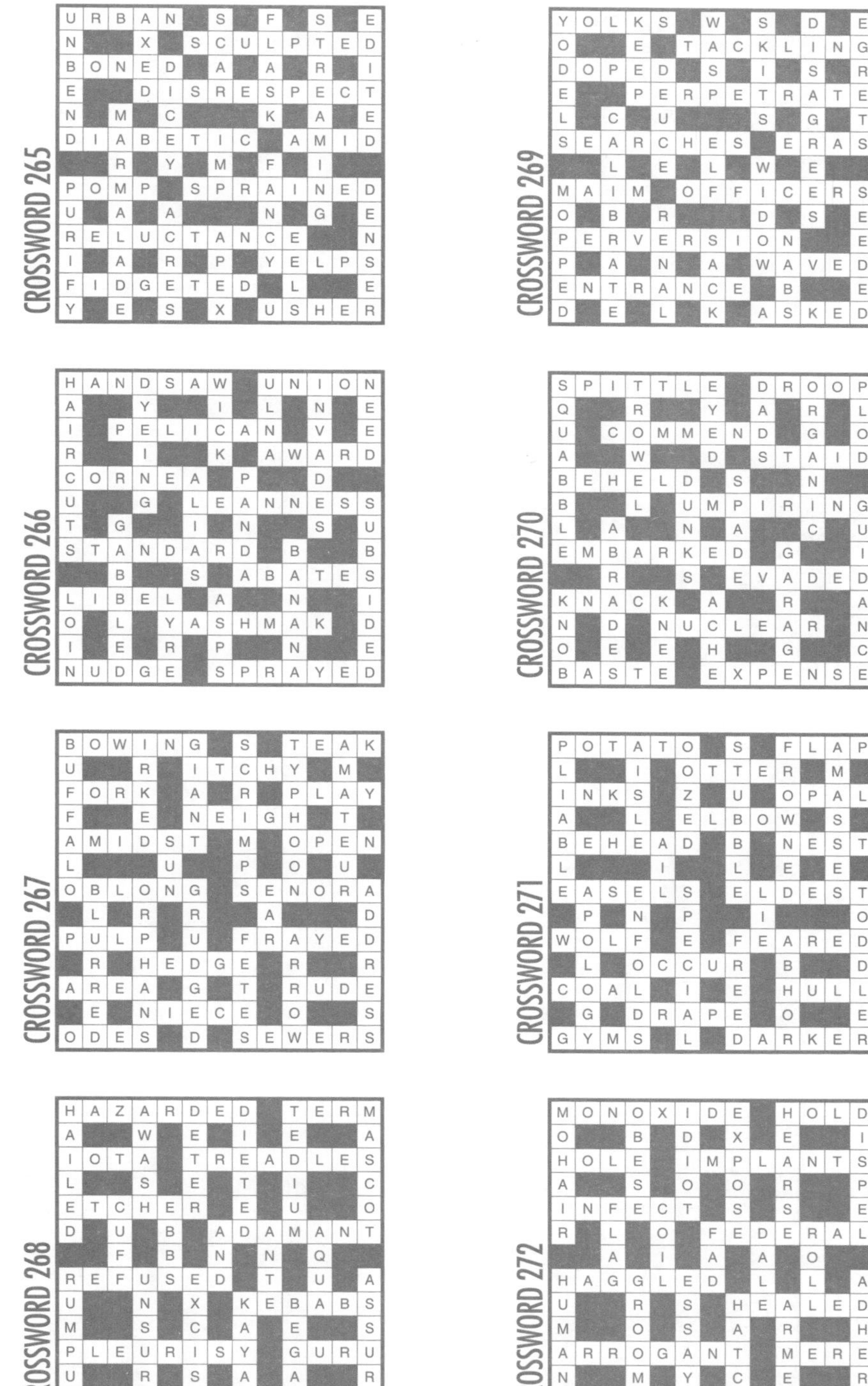
CROSSWORD 265
CROSSWORD 269
CROSSWORD 266
CROSSWORD 270
CROSSWORD 267
CROSSWORD 271
CROSSWORD 268
CROSSWORD 272

# SOLUTIONS

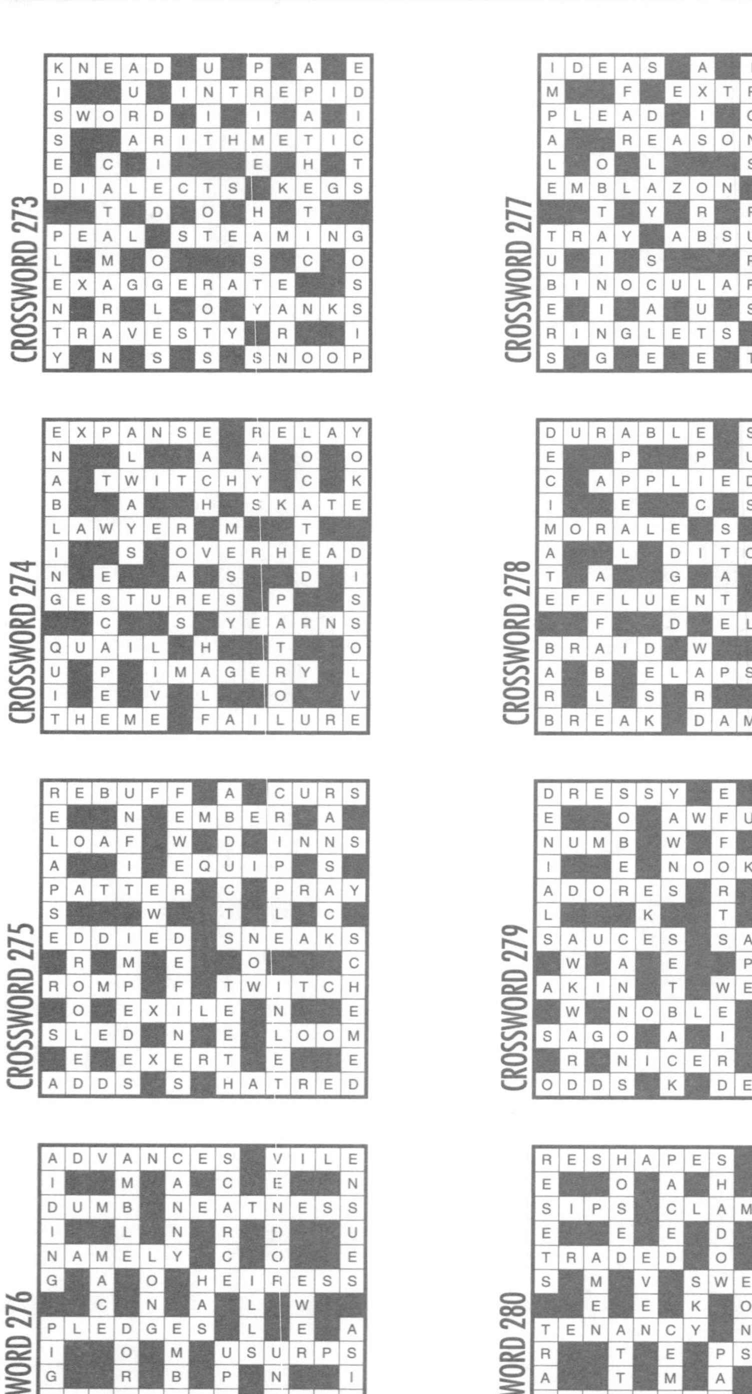
CROSSWORD 273
CROSSWORD 277
CROSSWORD 274
CROSSWORD 278
CROSSWORD 275
CROSSWORD 279
CROSSWORD 276
CROSSWORD 280

# SOLUTIONS

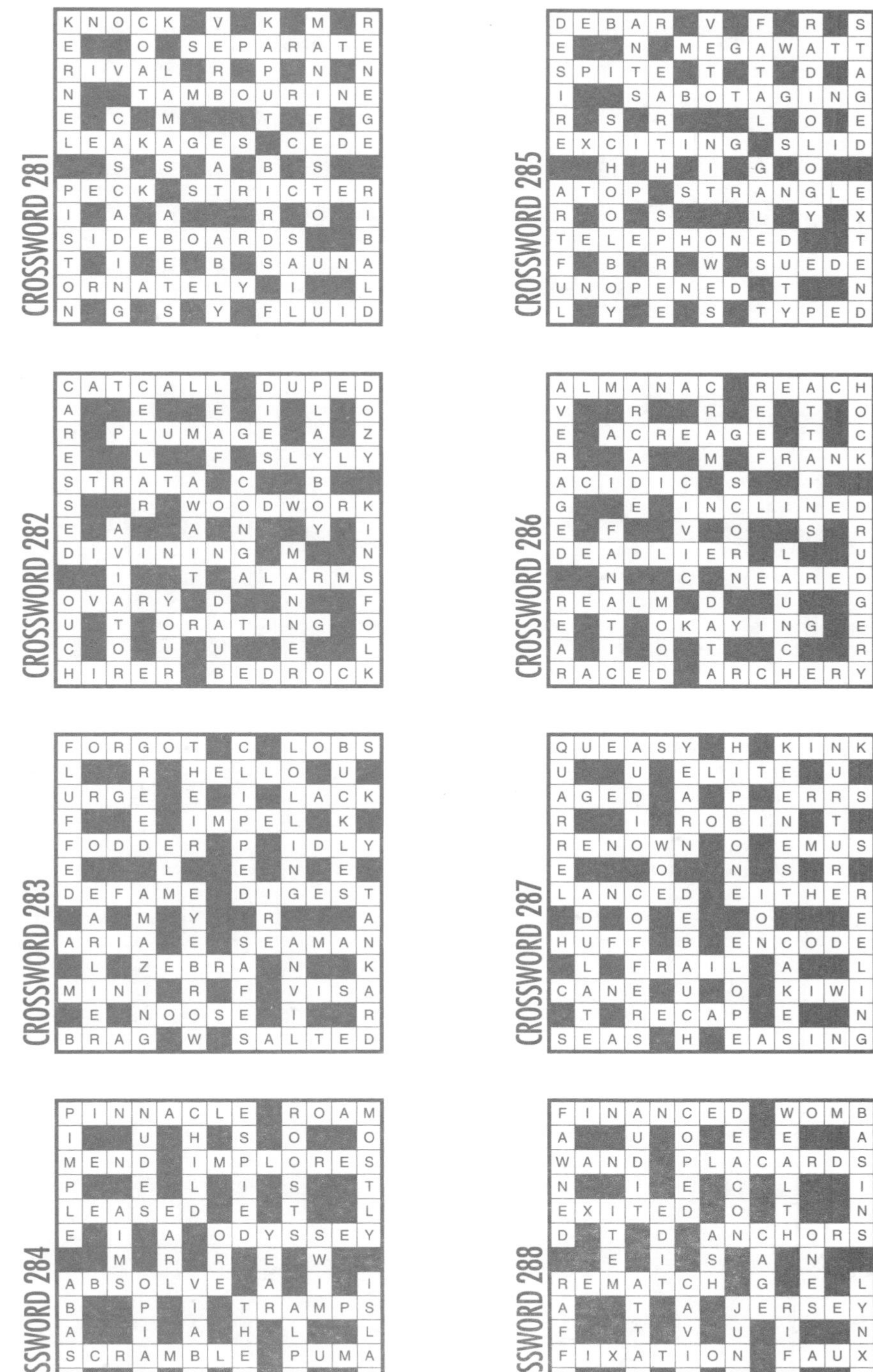
CROSSWORD 281
CROSSWORD 285
CROSSWORD 282
CROSSWORD 286
CROSSWORD 283
CROSSWORD 287
CROSSWORD 284
CROSSWORD 288

# SOLUTIONS

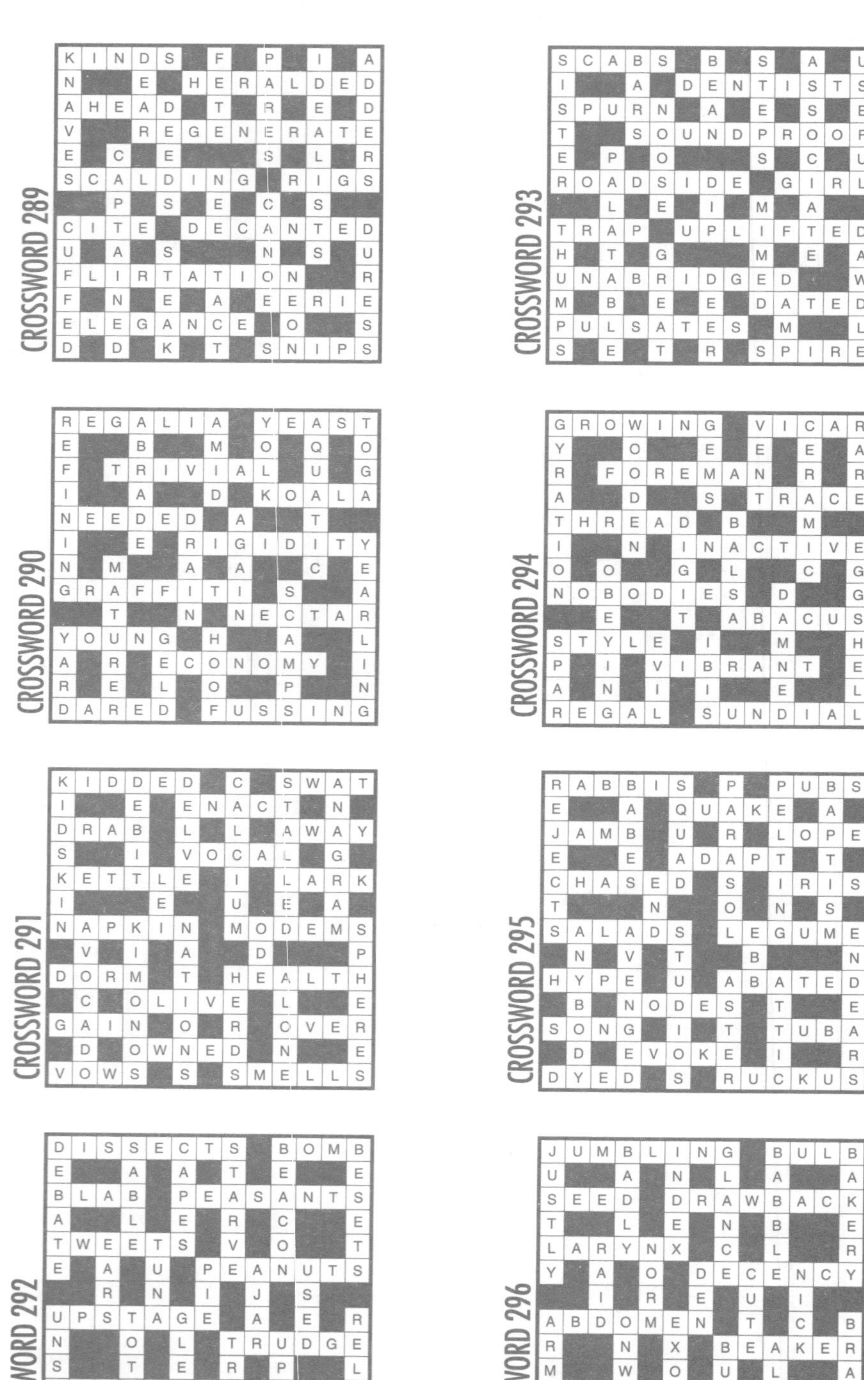

CROSSWORD 289
CROSSWORD 293
CROSSWORD 290
CROSSWORD 294
CROSSWORD 291
CROSSWORD 295
CROSSWORD 292
CROSSWORD 296

# SOLUTIONS

CROSSWORD 297

CROSSWORD 298

CROSSWORD 299

CROSSWORD 300

CROSSWORD 301

CROSSWORD 302

CROSSWORD 303

CROSSWORD 304

# SOLUTIONS

## CROSSWORD 305

| M | O | L | A | R | | T | | L | | B | | S |
|---|---|---|---|---|---|---|---|---|---|---|---|---|
| O | | | S | | S | W | E | E | T | E | S | T |
| C | O | C | K | Y | | I | | V | | W | | A |
| K | | | S | A | U | N | T | E | R | I | N | G |
| E | | H | | R | | | | E | | T | | E |
| D | E | A | F | N | E | S | S | | A | C | T | S |
| | | Z | | S | | O | | M | | H | | |
| B | E | A | M | | S | W | E | A | T | E | R | S |
| E | | R | | E | | | | D | | D | | T |
| W | I | D | E | S | P | R | E | A | D | | | R |
| A | | I | | S | | A | | M | A | N | I | A |
| R | A | N | S | A | C | K | S | | R | | | N |
| E | | G | | Y | | E | | U | N | F | E | D |

## CROSSWORD 306

| F | U | L | L | E | S | T | | D | R | A | M | A |
|---|---|---|---|---|---|---|---|---|---|---|---|---|
| I | | | I | | | H | | E | | M | | R |
| S | | I | N | F | L | A | M | E | | U | | I |
| H | | | K | | | W | | P | O | S | E | D |
| B | R | E | E | Z | E | | C | | | I | | |
| O | | | D | | M | A | R | G | I | N | A | L |
| W | | M | | | B | | U | | | G | | O |
| L | E | A | R | N | E | R | S | | C | | | U |
| | | N | | | D | | H | E | A | T | E | D |
| D | W | A | R | F | | T | | | R | | | N |
| E | | G | | R | E | A | C | H | E | S | | E |
| M | | E | | A | | L | | | E | | | S |
| O | D | D | L | Y | | C | O | R | R | A | L | S |

## CROSSWORD 307

| P | A | S | T | R | Y | | M | | T | E | E | M |
|---|---|---|---|---|---|---|---|---|---|---|---|---|
| U | | | I | | A | M | A | Z | E | | M | |
| F | L | E | A | | C | | T | | N | I | B | S |
| F | | | R | | H | O | A | R | D | | R | |
| I | M | P | A | C | T | | D | | I | R | O | N |
| N | | | | O | | | O | | N | | I | |
| G | A | M | B | O | L | | R | E | G | A | L | E |
| | G | | A | | A | | | R | | | | L |
| L | I | M | B | | Y | | H | E | A | V | E | D |
| | L | | O | Z | O | N | E | | F | | | E |
| S | I | L | O | | U | | E | | F | A | I | R |
| | T | | N | O | T | E | D | | I | | | L |
| E | Y | E | S | | S | | S | E | X | I | L | Y |

## CROSSWORD 308

| R | E | L | E | V | A | N | T | | T | O | A | D |
|---|---|---|---|---|---|---|---|---|---|---|---|---|
| A | | | N | | S | | W | | A | | | O |
| T | O | L | D | | S | P | E | C | I | F | I | C |
| I | | | O | | E | | L | | L | | | T |
| F | R | O | W | N | S | | V | | O | | | O |
| Y | | O | | E | | W | E | I | R | D | E | R |
| | | Z | | A | | A | | N | | O | | |
| Q | U | E | E | R | L | Y | | T | | T | | I |
| U | | | X | | A | | G | O | V | E | R | N |
| E | | | P | | U | | L | | E | | | T |
| S | T | R | A | D | D | L | E | | R | I | S | E |
| T | | | N | | E | | A | | V | | | R |
| S | O | L | D | | D | U | N | G | E | O | N | S |

## CROSSWORD 309

| S | O | D | A | S | | A | | S | | M | | V |
|---|---|---|---|---|---|---|---|---|---|---|---|---|
| A | | | L | | I | N | S | C | R | I | B | E |
| W | H | E | A | T | | T | | R | | N | | R |
| I | | | S | A | L | I | V | A | T | I | N | G |
| N | | B | | B | | | | M | | S | | E |
| G | R | A | B | B | I | N | G | | S | T | U | D |
| | | R | | Y | | I | | O | | E | | |
| Z | O | O | S | | C | L | E | V | E | R | L | Y |
| A | | M | | A | | | | A | | S | | A |
| N | E | E | D | L | E | S | S | L | Y | | | W |
| I | | T | | L | | H | | S | E | V | E | N |
| E | L | E | V | A | T | E | S | | L | | | E |
| R | | R | | Y | | D | | F | L | O | O | D |

## CROSSWORD 310

| Y | I | E | L | D | E | D | | B | O | A | R | D |
|---|---|---|---|---|---|---|---|---|---|---|---|---|
| O | | | A | | | U | | U | | F | | A |
| U | | A | C | C | L | A | I | M | | F | | S |
| T | | | K | | | L | | P | E | A | C | H |
| H | O | T | E | L | S | | A | | | I | | |
| F | | | D | | I | N | F | E | R | R | E | D |
| U | | E | | | G | | T | | | S | | E |
| L | E | N | I | E | N | C | E | | C | | | A |
| | | R | | | S | | R | E | A | P | E | D |
| B | L | A | S | E | | T | | | N | | | E |
| L | | G | | A | V | A | R | I | C | E | | N |
| O | | E | | S | | X | | | E | | | E |
| B | A | D | G | E | | I | M | P | L | I | E | D |

## CROSSWORD 311

| I | G | U | A | N | A | | P | | A | C | E | S |
|---|---|---|---|---|---|---|---|---|---|---|---|---|
| M | | | I | | L | E | A | S | E | | M | |
| B | O | W | L | | O | | D | | R | E | A | L |
| I | | | E | | F | O | L | I | O | | N | |
| B | A | N | D | I | T | | O | | B | O | A | R |
| E | | | | L | | | C | | I | | T | |
| D | A | B | B | L | E | | K | I | C | K | E | D |
| | N | | I | | Q | | | V | | | | O |
| A | G | O | G | | U | | H | Y | B | R | I | D |
| | U | | H | E | A | V | Y | | U | | | D |
| W | I | D | E | | T | | M | | D | A | M | E |
| | S | | A | D | O | R | N | | G | | | R |
| S | H | O | D | | R | | S | N | E | A | K | Y |

## CROSSWORD 312

| P | L | E | A | S | A | N | T | | B | R | E | D |
|---|---|---|---|---|---|---|---|---|---|---|---|---|
| E | | | S | | B | | R | | O | | | A |
| B | U | S | H | | A | W | A | R | D | I | N | G |
| B | | | E | | S | | D | | I | | | G |
| L | A | S | S | I | E | | E | | C | | | E |
| E | | E | | C | | F | R | E | E | Z | E | R |
| | | A | | O | | O | | P | | E | | |
| A | R | R | A | N | G | E | | E | | A | | D |
| D | | | S | | U | | Y | E | L | L | O | W |
| O | | | S | | S | | O | | O | | | E |
| P | R | E | A | C | H | E | D | | W | I | L | L |
| T | | | I | | E | | E | | E | | | L |
| S | O | I | L | | S | A | L | A | R | I | E | S |

## CROSSWORD 313

| G | A | N | G | S |  | F |  | N |  | G |  | S |
|---|---|---|---|---|---|---|---|---|---|---|---|---|
| A |  |  | I |  | C | L | E | A | R | E | S | T |
| S | W | I | F | T |  | A |  | T |  | N |  | O |
| H |  |  | T | A | S | K | M | A | S | T | E | R |
| E |  | B |  | R |  |  |  | L |  | L |  | E |
| S | C | A | N | D | A | L | S |  | D | E | E | D |
|  |  | R |  | Y |  | E |  | T |  | M |  |  |
| J | O | B | S |  | I | G | N | O | R | A | N | T |
| A |  | E |  | R |  |  |  | U |  | N |  | H |
| B | U | C | C | A | N | E | E | R | S |  |  | I |
| B |  | U |  | D |  | D |  | S | N | A | K | E |
| E | M | E | R | A | L | D | S |  | O |  |  | V |
| R |  | D |  | R |  | Y |  | A | B | I | D | E |

## CROSSWORD 314

| Q | U | I | E | T | E | R |  | T | U | B | B | Y |
|---|---|---|---|---|---|---|---|---|---|---|---|---|
| U |  |  | L |  |  | I |  | O |  | A |  | O |
| I |  | C | I | C | A | D | A | S |  | R |  | G |
| Z |  |  | C |  |  | S |  | S | A | M | B | A |
| Z | E | N | I | T | H |  | O |  |  | A |  |  |
| I |  |  | T |  | U | N | F | A | D | I | N | G |
| N |  | P |  |  | M |  | F |  |  | D |  | A |
| G | R | A | D | U | A | T | E |  | T |  |  | U |
|  |  | R |  |  | N |  | R | E | A | S | O | N |
| G | R | A | N | D |  | C |  |  | V |  |  | T |
| L |  | D |  | A | L | A | R | M | E | D |  | L |
| O |  | E |  | B |  | P |  |  | R |  |  | E |
| W | A | S | P | S |  | E | A | R | N | E | S | T |

## CROSSWORD 315

| W | R | E | A | T | H |  | C |  | R | E | A | M |
|---|---|---|---|---|---|---|---|---|---|---|---|---|
| A |  |  | O |  | U | S | A | G | E |  | U |  |
| D | O | U | R |  | F |  | R |  | C | O | D | E |
| D |  |  | T |  | F | L | A | S | K |  | I |  |
| L | I | L | A | C | S |  | M |  | O | N | T | O |
| E |  |  |  | U |  |  | E |  | N |  | O |  |
| D | A | N | C | E | R |  | L | A | S | E | R | S |
|  | D |  | O |  | U |  |  | I |  |  |  | A |
| T | O | M | B |  | N |  | E | R | A | S | E | D |
|  | R |  | W | H | A | C | K |  | L |  |  | N |
| D | I | V | E |  | W |  | I |  | I | D | L | E |
|  | N |  | B | R | A | I | N |  | B |  |  | S |
| E | G | G | S |  | Y |  | G | U | I | D | E | S |

## CROSSWORD 316

| S | Q | U | A | N | D | E | R |  | H | E | R | B |
|---|---|---|---|---|---|---|---|---|---|---|---|---|
| C |  |  | B |  | E |  | O |  | A |  |  | U |
| O | U | Z | O |  | B | R | A | I | S | I | N | G |
| U |  |  | D |  | T |  | R |  | S |  |  | G |
| R | I | V | E | T | S |  | E |  | L |  |  | E |
| S |  | I |  | E |  | A | D | H | E | R | E | D |
|  |  | C |  | E |  | D |  | O |  | E |  |  |
| P | R | E | E | N | E | D |  | P |  | V |  | I |
| A |  |  | L |  | M |  | C | E | A | S | E | D |
| R |  |  | O |  | B |  | A |  | R |  |  | E |
| C | O | M | P | L | A | I | N |  | S | A | G | A |
| E |  |  | E |  | L |  | A |  | O |  |  | L |
| L | E | A | D |  | M | I | L | D | N | E | S | S |

## CROSSWORD 317

| H | A | W | K | S |  | G |  | A |  | K |  | A |
|---|---|---|---|---|---|---|---|---|---|---|---|---|
| I |  |  | E |  | T | E | A | C | H | E | R | S |
| K | N | E | E | L |  | N |  | U |  | Y |  | C |
| I |  |  | L | A | M | E | N | T | A | B | L | E |
| N |  | T |  | T |  |  |  | E |  | O |  | N |
| G | L | A | N | C | I | N | G |  | H | A | N | D |
|  |  | R |  | H |  | U |  | F |  | R |  |  |
| B | O | A | S |  | U | N | S | A | D | D | L | E |
| O |  | N |  | P |  |  |  | U |  | S |  | X |
| D | E | T | R | A | C | T | I | N | G |  |  | U |
| I |  | U |  | U |  | E |  | A | I | M | E | D |
| E | N | L | I | S | T | E | D |  | B |  |  | E |
| S |  | A |  | E |  | S |  | C | E | D | E | D |

## CROSSWORD 318

| H | I | J | A | C | K | S |  | S | C | A | L | D |
|---|---|---|---|---|---|---|---|---|---|---|---|---|
| A |  |  | F |  |  | O |  | A |  | B |  | U |
| R |  | B | L | O | T | C | H | Y |  | R |  | K |
| A |  |  | O |  |  | K |  | S | L | A | V | E |
| N | E | G | A | T | E |  | R |  |  | D |  |  |
| G |  |  | T |  | L | E | A | F | L | E | T | S |
| U |  | A |  |  | E |  | I |  |  | D |  | T |
| E | M | B | R | A | C | E | D |  | B |  |  | A |
|  |  | A |  |  | T |  | S | W | A | Y | E | D |
| S | E | N | S | E |  | M |  |  | N |  |  | I |
| W |  | D |  | C | O | A | S | T | A | L |  | U |
| A |  | O |  | H |  | C |  |  | N |  |  | M |
| M | A | N | G | O |  | H | E | R | A | L | D | S |

## CROSSWORD 319

| U | N | P | A | I | D |  | O |  | D | U | L | Y |
|---|---|---|---|---|---|---|---|---|---|---|---|---|
| P |  |  | S |  | E | N | V | O | Y |  | I |  |
| S | U | C | H |  | A |  | E |  | N | A | B | S |
| U |  |  | E |  | L | A | R | V | A |  | R |  |
| R | O | U | N | D | S |  | F |  | M | E | A | T |
| G |  |  |  | I |  |  | E |  | I |  | R |  |
| E | A | G | L | E | S |  | D | E | C | O | Y | S |
|  | W |  | E |  | L |  |  | A |  |  |  | N |
| S | N | I | P |  | O |  | P | R | A | N | C | E |
|  | I |  | R | A | B | B | I |  | D |  |  | A |
| U | N | D | O |  | B |  | P |  | M | I | N | K |
|  | G |  | S | I | E | V | E |  | I |  |  | E |
| E | S | P | Y |  | R |  | R | O | T | T | E | D |

## CROSSWORD 320

| D | E | S | I | G | N | E | D |  | G | L | I | B |
|---|---|---|---|---|---|---|---|---|---|---|---|---|
| I |  |  | T |  | E |  | E |  | A |  |  | U |
| G | A | T | E |  | C | O | R | D | U | R | O | Y |
| I |  |  | M |  | K |  | I |  | G |  |  | I |
| T | E | A | S | E | S |  | D |  | E |  |  | N |
| S |  | R |  | M |  | N | E | E | D | I | N | G |
|  |  | E |  | I |  | O |  | L |  | S |  |  |
| C | H | A | P | T | E | R |  | S |  | L |  | A |
| A |  |  | O |  | M |  | D | E | T | E | C | T |
| P |  |  | L |  | P |  | I |  | I |  |  | T |
| P | E | T | I | T | I | O | N |  | G | L | E | E |
| E |  |  | C |  | R |  | E |  | E |  |  | N |
| D | U | N | E |  | E | N | D | O | R | S | E | D |

# SOLUTIONS

## CROSSWORD 321

| K | N | O | B | S |  | L |  | A |  | M |  | A |
|---|---|---|---|---|---|---|---|---|---|---|---|---|
| E |  |  | E |  | P | I | L | C | H | A | R | D |
| E | Q | U | A | L |  | S |  | O |  | N |  | V |
| N |  |  | T | E | M | P | E | R | A | N | C | E |
| L |  | S |  | A |  |  |  | N |  | E |  | R |
| Y | E | A | R | N | I | N | G |  | C | R | I | B |
|  |  | C |  | S |  | A |  | R |  | I |  |  |
| D | O | C | K |  | B | Y | P | A | S | S | E | D |
| O |  | H |  | A |  |  |  | N |  | M |  | A |
| D | R | A | W | B | R | I | D | G | E |  |  | M |
| G |  | R |  | B |  | C |  | Y | A | R | D | S |
| E | P | I | S | O | D | E | S |  | S |  |  | O |
| S |  | N |  | T |  | S |  | N | Y | L | O | N |

## CROSSWORD 322

| C | A | S | K | E | T | S |  | V | O | I | C | E |
|---|---|---|---|---|---|---|---|---|---|---|---|---|
| O |  |  | N |  |  | T |  | E |  | N |  | X |
| N |  | P | I | L | L | A | G | E |  | H |  | I |
| S |  |  | G |  |  | B |  | R | E | A | C | T |
| U | R | C | H | I | N |  | S |  |  | B |  |  |
| L |  |  | T |  | I | M | P | O | L | I | T | E |
| T |  | G |  |  | G |  | A |  |  | T |  | V |
| S | T | A | R | C | H | E | D |  | P |  |  | I |
|  |  | R |  |  | T |  | E | V | A | D | E | D |
| T | W | A | N | G |  | E |  |  | U |  |  | E |
| I |  | G |  | E | N | V | Y | I | N | G |  | N |
| N |  | E |  | T |  | E |  |  | C |  |  | C |
| T | I | D | E | S |  | R | E | S | H | A | P | E |

## CROSSWORD 323

| J | A | B | B | E | D |  | D |  | P | L | A | N |
|---|---|---|---|---|---|---|---|---|---|---|---|---|
| U |  |  | U |  | R | O | A | M | S |  | L |  |
| D | R | A | G |  | E |  | P |  | Y | E | L | P |
| G |  |  | L |  | A | S | P | I | C |  | U |  |
| I | N | D | E | E | D |  | L |  | H | I | D | E |
| N |  |  |  | E |  |  | E |  | I |  | E |  |
| G | A | B | B | L | E |  | D | E | C | A | D | E |
|  | L |  | E |  | X |  |  | R |  |  |  | N |
| A | G | E | S |  | H |  | U | R | G | I | N | G |
|  | E |  | E | X | A | C | T |  | I |  |  | U |
| A | B | L | E |  | U |  | T |  | D | O | L | L |
|  | R |  | C | A | S | T | E |  | D |  |  | F |
| H | A | S | H |  | T |  | R | H | Y | M | E | S |

## CROSSWORD 324

| B | E | S | I | E | G | E | D |  | G | U | L | P |
|---|---|---|---|---|---|---|---|---|---|---|---|---|
| A |  |  | N |  | E |  | E |  | R |  |  | A |
| T | H | U | G |  | N | O | B | L | E | M | E | N |
| T |  |  | O |  | I |  | I |  | A |  |  | D |
| L | O | A | T | H | E |  | T |  | S |  |  | A |
| E |  | L |  | A |  | A | S | P | E | C | T | S |
|  |  | T |  | L |  | F |  | L |  | O |  |  |
| M | O | O | N | L | I | T |  | E |  | M |  | R |
| I |  |  | A |  | M |  | K | A | R | A | T | E |
| D |  |  | P |  | P |  | I |  | U |  |  | N |
| G | R | E | A | T | E | S | T |  | L | A | V | A |
| E |  |  | L |  | D |  | E |  | E |  |  | M |
| T | R | A | M |  | E | N | S | H | R | I | N | E |

## CROSSWORD 325

| E | R | E | C | T |  | S |  | S |  | L |  | U |
|---|---|---|---|---|---|---|---|---|---|---|---|---|
| T |  |  | L |  | C | O | C | K | E | Y | E | D |
| C | R | O | A | K |  | L |  | I |  | R |  | D |
| H |  |  | M | A | Y | O | N | N | A | I | S | E |
| E |  | A |  | Y |  |  |  | S |  | C |  | R |
| D | I | C | T | A | T | E | D |  | L | I | D | S |
|  |  | T |  | K |  | W |  | M |  | S |  |  |
| U | N | I | T |  | D | E | M | E | N | T | I | A |
| N |  | V |  | B |  |  |  | S |  | S |  | B |
| L | E | A | D | E | R | L | E | S | S |  |  | U |
| O |  | T |  | E |  | I |  | Y | A | N | K | S |
| C | L | E | N | C | H | E | D |  | N |  |  | E |
| K |  | S |  | H |  | D |  | S | K | I | M | S |

## CROSSWORD 326

| R | O | O | M | I | E | R |  | O | R | A | T | E |
|---|---|---|---|---|---|---|---|---|---|---|---|---|
| O |  |  | O |  |  | A |  | U |  | D |  | A |
| W |  | O | B | J | E | C | T | S |  | V |  | R |
| D |  |  | B |  |  | K |  | T | R | A | I | N |
| I | N | T | E | N | D |  | O |  |  | N |  |  |
| E |  |  | D |  | U | N | B | L | O | C | K | S |
| S |  | C |  |  | L |  | E |  |  | E |  | I |
| T | R | A | M | P | L | E | S |  | G |  |  | D |
|  |  | L |  |  | Y |  | E | N | A | B | L | E |
| M | A | Y | B | E |  | S |  |  | L |  |  | W |
| E |  | P |  | N | E | W | S | B | O | Y |  | A |
| M |  | S |  | D |  | U |  |  | R |  |  | Y |
| O | B | O | E | S |  | M | U | S | E | U | M | S |

## CROSSWORD 327

| K | I | S | S | E | D |  | G |  | S | N | A | G |
|---|---|---|---|---|---|---|---|---|---|---|---|---|
| E |  |  | C |  | R | O | A | S | T |  | R |  |
| R | O | S | E |  | I |  | R |  | E | A | T | S |
| N |  |  | N |  | E | M | B | E | R |  | I |  |
| E | M | B | E | D | S |  | A |  | I | N | C | H |
| L |  |  |  | O |  |  | G |  | L |  | L |  |
| S | A | F | E | T | Y |  | E | L | E | V | E | N |
|  | D |  | G |  | O |  |  | A |  |  |  | A |
| S | M | O | G |  | U |  | A | W | O | K | E | N |
|  | I |  | H | I | N | T | S |  | A |  |  | N |
| F | R | E | E |  | G |  | I |  | S | E | M | I |
|  | E |  | A | M | E | N | D |  | E |  |  | E |
| P | R | O | D |  | R |  | E | A | S | E | L | S |

## CROSSWORD 328

| G | I | R | A | F | F | E | S |  | M | A | M | A |
|---|---|---|---|---|---|---|---|---|---|---|---|---|
| A |  |  | X |  | I |  | A |  | A |  |  | S |
| R | O | L | L |  | S | N | I | G | G | E | R | S |
| I |  |  | E |  | T |  | L |  | N |  |  | E |
| S | P | A | S | M | S |  | E |  | U |  |  | N |
| H |  | U |  | E |  | A | D | A | M | A | N | T |
|  |  | R |  | R |  | C |  | Q |  | T |  |  |
| N | E | A | R | E | S | T |  | U |  | O |  | E |
| U |  |  | E |  | E |  | R | A | M | M | E | D |
| D |  |  | V |  | X |  | I |  | E |  |  | I |
| G | A | Z | E | T | T | E | S |  | R | A | P | T |
| E |  |  | R |  | E |  | E |  | G |  |  | E |
| S | A | G | E |  | T | I | N | K | E | R | E | D |

## CROSSWORD 329

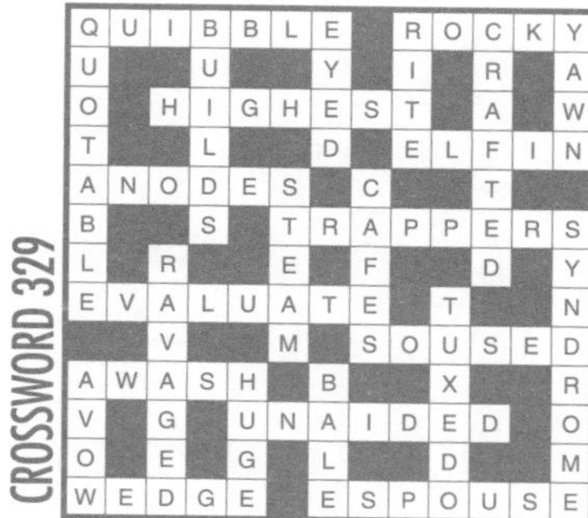

| Q | U | I | B | B | L | E |  | R | O | C | K | Y |
|---|---|---|---|---|---|---|---|---|---|---|---|---|
| U |  |  | U |  |  | Y |  | I |  | R |  | A |
| O |  | H | I | G | H | E | S | T |  | A |  | W |
| T |  |  | L |  |  | D |  | E | L | F | I | N |
| A | N | O | D | E | S |  | C |  |  | T |  |  |
| B |  |  | S |  | T | R | A | P | P | E | R | S |
| L |  | R |  |  | E |  | F |  |  | D |  | Y |
| E | V | A | L | U | A | T | E |  | T |  |  | N |
|  |  | V |  |  | M |  | S | O | U | S | E | D |
| A | W | A | S | H |  | B |  |  | X |  |  | R |
| V |  | G |  | U | N | A | I | D | E | D |  | O |
| O |  | E |  | G |  | L |  |  | D |  |  | M |
| W | E | D | G | E |  | E | S | P | O | U | S | E |

## CROSSWORD 330

| V | I | S | I | O | N |  | D |  | H | E | A | T |
|---|---|---|---|---|---|---|---|---|---|---|---|---|
| O |  |  | N |  | O | P | E | R | A |  | D |  |
| L | A | W | N |  | R |  | F |  | R | O | V | E |
| U |  |  | E |  | M | E | A | N | S |  | E |  |
| M | O | U | R | N | S |  | U |  | H | A | R | M |
| E |  |  |  | E |  |  | L |  | E |  | S |  |
| S | A | N | I | T | Y |  | T | A | R | R | E | D |
|  | N |  | G |  | A |  |  | I |  |  |  | E |
| H | Y | M | N |  | S |  | F | L | A | G | O | N |
|  | T |  | O | T | H | E | R |  | B |  |  | U |
| P | I | E | R |  | M |  | I |  | H | E | R | D |
|  | M |  | E | L | A | T | E |  | O |  |  | E |
| M | E | A | D |  | K |  | S | E | R | I | E | S |

## CROSSWORD 331

| E | X | P | E | N | S | E | S |  | R | O | B | S |
|---|---|---|---|---|---|---|---|---|---|---|---|---|
| F |  |  | B |  | L |  | O |  | A |  |  | U |
| F | L | A | B |  | Y | A | C | H | T | I | N | G |
| O |  |  | E |  | E |  | I |  | H |  |  | A |
| R | U | D | D | E | R |  | A |  | E |  |  | R |
| T |  | A |  | V |  | A | L | E | R | T | L | Y |
|  |  | U |  | E |  | S |  | A |  | O |  |  |
| A | L | B | I | N | O | S |  | C |  | R |  | I |
| D |  |  | N |  | V |  | T | H | A | N | K | S |
| A |  |  | S |  | E |  | I |  | R |  |  | S |
| P | A | S | T | O | R | A | L |  | G | U | R | U |
| T |  |  | E |  | D |  | E |  | U |  |  | E |
| S | L | A | P |  | O | D | D | M | E | N | T | S |

## CROSSWORD 332

| A | U | N | T | S |  | G |  | L |  | D |  | A |
|---|---|---|---|---|---|---|---|---|---|---|---|---|
| D |  |  | H |  | G | Y | R | A | T | I | N | G |
| V | I | T | A | L |  | M |  | I |  | A |  | E |
| I |  |  | N | U | R | S | E | R | Y | M | A | N |
| C |  | P |  | N |  |  |  | S |  | E |  | C |
| E | M | A | N | A | T | E | D |  | S | T | A | Y |
|  |  | R |  | R |  | L |  | S |  | E |  |  |
| W | E | A | N |  | S | K | E | W | E | R | E | D |
| O |  | M |  | I |  |  |  | I |  | S |  | R |
| B | R | O | A | D | E | N | I | N | G |  |  | E |
| B |  | U |  | O |  | O |  | E | A | S | E | D |
| L | I | N | O | L | E | U | M |  | S |  |  | G |
| Y |  | T |  | S |  | N |  | A | P | P | L | E |

## CROSSWORD 333

| E | R | R | A | T | I | C |  | T | U | L | I | P |
|---|---|---|---|---|---|---|---|---|---|---|---|---|
| S |  |  | S |  |  | H |  | R |  | U |  | E |
| C |  | U | K | U | L | E | L | E |  | N |  | A |
| A |  |  | I |  |  | F |  | E | X | A | L | T |
| P | L | A | N | E | T |  | H |  |  | T |  |  |
| A |  |  | G |  | I | N | A | C | T | I | O | N |
| D |  | V |  |  | T |  | R |  |  | C |  | E |
| E | V | A | C | U | A | T | E |  | H |  |  | E |
|  |  | L |  |  | N |  | M | O | A | N | E | D |
| P | L | U | M | E |  | R |  |  | Z |  |  | L |
| U |  | I |  | D | E | A | D | P | A | N |  | I |
| F |  | N |  | G |  | S |  |  | R |  |  | N |
| F | O | G | G | Y |  | P | A | D | D | I | N | G |

## CROSSWORD 334

| K | E | B | A | B | S |  | S |  | A | F | A | R |
|---|---|---|---|---|---|---|---|---|---|---|---|---|
| I |  |  | M |  | N | I | C | H | E |  | R |  |
| D | U | M | B |  | I |  | A |  | R | I | C | H |
| N |  |  | E |  | D | I | N | G | O |  | A |  |
| E | N | T | R | E | E |  | N |  | S | I | D | E |
| Y |  |  |  | K |  |  | E |  | O |  | E |  |
| S | A | U | C | E | S |  | R | E | L | I | S | H |
|  | I |  | H |  | H |  |  | R |  |  |  | A |
| T | R | U | E |  | O |  | P | A | C | I | N | G |
|  | L |  | M | O | V | I | E |  | A |  |  | G |
| M | I | N | I |  | E |  | T |  | R | E | E | L |
|  | N |  | S | O | L | V | E |  | E |  |  | E |
| M | E | R | E |  | S |  | R | I | D | G | E | D |

## CROSSWORD 335

| I | M | P | L | Y | I | N | G |  | T | W | I | G |
|---|---|---|---|---|---|---|---|---|---|---|---|---|
| R |  |  | O |  | N |  | O |  | I |  |  | A |
| O | W | E | D |  | S | H | U | D | D | E | R | S |
| N |  |  | G |  | E |  | G |  | I |  |  | S |
| I | N | F | E | C | T |  | E |  | E |  |  | E |
| C |  | I |  | O |  | A | D | O | R | N | E | D |
|  |  | V |  | A |  | N |  | V |  | O |  |  |
| S | W | E | A | T | E | D |  | A |  | S |  | S |
| C |  |  | R |  | N |  | O | L | D | E | S | T |
| H |  |  | M |  | D |  | P |  | I |  |  | O |
| O | R | N | A | M | E | N | T |  | C | H | U | M |
| O |  |  | D |  | A |  | E |  | E |  |  | P |
| L | A | M | A |  | R | A | D | I | S | H | E | S |

## CROSSWORD 336

| B | A | R | N | S |  | A |  | S |  | E |  | A |
|---|---|---|---|---|---|---|---|---|---|---|---|---|
| I |  |  | I |  | E | N | T | H | U | S | E | D |
| T | W | I | C | E |  | T |  | O |  | T |  | H |
| I |  |  | E | N | T | E | R | P | R | I | S | E |
| N |  | H |  | S |  |  |  | S |  | M |  | R |
| G | R | A | N | U | L | E | S |  | F | A | C | E |
|  |  | V |  | E |  | G |  | A |  | T |  |  |
| V | I | E | S |  | D | O | W | N | P | O | U | R |
| E |  | R |  | D |  |  |  | N |  | R |  | I |
| S | U | S | P | I | C | I | O | U | S |  |  | D |
| S |  | A |  | V |  | O |  | L | A | C | E | D |
| E | N | C | H | A | N | T | S |  | W |  |  | L |
| L |  | K |  | S |  | A |  | G | N | O | M | E |

# SOLUTIONS

CROSSWORD 341

| A | N | T | A | C | I | D |  | B | E | I | N | G |
|---|---|---|---|---|---|---|---|---|---|---|---|---|
| S |  | W |  |  | E |  | A |  | N |  | H |  |
| S |  | R | H | U | B | A | R | B |  | V |  | E |
| E |  |  | I |  |  | L |  | E | V | A | D | E |
| M | A | U | L | E | D |  | H |  |  | L |  |  |
| B |  |  | E |  | Y | E | A | R | L | I | N | G |
| L |  | S |  |  | I |  | I |  |  | D |  | R |
| E | X | A | M | I | N | E | R |  | R |  |  | A |
|  |  | M |  |  | G |  | S | T | A | R | E | D |
| E | X | P | E | L |  | T |  |  | N |  |  | I |
| W |  | L |  | I | T | A | L | I | C | S |  | E |
| E |  | E |  | P |  | L |  |  | I |  |  | N |
| R | I | D | E | S |  | E | V | I | D | E | N | T |

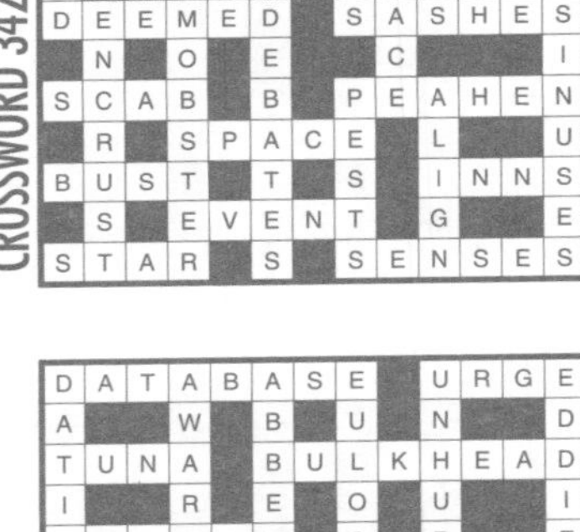


CROSSWORD 343

| D | A | T | A | B | A | S | E |  | U | R | G | E |
|---|---|---|---|---|---|---|---|---|---|---|---|---|
| A |  |  | W |  | B |  | U |  | N |  |  | D |
| T | U | N | A |  | B | U | L | K | H | E | A | D |
| I |  |  | R |  | E |  | O |  | U |  |  | I |
| N | A | M | E | L | Y |  | G |  | R |  |  | E |
| G |  | O |  | I |  | O | Y | S | T | E | R | S |
|  |  | T |  | K |  | N |  | O |  | V |  |  |
| A | C | H | I | E | V | E |  | F |  | I |  | S |
| M |  |  | N |  | E |  | T | A | B | L | E | T |
| I |  |  | W |  | N |  | A |  | U |  |  | A |
| D | R | E | A | M | E | R | S |  | F | O | R | K |
| S |  |  | R |  | E |  | K |  | F |  |  | E |
| T | H | U | D |  | R | E | S | I | S | T | E | D |

CROSSWORD 344

| S | T | R | A | Y |  | F |  | C |  | R |  | A |
|---|---|---|---|---|---|---|---|---|---|---|---|---|
| I |  |  | R |  | C | L | E | A | N | E | R | S |
| S | L | I | C | E |  | E |  | C |  | B |  | T |
| T |  |  | S | E | V | E | N | T | I | E | T | H |
| E |  | H |  | R |  |  |  | I |  | L |  | M |
| R | E | A | L | I | S | T | S |  | U | L | N | A |
|  |  | R |  | E |  | R |  | T |  | I |  |  |
| W | H | A | T |  | T | Y | P | H | O | O | N | S |
| R |  | S |  | A |  |  |  | I |  | N |  | O |
| O | B | S | E | R | V | A | N | C | E |  |  | R |
| N |  | I |  | I |  | B |  | K | N | E | A | D |
| G | E | N | I | A | L | L | Y |  | V |  |  | I |
| S |  | G |  | S |  | Y |  | T | Y | P | E | D |

# SOLUTIONS

## CROSSWORD 345

| | | | | | | | | | | | | |
|---|---|---|---|---|---|---|---|---|---|---|---|---|
| F | O | S | S | I | L | S | | E | N | A | C | T |
| L | | | O | | | N | | W | | L | | I |
| I | | C | L | I | M | A | T | E | | M | | F |
| P | | | E | | | P | | S | T | A | F | F |
| P | O | L | L | E | N | | S | | | N | | |
| E | | | Y | | I | N | C | R | E | A | S | E |
| R | | A | | | N | | R | | | C | | P |
| S | U | B | T | I | T | L | E | | B | | | I |
| | | R | | | H | | W | E | A | S | E | L |
| T | R | A | M | P | | V | | | B | | | E |
| O | | D | | O | V | A | T | I | O | N | | P |
| W | | E | | N | | I | | | O | | | S |
| N | A | S | T | Y | | N | U | N | N | E | R | Y |

## CROSSWORD 346

| | | | | | | | | | | | | |
|---|---|---|---|---|---|---|---|---|---|---|---|---|
| J | U | M | B | L | E | | S | | I | T | C | H |
| U | | | L | | T | O | T | A | L | | H | |
| M | O | N | O | | H | | R | | L | O | A | N |
| P | | | W | | I | R | A | T | E | | R | |
| E | T | H | N | I | C | | T | | G | R | A | M |
| R | | | | R | | | U | | A | | D | |
| S | H | A | C | K | S | | M | A | L | L | E | T |
| | A | | O | | H | | | Y | | | | A |
| D | Y | E | D | | O | | A | E | R | I | A | L |
| | W | | E | X | C | E | L | | A | | | E |
| K | I | W | I | | K | | I | | R | E | I | N |
| | R | | N | I | E | C | E | | E | | | T |
| M | E | T | E | | D | | N | E | R | V | E | S |

## CROSSWORD 347

| | | | | | | | | | | | | |
|---|---|---|---|---|---|---|---|---|---|---|---|---|
| I | D | E | A | L | I | S | M | | T | R | I | O |
| N | | | L | | S | | E | | O | | | U |
| C | R | A | B | | L | E | A | K | A | G | E | S |
| I | | | U | | E | | N | | S | | | T |
| T | H | E | M | E | S | | E | | T | | | E |
| E | | D | | T | | G | R | A | S | P | E | D |
| | | I | | C | | A | | C | | E | | |
| P | I | T | C | H | E | D | | N | | A | | G |
| O | | | O | | N | | S | E | L | L | E | R |
| D | | | W | | R | | U | | A | | | I |
| I | N | H | A | B | I | T | S | | B | L | I | P |
| U | | | R | | C | | H | | E | | | E |
| M | I | N | D | | H | A | I | R | L | E | S | S |

## CROSSWORD 348

| | | | | | | | | | | | | |
|---|---|---|---|---|---|---|---|---|---|---|---|---|
| M | O | R | A | L | | S | | W | | R | | A |
| O | | | W | | S | P | E | A | K | E | R | S |
| L | I | N | E | D | | A | | I | | S | | I |
| A | | | S | A | C | R | I | F | I | C | E | D |
| R | | T | | R | | | | S | | I | | E |
| S | A | U | N | T | E | R | S | | G | N | U | S |
| | | R | | S | | A | | S | | D | | |
| M | O | B | S | | A | P | P | A | R | E | N | T |
| A | | U | | A | | | | L | | D | | A |
| M | E | L | O | D | R | A | M | A | S | | | M |
| M | | E | | O | | W | | D | A | N | C | E |
| A | B | N | O | R | M | A | L | | G | | | S |
| L | | T | | E | | Y | | A | S | S | E | T |

## CROSSWORD 349

| | | | | | | | | | | | | |
|---|---|---|---|---|---|---|---|---|---|---|---|---|
| L | E | A | R | N | E | R | | U | R | B | A | N |
| O | | | I | | | O | | G | | L | | E |
| U | | C | O | U | N | C | I | L | | O | | O |
| N | | | T | | | K | | Y | E | A | R | N |
| G | R | I | E | V | E | | F | | | T | | |
| I | | | D | | N | E | A | R | N | E | S | S |
| N | | P | | | D | | I | | | D | | E |
| G | R | A | N | D | E | U | R | | A | | | E |
| | | R | | | D | | Y | O | D | E | L | S |
| U | L | C | E | R | | C | | | J | | | A |
| P | | H | | A | M | A | T | E | U | R | | W |
| O | | E | | C | | L | | | S | | | E |
| N | U | D | G | E | | M | O | T | T | L | E | D |

## CROSSWORD 350

| | | | | | | | | | | | | |
|---|---|---|---|---|---|---|---|---|---|---|---|---|
| N | U | M | B | E | D | | T | | S | O | A | P |
| O | | | O | | A | B | A | T | E | | W | |
| S | L | E | W | | T | | X | | S | H | A | M |
| T | | | E | | U | N | I | T | S | | K | |
| R | A | N | D | O | M | | C | | I | T | E | M |
| I | | | | R | | | A | | O | | N | |
| L | A | N | C | E | D | | B | A | N | I | S | H |
| | N | | A | | Y | | | M | | | | E |
| D | A | W | N | | N | | O | P | A | Q | U | E |
| | G | | D | R | A | W | N | | T | | | D |
| O | R | A | L | | M | | S | | L | O | A | F |
| | A | | E | L | O | P | E | | A | | | U |
| I | M | P | S | | S | | T | A | S | S | E | L |

## CROSSWORD 351

| | | | | | | | | | | | | |
|---|---|---|---|---|---|---|---|---|---|---|---|---|
| G | U | N | S | H | O | T | S | | C | U | R | B |
| A | | | I | | R | | T | | H | | | R |
| R | O | P | E | | B | E | A | R | A | B | L | E |
| T | | | G | | I | | B | | N | | | A |
| E | X | C | E | P | T | | L | | T | | | S |
| R | | H | | R | | P | E | A | S | A | N | T |
| | | I | | E | | O | | N | | C | | |
| D | E | C | A | Y | E | D | | O | | R | | A |
| A | | | L | | N | | A | N | G | E | R | S |
| R | | | I | | C | | D | | I | | | T |
| K | E | Y | B | O | A | R | D | | A | I | D | E |
| E | | | I | | S | | L | | N | | | R |
| R | U | N | S | | E | X | E | R | T | I | O | N |

## CROSSWORD 352

| | | | | | | | | | | | | |
|---|---|---|---|---|---|---|---|---|---|---|---|---|
| V | I | S | A | S | | H | | B | | H | | D |
| I | | | J | | S | E | P | A | R | A | T | E |
| A | H | E | A | D | | R | | T | | I | | M |
| B | | | R | A | C | E | C | O | U | R | S | E |
| L | | P | | L | | | | N | | S | | A |
| E | N | A | B | L | I | N | G | | S | T | U | N |
| | | T | | Y | | I | | F | | Y | | |
| A | C | H | E | | S | P | R | A | W | L | E | D |
| R | | O | | S | | | | R | | E | | O |
| R | E | L | U | C | T | A | N | C | E | | | R |
| O | | O | | A | | U | | E | L | V | E | S |
| W | I | G | G | L | I | N | G | | K | | | A |
| S | | Y | | P | | T | | U | S | U | A | L |

# SOLUTIONS

## CROSSWORD 353

| I | C | E | B | E | R | G |  | D | R | A | P | E |
|---|---|---|---|---|---|---|---|---|---|---|---|---|
| M |  |  | R |  |  | O |  | I |  | Q |  | D |
| I |  | M | A | N | U | A | L | S |  | U |  | G |
| T |  |  | W |  |  | D |  | H | E | A | V | E |
| A | S | Y | L | U | M |  | W |  |  | T |  |  |
| T |  |  | S |  | Y | I | E | L | D | I | N | G |
| O |  | S |  |  | R |  | E |  |  | C |  | R |
| R | E | C | U | R | R | E | D |  | L |  |  | A |
|  |  | H |  |  | H |  | S | T | A | T | I | C |
| C | H | E | F | S |  | A |  |  | U |  |  | I |
| A |  | M |  | H | O | S | T | I | N | G |  | O |
| S |  | E |  | O |  | P |  |  | C |  |  | U |
| H | E | D | G | E |  | S | I | P | H | O | N | S |

## CROSSWORD 354

| R | O | A | S | T | S |  | P |  | N | O | D | S |
|---|---|---|---|---|---|---|---|---|---|---|---|---|
| E |  |  | E |  | E | X | I | L | E |  | I |  |
| S | H | I | P |  | A |  | V |  | S | W | A | T |
| T |  |  | I |  | R | O | O | S | T |  | L |  |
| F | R | E | A | K | S |  | T |  | I | D | E | A |
| U |  |  |  | I |  |  | A |  | N |  | C |  |
| L | A | M | E | N | T |  | L | I | G | H | T | S |
|  | L |  | N |  | U |  |  | O |  |  |  | I |
| Z | I | N | C |  | M |  | A | N | G | L | E | D |
|  | M |  | L | I | B | E | L |  | A |  |  | I |
| H | O | B | O |  | L |  | T |  | V | E | I | N |
|  | N |  | S | U | E | D | E |  | E |  |  | G |
| L | Y | R | E |  | S |  | R | E | L | A | Y | S |

## CROSSWORD 355

| M | A | R | S | H | A | L | S |  | A | R | M | Y |
|---|---|---|---|---|---|---|---|---|---|---|---|---|
| A |  |  | A |  | G |  | E |  | B |  |  | A |
| K | N | O | B |  | R | E | S | T | R | A | I | N |
| E |  |  | L |  | E |  | A |  | O |  |  | K |
| R | E | C | E | D | E |  | M |  | A |  |  | E |
| S |  | L |  | O |  | M | E | D | D | L | E | D |
|  |  | O |  | P |  | A |  | I |  | I |  |  |
| V | A | G | U | E | S | T |  | N |  | F |  | T |
| E |  |  | N |  | T |  | N | E | A | T | E | R |
| R |  |  | S |  | R |  | O |  | S |  |  | U |
| M | E | G | A | W | A | T | T |  | K | I | N | D |
| I |  |  | I |  | I |  | E |  | E |  |  | G |
| N | E | E | D |  | N | O | S | E | D | I | V | E |

## CROSSWORD 356

| Y | A | C | H | T |  | T |  | S |  | I |  | F |
|---|---|---|---|---|---|---|---|---|---|---|---|---|
| E |  |  | E |  | P | I | T | T | A | N | C | E |
| A | U | R | A | L |  | E |  | E |  | D |  | A |
| R |  |  | L | A | N | D | L | A | D | I | E | S |
| L |  | A |  | S |  |  |  | L |  | G |  | T |
| Y | U | L | E | T | I | D | E |  | A | N | T | S |
|  |  | L |  | S |  | U |  | P |  | A |  |  |
| H | U | E | S |  | D | E | T | A | I | N | E | D |
| O |  | G |  | A |  |  |  | S |  | T |  | E |
| A | M | E | N | D | M | E | N | T | S |  |  | P |
| R |  | D |  | A |  | O |  | A | I | S | L | E |
| D | I | L | I | G | E | N | T |  | L |  |  | N |
| S |  | Y |  | E |  | S |  | S | T | E | E | D |

## CROSSWORD 357

| S | W | I | R | L | E | D |  | S | T | A | I | D |
|---|---|---|---|---|---|---|---|---|---|---|---|---|
| H |  |  | E |  |  | R |  | I |  | F |  | A |
| E |  | O | V | E | R | A | L | L |  | F |  | L |
| A |  |  | E |  |  | B |  | L | E | A | V | E |
| R | I | B | A | L | D |  | S |  |  | B |  |  |
| I |  |  | L |  | R | E | T | A | I | L | E | D |
| N |  | S |  |  | I |  | A |  |  | E |  | E |
| G | L | A | Z | I | E | R | S |  | C |  |  | F |
|  |  | V |  |  | D |  | H | O | A | R | S | E |
| S | H | A | V | E |  | F |  |  | R |  |  | R |
| H |  | G |  | R | E | A | C | H | E | D |  | R |
| I |  | E |  | R |  | I |  |  | E |  |  | E |
| N | O | D | E | S |  | R | E | T | R | E | A | D |

## CROSSWORD 358

| O | P | E | N | E | D |  | D |  | M | U | R | K |
|---|---|---|---|---|---|---|---|---|---|---|---|---|
| N |  |  | O |  | U | N | I | T | E |  | E |  |
| G | R | U | B |  | N |  | L |  | L | E | A | F |
| O |  |  | L |  | K | N | E | L | L |  | D |  |
| I | M | P | E | L | S |  | M |  | O | M | E | N |
| N |  |  |  | O |  |  | M |  | W |  | R |  |
| G | A | R | A | G | E |  | A | S | S | E | S | S |
|  | W |  | R |  | R |  |  | E |  |  |  | E |
| S | K | I | D |  | E |  | H | E | R | O | I | C |
|  | W |  | U | N | C | L | E |  | A |  |  | L |
| H | A | L | O |  | T |  | A |  | B | E | A | U |
|  | R |  | U | N | L | I | T |  | I |  |  | D |
| O | D | E | S |  | Y |  | S | E | D | U | C | E |

## CROSSWORD 359

| P | H | E | A | S | A | N | T |  | D | E | A | D |
|---|---|---|---|---|---|---|---|---|---|---|---|---|
| R |  |  | L |  | L |  | R |  | A |  |  | O |
| I | D | O | L |  | L | E | A | P | F | R | O | G |
| N |  |  | O |  | O |  | G |  | T |  |  | G |
| C | H | A | T | T | Y |  | I |  | E |  |  | E |
| E |  | N |  | W |  | A | C | C | R | U | E | D |
|  |  | T |  | I |  | I |  | A |  | S |  |  |
| R | E | I | G | N | E | D |  | K |  | E |  | U |
| I |  |  | Y |  | D |  | C | E | A | S | E | S |
| P |  |  | R |  | I |  | H |  | N |  |  | H |
| P | R | E | A | M | B | L | E |  | G | O | N | E |
| L |  |  | T |  | L |  | E |  | E |  |  | R |
| E | A | S | E |  | E | A | R | P | L | U | G | S |

## CROSSWORD 360

| S | O | A | K | S |  | K |  | G |  | I |  | U |
|---|---|---|---|---|---|---|---|---|---|---|---|---|
| T |  |  | N |  | E | N | T | R | A | N | T | S |
| I | D | L | E | D |  | E |  | I |  | N |  | E |
| F |  |  | W | A | T | E | R | P | R | O | O | F |
| L |  | P |  | I |  |  |  | S |  | V |  | U |
| E | L | A | P | S | I | N | G |  | H | A | I | L |
|  |  | P |  | Y |  | O |  | S |  | T |  |  |
| K | E | E | L |  | S | W | E | A | T | E | R | S |
| I |  | R |  | R |  |  |  | U |  | S |  | U |
| L | I | B | R | A | R | I | A | N | S |  |  | N |
| L |  | A |  | L |  | N |  | A | C | T | E | D |
| E | S | C | A | L | A | T | E |  | A |  |  | A |
| R |  | K |  | Y |  | O |  | T | R | U | C | E |

# SOLUTIONS

## CROSSWORD 361

| H | O | R | M | O | N | E |   | Q | U | A | K | E |
|---|---|---|---|---|---|---|---|---|---|---|---|---|
| O |   |   | O |   |   | M |   | U |   | V |   | A |
| S |   | F | O | R | M | U | L | A |   | I |   | S |
| T |   |   | R |   |   | S |   | Y | E | A | S | T |
| A | F | R | E | S | H |   | C |   |   | T |   |   |
| G |   |   | D |   | A | B | A | T | T | O | I | R |
| E |   | V |   |   | R |   | M |   |   | R |   | E |
| S | T | A | M | P | E | D | E |   | B |   |   | V |
|   |   | N |   |   | S |   | O | R | A | N | G | E |
| K | N | I | F | E |   | S |   |   | Z |   |   | R |
| N |   | L |   | B | E | A | N | B | A | G |   | E |
| I |   | L |   | B |   | N |   |   | A |   |   | N |
| T | O | A | D | S |   | G | O | U | R | M | E | T |

## CROSSWORD 362

| I | G | U | A | N | A |   | P |   | O | U | R | S |
|---|---|---|---|---|---|---|---|---|---|---|---|---|
| N |   |   | L |   | B | O | A | R | D |   | E |   |
| T | E | M | P |   | U |   | R |   | Y | O | L | K |
| E |   |   | H |   | T | H | A | W | S |   | E |   |
| R | E | C | A | P | S |   | S |   | S | O | A | R |
| N |   |   |   | E |   |   | O |   | E |   | S |   |
| S | A | F | A | R | I |   | L | A | Y | M | E | N |
|   | P |   | I |   | M |   |   | T |   |   |   | U |
| C | O | A | L |   | P |   | S | E | A | T | E | D |
|   | L |   | M | E | A | N | T |   | L |   |   | I |
| M | O | P | E |   | I |   | E |   | L | E | S | S |
|   | G |   | N | U | R | S | E |   | O |   |   | T |
| C | Y | S | T |   | S |   | R | O | W | E | R | S |

## CROSSWORD 363

| L | I | G | A | M | E | N | T |   | W | O | M | B |
|---|---|---|---|---|---|---|---|---|---|---|---|---|
| I |   |   | P |   | N |   | R |   | I |   |   | U |
| B | O | A | R |   | T | H | A | T | C | H | E | D |
| I |   |   | O |   | R |   | D |   | K |   |   | D |
| D | A | I | N | T | Y |   | E |   | E |   |   | E |
| O |   | R |   | H |   | C | R | A | D | L | E | D |
|   |   | O |   | E |   | U |   | L |   | U |   |   |
| U | N | N | A | M | E | D |   | S |   | L |   | T |
| N |   |   | T |   | N |   | F | O | L | L | O | W |
| C |   |   | T |   | L |   | R |   | A |   |   | E |
| L | A | X | A | T | I | V | E |   | D | O | S | E |
| A |   |   | C |   | S |   | E |   | E |   |   | T |
| D | A | S | H |   | T | I | D | I | N | E | S | S |

## CROSSWORD 364

| N | A | T | A | L |   | T |   | L |   | P |   | S |
|---|---|---|---|---|---|---|---|---|---|---|---|---|
| O |   |   | L |   | Q | U | E | E | R | E | S | T |
| V | O | C | A | L |   | B |   | M |   | D |   | A |
| E |   |   | S | A | N | A | T | O | R | I | U | M |
| L |   | P |   | U |   |   |   | N |   | G |   | E |
| S | C | A | N | D | A | L | S |   | W | R | E | N |
|   |   | W |   | S |   | O |   | I |   | E |   |   |
| K | I | N | G |   | S | P | I | C | I | E | S | T |
| I |   | S |   | E |   |   |   | I |   | S |   | A |
| S | C | H | E | D | U | L | I | N | G |   |   | N |
| S |   | O |   | I |   | E |   | G | A | Z | E | D |
| E | X | P | E | C | T | E | D |   | G |   |   | E |
| S |   | S |   | T |   | R |   | P | S | A | L | M |

## CROSSWORD 365

| N | O | M | A | D | I | C |   | F | L | O | U | T |
|---|---|---|---|---|---|---|---|---|---|---|---|---|
| A |   |   | B |   |   | O |   | A |   | C |   | U |
| V |   | P | L | A | C | A | R | D |   | T |   | B |
| I |   |   | O |   |   | X |   | E | R | A | S | E |
| G | R | O | O | V | E |   | G |   |   | V |   |   |
| A |   |   | M |   | R | E | A | P | P | E | A | R |
| T |   | S |   |   | U |   | S |   |   | S |   | E |
| E | X | C | E | R | P | T | S |   | S |   |   | D |
|   |   | R |   |   | T |   | Y | E | L | P | E | D |
| K | O | A | L | A |   | F |   |   | Y |   |   | E |
| I |   | P |   | W | E | A | R | I | E | R |   | N |
| T |   | E |   | R |   | W |   |   | S |   |   | E |
| E | A | R | L | Y |   | N | E | S | T | L | E | D |